II CHRONICLES

THE ANCHOR BIBLE is a fresh approach to the world's greatest classic. Its object is to make the Bible accessible to the modern reader; its method is to arrive at the meaning of biblical literature through exact translation and extended exposition, and to reconstruct the ancient setting of the biblical story, as well as the circumstances of its transcription and the characteristics of its transcribers.

THE ANCHOR BIBLE is a project of international and interfaith scope: Protestant, Catholic, and Jewish scholars from many countries contribute individual volumes. The project is not sponsored by any ecclesiastical organization and is not intended to reflect any particular theological doctrine. Prepared under our joint supervision, THE ANCHOR BIBLE is an effort to make available all the significant historical and linguistic knowledge which bears on the interpretation of the biblical record.

THE ANCHOR BIBLE is aimed at the general reader with no special formal training in biblical studies; yet, it is written with the most exacting standards of scholarship, reflecting the highest technical accomplishment.

This project marks the beginning of a new era of co-operation among scholars in biblical research, thus forming a common body of knowledge to be shared by all.

William Foxwell Albright
David Noel Freedman
GENERAL EDITORS

THE ANCHOR BIBLE

II CHRONICLES

TRANSLATION AND NOTES
BY
JACOB M. MYERS

Doubleday & Company, Inc.
Garden City, New York
1965

TRANSLATOR'S NOTE

The biblical book of Chronicles is actually one book which, because of its length when translated from Hebrew into Greek, was divided into what we now know as I and II Chronicles. The division into two volumes has been retained here, but the interrelatedness of the two precluded two separate introductions that would, by avoiding repetition, tend to mislead the reader into thinking that I and II Chronicles were two distinct works.

Therefore, the general introduction to the Chronicler's work appears at the beginning of I Chronicles, and a shorter introduction—relevant specifically to II Chronicles—appears here. The appendixes for all of Chronicles are to be found at the end of II Chronicles. Appendix I gives a complete list of the parallel and comparative passages that the Chronicler drew upon for both I and II Chronicles; Appendix II contains genealogical charts based upon the first nine chapters of I Chronicles. Each volume also includes an index of place and personal names that appear *in the biblical text of that volume,* but if a name occurs in any other of the Chronicler's works (I and II Chronicles and Ezra-Nehemiah), all of these occurrences are cited in order to illustrate the basic unity of the narrative contained in these volumes.

J.M.M.

CONTENTS

APPENDIXES

PRINCIPAL ABBREVIATIONS

1. PUBLICATIONS

AASOR	Annual of the American Schools of Oriental Research
AfO	Archiv für Orientforschung
AJSL	American Journal of Semitic Languages and Literature
AMJV	*Alexander Marx Jubilee Volume,* English Section
ANEP	*The Ancient Near East in Pictures,* ed. J. B. Pritchard
ANET	*Ancient Near Eastern Texts,* ed. J. B. Pritchard
AOT	*Altorientalische Bilder zum Alten Testament,* ed. H. Gressmann
AP	*Aramaic Papyri of the Fifth Century B.C.,* ed. and tr. A. Cowley
ARAB	*Ancient Records of Assyria and Babylonia,* ed. D. D. Luckenbill
ARI	*Archaeology and the Religion of Israel,* by W. F. Albright
BA	The Biblical Archaeologist
BASOR	Bulletin of the American Schools of Oriental Research
BBLA	Beiträge zur biblischen Landes—und Altertumskunde
BH	Biblia Hebraica, ed. R. Kittel
BJPES	Bulletin of the Jewish Palestine Exploration Society
BJRL	Bulletin of the John Rylands Library
BMAP	*The Brooklyn Museum Aramaic Papyri,* ed. E. G. H. Kraeling
BP	"The Biblical Period," by W. F. Albright
BRL	*Biblisches Reallexikon,* 1937
BZAW	Beihefte zur Zeitschrift für die alttestamentliche Wissenschaft
CAD	The Assyrian Dictionary, Oriental Institute of the University of Chicago
CBQ	Catholic Biblical Quarterly
EJ	*Die Entstehung des Judenthums,* by Eduard Meyer
FAB	*Festschrift für Alfred Bertholet*
FSAC	*From the Stone Age to Christianity,* by W. F. Albright
GA	*Geschichte des Altertums,* by Eduard Meyer
GVI	*Geschichte des Volkes Israel,* by Rudolph Kittel

IB	The Interpreter's Bible
ICC	The International Critical Commentary
IDB	The Interpreter's Dictionary of the Bible, 1962
IEJ	Israel Exploration Journal
IPN	*Die israelitischen Personennamen im Rahmen der gemeinsemitischen Namengebung*, by M. Noth
1QH	Qumran Hymns of Thanksgiving
1QM	Qumran Manual of Discipline
1QS	Qumran War Scroll
JAOS	Journal of the American Oriental Society
JBL	Journal of Biblical Literature and Exegesis
JBR	Journal of Bible and Religion
JNES	Journal of Near Eastern Studies
JPOS	Journal of the Palestine Oriental Society
JTS	Journal of Theological Studies
KS	*Kleine Schriften zur Geschichte des Volkes Israel*, by A. Alt
LCQ	Lutheran Church Quarterly
LGJV	*Louis Ginzberg Jubilee Volume*, English Section
MGWJ	Monatsschrift für Geschichte und Wissenschaft des Judentums
MVAG	Mitteilungen der vorderasiatisch-aegyptischen Gesellschaft
OIC	Oriental Institute Communications
OTS	Oudtestamentische Studien
PEQ	Palestine Exploration Quarterly
PJB	Palästinajahrbuch des deutschen evangelischen Instituts für Altertumswissenschaft des heiligen Landes zu Jerusalem
QDAP	Quarterly of the Department of Antiquities in Palestine
RB	Revue biblique
SVT	Supplements to Vetus Testamentum
TLZ	Theologische Literaturzeitung
TZ	Theologische Zeitschrifte
ÜS	*Überlieferungsgeschichtliche Studien*, by M. Noth
VT	Vetus Testamentum
WO	Die Welt des Orients
ZAW	Zeitschrift für die alttestamentliche Wissenschaft
ZDPV	Zeitschrift des deutschen Palästina-Vereins

For references to books, see Selected Bibliography.

2. Versions

Aq.	Ancient Greek translation of the Old Testament by Aquila
ATD	Das Alte Testament Deutsch
LXX	The Septuagint
MT	Masoretic Text
RSV	Revised Standard Version
Syr.	Syriac version, the Peshitta
Targ.	Targum, Aramaic translation or paraphrase
Vrs.	Ancient versions generally
Vulg.	The Vulgate

3. Other Abbreviations

Akk.	Akkadian
Ar.	Arabic
Aram.	Aramaic
Bab.	Babylonian
Eg.	Egyptian
Eng.	English
Fr.	French
Ger.	German
Gr.	Greek
Heb.	Hebrew
Kh.	Khirbet
Lat.	Latin
OT	Old Testament
Phoen.	Phoenician
Sem.	Semitic
Sum.	Sumerian

INTRODUCTION

THE WORK OF THE CHRONICLER IN THE BIBLE

In many respects the work of the Chronicler—I Chronicles, II Chronicles, Ezra, and Nehemiah—has been one of the most neglected portions of the Old Testament. Where it had to be dealt with, it was done grudgingly, often with misunderstanding, misgiving, or downright hostility. However, archaeological and historical studies have now rendered it more respectable and have shown it to be at times more accurate than some of its parallel sources. Naturally the Chronicler had a particular purpose in mind and, where he found more than one source to draw from for a story he wanted to use, he followed the one more harmonious with and adequate for his purpose.

Doubtless the position of Ezra, Nehemiah, and Chronicles in both Jewish and Christian canons has had much to do with the attitude of general Bible readers toward them. Their form and content, dictated in large measure by the peculiar interests of the writer(s), makes them rather dull for the modern reader. To those without an understanding and appreciation of the historical milieu and purpose of the work, genealogies, lists, exaggerated statistics, lengthy and detailed descriptions of religious forms and institutions, etc., can be rather depressing. The contrast is striking when the Chronicler's work is compared with the immediately preceding (Christian canon) Deuteronomic history, which reads much better because it appears more in line with the methods of modern historiography.

It seems a bit strange that the Chronicler's efforts should have been dismissed so lightly in view of the fact that his work comes from just that period in Hebrew history about which so little is otherwise known. The spade of the archaeologist is beginning to fill in the gaps of that period and, with a more appreciative and controlled study of the written materials, we can now be fairly certain of a good many of the hitherto obscure references and details. Supplementing the historical materials of Samuel and Kings and carrying the history of the fortunes of the Jews down to the fourth century

B.C., these books become extremely important. Properly understood and interpreted, they throw much welcome light on this confused period.

THE TITLE OF THE HEBREW BOOKS

The title of Chronicles in Hebrew is *dibrē hayyāmīm,* that is, chronicles of events, happenings of the days, records of the days or times. It was a rather widely used expression in Kings where it occurs some thirty-two times, referring to the book or record of the chronicles of the kings of Israel and Judah; it occurs twice in Esther (x 2)—the chronicles of the kings of Media and Persia. In Esther vi 1 it is used to cite the record of the memorable events in the history of Persia. Interestingly enough, the expression is found only twice in the work of the Chronicler—I Chron xxvii 24 and Neh xii 23. The present books of Chronicles were originally reckoned as one book.

THE TITLE IN THE VERSIONS

Our present Greek and Latin versions of Chronicles are called *Paraleipomena,* that is, things left over or omitted in the histories of Samuel and Kings, especially as they involve Judah. The use of the term Chronicles goes back to Luther who took it from St. Jerome's *Prologus geleatus* which has the following notice: *Dabre Aiamim, id est Verba Dierum, quod significatius totius divinae historiae possumus appellare, qui liber apud nos primus et secundus inscribitur* (Dabre Aiamim, that is the events of the days which we might significantly call the meaning of the whole sacred history, which book is entitled first and second by us). The Syriac follows the Hebrew.

PLACE IN THE CANON

In the Hebrew canon, the work of the Chronicler stands in the third division—the *Kethubim* (writings)—and last in that division. In our present canonical arrangement, Ezra-Nehemiah appears to be the sequel to Samuel and Kings. Though that was not originally the case, it may have been the origin of the division at the end of II Chronicles. Hence the history of Ezra begins just after the end of II Kings. This also explains the order of the books, that is, Chronicles after Ezra-Nehemiah, and accounts for the repetition of the ending of II Chronicles at the beginning of Ezra (indicating that the present order of the books is awkward). The separation of Ezra from Chronicles may have resulted from the incorporation of Ezra-Nehemiah into the Bible as a supplement to the story of Samuel and Kings, which occurred after Samuel and Kings had been canonized and therefore could no longer be tampered with. Chronicles, then, was added later. It is the last book in the Hebrew Bible and may have been viewed as a kind of appendix to the writings. The Greek Bible placed Chronicles, Ezra, and Nehemiah in the historical section in the following order: Chronicles, Esdras A, Esdras B (our Ezra-Nehemiah). That was the order followed by St. Jerome and Luther, and hence in our English Bibles, except that Esdras A (apocryphal Ezra) has been relegated to the Apocrypha while Esdras B appears as Ezra and Nehemiah.

THE INTENTION OF THE CHRONICLER[1]

Chronicles, Ezra, and Nehemiah are so closely related in thought, language, and theology that not only must they have come from a single hand, with possibly a few exceptions, but, like the other great literature of Israel, their author must have had in view a purpose that the earlier histories of his people did not meet in the form in which they had been transmitted.

The intent of the Chronicler was neither to rewrite the history of Judah nor specifically to gather together what had not been covered by his predecessors. His work is a lesson for the people of his time and situation drawn from the history of his people.[2] It might be referred to as a series of lectures or sermons on the bearing of that history upon the needs of the hour. Benzinger has said, "The Chronicler is not at all a writer of history in our sense of the term; he does not aim to relate what took place but what serves to edify; he is not a historian but a Midrashist."[3] C. C. Torrey has written in almost the same vein.[4] But just because the Chronicler is a "Midrashist" does not necessarily mean that he is a purveyor of pure fiction; he may look at history with some bias and omit or add material when it suits his purpose.

[1] For a summary of the historicoreligious situation and a discussion of the aim of the Chronicler in the light of his situation, see the comprehensive introduction to the Chronicler's work in *I Chronicles*.

[2] See G. von Rad, "Die levitische Predigt in den Bücher der Chronik" in *Gesammelte Studien zum Alten Testament*, pp. 248–61; *Das Geschichtsbild des Chronistischen Werkes*, pp. 133 f. (For complete references, see Selected Bibliography.)

[3] *Die Bücher der Chronik*, p. x (see Benzinger, Selected Bibliography, Commentaries).

[4] "The Composition and Historical Value of Ezra-Nehemiah," BZAW 2 (1896), 65. Cf. *Ezra Studies*, pp. 153–55, 208–13 (see Torrey, Selected Bibliography).

CONTENTS OF II CHRONICLES[5]

II Chron i–ix is devoted to the activities of Solomon. It begins with the new king's establishing himself in his position and his prayer for wisdom (i 1–17) and then proceeds immediately to a particularization of preparations for the construction of the temple (ii 1–18) and the formation of the corvée. The plans for the temple (iii), provision for its equipment (iv) and the dedication (v 1–vii 10) follow. Solomon's vision, administrative activity—both secular and religious—(vii 11–viii 18), the visit of the queen of Sheba (ix 1–12) and an inventory of the royal revenue and trade activity (ix 13–31) conclude the part. In the estimation of the Chronicler, Solomon is an extension of David, that is, the one who carried out the directions issued by the great king, though he did reflect wisdom and piety in his own right.

II Chron x–xxxvi rehearses the story of Judah as seen by the writer and enacted through its kings. In some respects, this story is the fulfillment of the divine promise to David by Nathan (I Chron xvii 13) and reaffirmed by Yahweh to Solomon (II Chron vii 18). In line with his method of dealing with history, this part centers about personalities, generally kings of Judah. The story begins with an account of the attitude of Rehoboam which led to a division of the kingdom (x) and a report on the progress of his plans for a separate administration—dissuasion from attacking Jeroboam, construction of fortress cities, the gravitation of the Levites to his territory (xi). Chapter xii deals with the invasion of Shishak with its consequences and the Chronicler's emphasis on the submission of the king in harmony with the demands of prophecy; it closes with the usual notice of the king's character, years of reign, death, and burial. The reign of Abijah is covered in a single chapter (xiii)

[5] A full discussion of the literary considerations in Chronicles may be found in the general introduction to *I Chronicles*.

which limits itself almost entirely to that king's campaign against Jeroboam which ended disastrously for the latter. The Chronicler's narrative of Asa includes a note on the ten years of peace at the beginning of his reign, his active participation in the religious purification of the land, and a more lengthy reference to Asa's defense against Zerah the Ethiopian (xiv). Chapter xv contains the prophecy of Azariah, son of Oded, and its results. The third chapter (xvi) devoted to Asa describes his altercation with Baasha of Israel, which involved an alliance between the former and Benhadad of Damascus against Baasha, and the prophecy of Hanani against Asa and its consequences. One of the favorite characters of our author was Jehoshaphat (xvii 1–xxi 1) whose exploits are set forth at some length. Chapter xvii begins with a general summation of Jehoshaphat's reign and then enumerates some of the deeds of the king—the instruction of the people (7–9), the tribute received by him (10–13) and the garrisoning of the fortified cities of Judah (14–19). His association with Ahab, king of Israel, in the Ramoth-gilead campaign, the prophecy of Micaiah ben Imlah associated with it and the outcome of the battle are related in chapter xviii. Jehoshaphat was rebuked for participating by Jehu ben Hanani (xix 1–3) a prophet. The judicial reform (xix 11) was of great significance. The campaign against the Transjordan confederation composed of Ammonites, Moabites, and Meunites is the subject of xx 1–30. The summary of Jehoshaphat's reign, his alliance with Ahaziah, the maritime fiasco at Ezion-geber, and his death and burial are recounted in xx 31–xxi 1. The remainder of chapter xxi deals with the reign of the wicked Jehoram, who slew his brothers, was allied by marriage with the house of Ahab, defeated the Edomites, received a letter from Elijah, suffered an invasion by Philistines and Arabs, and was the victim of a loathsome disease. Chapter xxii presents the story of Ahaziah, his death at the hands of Jehu, and the usurpation of the throne by Athaliah, his mother. The purge was not long in coming, as we learn from the success of Jehoiada in putting Joash on the throne (xxiii). Things went well while Jehoiada lived (xxiv 1–16), but after his death the king defected. When Zechariah, son of Jehoiada, reprimanded him, Joash put Zechariah to death. An Aramaean invasion followed and Joash was killed, the victim of a palace intrigue (xxiv 17–27). Joash was succeeded by Amaziah who, in accordance with prophetic advice, rejected Israelite assistance in his war with Edom. But, like his father, he turned away from Yahweh and became proud. The end was defeat, humiliation, and capture at the hands of Joash of Israel. Finally Amaziah was slain, by conspirators, at Lachish (xxv). The reigns of Uzziah and Jotham are of more than ordinary importance. The former was apparently a successful ruler (xxvi 1–15), but, like many others, overstepped his bounds (xxvi 16–23). Jotham's policy was a continuation of his father's (xxvii). The rule of the wicked Ahaz is dealt with most unsympathetically (xxviii). As in the case of Jehoshaphat, four chapters are devoted to Hezekiah (xxix–xxxii). The first act of Hezekiah was to issue orders for the cleansing of the temple (xxix) and the reinstitution of orderly worship. The Chronicler's ascription of a magnificent passover celebration to this king is given in chapter xxx; the following chapter (xxxi) is devoted to the religious reformation of Hezekiah. Chapter xxxii 1–23 is concerned with the invasion of Sennacherib and Hezekiah's reaction to it—his strengthening of the capital and his and Isaiah's prayers about the insults of the Assyrians hurled against the city and people—and the miraculous deliverance of Jerusalem. A summary statement on the achievements of the king follows (xxxii 24–33). Manasseh, the son of Hezekiah, acted haughtily toward Yahweh, followed the Assyrian cult, and desecrated the house of God (xxxiii 1–9). Finally there is the account of his capture by the Assyrians, his repentance and amends, and an evaluation of his reign (xxxiii 10–20). Nothing good is said about Amon who reverted to the evils practiced by his father before his repentance. He was slain by his own servants (xxxiii 21–25). Josiah is portrayed in almost the same glowing terms as Hezekiah. As soon as he reached the proper age he began the general reform (xxxiv 1–7) that led to the repair of the temple and finding the book of the law, which became the program for further cultic reformation (xxxiv 8–35). A spectacular observance of the passover followed (xxxv 1–19). The account of Josiah closes with the king's death at Megiddo where he attempted to thwart Pharaoh Neco in his hasty march to the Euphrates to assist the Assyrians against their opponents (xxxv 20–27). Succeeding reigns are passed over rapidly (xxxvi 1–21). Chronicles ends with a reference to the rise of Cyrus and his benevolent attitude toward the captive Jews in Babylon (xxxvi 22–23).

USE OF THE SOURCES[6]

One of the most difficult problems arising from the study of the literary composition of Chronicles, Ezra, and Nehemiah is the origin and use of the compiler's sources. Can his references to the sources noted in the previous section be taken seriously or were they already present in the anthology employed by him? The answer to that question will, to some extent, determine the evaluation placed on materials transmitted by the Chronicler which are not found elsewhere. R. H. Pfeiffer thinks he draws about one half of his material from earlier biblical books, while the other half consists, for the most part, of more or less historical fiction.[7] B. Maisler thinks that both Kings and Chronicles were dependent on "the words" of the prophets and famous personalities to a very large extent and to a lesser degree on the temple chronicles and official records.[8] The Chronicler's use of his sources is closely related to his purpose, his theology and general point of view,[9] which in turn depend on one's interpretation.[10] In the following resume only the barest facts can be stated, but it is absolutely essential for purposes of evaluation of the problem. For the sake of convenience, the outline follows the one above on content.

Solomon's reign and activity (II Chron i–ix)[11]

    i—Solomon's prayer with Yahweh's response (i 7–12 ‖ I Kings iii 5–15; i 14–17 ‖ I Kings x 26–29; i 5 ‖ Exod xxxviii 1 ff.).

[6] Based on M. Noth's analysis in ÜS, pp. 131–50. A complete discussion of the sources of the Chronicler's work is given in the comprehensive introduction to *I Chronicles*.

[7] *Introduction to the Old Testament,* pp. 803 ff.

[8] "Ancient Israelite Historiography," IEJ 2 (1952), 82–88.

[9] See A. M. Burnet, "Le Chroniste et ses sources," RB 60 (1953), 481–508; RB 60 (1954), 349–86.

[10] Cf. Noth, ÜS, pp. 110–80. Also Rothstein and Hänel, *Kommentar zum ersten Buch der Chronik,* pp. ix–lxxxii; Galling, *Die Bücher der Chronik, Esra, Nehemia,* pp. 8–12; Rudolph, pp. x–xxiv; Goettsberger, *Die Bücher der Chronik oder Paralipomenon,* pp. 6–17; Curtis and Madsen, pp. 17–26; and the various introductions (for complete references, see Selected Bibliography, Commentaries).

[11] Noth is certainly correct in assuming that the material of this section is pretty much as it left the hand of the Chronicler—ÜS, pp. 116 f.

Note resort to Gibeon for sacrifice where altar of Bezalel was located at the tent of meeting. Jerusalem had not yet attained its later status. The ark was at Jerusalem, but was associated only with musical service and not with sacrifices.

ii–vii—Temple affairs (ii 3 || I Kings v 3 ff.; ii 7 || v 6; ii 11 || v 7; ii 16–17 || v 13–18, not very close, iii || v, vii, not close; iv 2–5 || vii 23–26; iv 10–22 || vii 39–50; v 1–14 || vii 51–viii 11; vi 1–40 || viii 12–53; vi 41–42 || Ps cxxxii 8–11; vii 1–10 || viii 54–66, not verbally close; vii 11–22 || ix 1–9; vii 1–3a || Exod xl 34 f. and Lev ix 24). Nearly all commentators agree that the writer's source here was the Deuteronomic book of Kings. There may be a few minor additions such as v 11b–13a, vii 6, 9, vii 12b–15. But the author has not lost sight of his aim, that is, the temple, and has omitted matters apparently irrelevant to him (cf. rest of the records and II Chron ix 29); he has transmitted the tradition in his own words.

viii–ix, External matters pertaining to Solomon: his campaign to Hamath-zobah, corvée, fulfillment of religious obligations in accordance with the commands of David, shipping and trade through Ezion-geber, the visit of the queen of Sheba which reminds the writer of the wealth of Solomon made to minister to the glory of God (ix 11). Omissions and inclusions may be seen from the following: viii 1–18 || I Kings ix 10–28; ix 1–28 || I Kings x 1–29 (ix 26 || I Kings v 1); ix 29–31 || I Kings xi 41–43.[12]

Other kings of Judah (II Chronicles x–xxxvi)

x–xii, Rehoboam's reign (x 1–19 || I Kings i–xx [Chronicles omits vs. 20]; xi 1–4 || I Kings xii 21–24; xi 5–17 || xii 25–23). Chronicles expands and omits in last passage. The list of Rehoboam's fortified cities is historically trustworthy.[13] The Levitical exodus from Israel to Jerusalem fortified the Chronicler's

[12] On II Chron viii 2–6 see C. H. Gordon, IEJ 5 (1955), 88.
[13] G. Beyer, "Das Festungssystem Rehabeams," ZDPV 54 (1931), 113–34; K. Elliger, ZDPV 57 (1934), 87 ff.; Alt, "Festungen und Levitenorte im Land Juda," KS, II, pp. 306–15; W. F. Albright, "The Judicial Reform of Jehoshaphat," AMJV, pp. 66 f. Whether the fortification took place before or after the Shishak invasion is not clear, but R. Kittel, (GVI, II, p. 223) suggests it was afterward.

conception that only at Jerusalem is true Yahwism to be found and thus is doubtless tendentious, though it rests on a factual basis as may be judged by Jeroboam's construction in his kingdom of religious centers with a more conservative tendency (I Kings xii 27 ff.). The family list of Rehoboam[14] is derived from a special source and is at least partially historical. Chapter xi 23 indicates that he carried out the policies of his father (I Kings iv 8–19). Chapter xii 1–12, the invasion of Shishak, depends on I Kings xiv 25–28; xii 13–14 ‖ I Kings xiv 21–22; xii 15–16 is a variant of I Kings xiv 29–31, but not because different sources are mentioned.

xiii—Abijah. Greatly expanded from I Kings xv 1–8. Abijah's successful war with Israel is probably historical,[15] though it has some typical Chronicler touches. The Northerners were probably more numerous and powerful than the Judeans— as was the case between Samaritans and returnees in the time of the writer. Abijah's victory was due to an alliance with the Aramaeans (cf. I Kings xv 19) and brought Benjamin into the camp of Judah. Observe the theological tendency of Abijah's address to Jeroboam. In the reign of Asa, a portion of Benjamin was in Southern hands, thanks to the intervention of Benhadad (I Kings xv 19–22).[16] The best proof of the Chronicler's assertion is Baasha's attempt to retake some of the lost territory (I Kings xv 17).

xiv–xvi—Asa (xiv 1 ‖ I Kings xv 11; xv 16–19 ‖ I Kings xv 13–15; xvi 1–6 ‖ I Kings xv 17–22; xvi 11–14 ‖ I Kings xv 23–24). The Chronicler has greatly embellished the material found in Kings, for which he had other unutilized sources at his command. Albright thinks an Egyptian colony composed of Cushites was settled between Egypt and Judah by Shishak. This was the force that Asa subdued in part (xiv 9–15), but he did not succeed in taking their capital at Gerar. Since the booty included camels, the Cushites were doubtless assisted by

---

[14] See Noth, ÜS, p. 143, n. 1.

[15] Cf. Kittel, GVI, II, pp. 224 f. Noth, The History of Israel, p. 233, attributes it to Rehoboam. Cf. Noth, ÜS, p. 142. Bright, A History of Israel, p. 215, and Rudolph, pp. 235–39, also think it is historical.

[16] On Benhadad's first invasion of Israel (II Chron xv 19–xvi 6) see W. F. Albright in BASOR 87 (October 1942), 27 f.

the bedouin.[17] In view of this fact it is within the range of possibility that Asa built, perhaps rebuilt, fortified cities (xiv 6). That he engaged in reforming activity is attested also by Kings.[18] xvii–xx—Jehoshaphat (xviii 1–34 || I Kings xx 1–36; xx 31–37 || I Kings xxii 41–47). The Kings parallels may safely be regarded as representing the Chronicler's views of the received tradition. The judicial reform is factual.[19] The miraculous deliverance of Jehoshaphat from a coalition of Moabites, Ammonites, and Arabs sounds very much like the Israel-Aramaean affair described in II Kings vii. Behind it lies a historical nucleus,[20] though it is difficult to get at the precise facts. As usual the story is shot through with Levitical themes of the Chronicler—the piety of Jehoshaphat, the message of the Levitical prophet (xx 14), the Levitical praises (19 f.), singers appointed to praise Yahweh (21) and the valley of Beracah (blessing). Note the reasons given for the failure of the maritime venture (36–37; cf. I Kings xxii 47–50a).[21]

xxi—Jehoram (xxi 1 || I Kings xxii 51; xxi 2–11 || II Kings viii 16–22). Apparently the Chronicler had another source besides Kings since he reports Jehoram's slaying of his brothers, which is not beyond belief because other kings had done the same and because they may have objected to his policies (cf. II Chron xxi 13). The revolt of Edom and Libnah is reported also in Kings. The defection of Philistine areas (submissive under Jehoshaphat, II Chron xvii 11) and the restlessness of the bedouin in the south is quite possible under such unstable conditions—a legitimate assumption on the basis of other revolts successfully carried out against the king of Judah.[22]

xxii—Ahaziah and Athaliah (xxii 1–6 || II Kings viii 24b–29; xxii 7–9 || II Kings ix 20, 21, 27, 28; xxii 10–12 || II Kings xi 1–3). The slaying of Ahaziah's sons is utilized by the writer as

[17] W. F. Albright, "Egypt and the Early History of the Negeb," JPOS 4 (1924), 146 f.
[18] Albright, ARI, pp. 157–59.
[19] Albright, AMJV, pp. 74–82. I Chron xvii 7–9 may be a doublet describing the reform movement.
[20] M. Noth, "Eline palästinische Lokalüberlieferung in 2 Chron. 20," ZDPV 67 (1944/45), 45 ff.
[21] Cf. N. Glueck in BASOR 79 (October 1940), 8.
[22] Cf. Kittel, GVI, p. 264, n. 6.

retaliation for Jehoram's slaying of his brothers (xxii 1). His enthronement was probably the act of Jerusalem's officialdom who assumed the function of the am-ha-aretz. The latter had apparently been pushed into the background by the adoption of Northern policy in Judah because of the close relationship with the Ahab dynasty. That policy was doubtless followed by Athaliah. The rest of the material is from Kings.

xxiii—Jehoiada's acts in behalf of Joash (xxiii 1–21 || II Kings xi 4–20, with some additions by the Chronicler). The additions are interesting; the priests and Levites participate in the plot to thwart Athaliah whereas in Kings only the Carians and guards are mentioned.[23]

xxiv—The reign of Joash (|| II Kings xii). In addition to the three facts mentioned in Kings, the Chronicler supplies from his source the reference to his family (vs. 3), the death of Jehoiada (vss. 15–16) and the murder of Zechariah, the priest's son (vss. 20–22). In connection with the restoration of the temple, the Levites occupy the center of the stage rather than the priests. The Aramaean invasion is toned down considerably. These additions may well be historical, at least in essence; the Zechariah incident reflects the writer's interest in the prophets though, if historical, was given a peculiar religious twist.

xxv—Amaziah (xxv 1–4 || II Kings xiv 1–6; xxv 11 || II Kings xiv 7; xxv 17–24 || II Kings xiv 8–14; xxv 25–28 || II Kings xiv 17–20). Theologizing is very evident at two points: the prophet forbidding the use of Israelite mercenaries because Yahweh is not with Israel, and the statement that Amaziah served the gods of Edom which he had captured and brought to Jerusalem. There may have been some provocation for Amaziah's challenge of Joash (vs. 13), though the allegory of the thistle and the cedar in both accounts strongly suggests the pride of the former. The defeat of Amaziah and the conspiracy against him are interpreted as punishment for his failure to heed the prophet.

xxvi—Uzziah (Azariah) (xxvi 1–2 || II Kings xiv 21–22; xxvi 3–4 || II Kings xv 2–3; xxvi 20–23 || II Kings xv 5–7). A whole

---

[23] On the whole episode see W. Rudolph, "Die Einheitlichkeit der Erzählung vom Sturz Atalja," FAB, pp. 473–78, and Würthwein, Der 'amm . . . , pp. 22 ff.

mass of information is preserved here that is not found in Kings. Archaeological discoveries offer ample evidence of great building activity in this period. Towers were constructed in the wilderness and cisterns carved out.[24] Elath was rebuilt and Jerusalem fortified. The position of the priests is shown by their rebuke of Uzziah for overstepping his bounds in offering incense.[25]

xxvii—Jotham (xxvii 1–3 || II Kings xv 33–35; xxvii 7 || II Kings xv 36; xxvii 9 || II Kings xv 38). The Chronicler notes that Jotham continued the policies of his father. That appears pretty well established by archaeological results. His success is attributed to the fact that "he did what was right in the sight of Yahweh" and did not go into the temple.

xxviii—Ahaz (xxviii 1–5 || II Kings xvi 2–5; xxviii 16 || II Kings xvi 6–7; xxviii 20 || II Kings xvi 9; xxviii 26–27 || II Kings xvi 19–20). Chapter preserves some historical material not in Kings. The Edomite-Philistine uprising is quite plausible in the light of Assyrian inscriptions.[26] The list of Ephraimite chiefs came from the source. Of interest is the notice of the prophet Oded and his declaration of Israel's guilt; so also the reference to the Israelites as brothers of the Judahites (vss. 8, 11, 15), which may be due to his theology.

xxix–xxxii—Hezekiah (xxix 1–2 || II Kings xviii 1–3; xxxi 1 || II Kings xviii 4; xxxii 1–2 || II Kings xviii 13, Isa xxxvi 1; xxxii 9–15 || II Kings xviii 17, 19, 22, 35, 33, 29, Isa xxxvi 2, 4, 7, 14, 20, 18; xxxii 20–21 || II Kings xix 15, 35–37, Isa xxxvii 36–38; xxxii 24 || II Kings xx 1–2, Isa xxxviii 1–2; xxxii 31 || II Kings xx 12–13, Isa xxxix 1–2; xxxii 33 || II Kings xx 20–21). The Chronicler reflects only eighteen verses of Kings; the other material is his own (approximately 100 verses). He regards Hezekiah as more than a descendant of David; he is vir-

---

[24] Cf. F. M. Cross, Jr., and J. T. Milik, BASOR 142 (April 1956), 5–17. They favor the age of Jehoshaphat but admit that the activity in the Judean Buqeʻah could have taken place under Uzziah. Iron II sherds and an inscribed ostracon were found at Qumran (RB 61 [1954], 567); also an Israelite installation and cistern attributed by Father de Vaux to Jotham or Uzziah (RB 63 [1956], 535 f.). Cf. the fortress at Hurvat ʻUzzah; see Y. Aharoni, "The Negeb of Judah," IEJ 8 (1958), 37. For an archaeological summary, see F. Feuillet, VT 11 (1961), 270–91.
[25] See further the discussion in the COMMENT on Sec. 28.
[26] See references in COMMENT on Sec. 30.

tually a second David. The Levites figure prominently in his special material; he combines the musical services with sacrifices at the temple. Emphasis is placed on the king's observance of the commandments of David. There is nothing improbable in the outline of Hezekiah's reforming and missionary activity.[27] The fortification of Jerusalem and preparations for siege are doubtless historical.

xxxiii 1–20—Manasseh (xxxiii 1–10 || II Kings xxi 1–10; xxxiii 18–20 || II Kings xxi 17–18). The Chronicles source included the story of Manasseh's conversion, an attempt to explain the long reign of Judah's worst king.[28] Some of the story may be true, especially that dealing with the Assyrian captivity.

xxxiii 21–25—Amon (|| II Kings xxi 19–24). Source here was Kings, which was somewhat curtailed.

xxxiv–xxxv—Josiah (xxxiv 1–2 || II Kings xxii 1–2; xxxiv 8–28 || II Kings xxii 3–20; xxxiv 29–33 || II Kings xxiii 1–3; xxxv 1 || II Kings xxiii 21; xxxv 18–19 || II Kings xxiii 22–23; xxxv 20 || II Kings xxiii 29; xxxv 24 || II Kings xxiii 30a). Of the fifty verses of II Kings, some thirty are paralleled in II Chron. The Chronicler has expanded the story by using materials unknown or rejected by the Deuteronomist. Josiah's reforming activity began in his twelfth year (ca. 629 B.C.), a few years before the death of Asshurbanipal, and the relative inactivity of the Assyrians in the west. His concern for the people of the north follows that of Hezekiah. His conflict with Neco is correctly interpreted (xxxv 20) and must come from his source.[29] Josiah aspired to become another David and his religio-political activity is, in general, correctly reflected by the writer. He brings in his favorite Levites and mentions the prophetess Huldah. The Levites were the teachers of all Israel (xxxv 3) and participants in the preparations for the passover.

xxxvi 1–4—Jehoahaz (|| II Kings xxiii 30b–34). Source curtailed.

---

[27] Chapter xxx has been unduly suspected (cf. W. F. Albright, JBL 58 [1939], 185). On the whole situation see Albright, BP, p. 42; Kittel, GVI, II, p. 376.

[28] E. Meyer, GA, III p. 60, n. 1. For other references see COMMENT on Sec. 36.

[29] Cf. Couroyer, "Le litige entre Josias et Nechao," RB 55 (1948), 388–96; M. B. Rowton, "Jeremiah and the Death of Josiah," JNES 10 (1951), 128–30; D. J. Wiseman, *Chronicles of Chaldaean Kings*, 1956, pp. 18 ff.

xxxvi 5–8—Jehoiakim (‖ II Kings xxiii 34–37; xxiv 1, 5, 6). Also
somewhat shortened. His being bound in chains is connected with
a revolt against Nebuchadnezzar after the latter's indecisive
campaign against Egypt in 601 B.C.[30]
xxxvi 9–10—Jehoiachin (‖ II Kings xxiv 8–10, 16b–17). A greatly
condensed version of the essentials as given in Kings and now
known from the Weidner texts.[31]
xxxvi 11–21—Zedekiah (11–13a ‖ II Kings xxiv 18–20, Jer lii
1–3). The twenty-five verses of Kings have been condensed to
eleven and the historical events theologized. The writer's reference to the duration of the Exile (20) marks a good transition point for the last verses, which were added after the
completion of the work.
xxxvi 22–23—The decree of Cyrus (‖ Ezra i 1–3a).

Conclusion

The Chronicler had at his disposal the priestly redaction of the
tetrateuch and the great history of the Deuteronomist, which included the books of Deuteronomy, Joshua, Judges, Samuel, and
Kings. The fact that he omitted much material indicates only that
it did not contribute to his purpose—not that he rejected it as
untrue; it was clearly available to him, as his use of surrounding
matter demonstrates. The inclusion of material supplementary to that
of the Deuteronomist does not of itself mean that he wanted to add
to the sum total of historical knowledge; it may indicate only that
additions or omissions supported his main thesis in a given situation. Where he followed the Deuteronomist exactly, it may be presumed to have represented his point of view.

It is fairly certain that he was in possession of copies of official
documents and memoirs (Ezra and Nehemiah), as well as of official
lists of various types which he may have completed partly from oral
tradition and partly from studies and collections of his own. The
availability and use of some independent prophetic materials appear
quite plausible. Moreover, sources of information not found elsewhere but which were drawn from the archives of the temple and

[30] He may have bought off Nebuchadnezzar. See Wiseman, *op. cit.*, pp.
29 f.; D. N. Freedman, *The Biblical Archaeologist Reader*, 1961, pp. 113–
27.
[31] W. F. Albright, "King Jehoiachin in Exile," BA 5 (1942), 49–55.

were authentic, as can be shown from archaeological discoveries and topographical studies, were utilized.

The matter of recensions is difficult and no firm conclusion is possible. That there were later additions to some stories, perhaps whole stories compiled and inserted, can hardly be doubted, but it seems unwise to conclude that there was wholesale revision or major rewriting of the original work. It would appear that the work is pretty much as it was when it left the hands of the author, with the exception of the additions which may have been intended to bring it up to date or make it applicable to a slightly later period. Furthermore, within the limits of its purpose, the Chronicler's story is accurate wherever it can be checked, though the method of presentation is homiletical. The only valid objection to the foregoing statement could be his numbers which, by any interpretation, are impossibly high. This fact perhaps more than any other has made the Chronicler's work suspect.

The reader may wish to consult the general introduction to the work of the Chronicler, which appears as the Introduction to *I Chronicles,* on THE THEOLOGY OF THE CHRONICLER (The Chronicler's Conception of God, Worship, Israel as God's People, The Prophets and the Torah, and Messianism) and AUTHORSHIP AND DATE.

SELECTED BIBLIOGRAPHY

COMMENTARIES

Barnes, W. E., *The Books of the Chronicles* (Cambridge Bible for Schools and Colleges). Cambridge, 1899.

Benzinger, I., *Die Bücher der Chronik* (Kurzer Hand-Commentar zum Alten Testament). Tübingen und Leipzig: Mohr, 1901.

Cazelles, H., *Les Livres des Chroniques* (La Sainte Bible). Paris: Cerf, 1954.

Curtis, E. L., and Madsen, A. A., *A Critical and Exegetical Commentary on the Books of Chronicles* (The International Critical Commentary). New York: Scribner's, 1910.

Elmslie, W. A. L., "The First and Second Books of Chronicles," *The Interpreter's Bible*, III, pp. 339–548. New York and Nashville: Abingdon Press, 1954.

Galling, K., *Die Bücher der Chronik, Esra, Nehemia* (Das Alte Testament Deutsch). Göttingen: Vandenhoeck & Ruprecht, 1954.

Goettsberger, J., *Die Bücher der Chronik oder Paralipomenon* (Die heilige Schrift des Alten Testaments, XII). Bonn: Peter Hanstein, 1939.

Haller, M., *Chronik* (Die Schriften des Alten Testaments, II, 3, pp. 330–54). Göttingen: Vandenhoeck & Ruprecht, 2d ed., 1925.

Kittel, R., *Die Bücher der Chronik und Esra, Nehemia und Esther* (Handkommentar zum Alten Testament). Göttingen: Vandenhoeck & Ruprecht, 1902.

Noordtzij, A., *De Boeken der Kronieken* (Korte Verklaring der Heilige Schrift). Kampen: J. H. Kok, 2d ed., 1957 (2 vols.).

Rehm, M., *Die Bücher der Chronik* (Echter-Bibel). Würzburg: Echter-Verlag, 1934.

Rothstein, J. W., and Hänel, J., *Kommentar zum ersten Buch der Chronik* (Kommentar zum Alten Testament). Leipzig: A. Deichert, 1927.

Rudolph, W., *Chronikbücher* (Handbuch zum Alten Testament). Tübingen: Mohr, 1955.

Slotki, I. W., *Chronicles* (Soncino Books of the Bible). London: The Soncino Press, 1952.

Van Den Born, A., *Kronieken* (De Boeken van Het Oude Testament). Roermond en Maaseik: J. J. Romen & Zonen, 1960.

Van Selms, A., *I-II Kronieken* (Tekst en Uitleg). Groningen-Batavia: J. B. Wolter, 1939, 1947.

OTHER WORKS

Abel, F. M., *Géographie de la Palestine*. Paris: Gabalda, 1933, 1938.

Albright, W. F., *Archaeology and the Religion of Israel* (abbr. ARI). Johns Hopkins Press, 1942.

————, *From the Stone Age to Christianity* (abbr. FSAC). New York: Doubleday Anchor Books, 1957.

Alexander Marx Jubilee Volume, English Section (abbr. AMJV). New York: The Jewish Theological Seminary of America, 1950.

Alt, A., *Kleine Schriften zur Geschichte des Volkes Israel* (abbr. KS). Munich: Beck, 3 vols., 1953–59.

Bright, John, *A History of Israel*. Philadelphia: Westminster Press, 1959.

Cowley, A., ed. and tr., *Aramaic Papyri of the Fifth Century B.C.* (abbr. AP). Oxford: Clarendon Press, 1923.

Ehrlich, A. B., *Randglossen zur hebräischen Bibel,* VII. Leipzig: Hinrichs, 1914.

Festschrift für Alfred Bertholet (abbr. FAB). Tübingen: Mohr, 1950.

Gressmann, H., ed., *Altorientalische Bilder zum Alten Testament* (abbr. AOT). Berlin and Leipzig: Walter de Gruyter, 2d ed., 1927.

Junge, E., *Die Wiederaufbau des Heerwesens des Reiches Juda unter Josia.* Stuttgart: Kohlhammer, 1937.

Kittel, R., *Geschichte des Volkes Israel* (abbr. GVI). 3 vols., 1923–29: Vols. I, II (Gotha: Leopold Klotz Verlag, 1923, 1925); Vol. III (Stuttgart: Kohlhammer, 1927, 1929).

Kraeling, E. G. H., ed., *The Brooklyn Museum Aramaic Papyri* (abbr. BMAP). Yale University Press, 1953.

Kropat, A., "Die Syntax des Autors der Chronik" (*Beihefte zur Zeitschrift für die alttestamentliche Wissenschaft*). Giessen: A. Töpelmann, 1909.

Kugler, F. X., *Von Moses bis Paulus* (pp. 234–300). Munster: 1922.

Louis Ginzberg Jubilee Volume, English Section (abbr. LGJV). New York: The Jewish Theological Seminary of America, 1945.

Luckenbill, D. D., ed., *Ancient Records of Assyria and Babylonia* (abbr. ARAB). University of Chicago Press, 1926, 1927.

Meyer, E., *Die Entstehung des Judenthums* (abbr. EJ). Halle: Niemeyer, 1896.

———, *Geschichte des Altertums* (abbr. GA). Darmstadt: Wissenschaftliche Buchgemeinschaft (reprint), 1953–58, 3d ed., 1954.

———, *Kleine Schriften*. Halle: Niemeyer, 2d ed., 1924.

Noth, M., *Die israelitischen Personennamen im Rahmen der gemeinsemitischen Namengebung* (abbr. IPN) (*Beiträge zur Wissenschaft vom Alten und Neuen Testament*). Stuttgart: Kohlhammer, 1928.

———, *The History of Israel*. New York: Harper, 1958.

———, *Überlieferungsgeschichtliche Studien* (abbr. ÜS). Tübingen: Niemeyer Verlag, 2d ed., 1957.

Pritchard, J. B., ed., *The Ancient Near East in Pictures Relating to the Old Testament* (abbr. ANEP). Princeton University Press, 1954.

———, *Ancient Near Eastern Texts Relating to the Old Testament* (abbr. ANET). Princeton University Press, 2d ed., 1955.

Rehm, M., *Textkritische Untersuchungen zu den Parallelstellen der Samuel-Königsbücher und der Chronik* (Alttestamentliche Abhandlungen). Münster: Aschendorff, 1937.

Torrey, C. C., *Ezra Studies*. University of Chicago Press, 1910.

———, *The Chronicler's History of Israel*. Yale University Press, 1954.

Vannutelli, P., *Libri Synoptici Veteris Testamenti seu Librorum Regum et Chronicorum loci paralleli*. Rome: Pontificio Instituto Biblico, 1931.

von Rad, G., *Das Geschichtsbild des chronistischen Werkes* (Beiträge zur Wissenschaft vom Alten und Neuen Testament). Stuttgart: Kohlhammer, 1930.

Welch, A. C., *The Work of the Chronicler*. London: The British Academy, 1939.

———, *Post-Exilic Judaism*. Edinburgh and London: William Blackwood, 1935.

ARTICLES

Albright, W. F., "The Biblical Period" (abbr. BP), *The Jews: Their History, Culture, and Religion,* ed. L. Finkelstein (New York: Harper, 1949), I, pp. 3–69.

———, "The Date and Personality of the Chronicler," JBL 40 (1921), 104–24.

———, "The Judicial Reform of Jehoshaphat," *Alexander Marx Jubilee Volume,* English Section (abbr. AMJV).

——, "The List of Levitic Cities," *Louis Ginzberg Jubilee Volume* I, English Section (abbr. LGJV).

Bea, A., "Neuere Arbeiten zum Problem der biblischen Chronikbucher," *Biblica* 22 (1941), 46–58.

Beyer, G., "Das Festungssystem Rehabeams," ZDPV 54 (1931), 113–34.

Burnet, A. M., "Le Chroniste et ses sources," RB 60 (1953), 481–508; RB 61 (1954), 349–86.

——, "La théologie du Chroniste. Théocratie et messianisme," *Sacra Pagina*, I, 1959, pp. 384–97.

Freedman, D. N., "The Chronicler's Purpose," CBQ 23 (1961), 436–42.

Klein, S., "Kleine Beiträge zur Erklarung der Chronik," MGWJ 70 (1926), 410–16; MGWJ 80 (1936), 195–206.

Noordtzij, A., "Les intentions du Chroniste," RB 21 (1940), 161–68.

North, R., "The Cain Music," JBL 83 (1964), 373–89.

——, "Theology of the Chronicler," JBL 82 (1963), 369–81.

Richardson, H. N., "The Historical Reliability of Chronicles," JBR 26 (1958), 9–12.

Rudolph, W., "Problems of the Books of Chronicles," VT 4 (1954), 401–9.

von Rad, G., "Die levitische Predigt in den Bücher der Chronik," *Gesammelte Studien zum Alten Testament* (München: Kaiser Verlag, 1958), pp. 248–61.

Zimmerman, F., "Chronicles as a Partially Translated Book," JQR 42 (1951–52), 265–82, 387–412.

I. THE REIGN OF SOLOMON

(ca. 962–922 B.C.)

1. SOLOMON TAKES OVER THE KINGDOM
(i 1–17)†

Formal religious ceremony

I ¹ Solomon the son of David then established himself firmly over the kingdom and Yahweh his God was with him and magnified him very greatly. ² Solomon spoke to all Israel, to the captains of the thousands and hundreds, to the judges and to every leader in all Israel, the heads of families. ³ Then Solomon, with the whole congregation, went to the high place at Gibeon because the tent of meeting of God which Moses the servant of Yahweh had made in the desert was there. ⁴ [But David had brought up the ark of God from Kiriath-jearim to the place which David had provided for it, for he had pitched a tent for it at Jerusalem]. ⁵ The bronze altar, which Bezalel the son of Uri the son of Hur had made, [was] there*a* before the tabernacle of Yahweh where Solomon and the congregation consulted him*b*. ⁶ Solomon made an offering there before Yahweh upon the bronze altar of the tent of meeting, offering upon it a thousand burnt offerings. ⁷ That night God appeared to Solomon and said to him, "Ask, what I shall give to you!" ⁸ Solomon replied to God, "You have displayed great loyalty to David my father and you have made me king in his place. ⁹ Now, O Yahweh God, may your promise to David my father be confirmed, in as much as you have made me king over a people as numerous as the dust of the earth. ¹⁰ Grant me, therefore, wisdom and knowledge to go out and come in before this people,

† **II Chron i 1–13:** cf. I Kings iii 1–15, iv 1; **14–17:** cf. I Kings x 26–29.

a Heb. "he put" has the same consonants as "there."
b I.e., Yahweh. LXX, Vulg. "it," referring to the altar.

for who can otherwise govern this people of yours that is so great?" 11 Then God said to Solomon, "Because you had this in mind and did not request riches, wealth, honor, or the death of your enemies and did not even request long life but asked for wisdom and knowledge that you may direct my people over whom I have made you king, 12 wisdom and knowledge have been granted to you, and in addition I am giving you riches, wealth, and honor such as no kings before you possessed or such as none after you shall possess." 13 So Solomon came away from the high place at Gibeon, from the tent of meeting, to Jerusalem and assumed his duties as king over Israel.

Solomon's wealth

14 Solomon then amassed chariots and horsemen; he had fourteen hundred chariots and twelve thousand horsemen which he kept in the chariot-cities and at the royal establishment at Jerusalem. 15 The king made silver and gold as plentiful in Jerusalem as stones and cedar as common as sycamore in the Shephelah. 16 Solomon's horses were imported from Cilicia; the merchants of the king acquired them at the prevailing price. 17 They imported a chariot from Egypt for six hundred shekels of silver and a horse [from Cilicia] for one hundred and fifty shekels and thus [at that price] they conveyed them through their agents to the kings of the Hittites and to the kings of Aram.

NOTES

i 10. *to go out and come in.* Originally a military expression (cf. I Sam xviii 13, 16; I Chron xi 2) but here it means to govern the people adequately and with dignity befitting a king.

11. *the death of your enemies.* Literally "the life of those who hate you." Cf. I Kings iii 11 "enemies." In fact, Solomon did remove those who opposed or threatened his position.

15. This verse is the Chronicler's contribution to the description of the quantity of Solomon's wealth. Palestine is one of the stoniest places on earth. Sycamores, not highly esteemed, grew in great numbers in the Shephelah, the low hills between the central highland and the mari-

time plain to the southwest of Bethlehem. Cedar, on the other hand, was rare and greatly prized as may be seen from the many references to the cedars of Lebanon, a few of which grow today as ornamental trees in the Augusta Victoria Hospital compound.

16. *from Cilicia.* Omitting "Egypt" here in harmony with the second part of the verse and because horses were not bred in Egypt. On Cilicia see W. F. Albright, BASOR 120 (December 1950), 22 ff.

the prevailing price. On meaning of *mehīr* see A. Goetze, "The Laws of Eshnunna," AASOR 31 (1956), 111 f.

17. Six hundred shekels is about 15⅒ lbs., 150 about 3¾ lbs. Solomon was a great merchant prince who knew how to turn every opportunity to advantage. Among other occupations, he was a dealer in Cilician horses (reported by Herodotus III.90 to be of excellent quality) and Egyptian chariots, equally fine. There can be no doubt on the rendering of *mqwh* ("from Cilicia"). Que (=Cilicia) occurs frequently in Assyrian letters and inscriptions from the time of Shalmaneser III (ninth century). Chariots were four times as expensive as horses, chiefly because wood had to be imported from Egypt and chariot making required great skill and expert workmanship. Moreover, after manufacture the cost of delivering of the product must have been high too. Horses, on the other hand, were simply raised; there is no evidence for pedigrees of any kind. See Albright, ARI, p. 135.

COMMENT

Chapter i serves, for the most part, as an introduction to the work of Solomon which, according to the Chronicler, centers almost exclusively around the building of the temple. Solomon thus carries on the work of his father as it pertains to the religious aspects of the kingdom. Here note is taken of his accession and his wealth, a subject amplified later (ch. ix), probably to emphasize the blessing of Yahweh attendant upon his concern for the cult.

[Assumption of duties as king, i 1–13]: In the background of this story is I Kings iii 1–15, with omission of the elements that did not lend themselves to the purpose the writer had in mind. The observation on Solomon's firm hold on the throne reflects the struggle for power shortly before the death of David (see COMMENT on I Chron xxix). But because God was with him, success crowned the efforts of his partisans. The first move of the new king was to summon the officials and the people to a religious service at Gibeon

—manifestly an official act rather than, as suggested by I Kings iii 4, a personal one. The references to high places in I Kings iii is carefully left out, though a parenthetical statement informs us that while the altar remained before the tent of meeting at Gibeon, the ark was in the tent pitched for it by David at Jerusalem. On the tent of meeting that Moses the servant of God had made special emphasis is laid to protect Solomon from violation of the priestly prohibition (Lev xvii 8, 9). No apology was required as was the case for the Deuteronomist (I Kings iii 3). Perhaps the Chronicler had imbibed something of the spirit of Ezekiel who discovered that the presence of Yahweh was more important than the place; that presence was symbolized by the altar and confirmed by the revelation given to Solomon. To legitimize further the national worship ceremony at the Gibeon high place, the presence of the altar of Bezalel is specifically stressed. Only here do we read of the altar at Gibeon (cf. I Chron xvi 39, 40, xxi 29) being that of Bezalel (Exod xxxi 2–11, xxxviii 1–2). Here it is said to be made of bronze but it was actually made of acacia wood (Exod xxvii 1–2) overlaid with bronze. The holding of this first national religious gathering at Gibeon gains added significance when it is recalled that Zadok was the officiating priest there (I Chron xvi 39–42). On the offerings themselves, cf. the source, I Kings iii 4c–5.

The nocturnal theophany is based on I Kings iii 5–13, 15, iv 1 but is effectively condensed—a fact that demonstrates the literary method of the writer and his use of his sources. God appears to Solomon directly and not in a dream. The Deuteronomist's expatiation on David is omitted because the attention is focused on the man of peace. In place of a discerning mind to judge the people rightly and an ability to distinguish between good and evil, the Chronicler appropriately speaks of wisdom and knowledge, though the significance is the same. Perhaps the most striking omission of all is the appearance of Solomon before the ark and offering sacrifices there (I Kings iii 15b). It is only after these elaborate cultic rites that Solomon assumes his duties as king.

[Amassing of wealth, 14–17]: The wealth and wisdom of Solomon are referred to also in chapter ix and as such can hardly be incidental. The story of the harlots, so vividly told in I Kings iii 16–28 to illustrate his wisdom, is passed over by the Chronicler but the material wealth of the king is accentuated not only here but throughout the narrative to prove the fulfillment of the divine promise of blessings—riches, wealth, and honor—such as no king before or after him possessed. This is a cliché not to be applied literally. Though the divine promise veers away a bit from the Deuteronomic formula—blessing equals prosperity and wealth and riches may derive from wisdom—the end result is the same: Blessing equals wisdom equals wealth. It is striking that this little pericope stands at the beginning of the story and that to the horses, chariots, horsemen, silver, and cedar, gold is added; otherwise I Kings x 26–29 is followed practically verbatim. The writer has in mind two things as he proceeds with his account of Solomon: (a) the fact that Yahweh had blessed him beyond parallel and (b) that his interest in the temple—religious institutions—must not be obscured by other matters however important. That is why he disposes of the other matters pertaining to Solomon's kingdom so quickly.

2. BUILDING THE TEMPLE: PREPARATIONS
(i 18 [ii 1E], ii 1–17 [ii 2–18E]†

I 18 Then Solomon gave the order to build a house for the name of Yahweh and a palace for himself.

II 1 Solomon allotted seventy thousand burden-bearers, eighty thousand quarrymen in the mountain and thirty-six hundred overseers over them. 2 Then Solomon sent the following message to King Huram[a] of Tyre: "As you did for David, my father, when you sent him cedars to build for himself a house to dwell in—3 For you see, I am going to build a house to the name of Yahweh my God, dedicating it to him that perfumed incense may be burned before him, the layer bread set out continually, burnt offerings offered in the morning, in the evening, on the Sabbaths, at the time of the new moons and the festivals of Yahweh our God, as prescribed eternally for Israel. 4 The house I am building must be great, for our God is greater than all [other] gods. 5 Yet who can summon strength to build a house for him when heaven and the highest heavens cannot contain him? Who am I that I should build a house for him, except to burn incense before him?—6 So send me now a man trained to work in gold, silver, bronze, iron, purple, crimson, and violet materials, and who knows how to make engravings; he is to work with my trained men in Judah and Jerusalem whom David my father has provided. 7 Send me also cedar, cypress, and algum lumber from Lebanon, for I know that your servants are experienced in cutting Lebanon timber; indeed, my servants will assist your servants 8 to prepare timber in abun-

† II Chron i 18–ii 17: cf. I Kings v 1–18 (v 15–32H), vii 13–14.

[a] Some manuscripts, Vulg., LXX read "Hiram."

dance for me, because the house that I am building is to be
wondrously great. ⁹ I will provide one hundred thirty thousand
bushels of wheat, one hundred thirty thousand bushels of barley,
one hundred twenty thousand gallons of wine, and one hundred
twenty thousand gallons of oil for the board of your servants,
the woodsmen cutting the timbers." ¹⁰ Huram^a king of Tyre sent
to Solomon the following written reply: "Because Yahweh loves
his people, he has made you king over them." ¹¹ Huram said
further, "Praised be Yahweh God of Israel, who made heaven
and earth and has given David a wise son, endowed with such
insight and understanding, to build a house for Yahweh and a
palace for his kingdom. ¹² I have just now sent a trained man,
endowed with good judgment, namely Huramabi, ¹³ who is the
son of a Danite woman but his father is a Tyrian. He is trained
to work in gold, silver, bronze, iron, stone, and wood, and in
purple, violet, linen and crimson materials; also to do all kinds
of engraving and to work out any artistic design that may be
entrusted to him in conjunction with your artists and the artists
of my lord David, your father. ¹⁴ Now let my lord send the
wheat, the barley, the oil, and the wine to his servants as he
promised, ¹⁵ and we will cut all the timber you need from Lebanon and ship it to you in sea rafts as far as Joppa, but you must
transfer it from there to Jerusalem." ¹⁶ Then Solomon took a
census of all the foreigners in the land of Israel similar to the
census which David his father had taken and one hundred fifty-
three thousand six hundred were found. ¹⁷ He made seventy
thousand of them burden-bearers, eighty thousand of them
quarrymen in the mountain, and three thousand six hundred
of them overseers to keep the people at work.

NOTES

ii 1. See NOTE on vs. 17 below.

3. *layer bread.* Also known as show bread, presence bread, continual
bread. The loaves of bread placed on the acacia table standing before
Yahweh in the temple (cf. Heb ix 2 ff.; Exod xxv 30).

9. Since a kor contained about 6½ bushels, there were about 130,000 bushels each of barley and wheat. A bath was slightly more than 6 gallons, thus making 120,000 gallons each of oil and wine.

the board. Reading *makkōlet* with Vulg. for *makkōt* "crushed" (cf. I Kings v 25, with syncopation of *aleph*).

12. *Huramabi.* The Kings parallels (I Kings vii 13, 40, 45) all have Hiram (originally Ahiram). The text could be read "Huram my father," but King Hiram's father was Abibaal. Rudolph (*Chronikbücher*, p. 200 [see Selected Bibliography, Commentaries]) suggests "Huram, my master" and points out that *'ab* sometimes means adviser, master, as in Gen xlv 8; Judg xvii 10; I Maccabees xi 32. If that is correct, the meaning here might be "Huram, my master (craftsman)."

13. *the son . . . Tyrian.* Rudolph, p. 225, thinks this tradition may be based on an oral source.

15. A copper axhead found in Syria belonged to an ancient Egyptian boat crew possibly engaged in procuring cedar from Lebanon. See BJRL 44 (1961–62), 110.

17. According to I Kings v 13 ff., Solomon raised a levy of forced laborers from "all Israel." The Chronicler modified the claims of his source by limiting the levy to foreigners in Israel. The Deuteronomist has the levies working in relays of three months. Corvées in early Egypt also served in relays of three months, the system being based on the duration of the inundation of the Nile. Cf. Herodotus II.124 and H. Kees, *Ancient Egypt* (London, 1961), p. 55. How to interpret the numbers is a question. If they are based on the unit principle, there would be 153 units, each with 600 persons, yielding a total of 91,800. The 150 units (perhaps a round number) would comprise 90,000 workmen, assuming the same number of persons per unit (i.e., 600). For these 90,000 workmen, there were three units of overseers which (on the same basis) would comprise 1800 individuals, or one overseer for 50 workmen.

COMMENT

[Preparations for the construction of the temple, i 18]: Despite the fact that the amassing of wealth and the formation of a "mechanized" army stationed in chariot-cities in various centers of the kingdom took some time and required no little effort and planning, these developments are passed over hurriedly because the author was concerned about getting to the most significant aspect of Solomon's reign—the construction of the temple and the palace for which the order was given forthwith. That order meant simply the carrying out of the blueprints submitted to Solomon by David as set forth in I Chron xxviii 11–19. While the building of a palace is mentioned by the Chronicler, here and elsewhere (ii 11, vii 11, viii 1, ix 11), he nowhere gives details about it. Perhaps we are to think of the whole complex of buildings of which the temple was itself but the royal chapel (cf. K. Möhlenbrink, *Der Tempel Salomos,* 1932; E. Renan, *Histoire du peuple d'Israel,* II, 1891, p. 142; A. Parrot, *The Temple of Jerusalem,* 1957, pp. 51–55), or it may be that knowledge of the temple from other sources (I Kings vii 1–12) is taken for granted.

[Preparations for the construction of the temple (continued), ii 1–17]: The order of the king to proceed at once with the building of temple and palace, could not be carried out without a great deal of preparation. Such a gigantic enterprise required more than wealth and wisdom; arrangements had to be made with Hiram (Huram) of Tyre, and manpower and organization provided for the actual work. Verse 1 is a repetition of vs. 17, both of which are dependent upon the census of foreigners referred to in vs. 16 (cf. I Kings v 13 ff. (v 27H ff.) where the forced labor is drawn from all Israel). The Chronicler has thus toned down the Kings report in both scope and applicability. He has, in effect, recast the whole story to bring it into harmony with his ideas, omitting some aspects of the Deuteronomic narrative and supplying others. Solomon is a much more independent king here since he takes the initiative in carrying out the obligations to build the temple laid upon him by his father. Kings (I Kings v 1) says Hiram sent ambassadors to Solomon after David's death to console him and to congratulate him upon his own accession. Through these ambassadors of good will Solomon then made his request for men and materials. In the message conveyed to Hiram, I Chron xiv 1 is recalled and made a precedent for that of Solomon, though no mention is made of the reason for David's failure to build the temple—not a thing is said about the latter's plan for the venture, possibly because it was so fully dealt with in earlier chapters. So far as this chapter is concerned, the credit for initiative in the project belongs to Solomon. The purpose for the temple as envisioned by Solomon is worship in all its forms; it must be congruous with the greatness of Yahweh who is above all gods, though he cannot really be confined to a house made by man. Solomon's depreciation of himself conforms to the writer's view of the majesty of God in comparison with whom even the great and wealthy king pales into insignificance.

In contrast with the Kings chapter, the first request is for a man trained in the decorative crafts to direct Solomon's own craftsmen in their work—they had been provided by David, but the plans of the latter are only hinted here. In addition to the request for a skilled workman, there is the order for lumber—cedar, cypress, and algum (cf. *elammakku* in CAD, IV, pp. 75 f.). Algum was a precious wood used for furniture, palace, and temple construction; it occurs in an inventory list from Ugarit (120:10). II Chron ix 10 thinks of it as one of the products of Ophir, but it more likely came from Syria. The Kings parallel does not include it, having only cedar and cypress. Along with the order for lumber comes an offer of assistance from Solomon whose workmen are unskilled in logging (I Kings v 6 [20H]); this offer evidently was made because of the magnitude of the task. In return for Hiram's products and labor, Solomon offers to provide food and drink for the workmen. I Kings v 11 (25H) apparently thinks of the wheat and oil as tribute since it is for Hiram's household. Here barley and wine are added to the wheat and oil, a typical expansion of the Chronicler.

The reply of Hiram begins with a paean of praise to Yahweh who loves his people as shown by his selection of Solomon, David's wise son, to build the temple and palace. This marks an alteration of the Kings parallel which rather coldly, but more realistically, observes "blessed be Yahweh today who has given to David a wise son . . ." and offers to supply the needs of Solomon. Without delay, Hiram sent Huramabi, the son of a Tyrian father and a Danite mother, and urged the king to send on the supplies and laborers. Huramabi's (Hiram from Tyre in I Kings vii 13) abilities have been greatly expanded. Kings refers to him only as a worker in bronze. It has been pointed out that this expansion was due to the requirements of Solomon's temple (iii 7 ff., 14) and that the author thought of him as another Bezalel (Exod xxxi 2–5, xxxv 30–33) who was associated with two Danites. That may be the source of the Danite connection mentioned here, whereas Kings says Hiram was the son of a Naphtali widow.

The Chronicler is more definite in the agreement of Hiram to cut and ship the lumber to Joppa than is the Kings narrator. The former was aware of the port (Ezra iii 7; Jon i 3), which was the nearest to Jerusalem. According to Josh xix 46, Joppa was opposite the territory of Dan (its original allotment among Ephraim, Judah, and Philistia). It is mentioned in Egyptian documents and lists in the time of Thutmose III (fifteenth century B.C.)—see ANET, pp. 22, 242. It was one of the cities besieged by Sennacherib during his campaigns to the west—ANET, p. 287.

3. BUILDING THE TEMPLE: CONSTRUCTION
(iii 1–17)†

III ¹ So Solomon began to build the house of Yahweh in Jerusalem on Mount Moriah *which David his father had selected*—the place which David had prepared—on the threshing floor of Ornan the Jebusite. ² He began to build it on the second day in the second month of the fourth year of his reign. ³ Now these are *ᵇthe measurementsᵇ* which Solomon fixed for the building of the house of God: its length in cubits, according to the old standard, was sixty cubits and its width was twenty cubits; ⁴ the portico in front of the house was as long as the width of the house, that is, twenty cubits, and the height was one hundred and twenty cubits. On the inside he overlaid it with pure gold. ⁵ The nave he paneled with cypress wood which he overlaid with fine gold and ornamented with palm and chain designs. ⁶ He decorated the house beautifully with precious stones and with gold from Parvaim. ⁷ Thus he overlaid with gold the house, the rafters, the thresholds, its walls and its doors, and engraved the walls with cherubs. ⁸ He made the holy of holies, its length corresponding to the width of the house, twenty cubits long and twenty cubits wide and overlaid it with genuine gold weighing six hundred talents. ⁹ The weight of the nails was fifty shekels of gold. He also overlaid the upper rooms with gold.

† II Chron iii 1–17 ‖ I Kings vi 1–38, cf. vii 15–22.

ᵃ⁻ᵃ Vulg. reads *qui demonstratus fuerat David patri eius*. LXX reads "where the Lord appeared to David his father," but "Yahweh" does not appear in either MT or Vulg. See NOTE.
ᵇ⁻ᵇ Insert, with Targ., to bring out meaning. Targ. takes *hwsd* as an abbreviation for *hmdwt 'šr ysd*, "the measures which he fixed."

10 He made two molten* cherubs for the holy of holies which he likewise overlaid with gold. 11 The wings of the cherubs had a spread of twenty cubits; one wing of each (being five cubits) touched the wall of the house and the other wing (also of five cubits) touched the wing of the other cherub. 12 On the other hand, one wing of the second cherub touched the other wall of the house, while the other wing, also of five cubits, touched the wing of the first cherub. 13 The wings of these cherubs had a spread of twenty cubits. They stood on their feet with their faces toward the house. 14 He made the curtain of violet, purple, and crimson materials and linen and worked a cherub design upon it. 15 He made two pillars thirty-five cubits long for the front of the house; the capitals on top of them were five cubits. 16 He made chain designs like a necklace and placed them at the top of the pillars; he also made a hundred pomegranates which he put on the chain designs. 17 He set up the pillars in front of the temple, one on the right and the other on the left, and called the name of the one on the right Jachin and the name of the one on the left Boaz.

*The word is uncertain but probably refers to a figure of precious metal. LXX has "wood"; Vulg. *statuario opera;* I Kings vi 32 "fir" or "pine"; RSV "olivewood"; Rudolph "plastic"; Goettsberger (see Selected Bibliography, Commentaries) "sculptured work."

NOTES

iii 1. *had selected.* So with Ehrlich (*Randglossen zur hebräischen Bibel,* VII; see Selected Bibliography) and Rudolph. For this meaning of Heb. *rā'āh* see Gen xxii 8, xli 33.

—*the place . . . prepared.* This is an explanatory clause.

3. *fixed.* Reading pi. pf. for hoph.; dittography of *h.*

cubits. The cubit was 17.49 inches; that of Ezekiel (xl 5, xliii 13) was about 20.405 inches.

the old standard. The old standard was that adopted by Ezekiel and used in the time of Solomon.

4. *the portico . . . width of the house.* Cf. I Kings vi 3. A difficult verse and not very smooth Hebrew. Translation is based on LXX in

part; literally "the portico which [was] in front of the house was the length in front of the width of the house." What is apparently meant is that the length of the portico extending across the front of the house was 20 cubits. Cf. Möhlenbrink, *Der Tempel Salomos*, p. 27.

one hundred and twenty cubits. Certainly exaggerated. Original may have read 20 cubits, for which there is some evidence in the versions; *mē'āh* may be a corruption of the term for cubit. Cf. vs. 8 and iv 1. But the same figure appears in LXX.

5. *chain designs*. Cf. Akk. *šaršarratu* "chain." Chain designs were also used on the capitals (I Kings vii 17; vs. 16) of the two pillars; these were probably Phoenician. Cf. G. E. Wright, *Biblical Archaeology*, 1957, p. 140.

6. *Parvaim*. "Parvaim" is unknown; perhaps the "el Farwaim" of the Arab historian Hamdani. See H. E. del Medico, "ZAHAB PARWAYIM: L'or fructifère dans la tradition juive," VT 13 (1963), 156–86.

8. *six hundred talents*. Something over 22½ tons.

9. *fifty shekels*. Approximately 1¼ lbs.

11. *twenty cubits*. About 30 ft.

five cubits. Slightly more than 7½ ft.

12. *other*. So for clarity.

16. *like a necklace*. So with most commentators for "inner room, sanctuary," which is hardly possible here.

17. *Jachin . . . Boaz*. For possible interpretation of the names see R. B. Y. Scott, JBL 58 (1939), 143 ff.

COMMENT

Although the Chronicler has a dominant interest in the temple and its institutions, he has considerably curtailed the account now standing in I Kings. There appears to be a greater concern for the cultus than for the building itself which may be explained by the fact that the postexilic temple was evidently less elaborate than the old Solomonic one had been (cf. Josephus *Antiquities* XV.xi).

[The site and the beginning of the construction, iii 1–2]: Solomon built the temple on the site selected by David, not specified by the Kings narrative. Mount Moriah is not elsewhere connected with it. The writer thus associates the site with the land of Moriah where Abraham was to offer Isaac (Gen xxii 2), doubtless because it was designated as the mount of Yahweh (Gen xxii 14). He may have been influenced in part by Isaiah who has a great deal to say about the mountain of Yahweh (ii 2, 3, xxx 29, lxv 25, lxvi 20; cf. also Joel iii 17; Mic iv 1; Zech viii 3). The threshing floor of Ornan is not mentioned in the Kings parallel though it is possibly assumed. The date for the beginning of the building corresponds exactly with that in I Kings, though it is not so broad (for date of Solomon's temple see M. B. Rowton in BASOR 119 [October 1950], 20–22 and references cited there to others who disagree; Parrot, *The Temple of Jerusalem,* pp. 21 f.). The reference to the exodus from Egypt is not included, nor is the name of the month (I Kings vi 1 has "Ziv," i.e., "April–May"). Delay in beginning until the fourth year of his reign was due to the organizational preparations, arrangements for and transport of materials to Jerusalem and the procurement of technicians.

[The temple itself, 3–17]: The full measurements of the temple are not given. The length of the building without the portico was sixty cubits. According to I Kings vi 3, 17, 20, the dimensions of the portico were 20×10 cubits, of the nave 20×40, of the *debir* 20×20, or an over-all length of seventy cubits and breadth of twenty cubits. The $d^e b\bar{i}r$ was the "holy of holies." It means literally, "oracle," since it was the special dwelling place of the Lord. The temple consisted of three parts: the *'ūlām*—portico or vestibule, the *hēkāl* —the "holy place" or the main room of the sanctuary, and the $d^e b\bar{i}r$. The size of these parts of the temple, in terms of feet, using the long cubit, was approximately 34×17, 34×68, 34×34. For descriptions of the temple see Parrot, *The Temple of Jerusalem;* Möhlenbrink, *Der Tempel Salomos;* G. E. Wright, BA 4 (1941), 17–31, BA 18 (1955), 41–44; P. L. Garber, BA 14 (1951), 2–24. The height is given as thirty cubits for the nave in I Kings vi 2; the *debir* was a cube of 20×20×20, possibly on a platform of ten cubits so that the height of both the nave and *debir* would be the same (see Parrot, *The Temple of Jerusalem,* p. 33, and n. 5; Garber, BA 14 [1951], 18 f. and references there; Möhlenbrink, *Der Tempel Salomos,* pp. 131–41).

The portico was overlaid on the inside with pure gold (cf. I Kings vi 22). The nave paneled with cypress—I Kings vi 15 has cedar, with floor of cypress—was overlaid with gold decorated with palm and chain designs (only here). The decoration of the house with precious stones is explained by Vulg. as follows: "He laid the floor of the temple with costly marble." David had collected precious

stones which may have been used in mosaics on the floor of the
nave. The cherubs engraved on the walls are referred to also in
I Kings vi 29 where, in addition to the designs mentioned in 5b,
open flower patterns are specified.

With the exception that the height is not given, the measurement
of the *debir* corresponds to that in the Kings parallel. The enormous
amount of gold used in encasing the inside of the *debir* is com-
mensurate with I Chron xxix 4, though there is no reference to it in
Kings. Nor is there any parallel to the golden nails (really spikes),
though the golden hooks of the tabernacle (Exod xxvi 32, 37) may
have been in the mind of the writer. The "upper rooms" of the
debir are not referred to elsewhere. The cast cherubs with a total
wingspread of twenty cubits—five cubits for each of their two
wings—were placed side by side with tips touching the wall and
the other cherub and facing toward the nave (on Cherubs see BA
1 [1938], 1–3).

The curtain between the *debir* and the nave is not noticed in
I Kings, nor does it appear in Ezekiel's description of the temple.
Some think it was originally present in I Kings vi 21b but fell out
through a similarity of consonants (in Hebrew) between *curtain*
and *chains*. See Rudolph, pp. 204 f. The Kings parallel has wooden
doors between them. The reference here is based on the tabernacle
curtain (Exod xxvi 31–35) whose description is identical with this
one. According to Josephus (*Wars* V.v) there was a curtain between
debir and nave in the Herodian temple.

The most interesting feature of the two pillars is that they stood
"in front of the temple" and were thus not built into it as an integral
part of the structure (cf. Möhlenbrink, *Der Tempel Salomos*, pp.
111 f.). Albright (ARI, pp. 144–48) has shown that they were
cressets similar to those connected with Phoenician temples and
obviously had special symbolic significance for the worshipers; their
possible significance is outlined by Albright on p. 148. Cf. S. Yeivin,
"Jachin and Boaz," *Eretz Israel*, V, 1958, pp. 97–104 (in Hebrew).

4. BUILDING THE TEMPLE: FURNISHINGS
(iv 1–22, v 1)†

IV ¹ He made a bronze altar twenty cubits long, twenty cubits wide and ten cubits high. ² He made the cast-metal sea which was circular in shape, ten cubits from brim to brim, five cubits high, and thirty cubits in circumference. ³ Something like oxen under it went the whole way around it, ten per cubit around the entire sea; there were two rows of oxen cast into a solid piece with it. ⁴ It stood upon twelve oxen, three looking north, three looking west, three looking south, and three looking east, while the sea rested upon them and the hindquarters of all of them were turned inward. ⁵ It was a handbreadth in thickness, its brim was shaped like the brim of a cup, like a lily blossom, and its capacity was three thousand baths. ⁶ He made ten basins, placing five on the right and five on the left, in which to wash; they were to rinse the articles for the burnt offering in them, but the sea was for the priests to wash in. ⁷ He made ten golden lampstands according to pattern which he placed in the temple, five on the right and five on the left. ⁸ He made ten tables which he set up in the temple, five on the right and five on the left; he also made a hundred golden bowls. ⁹ He made the court of the priests and the great court together with doors for the court, which doors he overlaid with bronze. ¹⁰ He placed the sea on the right side *of the house* toward the southeast. ¹¹ Huram made the ash containers, the shovels, and the bowls; so Huram completed the work on the house of God which he had agreed to do for King Solomon; ¹² the two pillars and the basins and the capitals on top of the two pillars, the two gratings to cover

† **II Chron iv 1–22** ‖ I Kings vii 23–50; **II Chron v 1** ‖ I Kings vii 51.

ᵃ⁻ᵃ So with LXX and I Kings vii 39.

both of the basins of the capitals which were on top of the pillars, 13 the four hundred pomegranates for the two gratings —two rows of pomegranates per grating—to cover the two basins of the capitals which were upon the pillars, 14 the ten wheel bases and the ten basins for the wheel bases 15 the one sea with the twelve oxen under it, 16 the ash containers, the shovels, and the forks. Huramabi made for King Solomon all the utensils for the house of Yahweh of polished bronze. 17 The king cast them in the territory of the Jordan in the earthen foundries between Succoth and Zarethan. 18 Solomon made all these utensils in very great quantities, for the weight of the bronze was incalculable. 19 Solomon made all the utensils designed for the house of God, together with the golden altar and the tables upon which was the show bread, 20 the lampstands with their lamps, to be lighted before the *debir* according to plan, of fine gold; 21 the blossom ornaments, the lamps, and the tongs were of gold, the most precious gold. 22 The snuffers, the sprinkling bowls, the [incense] ladles, and the pans were made of genuine gold; as for the entrance to the house, its inner doors to the holy of holies as well as the doors of the house itself, that is of the temple, also were made of gold.

V   1 When all the work that Solomon did for the house of Yahweh was completed Solomon brought in the consecrated gifts of David his father: the silver, the gold, and all the utensils he had put into the treasuries of the house of God.

NOTES

iv 1. Roughly 30×30×15 feet.

3. *Something like oxen.* I Kings vii 24 "gourd-like ornaments." Note the attempt to avoid direct equation with oxen because of their resemblance to the golden bulls of the Northern Kingdom that were so obnoxious to the writer.

ten per cubit. With I Kings vii 24.

5. *a handbreadth.* Approximately three inches.

three thousand baths. I Kings vii 26 has two thousand baths. A bath=
6+ gallons.

6. *right . . . left.* I.e., of the molten sea.

rinse. This word occurs elsewhere in the OT only three times (Isa
iv 4; Ezek xl 38; Jer li 34). From Isa iv 4 we know it means "to wash."
Only here and in Ezekiel is it used in connection with the burnt offering.

11. *the bowls.* For a description of the type, see A. M. Honeyman,
PEQ (1939), 83 f.

12. *the basins.* See Zech iv 3; cf. W. F. Albright, BASOR 85 (February 1942), 25; the *gullāh* was the basin on top of the pillar.

14. *the ten . . . the ten.* Reading *'śr* and *'śrh* ("ten") for *'śh* ("he
made"), with I Kings vii 43. LXX has "ten bases." For a discussion
of the basins and bases, see L. H. Vincent in *Miscellanea Biblica B.
Ubach*, 1953, pp. 147–59.

16. *the forks.* I Kings vii 45 "bowls," as in vs. 11. For occurrence
of word elsewhere see BA 4 (1941), p. 29, n. 6.

Huramabi. See NOTE on ii 12.

all the utensils. So for "all their utensils" because of verse division.
For description see Wright, *Biblical Archaeology*, pp. 141 f.

17. *in the earthen foundries.* For this translation see N. Glueck,
BASOR 90 (April 1943), 13 f., where he discusses the difficulties involved in the generally accepted reading. His suggested reading is: "in
the earthen foundries (or in the thickened earthen moulds) between
Succoth and Zarethan." For W. F. Albright's views see "The Administrative Divisions of Israel and Judah," JPOS 5 (1925), 33, n. 37.

Zarethan. MT has *Zeredah.* With I Kings vii 46, since Zarethan, the
birthplace of Jeroboam I (I Kings xi 26), was probably in the hill
country of Ephraim. Cf. F. M. Abel, *Géographie de la Palestine*, II,
p. 457 (see Selected Bibliography).

20. *fine gold.* On *zhb sgwr* as red gold see G. R. Driver, *Ephemerides
Theologicae Lovanienses*, 1950, p. 352.

22. Note the Chronicler's glorification of the temple.

ladles. On the subject of incense spoons see W. F. Albright, *Tell Beit
Mirsim III: The Iron Age*, AASOR 21–22 (1943), par. 42; Y. Yadin et
al., *Hazor*, II, 1960, p. 63, and Pls. CVIII and CLXIV, 12, where the
object is referred to as an incense ladle.

COMMENT

[The bronze altar, iv 1]: There is no direct reference in I Kings to the construction of an altar of bronze, though its existence is demonstrated by reference thereto in I Kings viii 64, ix 25; II Kings xvi 14. The omission here is surely accidental and not deliberate, as its appearance in those passages indicates. Whether this verse is a secondary insertion is a matter for conjecture. Rudolph, p. 207, thinks it came originally from I Kings vii, where it stood between vss. 22 and 23, but fell out through homoioarkton. Both I Kings vii 23 and II Chron iv 1 begin with the same word in MT. Rudolph points out that the order in which the dimensions are given follows the Kings practice, that is, the number of cubits precedes the dimensions, whereas the Chronicler has the dimensions followed by the numbers. Then, two different words are used for height—Kings, *qūm;* Chronicles, *gbh.* Here there is no elaborate description of the block-levels of the altar as in Ezekiel. Only the top is detailed. (For a good illustration of the platform altars of Mesopotamia see ANEP, Fig. 627.)

The bronze altar of Bezalel that was in Gibeon before the tabernacle and upon which Solomon offered sacrifices (II Chron i 5-6) is certainly in the background. In the Yehawmilk inscription (fifth-fourth centuries B.C.) we read of a bronze altar made by the king of Byblos and presented to the Lady of Byblos who was, however, a goddess. (See ANET, p. 502.) The top of the altar was square, as was that of Ezekiel's temple (xliii 16). Its height was about fifteen feet, the same as that of Ezekiel, and it must have been approached by steps. For further information on the altar, see H. Wiener, *The Altars of the Old Testament,* 1927; J. de Groot, *Die Altäre des salomonischen Tempelhofes,* 1924; K. Galling, BRL, cols. 13-22; Albright, ARI, pp. 150 f.

[The cast-metal sea and the basins, 2-6]: Here the Chronicler follows Kings with only a few minor deviations, except for vs. 6. The description of the sea is clear and requires little interpretation. On the expression "something like oxen" for which Kings has "gourds were under its brim," see NOTE on vs. 3. The purpose of the sea was for the priests to wash in. The arrangement of the oxen probably had a

symbolical as well as a decorative significance. See ARI, pp. 148 f.;
Parrot, *The Temple of Jerusalem*, pp. 45 f., and drawing Fig. xi.
A connection of the twelve oxen with the twelve tribes of Israel
seems clear. The arrangement of the oxen may have something to do
with that of the tribes around the tabernacle in the desert, which
were also arranged in groups of three (Num ii). The connection of
the bull with fertility is well known; he was the symbol of Hadad,
the storm-god who was responsible for the life-giving waters. The
writer modifies the Canaanite associations by referring to the oxen
(bulls) as "something like" them. Their arrangement in groups of
three facing in the four directions may point to the four seasons,
though this is disputed by Parrot. While the Canaanite pattern is
obvious, its real meaning was probably forgotten by the writer's time,
but his description may be more accurate than the gourd pattern of
the Deuteronomist because of the latter's abhorrence of the golden
bulls of Jeroboam I.

The other variant is the capacity of the sea: Kings, two thousand
baths, Chronicles, three thousand. C. C. Wylie, BA 12 (1949),
86–90, explains the difference as due to the hemispherical shape
visualized by Kings and the cylindrical shape visualized by the
Chronicler. (For figure of forms cf. BA 4 [1941], 17, but cf.
Rudolph, p. 206; for calculations of capacity see R. B. Y. Scott in
JBL 77 [1958], 209–12, and BA 22 [1959], 29–32.) The ten
basins, placed five on the right and five on the left of the sea, were
for the washing of the burnt offering. The ten basins with their
stands are described in great detail in I Kings vii 27–39, especially
the stands. The basins were made for each stand (vs. 38). The
decorations of the stands were undoubtedly symbolic (for recon-
structions see AOT, Figs. 505, 507, 508; Parrot, *The Temple of
Jerusalem*, pp. 48 f.) and it may be that their description was omitted
by the Chronicler because of their character. The word for basin,
kiyor, derives ultimately from Sumerian and is used frequently
in the inscriptions of Sargon II in the sense of kettle or caldron
(see ARI, pp. 153 f., with notes there; and Honeyman, PEQ [1939],
82 f.).

[The lampstands, tables, bowls, 7–8]: The lampstands were
made according to pattern, which means according to the plan de-
vised for them. The tabernacle had only one lampstand with six
branches, that is, with seven light faucets (cf. Exod xxv 31 ff., xxxvii

17 ff.). That was also the case in later times (cf. I Maccabees i 21, iv 49). But I Chron xxviii 15 and Jer lii 19 refer to lampstands (plural). II Chron xiii 11 also refers to one lampstand with its lights. Nowhere else is there mention of ten tables. Ezek xl 38–43 mentions the use of tables for the slaying of sacrificial animals and the instruments of the priests are mentioned but the text is not clear as to the number, though probably there were only eight. The reference cannot be to the table of the layer bread since only one table is referred to in xiii 11, xxix 18; but the plural is used in I Chron xxviii 16 and in vs. 19 of this chapter. It has been suggested that the number ten is an exaggeration here, as the ten lampstands may be. The tables could have been used for the lampstands since they are in similar position and are equal in number. The hundred sprinkling bowls may have been used to catch the blood of the sacrificial victims for later sprinkling.

[The courts and the placement of the sea, 9–10]: The reference to two courts here is based on Ezekiel and the usages of the second temple. The term "the great court," *ha'zarah hag^edolah,* is used only in Chronicles and Ezekiel. The inner court of I Kings vi 36, vii 12 is the space immediately adjacent to the temple, and the great court of vii 12 is the whole area around the complex of Solomon's buildings. The second temple had two courts; an outer court for the general public and an inner one restricted to those who were ritually clean (cf. E. Bikerman, "Une proclamation séleucide relative au Temple de Jérusalem," *Syria* 25 [1946–48], 67–85). The doors are not mentioned in Kings. The reiteration of the placement of the sea is due to the source for the following verses, which is I Kings vii 39b–50.

[The work of Huram, 11–18]: The ash containers were for the ashes from the altar offerings (cf. Exod xxvii 3). Shovels, forks, and wheel bases have been discovered in a number of excavations (cf. Wright, *Biblical Archaeology,* pp. 141 f., and Fig. 96 on p. 142; for wheel bases, see AOT, Pls. cciii, cciv). The pillars have been discussed in the preceding chapter. The capitals of the pillars were decorated with lily designs (I Kings vii 19); above the basins were gratings decorated with pomegranate designs, two rows around each one. See tripod in C. F. A. Schaeffer, *The Cuneiform Texts of Ras Shamra-Ugarit,* 1939, Pl. xxiii, Fig. 2, for illustration of pomegranate design. The casting was done on the other side of the Jordan between Sukkoth and Zarethan. The bronze probably came from the mines in the wadis of Timna and Amram in the fifteen-kilometer-long valley north of Elath on the Gulf of Aqabah. For the exploration and description of the location see *Illustrated London News,* September 3, 1960, pp. 383–85.

[Summary of utensils, 19–22]: With few changes, this list of temple equipment follows that of I Kings. Of special interest is the golden altar used for burning incense. It was modeled after that of the tabernacle in Exod xxx 1 ff. R. de Langhe in *Biblica* 40 (1959), 476–94, gives a full discussion of the golden altar.

Under the influence of vs. 8, the writer speaks of altars for the show bread. All of the utensils were made of gold. So also were the inner doors of the *debir* and the doors of the temple itself.

[Gifts moved into the temple, v 1]: This verse marks the transition between the story of the construction and that of the dedication of the temple. It observes that when the temple was finished, the consecrated gifts of David (cf. I Chron xviii 11, xxvi 26) were moved into the treasuries, though the Chronicler says nothing about the latter in the preceding account of the building of the temple. The treasuries are probably to be connected with the "upper rooms" of iii 9 and the side chambers of I Kings vi 5 ff. The writer has followed his source in I Kings vii 51 almost exactly.

5. BUILDING THE TEMPLE: REMOVAL OF THE ARK. GOD'S APPROVAL
(v 2–14)†

Removal of the ark to the temple

V ² Then Solomon assembled at Jerusalem the elders of Israel and all the heads of the tribes, the Israelite family princes, for the purpose of bringing up the ark of the covenant of Yahweh from the city of David which is Zion. ³ All the men of Israel assembled themselves before the king at the time of the feast, that is the seventh month. ⁴ When all the elders of Israel had arrived, the Levites took up the ark; ⁵ they brought up the ark, the tent of meeting, and all the sacred utensils which were in the tent. The Levitical priests brought them up. ⁶ King Solomon and the whole congregation of Israel present with him before the ark sacrificed sheep and oxen in such abundance that they could neither be numbered nor counted. ⁷ The priests brought the ark of the covenant of Yahweh to its appointed place under the wings of the cherubs in the sanctuary of the house, in the holy of holies. ⁸ The cherubs spread out both their wings over the location of the ark, that is the cherubs formed a canopy for the ark and its poles. ⁹ However, the poles were so long that the ends of the poles of the ark could be seen in front of the sanctuary though they could not be seen from the outside; ªit remains there to this day.ª ¹⁰ There was nothing in the ark except the two tables [of the law] which Moses had placed in it at Horeb when Yahweh made a covenant with the Israelites at the time of their exodus from Egypt.

† II Chron v 2–14 ‖ I Kings viii 1–11.

ª⁻ª See NOTE.

The appearance of the glory of Yahweh

11 When the priests left the holy place—for all the priests present had sanctified themselves regardless of divisions, 12 and all of the Levitical singers, Asaph, Heman, Jeduthun, and their sons and their brothers garbed in linen were standing on the east side of the altar with cymbals, harps, and zithers; with them stood one hundred and twenty priests blowing the trumpets; 13 the harmony between the trumpeters and singers was [so perfect] that only one melody was audible when they praised and gave thanks to Yahweh—and the music began, accompanied by trumpets, cymbals, and [other] instruments of song, to render

> praise to Yahweh
> for he is good,
> and eternal his devotion

*b*the house was filled with a cloud,*b* 14 so that the priests were unable to remain to perform their service because of the cloud, for the glory of Yahweh filled the house of God.

b–b So, omitting "the house of Yahweh." May be an explanatory note. Cf. LXX "the house was filled by a cloud of the glory of Yahweh" and Vulg. "the house of God was filled by a cloud." The writer may have had in mind Isa vi 4 or the thought of Ezek x 4.

NOTES

v 9. *of the ark.* I Kings viii 8 reads "from the holy place."

it remains . . . day. Kings reads: "they [the poles] remain there until this day"; so also LXX and many manuscripts here. The meaning of the statement is the same since the presence of the poles would at the same time indicate the presence of the ark itself. The writer quoted his source, for the ark was no longer in existence when he wrote.

10. *when . . . covenant.* Required by context. Cf. vi 11.

12. *one hundred and twenty priests.* I.e., five for each of the twenty-four divisions (cf. I Chron xxiv).

13. *trumpeters.* The priests were the trumpeters (I Chron xv 24).

COMMENT

[The transfer of the ark from Zion to the temple, v 2–10]: The solemn assembly took place at the feast of the seventh month, unnamed here since the name was not in use in postexilic times. The name of the month Ethanim (I Kings viii 2) is Canaanite. The seventh month among the Hebrews was Tishri. The feast in the autumn was that of tabernacles. The removal of the ark to the temple certainly presupposes the completion of the work of building; but according to I Kings vi 38, construction was finished in the eighth month. That may, however, refer to the structure only and not to the other paraphernalia perfected by Huramabi. In any case, Solomon was assisted by all the officials of Israel, political and religious. The ark had been kept in the temporary structure (the tent) provided for it when David brought it to Jerusalem (I Chron xvi 1). I Kings viii 3 has the priests taking up the ark; the Chronicler follows the regulation laid down by David (I Chron xv 2) on the basis of the law of Moses (Deut x 8, xxxi 25; Num iii 31). The sharp distinction between priests and Levites was not always observed. The Chronicler has exalted the latter but in so doing does not encroach upon the prerogatives of the former. Thus he follows the *P* and *D* tradition of having the Levites bear the ark but the priests place it in the sanctuary. The Kings tradition follows that of Joshua (iii–iv). The combination of Levitical priests (or the priests, the Levites) follows Deuteronomy; however the Kings parallel has a conjunction: "the priests and Levites."

Just what is meant by vs. 5 is not quite certain. It could mean the religious articles in the tabernacle at Gibeon, though the context suggests it to have been concerned with the tent pitched for the ark by David. The term "tent of meeting" is used only of the tabernacle that was at Gibeon. It may be that both are meant to be included since no official religious service is recorded as taking place at Gibeon after the great sacrifice and subsequent revelation to Solomon there (II Chron i). Sacrifices naturally accompanied the event, their number and character in keeping with the magnitude of the occasion.

The ark itself was placed in the *debir* of the temple under the cherubs, whose wings formed a canopy over it. It is not clear how the structure was planned or oriented so as to make it possible to see them (see K. Galling, "Das Allerheiligste," JPOS 12 [1932], 43 ff.). It must mean that the ark was hidden behind the curtain (iii 14) but the poles stuck out on both sides. The cherubs must have covered everything from the top because their wings extended from wall to wall (iii 11–13). The contents of the ark were the tables of the *torah,* always closely associated with the ark of the covenant (cf. Deut x 2, 5). The Chronicler followed Kings closely here, and Kings was the work of the Deuteronomist. Later tradition suggested that the ark also contained a pot of manna and Aaron's rod (Heb ix 4), probably on the basis of Exod xvi 32–34, which does not say that it was put into the ark but that it was kept before the testimony (*'ēdūt*). Cf. Josephus *Antiquities* III.vi.5. For the Rabbinic tradition see H. L. Strack and P. Billerbeck, *Kommentar zum Neuen Testament aus Talmud u. Midrash,* III, 1926, pp. 737–40.

[The appearance of the glory of Yahweh, 11–14]: Here the Chronicler has substantially expanded the simple statement of his source. There it is said that when the priests withdrew from the *debir* where the ark had been deposited, the cloud filled the house so that they could not remain to perform their service. The cloud as a symbol of the presence of Yahweh is quite common (Exod xiii; Num ix; Ezek x 3–4) and here is intended to show the acceptance of the house dedicated to his name and now occupied by him. The origin of the passage is uncertain since the appearance of the glory of Yahweh is mentioned again after the dedication of the temple (vii 1–2). Here it may be connected with the festival rite conducted on the occasion of the transfer of the ark which appears to be a special ceremony. The ark played a vital role in Chronicles (the term occurs some fifty times). The auspicious rites conducted when it was brought to its final abode rivals those attending David's removal of it from the house of Obed-edom to Jerusalem. The Levitical singers were there, as were representatives of the twenty-four priestly divisions (on the musical guilds see I Chronicles, COMMENT on Sec. 25). Chronicles is the first to refer to the linen garb worn by the Levites (cf. I Chron xv 27), which was the material for the priestly vestments. That is another indication of the high regard for the Levites held by the writer whoever he was. These verses are generally denied to the Chronicler, possibly belong to the same hand responsible for I Chron xxiii–xxvii. Rudolph, p. 211, thinks they are a mechanical addition from I Kings vii. The rendition of such perfect music is to be observed and follows the repeated assertion of David's organization of the musical guilds. The passage may be an insertion but, if so, it follows the Chronicler's tradition.

6. BUILDING THE TEMPLE: SOLOMON'S DEDICATION AND PRAYER (vi 1–42)†

Solomon's dedicatory address

VI 1 Then Solomon said,

"Yahweh said he would dwell in darkness;
2 And I have built for you an exalted house,
An eternal dwelling place for you."

3 The king then turned around to bless the whole congregation of Israel while the whole congregation of Israel was standing. 4 He said, "Blessed be Yahweh God of Israel who by his deeds has fulfilled what he promised David my father orally when he said, 5 'At no time since I brought out my people from the land of Egypt, did I select a city out of all the tribes of Israel to build a house where my name should dwell, or choose a man as leader for my people Israel, 6 but I did select Jerusalem where my name should dwell and chose David to be [ruler] over my people Israel.' 7 David my father had set his heart on building a house for the name of Yahweh God of Israel, 8 but Yahweh said to David my father, 'When you set your heart upon building a house for my name, you did well in that you had it in your heart [to do so], 9 nevertheless you shall not build the house, but your son, your bodily descendant, shall build the house for my name.' 10 Yahweh has fulfilled now the promise which he made and I have risen to the place of David my father; I am occupying the throne of Israel as Yahweh promised and I have built the house for the name of Yahweh God of Israel 11 where I have placed the ark wherein is the covenant of Yahweh which he made with the people of Israel."

† **II Chron vi 1–42** ‖ I Kings viii 12–52.

Solomon's prayer

12 Then he stood up before the altar of Yahweh in the sight of the whole congregation of Israel and spread out his hands— 13 For Solomon had made a bronze platform five cubits long, five cubits wide, and three cubits high which he placed inside the court and upon which he stood. He knelt down upon his knees in the sight of the whole congregation of Israel and spread out his hands toward the heavens—14 and said, "O Yahweh God of Israel, there is no God like you in the heavens or upon the earth who keeps covenant faith with your servants who walk before you with all their heart 15 and which you observed with your servant David my father as you promised him. You have spoken it with your own mouth and have fulfilled it as is evident this very day. 16 Now, O Yahweh God of Israel, for the sake of your servant David, my father, keep your promise to him when you said, 'You shall never lack a descendant to sit upon the throne of Israel before me, if only your sons will guard their conduct, to conform to my instructions, as you have conducted yourself before me.' 17 Now, O Yahweh God of Israel, may your word which you spoke to your servant David prove true! 18 But can God, in truth, dwell among men upon the earth? Behold, the heavens and the highest heavens cannot contain you, how much less this house I have built! 19 Consider, therefore, the prayer and supplication of your servant, Yahweh my God, listen to the entreaty and the prayer your servant is offering before you; 20 that your eyes may be open to this house day and night, to the place where you promised to put your name, so that you may hear the prayer your servant offers toward this place. 21 Listen also to the entreaties of your servant and your people Israel. Whenever they pray toward this place, do listen from your dwelling place, from the heavens, and when you hear [it], forgive. 22 If anyone has sinned against his neighbor and an oath is required of him to confirm it and the oath is taken before your altar in this house, 23 then listen from the heavens and render justice to your servants; requiting the guilty by making

him responsible for his conduct and justifying the righteous in accordance with his righteousness. 24 If your people Israel are defeated before their enemy because they have sinned against you but then repent, confess your name, pray, and implore favor before you in this house, 25 then listen from the heavens, forgive the sin of your people Israel and bring them back to the land which you gave to them and to their fathers. 26 When the heavens remain closed so that there is no rain because they have sinned against you and they pray toward this place, confess your name and turn from their sin because you ªhumble themª, 27 then listen from the heavens, forgive the sin of your servants, your people Israel—for you are continually teaching them the good way which they are to follow—and let it rain upon the land which you gave to your people as an inheritance. 28 Should there be a famine in the land or pestilence, or should there be blight, or mildew, or locusts, or caterpillars, or their enemies besiege them in their own land, or any plague, or any sickness, 29 whatever prayer or entreaty is made by any one or by all of your people Israel, when each one is acutely aware of his affliction and pain, and he spread out his hands toward this house, 30 then listen from the heavens, your dwelling place, forgive and deal with each one, whose mind you know, in accordance with all his deeds—for you alone know the mind of the sons of men— 31 that they may revere you by following your directions, which you gave to our fathers, throughout all the days of their life on the face of the earth. 32 Also when the foreigner, who is not a member of your people Israel and who comes from a distant land, attracted by your great name, your powerful hand, and your outstretched arm, comes and prays toward this house, 33 then listen from the heavens, your dwelling place, and act in accordance with all that the foreigner implores you to do, in order that all the peoples of the earth may acknowledge your name, revere you as your people Israel do, and know that this house which I have built bears your name. 34 When your people go out to battle against their enemies, on whatever mission you

ª–ª So with LXX, Vulg.; Hebrew reads "answer them" or "afflict them."

send them, and they pray to you in the direction of this city
which you have chosen and the house I have built for your name,
35 then listen from the heavens to their prayer and entreaty
and maintain their cause. 36 If they sin against you—for there
is not a man who does not sin—and you are angry with them,
and abandon them before the enemy so that their captors carry
them away to a distant or nearby land; 37 but then they wholeheartedly repent in the land where they have been taken as captives and entreat you once more in the land of their captivity,
saying, 'We have sinned, we have done wrong; we have rebelled,'
38 and return to you with all their mind and their soul in the
land of their captivity to which they were carried away as captives, and pray in the direction of their land which you gave
to their fathers and the city which you chose, and toward the
house that I have built for your name, 39 then listen from the
heavens, your dwelling place, to their prayer and their entreaties,
maintain their cause and forgive your people who sinned against
you. 40 Now, O my God, may your eyes be open and your ears
attentive to the prayer [offered] in this place.

41 And now go up, O Yahweh, God, to your resting place,
     you and your mighty ark;
  Let your priests, O Yahweh, God, put on salvation,
  Let your devotees rejoice in that which is good.
42 O Yahweh, God, do not reject your anointed ones;
  Remember the loyalties of David your servant."

NOTES

vi 2. *exalted.* Cf. W. F. Albright, JPOS 16 (1936), 17–20, on the
meaning of *z^ebūl.*

an eternal dwelling place. For idea see 1QH 18:29.

3. *turned around.* Literally "turned his face and blessed."

11. *where I . . . ark.* I Kings viii 21, "I have made a place for the
ark."

the people of Israel. Kings parallel reads "our fathers."

23. *making . . . conduct.* Literally "to put his way [deed] upon his head."

28. *their enemies . . . land.* Literally "his enemies besiege him in the land of his gates." I.e., lay siege to his cities.

29. *his affliction and pain.* Cf. 1QH 9:6, where the order of words is reversed.

33. *bears your name.* Literally "that your name has been called over . . ."

41. Cf. Ps cxxxii 8–11.

42. *anointed ones.* Some manuscripts and Ps cxxxii 10 have singular. For RSV expression "the face of," see 1QH 16:18. The "anointed ones" refers to kings and priests.

Remember . . . servant. Based on Isa lv 3—loyalties of David.

COMMENT

This section closely follows its source in I Kings viii 12–52. It contains two addresses, one to the people and the other to God in the form of a lengthy prayer just as appropriate for the Chronicler's time as for that of Solomon.

[The address to the people, vi 1–11]: Verses 1, 2 are apparently meant to be a part of the preceding episode and are Solomon's comment upon the appearance of the glory of Yahweh that descended upon the sanctuary when the ark of the covenant was moved into it. The king and the congregation of Israel followed the procession from the east; they stood behind the Levitical singers facing the altar and looking toward the temple. In response to the withdrawal of the priests from the sanctuary because of the presence of the glory of Yahweh, Solomon uttered these lines. That sequence of events connects the dedication with the placing of the ark in the *debir* (but see COMMENT on Sec. 5, v 5).

With some additions the address to the people reiterates the same principles enunciated by David in I Chron xxviii 2 ff. The passage begins with the note that Solomon turned from facing the altar toward the people who had been standing behind him. He observes that Yahweh has now fulfilled his promise to David by his deeds, that is, by permitting the house to be constructed and showing his approval by the appearance of his glory. I Kings viii 16 omits, by homoioteleuton, 5b–6a which the Chronicler has preserved for us.

[Solomon's prayer, 12–42]: Having addressed the people, Solomon turned toward the altar of Yahweh that was before him and offered up this prayer. According to the Chronicler, he stood upon a bronze platform—or knelt upon it—in full view of the assembled congregation. The Chronicler alone records the detail of the bronze platform. The *kiyyōr* (platform) is fairly well attested as a cult object used by dignitaries. Albright calls attention to a number of such representations from Egypt and Syria (ARI, pp. 152 f.; cf. also Parrot, *The Temple of Jerusalem*, pp. 44 f.). A king offering prayer to Baal is depicted on a stele from Ugarit (C. F. A. Schaeffer, *Ugaritica* 2 [1949], Pls. xxiii, xxiv; cf. H. Bossert, *Altsyrien*, 1951, Fig. 960, which shows a priest on a high platform with legs presenting an offering to the deity. The stele is from Daphne).

Both standing and kneeling positions are shown on the monuments. Pritchard (ANEP, p. 192, Fig. 576) has one of Tukulti-Ninurta I standing and kneeling before a cult socket. H. Schmökel (*Ur, Assur und Babylon*, 1955, Pl. 66) shows a bronze statue of a man kneeling in prayer. The statue comes from Larsa. Just why Solomon stood or knelt upon this platform is uncertain; it could have been that such a position made him more readily visible to the congregation or enabled the people to hear him better. For another view cf. G. von Rad, *Gesammelte Studien zum Alten Testament*, 1958, p. 207. The temple is, according to this theory, both the dwelling place of Yahweh and the place where he is worshiped. Yahweh is present in the temple, also in heaven.

The first portion of the prayer is characterized by praise for Yahweh who always remains faithful to his covenant, and by thanksgiving for the fulfillment of his promises to David. This is coupled with a petition that the promises made to David may remain forever true. An ascription of majesty to Yahweh follows, pointing out that since the very heavens cannot contain God, the temple, which is so infinitesimal, cannot hope to do so. That may be the reason for the Chronicler's frequent references to Yahweh's hearing "from heaven" (seven times in the chapter). Though the writer follows his source closely, it is significant that he stresses the house of Yahweh as the place where prayer is both offered and answered. It is thus the meeting place of God and man, for not only is Yahweh implored to hear the prayer of the king but also the prayers of "your people Israel." Also of special importance is the recognition of the people's need for forgiveness—an outstanding characteristic of the whole prayer of the king.

The seven petitions in vss. 22–39 deal almost exclusively with national affairs. Though the first petition appears to be individual in import, it is a matter of maintaining community order. It deals with the confirmation of the oath so as to vindicate the innocent and to requite the guilty. The second petition concerns Israel's recognition of its sin in its defeat at the hands of an enemy. If the people repent, God is implored to hear their prayer and restore them to their land. The third petition deals with drought; the fourth with famine, pestilence, and other calamities; the fifth with the foreigner who may be drawn to Israel's God by the observation of his mighty acts. It is significant that no condition is laid upon the foreigner; he is neither required to confess his faith nor to confess his sins, though both may be implied by an attraction to Yahweh. The sixth petition requests assistance from Yahweh for any military mission upon which he may have sent Israel. The final petition is on behalf of those who are in captivity and who recognize their sin by repentance and contrition. The broad application of the principle involved (vs. 36) is extraordinary. The petitionary portion of the prayer closes with the plea that Yahweh may ever hear those who pray "in this place." Verses 39–40 are a curtailed parallel of I Kings viii 50–52.

The conclusion of the prayer was added by the Chronicler from Ps cxxxii 8–11 and Isa lv. Since this conclusion is missing in the Kings parallel, the writer must have included it for a specific purpose. Psalms cxxxii is one of the royal psalms and as such centers about the idea of the enthronement of the king (see H. Gunkel and J. Begrich, *Einleitung in die Psalmen,* 1933, pp. 140–71, and S. Mowinckel, *Psalmenstudien,* II, 1922, pp. 112 ff.; for recent literature bearing on the Psalm see H. J. Kraus, *Psalmen,* II, 1960, p. 876). Amid the vicissitudes of the age, recalling the Deuteronomic theme of the rest of the people of God, the Chronicler has Solomon pray that Yahweh may take up his resting place with them (cf. von Rad, *Gesammelte Studien zum Alten Testament,* pp. 104 f.). Rest could be assured only if the mighty ark were present because it was the symbol of power. But that is not enough: the priests would have to put on salvation and the devotees delight in the good—a motif not present in the Psalm parallel. Once more the king prays, in the words of the Psalm, for the continuity of the Davidic line, which for the writer would have messianic significance. Only thus could the Davidic hope be realized and the promise to him be fulfilled (I Chron xxiii 25)—a blessing devoutly to be wished for in his time.

There may be a connection here between the dedication of the temple by Solomon and the second temple of Zerubbabel. The use of Ps cxxxii would be particularly suitable for such an occasion as the dedication of the second temple. Zerubbabel was the last pretender of whom we know until after the time of Ezra and Nehemiah. The variations from Ps cxxxii, based on Isa lv, look like a formulation of the Chronicler. If, therefore, the addition has Zerubbabel's temple as a frame of reference, the hope expressed is both messianic and historical.

7. BUILDING THE TEMPLE: THE DEDICATION CEREMONY
(vii 1–10)†

VII 1 As soon as Solomon had concluded his prayer, fire descended from the heavens and consumed the burnt offering and the sacrifices, and the glory of Yahweh filled the house, 2 so that the priests were unable to enter the house of Yahweh because the glory of Yahweh filled the house of Yahweh. 3 When all the Israelites saw the descent of the fire and the glory of Yahweh upon the house, they bowed down with their faces to the ground on the pavement, worshiped and praised Yahweh with

"For he is good and his loyalty eternal."

4 Then the king and all the people offered a sacrifice before Yahweh. 5 King Solomon offered a sacrifice of twenty-two thousand oxen and one hundred twenty thousand sheep when the king and all the people dedicated the house of God. 6 The priests occupied their posts and the Levites had the musical instruments of Yahweh which David the king had provided to [render]

"Give thanks to Yahweh, for eternal is his loyalty"

whenever David offered praise with their help; the priests on the other side blew trumpets while all Israel stood. 7 Solomon also dedicated the middle section of the court that was in front of the house of Yahweh, for he offered the burnt offerings and the fat pieces of the peace offerings there, because the bronze altar which Solomon had made could not hold the burnt offering, the meal offering and the pieces of fat. 8 At that time Solomon together with all Israel who had come from the entrance

† II Chron vii 1–10 ‖ I Kings viii 54, 62–66.

at Hamath to the wadi of Egypt—a very large congregation—
celebrated the feast for seven days. ⁹ On the eighth day they
had the final celebration, for they had devoted seven days to
the dedication of the altar and seven days to the feast. ¹⁰ On
the twenty-third day of the seventh month he sent the people to
their tents, rejoicing and delighted because of the goodness Yahweh had shown to David, to Solomon, and to Israel his people.

NOTES

vii 3. *the pavement*. Cf. Ezek xl 17–18, xlii 3 which locate the pavement in the outer court.
"For he . . . eternal." The title of the hymn.
6. *"Give thanks . . . loyalty."* The title of the hymn.
on the other side. Literally "in front of them." Could also be rendered
"responsively." While there may well have been an antiphonal arrangement, the reference here appears to be to a position in view of the
priests' posts mentioned at the beginning of the verse. According to
v 12 the Levitical musicians stood on the east side of the altar. The
priests "in front of them" would then have been on the west side,
between the altar and the temple proper.
8. *the entrance . . . Egypt*. The traditional limits of the holy land;
in other sources, the limits are more tightly drawn (from Dan to Beer-
sheba).

COMMENT

The source in I Kings is followed fairly closely, though there are
some deviations and some rearrangements. This section is concerned
with the actual dedication of the house of Yahweh, and the following section with Yahweh's response to Solomon's work in connection with the temple and his prayer.

The response of Yahweh to Solomon's dedication of the temple
was a gigantic holocaust ignited by fire from heaven, which confirmed his acceptance of both temple and offerings that had been
waiting (cf. v 6). The same phenomenon occurred when David offered sacrifices on the threshing floor of Ornan to stay the plague
(I Chron xxi 26). Verses 1c–3 replace Solomon's blessing of the
people in I Kings viii 54b–61. The glory of Yahweh now filled the

temple as it had filled the *debir* when the ark was placed therein
(v 13 f.). The people bowed reverently before Yahweh and worshiped him; they burst into praise with the hymn sung on the other
occasion just noted. The sacrifices referred to were those consumed by the heavenly fire (vs. 1). Verse 6 may be a later
insertion since it does not occur in Kings. But such a hymnal response
to the accompaniment of Levitical musicians and priestly trumpeters
may well have been part of the service, if, as is believed, musical
guilds were organized by David (for a discussion of David's provision of musical instruments and organization of musical guilds see
COMMENT in *I Chronicles,* Sec. 25).

The place where the sacrifices were offered, in the center of the
court, was consecrated especially for the purpose as the bronze altar
was too small for such enormous offerings. This was, in all probability, the rock upon which David offered the oxen purchased from
Ornan. According to the Chronicler, the bronze altar was made by
Solomon (vs. 7, iv 1). The Kings parallel says nothing about the
construction of such an altar, nor is it referred to elsewhere in
Chronicles. Evidently the Deuteronomist assumed that the bronze
altar of the tabernacle was moved into the temple complex where it
remained until it was displaced by Ahaz (II Kings xvi).

The feast of tabernacles was celebrated in connection with the
consecration of the altar as the phrase "at that time" (vs. 8) indicates. This was one of the feasts requiring the presence of all male
Israelites (Deut xvi 16). Not only does the writer repeat the assertion of I Kings viii 65 that all Israel from the Hamath entrance
to the wadi of Egypt was present but stresses the great size of the
congregation in attendance by adding "very." According to the
Kings parallel, Solomon dismissed the people on the eighth day;
here the eighth day marked the climax of the whole festival, a later
practice (cf. Lev xxiii 36b; Num xxviii 25 f.; Neh viii 18) not
mentioned in the earlier law (Deut xvi 13–15). The combined
time for dedication and the feast then was a total of fifteen days
plus one day for the dismissal of the people. As Rudolph, p. 217,
has pointed out, since the dismissal of the people took place on the
twenty-third day of the seventh month, the feast of dedication occupied the eighth to the fourteenth days, and the dedication, the
fifteenth to the twenty-second days. That the dedication of the temple
is here referred to as that of the altar is explained in vs. 12: the
place of sacrifice is the communion center of the temple complex.

8. BUILDING THE TEMPLE: YAHWEH'S RESPONSE
(vii 11–22)†

VII ¹¹ When Solomon had completed the house of Yahweh and the palace and brought to a successful conclusion all that was in the mind of Solomon to do with reference to the house of Yahweh and his own house, ¹² Yahweh appeared to Solomon that night and said to him, "I have heard your prayer and have chosen this place for myself as a house of sacrifice. ¹³ If I shut up the heavens so that it does not rain and command the locust to crop the land, or if I send a pestilence on my people, ¹⁴ and then my people over whom my name is called humble themselves, pray, seek my presence, and turn away from their evil ways, I will listen from the heavens, forgive their sin, and restore their land. ¹⁵ Now my eyes shall be open and my ears attentive to the prayer offered at this place. ¹⁶ Now I have chosen and consecrated this house where my name shall remain forever and where my eyes and my heart shall be continually. ¹⁷ If you walk before me as David your father did, strive to do everything that I command you, and keep my statutes and judgments, ¹⁸ I will uphold your royal throne as I covenanted with David your father, saying, 'You shall not lack one to rule Israel.' ¹⁹ But if you turn away, abandon my statutes and my commandments which I have laid down for you, and go to serve other gods and worship them, ²⁰ I will uproot ᵃyouᵃ from my land which I gave to ᵃyou,ᵃ and I will cast out of my sight this house which I have consecrated for my name and make it a derision and taunt among all the peoples. ²¹ And everyone who

† II Chron vii 11–22 ‖ I Kings ix 1–9.

ᵃ⁻ᵃ So with some of the versions, for Heb. "them" influenced by the pronoun at the end of the preceding vs. I Kings ix 7 reads "I will cut off Israel."

passes by it shall be appalled at this house which was so exalted and remark, 'Why has Yahweh done so to this land and to this house?' 22 Then shall they reply, 'Because they abandoned Yahweh God of their fathers who brought them up out of the land of Egypt, joined themselves to other gods, worshiped and served them; on that account he brought all this evil upon them.'"

NOTES

vii 18. *I covenanted.* I Kings ix 5 reads "I promised."

COMMENT

The appearance of Yahweh to Solomon is indicative of the acceptance of his work, as the descent of fire had been for the offerings and the glory of Yahweh for the *debir* when the ark was placed in it. While there is no special passage dealing with the palace or other structures (cf. I Kings vii), it must be remembered that they were all part of the same complex of buildings. In fact, the temple itself was in all probability a royal chapel in the days of Solomon and as such would be only one of the buildings involved in the gigantic enterprise. For a sketch of the buildings see Parrot, *The Temple of Jerusalem,* p. 20 (from Galling, BRL, cols. 411–12). For the royal chapel idea see Parrot, *op. cit.,* pp. 51 f.; Möhlenbrink, *Der Tempel Salomos,* pp. 48 ff.; Alt, KS, II, pp. 100–15. The king occupied a special place in Israel and hence the house of Yahweh adjacent to the house of the king is quite appropriate. In any case, Yahweh appeared to Solomon that night (Kings indicates this was the second time, the first at Gibeon) to reassure him that his work and prayer have been noted in heaven. The communication of Yahweh in the first statement follows the same line taken by the prayer of the king. Yahweh promises to be attentive to "this place," which may have more in it than the temple itself, referring to both the place of worship and the center of the rule of his anointed one.

So much is implied by vss. 17–18. There is certainly a messianic overtone in the phrase "one who rules over Israel" (cf. Mic v 2). The influence of the prophets is apparent here. The threat in vs. 20 is stronger here than in I Kings ix 7.

9. OTHER ACHIEVEMENTS OF SOLOMON
(viii 1–18)†

VIII 1 At the end of twenty years during which Solomon had built the house of Yahweh and his own house, 2 and *ᵃrestored the cities which Huram had given to himᵃ and colonized them with Israelites, 3 Solomon went to Hamath-zobah and seized it. 4 He also fortified Tadmor in the desert, as well as all the store cities he had built in Hamath. 5 He built Upper Beth-horon and Lower Beth-horon, fortress cities with walls, gates, and bars; 6 Baalath and all Solomon's store cities; all the chariot-cities and the cities for his teams of horses; and everything heᵇ wanted to build in Jerusalem, in the Lebanon, or in any [other] area under his dominion. 7 All the people left of the Hittites, the Amorites, the Perizzites, the Hivites, and the Jebusites who did not belong to Israel—8 that is, those of their descendants remaining in the land after them and whom the Israelites had not exterminated—Solomon reduced to slavery as they are to this day. 9 However Solomon did not make slaves of any of the Israelites for his work; for they were soldiers, chiefs of his adjutants, and chiefs of his chariots and his horsemen. 10 These were the chiefs of King Solomon's garrisons: two hundred and fifty of them who were in charge of the people. 11 Then Solomon brought up the daughter of Pharaoh from the city of David to the house he had built for her because, he said, "My wife must not live in the house of David the king of Israel, for the precinctsᶜ to which the ark of Yahweh has come are sacred."

† **II Chron viii 1–18** ‖ I Kings ix 10–28.

ᵃ Text repeats the name Solomon as subject of "restored" and as the object "him" in the relative clause.
ᵇ Text has "Solomon."
ᶜ Hebrew reads "these," referring to the total complex of buildings.

12 Then Solomon offered burnt offerings to Yahweh, upon the altar of Yahweh which he had erected before the portico, 13 in accordance with the regular prescriptions for offering as commanded by Moses, on the Sabbaths, the new moons, the festivals, and the three yearly feasts: the feast of unleavened bread, the feast of weeks, and the feast of tabernacles. 14 Following the prescription of David his father, he set up the divisions of priests for their service and the Levites for their duties of praise and ministration before the priests, in conformity with the daily requirements; also the porters according to their divisions for each gate, for such was the command of David the man of God. 15 Nor did they deviate in any respect from the command of the king concerning the priests, the Levites, and the storehouses. 16 Thus all the work of Solomon was carried out from*d* the day of the foundation of the house of Yahweh until its consummation—the house of Yahweh was complete in every detail. 17 Then Solomon went to Ezion-geber and to Eloth, on the seashore in the land of Edom. 18 Huram sent him ships through his agents as well as experienced seamen who went to Ophir with Solomon's servants where they took on four hundred and fifty talents of gold which they brought to King Solomon.

d So with the Vrs. for Heb. "until."

NOTES

viii 4. *Tadmor.* I Kings ix 18 has Tamar but vocalizes Tadmor.

6. *area.* Literally "land."

8. *slavery.* Cf. I Kings ix 21 where the phrase for total slavery occurs. See I. Mendelsohn, *Slavery in the Ancient Near East,* 1949, p. 97.

16. *the house of Yahweh was complete in every detail.* Based on I Kings ix 25c.

18. *experienced seamen.* Literally "servants who know the sea."

ophir. See COMMENT on vss. 17–18.

four hundred and fifty talents. I Kings ix 28 has "420 talents."

COMMENT

In most respects the Chronicler follows his source though he modifies certain points and expands others. This section is a good illustration of his method.

[Building and fortification of cities, viii 1–6]: The most striking thing in the section is vs. 2, which does not agree with the situation narrated in I Kings ix 10 ff. There it is stated that Solomon gave to Hiram twenty cities in Galilee in exchange for lumber and gold. Here it is said that Hiram gave to Solomon certain cities, presumably in Galilee though the location is not given, which Solomon colonized. If Kings is right about Hiram's reaction, Chronicles may have the sequel to the story. Hiram may have returned the cities to Solomon as worthless, which might explain why he "restored" them. There may be more involved in the transaction than meets the eye. Solomon may have made good on the original deal, with payment in gold or in some other way; in that case the cities may have been collateral until the time when payment could be made in gold. It has been suggested that the Chronicler refers to another situation than the one in I Kings ix 10 ff., but that seems unrealistic (cf. Rudolph, p. 219) in view of the context. Some feel that Hiram may have returned the cities, which may be correct, but that might reflect on the financial condition of Solomon.

The seizure of Hamath-zobah is not mentioned in I Kings ix. Hamath-zobah, which are brought together twice by the Chronicler (I Chron xviii 3 and here), reflect the situation in the Persian period when Zobah was part of the province of Hamath (see K. Elliger in PJB 32 [1936], 56; M. Noth, PJB 33 [1937], 47; C. H. Gordon, JNES 14 [1955], 56–58; Noth, ÜS, p. 159). David had trouble with Zobah (II Sam viii 9, x 8; I Chron xix 6), perhaps on more than one occasion. It is possible that the difficulty reappeared in Solomon's time or the Chronicler may have attributed David's conquest to Solomon. Zobah may have rebelled after David's death but it is hard to understand how Hamath would be involved; its friendship with David (II Sam viii 9–10) doubtless continued into Solomon's reign. A. Malamat thinks there may be a historical kernel present in the story of Hamath-zobah (cf. BA 21 [1958], 101, n.

22, and references there). Gordon thinks Israelites were settled there as enclaves during the period of the united monarchy (IEJ 5 [1955], 88).

Tadmor does not occur in the parallel (I Kings ix 18); the name given there is Tamar, which was a small village southwest of the Dead Sea (cf. Ezek xlvii 19, xlviii 28; the Thamara of Eusebius, presently identified with Qurnub, was some twenty-five miles southeast of Beer-sheba. For further discussion see J. A. Montgomery and H. S. Gehman, *The Book of Kings* [in ICC], 1951, p. 208). The alteration of Tamar to Tadmor is usually attributed to the Chronicler's attempt to glorify Solomon, since Tadmor was an important center east of Zobah on the caravan route to Mesopotamia (Tadmor later became Palmyra). It is to be noted that the Kings reference appears in a different context and thus the Chronicler may indeed preserve another tradition since he places it immediately after Hamath-zobah in whose territory Tadmor was located. There is no evidence that David did much fortifying; but there are numerous references to Solomon's fortifications, which are supported by archaeological explorations. See A. Dupont-Sommer, *Les Araméens*, 1949, pp. 28 f. But also see remarks of W. F. Albright, "The Judicial Reform of Jehoshaphat," AMJV, p. 69; in ARI, p. 133, he speaks of Solomon's control of the outlying district of Zobah, etc. Cf. also John Bright, *A History of Israel* (see Selected Bibliography), p. 192, n. 66. There is just a possibility that Solomon may have constructed some kind of fortification at or in the vicinity of Tadmor to check the Aramaeans, who threatened the outskirts of his empire. If we admit his endeavor to control Aramaean pressures then the fortifying of Tadmor or its environs is not impossible. See M. Gichon, "The Defences of the Solomonic Kingdom," PEQ (July–December 1963), pp. 116–19.

Beth-horon was some ten miles west northwest of Jerusalem on the boundary between Ephraim and Benjamin (Josh xviii 13) and a Levitical city (Josh xxi 22). Later it became Upper Beth-horon and Lower Beth-horon (Beit 'Ur el-Foqa and Beit 'Ur et-Tahta). It was a gateway into the hill country (cf. I Sam xiii 18). The I Kings parallel speaks only of Lower Beth-horon which was probably the more important of the two. It was a fortified place on the way from the Valley of Aijalon to Gibeon. Baalath was somewhere in Dan (Josh xix 44). Kings mentions in addition Hazor, Megiddo, and

Gezer, which are probably implied here in the phrase "all the chariot-cities and the cities for his teams of horses."

Solomon's building activity is attested by archaeology at Gezer, Megiddo, Hazor, Ezion-geber, and other places. A description of the results at Megiddo in the Solomonic period, including the famous stables, may be found in R. S. Lamon and G. M. Shipton, *Megiddo*, I, 1939, pp. 8–61; for Gezer, see G. E. Wright, BA 21 (1958), 103 f.; for Hazor, see Y. Yadin, BA 21 (1958), 46 f. See also Y. Aharoni's attribution to Solomon of casemate walls at Hazor, Gezer, Tell Qasile, Beth Shemesh, and Tell Beit Mirsim (BASOR 154 [April 1959], 35–39).

[Labor battalions, 7–10]: This passage follows I Kings ix 20–23 (fairly) closely. Both authors assert that forced labor was confined to the descendants of the peoples living in the land when Israel took over. The Chronicler says Israel did not exterminate them; the Deuteronomist says they could not do so. The Israelites were either soldiers or overseers over the labor battalions. But cf. I Kings v 13 ff., which the Chronicler conveniently overlooks earlier. The number of those set over the labor gangs is 250; in I Kings ix 23 it is 550. The former may be a scribal error, though it is to be observed that he has toned down the whole statement a bit by omitting the phrase "over the work."

[Moving day for the daughter of Pharaoh, 11]: I Kings ix 24 says the daughter of Pharaoh *came up* from the palace of David to the house that Solomon had made for her. Elsewhere in I Kings (ix 16) we learn that Gezer (perhaps Gerar) was given by the Pharaoh to Solomon as a marriage dowry for his daughter. All this is carefully excluded by the Chronicler because he wants to play down any relationship with Egypt. Here he stresses two points: (a) that Solomon *brought* the daughter of Pharaoh up to the house prepared for her, and (b) that she is separated from the royal palace because she is his wife and not because she is the daughter of Pharaoh. The reason for the separation was that she was a woman. Women were more frequently unclean in the ritual sense (Lev xv 19 ff.) than men. The Chronicler, in the interests of cult purity, thus endeavored to remove women from proximity to that which was sacred in line with the precepts of the *P* code. This led, later on in the days of the Herodian temple, to the provision of the court of women (cf. E. Schürer, *Geschichte des jüdischen Volkes im Zeitalter*

Jesu Christi, II, 3d ed., 1898, p. 285). The parallel verse of Kings speaks of the building of the Millo, which is not referred to here at all.

[Cultic provisions, 12–16]: The Chronicler has both curtailed and expanded the notice of offerings in his source (I Kings ix 25). The latter mentions burnt offerings and peace offerings as being offered three times a year, that is, at the annual feasts. He also says that Solomon also burned incense to Yahweh. The Chronicler, on the other hand, limits the scope of offerings to the burnt offering and says nothing about the offering of incense. Verses 13–16a are missing in I Kings ix. There it is said that the offerings were in accord with the prescription laid down by Moses (cf. Num xxviii–xxix) which are then detailed as referring to the Sabbath, new moon and festivals, as well as to the three annual feasts. Following the appointment of David, Solomon continued the priestly and Levitical orders (I Chron xxiii–xxvi) and those of the gatekeepers. They were followed exactly. So far as the writer is concerned, the carrying out of those prescriptions marked the completion of the work on the house of God, the fulfillment of the commands of David.

[Maritime mission to Ophir, 17–18]: The maritime venture of Solomon has been greatly illumined by the explorations and excavations of Nelson Glueck (see Glueck, *The Other Side of the Jordan*, 1940, Ch. iv; *Rivers in the Desert*, 1959, pp. 153–63; BA 1–3 [1938–40]; *National Geographic Magazine*, February 1944, 233–56). The Chronicler has the king himself go to Ezion-geber. As the maps indicate, Ezion-geber is near the northern end of the Gulf of Aqaba. The town was apparently known as Elath or Eloth in the time of Kings (I Kings ix 26). (See N. Glueck, "The Topography and History of Ezion-geber and Elath," BASOR 72 [1938], 2–13.) It is identified with present-day Tell el-Kheleifeh, west of Aqaba. Solomon had a seaport and large copper and iron works at Ezion-geber, and to judge from the remains, there was also a naval yard there for the construction and repair of ships. Copper and iron were derived from the surrounding area. On the problem of the source of Solomon's copper and the location of his copper mines see Y. Yadin, *Biblica* 36 (1955), 346, n. 2, and B. Rothenberg, "Ancient Copper Industries in the Western Araba," PEQ (January–June 1962), 5–64. Finished products were apparently exported in barter trade with South Arabia and Ophir, and thus broke the land

route monopoly of the South Arabians. Ophir was probably in
Somaliland across from South Arabia. (See Albright, ARI, pp. 133 f.;
J. A. Montgomery, *Arabia and the Bible,* 1934, p. 38, n. 5, and
pp. 176 ff. For further references to Solomon's activity at Ezion-
geber and its significance see Montgomery and Gehman, *The Book
of Kings,* pp. 211 f.)

The Tyrians were the best seamen of the time and once again
Hiram assisted Solomon by sending him shipbuilders and sailors.
Through their combined efforts they were quite successful, as the
archaeological remains indicate. The enormous quantity of gold
(over fifteen tons) is probably exaggerated.

10. SOLOMON'S WISDOM AND WEALTH
(ix 1–28)†

The visit of the queen of Sheba

IX 1 When the queen of Sheba heard about the renown of
Solomon, she came to Jerusalem, with a very large company of
attendants and camels bearing perfume, a large quantity of gold
and precious stones, to test Solomon with perplexing questions.
After she arrived, she conversed with Solomon about everything
that was on her mind. 2 Solomon answered all her questions and
nothing was concealed from Solomon that he could not interpret for her. 3 When the queen of Sheba saw the wisdom of
Solomon, the house he had built, 4 his table fare, his servants'
quarters, the position and attire of his ministers, his cupbearers
and their attire, and the steps^a by which he went up to the house
of Yahweh, she was breathless. 5 She said to the king, "The
report I heard in my country about your wisdom in handling
affairs of state is true. 6 I did not believe their reports until I
came and saw it for myself; yes, the greater half of your wisdom
had not been told me; you surpass the report I have heard.
7 Fortunate are ^byour men^b and fortunate these your servants
who stand before you continually and listen to your wisdom.
8 Blessed be Yahweh your God who was pleased with you and
put you on his throne as king for Yahweh your God. Because
your God loved Israel and wanted to give them eternal support,

† II Chron ix 1–12 ‖ I Kings x 1=13; 13–28 ‖ I Kings x 14–29, iv 21 (v 1H).

^a Hebrew reads "his upper chamber," on the roof of the temple. I Kings x 5
reads "his burnt offering." The interpretation is difficult with either reading.
Based on von Rad's suggestion.
^{b–b} LXX of I Kings x 8 reads "your wives," as do some Greek manuscripts
here.

he set you over them as king to maintain justice and righteousness." 9 Then she gave the king one hundred and twenty talents of gold, a great quantity of perfume and precious stones; there was no perfume like that which the queen of Sheba presented to King Solomon. 10 The servants of Hiram and the servants of Solomon who brought gold from Ophir, also brought algum wood and precious stones. 11 The king used the algum wood for steps° of the house of Yahweh and the house of the king, and for zithers and harps for the singers; their like had never been seen before in the land of Judah. 12 King Solomon gave the queen of Sheba every delightful thing for which she asked, apart from [what he gave her in exchange for] what she brought to the king. Then she returned to her country with her servants.

Solomon's wealth

13 The weight of the gold that Solomon received annually amounted to six hundred and sixty-six talents of gold, 14 apart from [what] the traders and merchants brought; all the Arabian kings and the governors of the land also brought gold and silver to Solomon. 15 King Solomon made two hundred large shields of beaten gold, six hundred shekels of beaten gold being inlaid in each shield; 16 and three hundred shields of beaten gold, three hundred shekels of beaten gold going into each shield; the king put them into the house of the forest of Lebanon. 17 The king also made a large ivory throne which he overlaid with pure gold. 18 The throne had six steps, and a footrest [made] of gold was attached to the throne and on both sides of the seat were armrests with two lions standing beside the armrests, 19 and twelve lions standing there, one on each side of the six steps. Nothing like it had been made for any kingdom. 20 All the drinking cups of King Solomon were made of gold and all the vessels of the house of the forest of Lebanon of fine gold; silver was of no estimation in the time of Solomon. 21 The king's fleet went to Tarshish with the servants of Huram, making a round trip every

° With LXX, Heb. "streets." The Kings parallel (I Kings x 12) is equally obscure. Rudolph (p. 222) renders "balustrades" or "banisters."

three years; the Tarshish fleet carried gold, silver, ivory, and two species of monkeys. 22 King Solomon surpassed all the kings of the earth in wealth and wisdom, 23 and all the kings of the earth consulted Solomon to listen to his wisdom which God had put in his mind. 24 Each one of them brought his gift—articles of silver and articles of gold, garments, weapons,*a* perfume, horses, and mules; so it was year after year. 25 Solomon also had four thousand stalls for horses and chariots together with twelve thousand horsemen whom he billeted in the chariot-cities and with the king at Jerusalem. 26 He was the ruler over all the kings from the river to the land of the Philistines as far as the border of Egypt. 27 The king made silver as cheap in Jerusalem as stones, and cedar as plentiful as sycamore in the Shephelah. 28 They brought Solomon horses from Egypt and from all [other] lands.

a LXX reads "oil of myrrh."

NOTES

ix 1. *After she arrived.* Literally "she came to Solomon, she conversed with him."

5. *your wisdom . . . state.* Literally "about your words and about your wisdom."

9. *one hundred and twenty talents of gold.* A little over 4½ tons.

10. *algum wood.* Cf. COMMENT on ii 1–17. Customarily rendered "sandalwood," which is not found in the Lebanon mountains.

12. *every delightful thing . . . asked.* The meaning seems to be that he gave her whatever she admired and said she wished to possess.

[*what he gave her in exchange for*]. Some such clarification is necessary. The mission of the queen of Sheba was mostly commercial, hence the exchange. Some complimentary presents were doubtless exchanged along with the conclusion of commercial agreements. The addition really combines the texts of Kings and Chronicles. If it is correct, we have a case of double haplography because the clauses begin and end in the same way. Thus I Kings x 13 reads: "Except for what he gave her as the hand of the King Solomon"; while the text here says, "Except for what she brought to the king." Putting the two together we read, "Except for what he gave her [according to the authority of King Solomon] for what she brought to the king."

13. *six hundred and sixty-six talents*. Slightly over 25⅛ tons.

14. *the traders*. Literally "from the men of caravan trade." The meaning seems to be the revenue derived from tolls and mercantile trade. See J. Gray, *The Legacy of Canaan*, 1957, p. 157.

15. *large shields*. For drawings of large (*sinnāh*) and small (*māgēn*) shields see Galling, BRL, cols. 457–58; also ANEP, 184, 372.

beaten gold. May be alloyed or inlaid gold; they were for ornamental purposes.

six hunded shekels. About 15 lbs.

16. *shields*. See first NOTE on vs. 15.

three hundred shekels. I Kings x 17 has "3 minas of gold," which equals 150 shekels or about 3¾ lbs.

the house of the forest of Lebanon. So called perhaps because of the extensive use of cedar.

19. *One . . . steps*. Literally "on both sides of the six steps."

20. *silver . . . Solomon*. This is of course oriental hyperbole. There was so much of it that it didn't count. Cf. the request of King Dushratta of Mitanni for Egyptian gold which he says is "as common as dust" (J. A. Knudtzon, *Die El-Amarna Tafeln*, No. 19, line 61).

21. *Tarshish*. On the problem of Tarshish and the Tarshish fleet as the refinery fleet see W. F. Albright, BASOR 83 (October 1941), 22; ARI, p. 136; *Eretz Israel*, V, 7–9. Since Tarshish means "refinery" in Phoenician and the trade was with Ophir and Punt, there can hardly be a reference to Tartessus in southern Spain. Taken literally, i.e., as Tartessus in Spain, a voyage around the tip of Africa would be involved. That is quite unlikely.

making . . . years. The round trip would require something over a year; if it began in a given year it would extend through the next and into the following year. Thus parts of two years plus the one full year between would be reckoned as three years. See ARI, p. 134 and notes.

two species of monkeys. The *qōphīm* and *tukkiyīm* were monkeys of different types, ARI, p. 212, n. 16.

26. *the river*. I.e., the Euphrates.

27. *the Shephelah*. Low hills southwest of Bethlehem.

28. Refers to the horse trade; see NOTES on i 16, 17.

COMMENT

These verses are closely paralleled in I Kings x, the source upon which the writer relied. There was no reason to deviate from the source since it fitted quite well into his scheme for the glorification of King Solomon.

[The visit of the queen of Sheba, ix 1–12]: From the viewpoint of the Chronicler, the two phases of Solomon's achievements—wisdom and wealth—are associated to illustrate his fame and splendor. But the underlying motive of the source he used is undoubtedly trade. The visit of the queen of Sheba can no longer be regarded as fictional. Recent archaeological explorations in South Arabia have added a whole new chapter to the wealth and trade of a hitherto obscure land. While the names of queens as rulers do not appear in the known Assyrian records before the eighth century (one, Samsi, is mentioned in the records of Tiglath-pileser III and Sargon II; ANET, pp. 283 ff.), they must have been prominent in South Arabian affairs before that time. The impact of Arabia upon Palestine was considerable, as may be seen from the numerous references in the Bible (cf. Montgomery, *Arabia and the Bible;* G. W. Van Beek, BA 15 [1952], 2–6; W. F. Albright, "Dedan," *Geschichte und Altes Testament,* 1953, pp. 1–12). Sheba (Saba, Sabaeans) is mentioned frequently (cf., in addition to this section and its parallel, Isa lx 6; Jer vi 20; Ezek xxvii 22, xxxviii 13; Joel iii 8; Job i 15, vi 19; Ps lxxii 10, 15), especially in connection with caravans and the spice trade. To judge from the results of excavations so far published, Marib, the ancient capital of Sheba, was an imposing center of activity. Furthermore, evidence of economic vitality is shown by trade carried on all over the area from South Arabia northward to Phoenicia and Syria. See R. L. Bowen and F. P. Albright, *Archaeological Discoveries in South Arabia,* 1958, especially Pt. II, and the popular account by W. Phillips, *Qataban and Sheba,* 1955, especially Chs. 10, 24. Part of the site of Hadjar Bin Humeid, about sixty miles south of Marib, has been excavated to the bottom of the Tell and shows the existence of a settlement there in the tenth century B.C. The depths of the deposits at Timna and Marib indicate much older settlements and are therefore reflective of an advanced civilization, widespread and prosperous, in South Arabia (see W. F. Albright in *Eretz Israel*, V, 7–9). The tenth century was apparently one of extraordinary growth and expansion from Syria to Ethiopia (W. F. Albright, "Zur Chronologie des vorislamischen Arabien," in *Von Ugarit nach Qumran*, 1958, pp. 1–8).

It is probably no accident that this episode is reported immediately after the reference to the establishment of Solomon's seaport at Ezion-geber, whose traffic with Ophir threatened the lucrative overland trade of the South Arabians. Thus the visit of the queen of Sheba takes on added significance; it is of the nature of a diplomatic and trade mission whose business was to establish a modus vivendi with the great merchant prince of Palestine. What the queen saw confirmed the reports that had reached her of Solomon's wisdom and enterprise. The Chronicler does not refer to the classic description of Solomon's wisdom (I Kings iv 29–34 [v 9–14H]) and the term here appears to include something other than songs and proverbs. As Alt has shown, KS, II, pp. 90–99, Solomon's wisdom as described in I Kings iv 33 (v 13H) is to be explained in the light of Egyptian and Babylonian parallels; Alt characterizes it as "Listenwissenschaft," the art of classification. As viewed here it seems to be the knowledge of how to do things (vss. 3–4), functional knowledge as applied to building, organization, arrangements in his court, etc. Along with these qualities went that of a shrewd trader, as the queen must have learned even before her mission to Jerusalem. In addition to the traditional exchange of gifts there was trade of goods as implied in vs. 12.

The widest departure from the sources occurs in vs. 8 where I Kings x 9 has David occupying the throne of Israel. Here, in line with the writer's general view that the throne is Yahweh's which the king occupies for him, it is his (i.e., Yahweh's) throne occupied by Solomon "as king for Yahweh your God" (cf. I Chron xvii 14, xxviii 5, xxix 23; II Chron xiii 8).

[Solomon's wealth, 13–28]: With few significant variants, the Chronicler follows his source, which is itself composed of an assortment of materials bearing on the general subject of the wealth of Solomon. While there is certainly a great deal of exaggeration connected with almost every item, there is doubtless truth in each one. He did have a tremendous income from various sources, particularly from tolls levied on merchants and as a merchant trader, refiner, and manufacturer (see COMMENT on Sec. 9, viii 17–18). The reference to Arabian kings may reflect trade in Solomon's period but also a later time as Arabian trade continued into post-exilic times and after. The tribute or taxes received from the governors (a late term) of the land may contain a kernel of truth, though couched in late terminology, if the reference is to tolls levied for economic privileges.

The golden shields, made for decorative purposes, may be no more than the persistence of a local tradition and brought into the picture here because of the mention of gold in the preceding verses. The great ivory throne overlaid with gold was a showpiece; the story was repeated here because it reflected the splendor and glory of the Solomonic empire. This is also true of the later exaggeration of the drinking cups and the other ornamental vessels in the house of the forest of Lebanon. For a description of the throne, with a note on Asshurbanipal's, see Montgomery and Gehman, *The Book of Kings*, pp. 221 f. Here, vss. 17–19, is one of the significant variations from Kings. According to the latter, the back of the throne contained the figure of a calf's head, which here is made into either a lamb or armrest (cf. C. North, ZAW 50 [1932], 28 f.), in order to avoid any reference to the golden calves of Jeroboam as already evident in the MT of Kings. For such ornaments see J. W. and Grace M. Crowfoot, *Early Ivories from Samaria*, 1938, Pl. 9, Fig. 1, and G. Loud, *The Megiddo Ivories*, 1939, Pl. 4, Figs. 2a, b. The throne of Bar Rekab had a footstool (ANEP, 460). For a good illustration of a throne, though with different decorations on the back, see H. Carter and A. C. Mace, *The Tomb of Tut-Ankh-Amen*, I, 1923, Pls. LXII–LXIV. For the lion features see M. Pongracz, "Löwendarstellungen an Podesten der Königsthrone," *Mitteilungen des deutschen archäologischen Instituts Alteilung Kairo*, XV, 1957, pp. 213–20.

The maritime adventures of Solomon are significant and again the Chronicler has shown his bias toward the king. His source stated that both Hiram and Solomon had ships plying the waterways between Ezion-geber and Ophir. But Hiram's maritime activity has been toned down, as may be seen from the translation, which fits in well with the following verses describing Solomon's wealth and fame. Verse 24 doubtless refers to mercantile activity, which was conducted on a barter basis. Tolls and taxes were also paid in kind.

What is involved in the reference to chariot-cities with their horse stables and chariot sheds may be seen from the excavations of Megiddo and elsewhere (see Lamon and Shipton, *Megiddo*, I, pp. 32–47). According to the calculations of the archaeologists there was room at Megiddo for about four hundred and fifty horses and one hundred and fifty chariots, along with exercising grounds, water tanks, houses for grooms, etc. The four thousand stalls is probably not an exaggeration (though I Kings iv 26 [v 6H] obviously is; possibly a scribal error) since there were stables of similar character at Tell el-Hesy, Gezer, Taanach, and perhaps at Hazor (see P. L. O. Guy, *New Light from Armageddon*, 1931, pp. 42–48). However, these structures may not have been stables but storage places, as may have been those at Hazor; see Yadin et al., *Hazor*, II, p. 9. On the extent of Solomon's rule see COMMENT on Sec. 9. While there may have been some shrinking of the Israelite empire under Solomon, there cannot have been much (cf. Bright, *A History of Israel*, p. 193, and references there). But Solomon's claims were, in all probability, largely of a commercial nature as is hinted at again and again in the account.

11. CONCLUSION
(ix 29–31)†

IX ²⁹ As for the remainder of the history of Solomon from beginning to end, is it not written down in the records of Nathan the prophet, in the prophecy of Ahijah the Shilonite, and in the visions of Iddo the seer concerning Jeroboam the son of Nebat? ³⁰ Solomon was king over all Israel at Jerusalem for forty years. ³¹ When Solomon slept with his fathers, they buried him in the city of David his father and Rehoboam his son became king in his place.

† II Chron ix 29–31 ‖ I Kings xi 41=43.

COMMENT

Omitting the stories of Solomon's defection through catering to foreign women, the Hadad and Rezon episodes, and the treason of Jeroboam with the support of Ahijah because they undermined his views of the king, the writer brings his account of Solomon to a conclusion. This section follows I Kings xi 41–43 with the exception of the reference to the sources in 29b. Whether they were actual sources current at the time or whether they refer to Kings is disputed. Three prophetic records are mentioned as in the case of David (I Chron xxix 29).

II. THE KINGS OF JUDAH

(ca. 922–587 B.C.)

12. THE REIGN OF REHOBOAM (ca. 922–915 B.C.): THE REBELLION OF ISRAEL (x 1–19)†

X ¹ Then Rehoboam went to Shechem, for all Israel had come to Shechem to make him king. ² When Jeroboam the son of Nebat heard about it—for he was in Egypt whither he had fled from the presence of Solomon the king—he returned from Egypt. ³ So they sent and summoned him. When Jeroboam and all Israel arrived, they said to Rehoboam, ⁴ "Your father made our yoke heavy; ease now the harsh servitude of your father and the heavy yoke he has imposed upon us and we will serve you." ⁵ He said to them, "Come back to me again in three days." So the people left. ⁶ Then King Rehoboam consulted the elders who served his father during his lifetime saying, "What reply do you advise for this people?" ⁷ They advised him as follows: "If you will be kind to this people, befriend them, and speak charitably to them, they will always remain your servants." ⁸ But he rejected the advice which the elders gave him and then consulted the younger men who grew up with him and were now his counselors. ⁹ He said to them, ᵃ"How do you advise meᵃ to reply to this people who have said to me, 'Ease the yoke which your father imposed upon us'?" ¹⁰ The younger men who grew up with him gave him the following advice: "This is how you ought to reply to the people who petitioned you:

'Your father made heavy our yoke;
you make [it] easier for us'!

† II Chron x 1–19 ‖ I Kings xii 1–20.

ᵃ⁻ᵃ MT has "how do you advise that we . . ."; LXX "how do you advise that I." May be the royal plural.

This is what you ought to tell them, 'My little finger is thicker than my father's loins; 11 Although my father laid a heavy yoke upon you, I will make it yet heavier;

> My father disciplined you with whips,
> I will [do it] with scorpions.'"

12 When Jeroboam and all the people came to Rehoboam on the third day, as the king had directed, saying, "Come back to me on the third day," 13 the king Rehoboam answered them harshly because the king had rejected the advice of the elders. 14 In accordance with the advice of the younger men, he replied to them as follows:

> *b*"My father made heavy your yoke,*b*
> I will add to it;
> My father disciplined you with whips,
> I will [do it] with scorpions."

15 So the king did not listen to the people, for it was a turn of affairs brought about by God that Yahweh might fulfill his word concerning Jeroboam the son of Nebat which he delivered through Ahijah the Shilonite. 16 When all Israel saw that the king would not listen to them, the people retorted to the king as follows:

> "What part have we in David,
> No inheritance with the son of Jesse;
> Each one to your tents, O Israel,
> Now look to your own house, O David."

So all Israel went to their tents. 17 Hence Rehoboam was king only over those of the Israelites who lived in the cities of Judah. 18 When King Rehoboam sent out Hadoram*c* the corvée chief, the Israelites stoned him to death but King Rehoboam managed to mount his chariot and escape to Jerusalem. 19 So Israel has remained in rebellion against the house of David until today.

b-b So with many manuscripts. Hebrew reads "I will increase your yoke."
c LXX*B* has "Adoniram." Cf. I Kings xii 18 "Adoram," a spelling variant.

Notes

x 2. *he returned from Egypt.* I Kings xii 2 "he lived in Egypt." I Kings xii 2–3a is missing in LXX and is in part an intrusion from this passage combined with reminiscences of xi 40.
7. *kind.* I Kings xii 7 "servant."
befriend them. I Kings xii 7 "serve them."
16. *all Israel.* Kings parallel reads "Israel."
saw. Add with I Kings xii 16.
19. The Chronicler was quoting his source here. It has no reference to the later Samaritan schism.

Comment

Apparently there was no question of Rehoboam's accession in Judah; the old Davidic structure of a double crown, one of Judah and the other of Israel, was maintained. Hence he had to receive the crown of the latter from the hands of the elders of Israel. To that end he traveled to Shechem, the old amphictyonic center of Israel. (On the amphictyonic character of the Israelite tribes see M. Noth, *Zwölf Stämme Israels,* 1930. The personal union of Israel and Judah initiated by David and continued under Solomon fell apart after the latter's death because of the refusal of Rehoboam to redress the grievances of Israel.) Before anointing him, the authorities demanded the lifting of the grievous burdens imposed upon them by the extravagant building program of Solomon.

The preceding chapter mentions Jeroboam only in connection with the prophecy of Ahijah. The Chronicler, having avoided any reference to discontent during Solomon's reign, does so here only to explain why Jeroboam was in Egypt from whence he returned when he was informed of the proposed accession of Rehoboam. "All Israel" (vss. 1, 3, 16[*bis*]) refers to all the Northern tribes. "The Israelites who lived in the cities of Judah" (vs. 17) and "all Israel in Judah and Benjamin" (xi 3) underline the Chronicler's view that only those elements of Israel that remained loyal to the Davidic line were the true Israel.

In vs. 7 the Chronicler has toned down the source which has "servant" for "kind," obviously too strong a word for him as it applied to the king. For the same reason he changed "serve them" into "please them." Although Solomon is glorified by the writer, he cannot and does not exclude the damaging reflections upon his rule provided by this chapter, which is telling evidence to the effect that he does not completely distort history, painful though it may have been for him.

13. THE REIGN OF REHOBOAM (ca. 922–915 B.C.): ESTABLISHING THE KINGDOM (xi 1–23)†

The prophecy of Shemaiah

XI ¹ When Rehoboam arrived at Jerusalem he mustered one hundred and eighty thousand select warriors from the house of Judah and of Benjamin to win back the kingdom for Rehoboam by war with Israel. ² Then the word of Yahweh came to Shemaiah, the man of God, saying, ³ "Tell Rehoboam the son of Solomon, the king of Judah and all Israel in Judah and Benjamin: ⁴ 'Thus has Yahweh said, you must not go up to fight with your brothers. Let each man return to his house, for this matter is my doing'." When they heard the words of Yahweh, they abandoned their pursuit of Jeroboam.

Cities for defense

⁵ Rehoboam resided in Jerusalem but built cities for the defense of Judah. ⁶ He built Bethlehem, Etam, Tekoa, ⁷ Beth-zur, Soco, Adullam, ⁸ Gath, Mareshah, Ziph, ⁹ Adoraim, Lachish, Azekah, ¹⁰ Zorah, Aijalon, and Hebron, which were the fortified cities for Judah and Benjamin. ¹¹ He strengthened the fortified places and put commanders and supplies of food, oil, and wine, in them. ¹² He also put large shields and spears in every single city and strengthened them very much. Thus Judah and Benjamin were retained by him.

Migration of priests and Levites

¹³ The priests and Levites from all over Israel came from their domain and placed themselves at his disposal. ¹⁴ The Levites left their pasture grounds and their property and went to Judah

† II Chron xi 1–4: cf. I Kings xii 21–24; 5–17 ‖ I Kings xii 25–33.

and Jerusalem because Jeroboam and his sons had excluded them from the priesthood of Yahweh, 15 and appointed priests of his own for the high places for the satyrs and for the calves he had made. 16 Those of all the tribes of Israel who had set their minds on seeking Yahweh God of Israel followed them to Jerusalem to sacrifice to Yahweh God of their fathers. 17 They strengthened the kingdom of Judah and supported Rehoboam the son of Solomon for three years, for they followed the way of David and Solomon for three years.

Rehoboam's family

18 Rehoboam took Mahalath the daughter of Jerimoth, David's son, and Abihail the daughter of Eliab, Jesse's son, as wife. 19 She bore him the following sons: Jeush, Shemariah, and Zaham. 20 After her he took Maacah the daughter of Absalom [as a wife] who bore him Abijah, Attai, Ziza, and Shelomith. 21 Rehoboam loved Maacah the daughter of Absalom more than all his [other] wives and concubines—for he had taken eighteen wives and sixty concubines and fathered twenty-eight sons and sixty daughters. 22 Rehoboam named Abijah the son of Maacah as the head and, therefore, leader of his brothers, for he wanted to make him king. 23 He acted wisely by distributing some of his sons to all the territories of Judah and Benjamin, that is to all the fortified cities, where he provided food in abundance for them and sought out wives *for them.*

a–a So for Heb. "multitude"; but cf. LXX. See NOTE.

NOTES

xi 1. *one hundred and eighty thousand.* Possibly the unit basis is involved here too since the reference is to a mustering of armed forces.

20. *Maacah the daughter of Absalom.* Cf. I Kings xv 2.

Abijah. "Abijam" in I Kings xv 1–7 (cf. Albright, AMJV, p. 81, n. 72).

22. *Rehoboam named Abijah . . . as the head.* Abijah was named "eldest" son and heir apparent. The use of the term *nāgīd* suggests the

possibility of a coregency here to secure succession against other claimants.

23. *and sought out wives for them.* Cazelles (*Les Livres des Chroniques* [see Selected Bibliography, Commentaries]) refers to the literal translation, approximately, "he consulted the multitude [of the gods] of his wives" which he takes with the following verse (xii 1). The rendering here adopted is based on the following division of words: *wayyiśśā' lāhem* [ ] *nāšim.* Rudolph suggests . . . *lāhem hᵃmōn nāšim* ("for them a multitude of wives").

COMMENT

[Prophecy of Shemaiah, xi 1–4]: To Shemaiah belongs the distinction of having averted further internecine war between Rehoboam and Jeroboam. "All Israel in Judah and Benjamin" in vs. 3 reflects the Chronicler's view, since I Kings xii 23 has "all the house of Judah and Benjamin" (cf. COMMENT on preceding section).

[Cities for defense, 5–12]: This passage is unique with the Chronicler and points clearly to the fact that he had sources at his disposal that were ignored by or unknown to the Deuteronomist. It also shows how he wove this material into his narrative in place of the latter's references to certain activities of Jeroboam.

G. Beyer ("Das Festungssystem Rehabeams," ZDPV 54 [1931], 113–34) has shown convincingly that the system of fortifications belongs to the period of Rehoboam; whether it dates from before the invasion of Shishak, as the Chronicler infers (xii 2), or after cannot now be determined (see also E. Junge, *Die Wiederaufbau des Heerwesens des Reiches Juda unter Josia,* 1938, who thinks the list is Josianic; and Alt, KS, II, pp. 306–15, who thinks it possible that it dates from the time of Rehoboam). Excavations at Azekah, Mareshah, Lachish, Beth-zur, and elsewhere have uncovered fortifications which may date from the period of Rehoboam (cf. Bliss and Macalister, *Excavations in Palestine, 1898–1900,* 1902; O. R. Sellars, *The Citadel of Beth-Zur,* 1933, and BA 21 [1958], 71–76; O. Tufnell, *Lachish III: The Iron Age,* 1953). If Beth-shemesh was in ruins at the time, that would account for its not being included (cf. F. M. Cross, Jr., and G. E. Wright, "The Boundary and Province Lists of the Kingdom of Judah," JBL 75 [1956], 216 f.); on the other hand both Beth-shemesh and Debir, present-day Tell

Beit Mirsim, may have been fortified already by Solomon (see BASOR 154 [April 1959], 38, n. 16). All of the places mentioned have now been identified. See the index in L. Grollenberg, *Atlas of the Bible*, 1956. On Etam, present-day Khirbet el-Khokh, see H. J. Kraus, ZDPV 72 (1956), 152–62. The fortifications were either in the hill country or at the edge of it and were intended for defense primarily against the Egyptians and Philistines, though they may have been erected in part also against the expansions of Edom. There was rebellion in Edom already in the time of Solomon (I Kings xi 14–22, 25), an incident not mentioned in Chronicles. The order of the listing in our passage does not follow the expected geographical sequence and, apart from 1 to 4, cannot be explained. Why Hebron should come last is also difficult to explain, unless it was a secondary fortress to which the hard-pressed defenders of Ziph might retreat if necessary. It is possible that others too were secondary fortifications, a line of fortified places where arms and other supplies were kept for emergency purposes, or for service in case the first line of defense was pierced. Rehoboam either regarded Jerusalem as fortification enough against Israel or he did not regard defense against Israel as imperative as against foreign elements.

[Migration of priests and Levites, 13–17]: The migration of priests and Levites is based on the report of I Kings xii 31–32, xiii 33 to the effect that Jeroboam appointed priests "from the whole people who were not Levites," though that does not imply necessarily that the latter were excluded as the Chronicler seems to think. But, as for the Deuteronomist, everything Jeroboam did was sinful in the sight of the Chronicler, who added satyrs to the high places and calves that he provided in Israel. Because of his feeling for Jerusalem as the worship center, he emphasizes the fact that all the really discerning Israelites followed the priests and Levites to the only legitimate shrine of the nation. Verse 17 may refer to the period before defection set in in the south, or that the Northerners came to Jerusalem for three years, that is, until the shrines of Jeroboam were set up when they, for the most part, worshiped there—a situation deplored by the writer.

[Family relationships of Rehoboam, 18–23]: Mahalath was a great-granddaughter of Jesse through both parents. Her father, Jerimoth, is nowhere else listed as a son of David and thus must have been the son of an inferior wife. Thus Mahalath was a cousin of the king Rehoboam. Maacah was either the granddaughter of Absalom, the son of David, or the daughter of another Absalom. Absalom, David's son, had only one daughter, Tamar, and three sons (II Sam xiv 27) who probably died in infancy (cf. II Sam xviii 18). Since no family connection is given, this appears to have been another Absalom. The oldest son of the beloved wife became the successor of Rehoboam.

Like his father Solomon (I Kings iv 11, 15), Rehoboam placed his sons in strategic centers to maintain his position and to guard against disloyalty.

14. THE REIGN OF REHOBOAM (ca. 922–915 B.C.): ABANDONMENT OF YAHWEH (xii 1–16)†

Shishak invasion

XII 1 ^aWhen the kingdom of Rehoboam was established^a and he had become strong, he, together with all Israel, abandoned the law of Yahweh. 2 In the fifth year of King Rehoboam, Shishak the king of Egypt came up against Jerusalem, because they were unfaithful to Yahweh, 3 with twelve hundred chariots and sixty thousand horsemen; the people who came with him from Egypt were innumerable—Libyans, Sukkiim, and Ethiopians. 4 They captured the fortified cities belonging to Judah and came as far as Jerusalem. 5 Then Shemaiah the prophet came to Rehoboam and the captains of Judah who had retreated to Jerusalem before Shishak and said to them, "Thus has Yahweh said, 'You have abandoned me and so I have abandoned you to the hand of Shishak.'" 6 Then the captains of Israel and the king humbled themselves and said, "Yahweh is righteous." 7 When Yahweh saw that they humbled themselves, the word of Yahweh came to Shemaiah, saying, "Because they have humbled themselves, I will not destroy them but I will grant them some measure of deliverance; my wrath shall not be poured out upon Jerusalem by the hand of Shishak, 8 but they shall be his servants that they may find out [the difference between] my service and the service of the kings of the [other] lands." 9 So Shishak the king of Egypt attacked Jerusalem and carried away

† **II Chron xii 1–9:** cf. I Kings xiv 25–26; **10–14:** cf. I Kings xiv 27–28, 21–22; **15–16** ‖ I Kings xiv 29–31, xv 6.

^{a–a} Reading k^ehikkōn for k^ehākīn. MT has "when Rehoboam established the kingdom."

the treasures of the house and the treasures of the king's house.
He carried away everything, including the golden shields which
Solomon had made.

More on Rehoboam

10 King Rehoboam then made bronze shields to replace them
and put them into the hand of the captains of the guard who
kept watch over the entrance to the king's house. 11 Whenever
the king entered the house of Yahweh the guards would come
and take them up and when he retired they would bring them
back again into the guard chamber. 12 When he humbled himself, the wrath of Yahweh turned away from him so as not to
destroy him completely. There were also some good things in
Judah. 13 So King Rehoboam grew strong in Jerusalem and continued as king. For Rehoboam was forty-one years old when he
became king and remained king for seventeen years in Jerusalem, the city where Yahweh had chosen, out of all the tribes of
Israel, to put his name. His mother's name was Naamah the
Ammonitess. 14 But he did wrong in that he did not set his
mind to seek Yahweh.

Conclusion

15 As for the history of Rehoboam from beginning to end, is
it not written down in the records of Shemaiah the prophet and
Iddo the seer; so also is the official genealogy? Wars between
Rehoboam and Jeroboam continued throughout the period.
16 When Rehoboam slept with his fathers, he was buried in
the city of David and Abijah his son became king in his place.

NOTES

xii 3. *Sukkiim.* There were foreign mercenaries in the Egyptian army
at the time. See W. F. Albright in *The Old Testament and Modern
Study*, ed. H. H. Rowley, 1951, p. 18.

8. *kings.* So on basis of Phoen. *mmlkt* "kings," rather than "kingdoms."

11. *chamber.* On *t'* as "chamber," see W. von Soden, WO 1 (1950), 356–61.

13. *His . . . Naamah the Ammonitess.* On the status of the queen mother, see H. Donner, "Art und Herkunft des Amtes der Königinmutter im Alten Testament," *Festschrift Johannes Friedrich,* 1959, pp. 105–45 and references cited there.

16. *Abijah.* I Kings xiv 31 has "Abijam." Cf. M. Noth, IPN, p. 234. Probably the given name, while Abijah was the throne name. Cf. Uzziah-Azariah, Eliakim-Jehoiakim, Mattaniah-Zedekiah.

COMMENT

The sources for chapter xii were I Kings xiv 21–28 and a special piece, probably the temple records of the prophecy of Shemaiah. The following table indicates the situation:

II Chron xii	I Kings xiv
1	—
2 ab	25
2 c–9 a	—
9 b–11	26–28
12	—
13–14	21–22
15–16	29–31

The order adopted by the writer points up the fact that he pursued his own methods for the purpose he had in mind.

[The Shishak invasion, xii 1–9]: The Deuteronomist devoted only two verses to this important episode. The Chronicler had access to another source which gave a fuller account and has thus preserved for us data corroborated by archaeological discoveries and Egyptian historical lists. Shishak was the first strong king of the twenty-second dynasty (Bubastite) whose aim doubtless was twofold: (a) to extend Egyptian power and (b) to teach Jeroboam a lesson. His invasion took place in the fifth year of Rehoboam (ca. 918 B.C.) and was a major operation, as indicated by the list of cities claimed as its victims. (See M. Noth, ZDPV 61 [1938], 277–304; Albright, AASOR 21–22 [1943], 38, n. 14; B. Mazar, "The Campaign of Pharaoh Shishak to Palestine," in SVT: *Volume du Congrès: Strasbourg, 1956* [Strasbourg, 1957], pp. 57–66, and IEJ 2 [1952], 82–88; W. F. Albright, BP, pp. 29 f., and BASOR

130 [1953], 4–8.) The names of towns in that list suggest that there was no major invasion of Judah proper, except for Aijalon. However both Kings and Chronicles assert that Jerusalem was attacked and there is evidence from archaeology that some of the cities of Judah were destroyed at the time, notably Lachish. Moreover, the Chronicler says that the fortified cities of Judah were captured and that the military leaders had retreated before the forces of Shishak to Jerusalem. It may be that Judah did escape more serious destruction by the payment of tribute. Despite the utilization of his excellent source, the Chronicler appears to have been concerned chiefly with the theological significance of the event. "All Israel" (Judah was for the Chronicler the true Israel, the only Israel that counted) and her king had abandoned the torah of Yahweh; that is why Shishak came against Jerusalem. Jerusalem was dealt a severe blow but was not destroyed because the leaders humbled themselves before Yahweh whose word was delivered by Shemaiah the prophet.

[Further observations on Rehoboam, 10–14]: The golden ornamental shields had to be replaced with shields of bronze. Again the Chronicler reverts to his theological view that Rehoboam and Judah escaped complete destruction because of his submission. There was still some good in Judah and so the wrath of God was turned away from him. Verse 13 is a concluding observation following the invasion of Shishak; it is placed here at the end of the narrative on Rehoboam rather than at the beginning (as in I Kings xiv 21), probably as a testimony to Yahweh's fulfillment of his promise to spare Jerusalem. Rehoboam became strong in Jerusalem and his reign continued for seventeen years. Verse 14 is an addition, a reminder of what was said in vs. 1.

[Conclusion, 15–16]: The statement on the sources used by the writer follows the pattern set in the references to the records of the reigns of David and Solomon. He thus departs from I Kings xiv 29 which speaks of the chronicles of the kings of Judah as the source for "the rest of the deeds of Rehoboam"; there is no mention of the prophetic records (see Introduction to *I Chronicles,* "The Sources Referred to by the Chronicler").

15. THE REIGN OF ABIJAH (ca. 915–913 B.C.) (xiii 1–23 [xiii 1–22, xiv 1E])†

Accession

XIII 1 In the eighteenth year of King Jeroboam, Abijah became king over Judah. 2 He was king for three years in Jerusalem and his mother's name was Micaiah the daughter of Uriel from Gibeah. When war broke out between Abijah and Jeroboam, 3 Abijah began the battle with an army of four hundred thousand choice warriors. Jeroboam engaged him in battle with eight hundred thousand choice warriors.

Address of Abijah

4 Then Abijah stood up on Mount Zemaraim, located in [the region of] Mount Ephraim, and said, "Listen to me, Jeroboam and all Israel: 5 Don't you know that Yahweh God of Israel has given eternal dominion over Israel to David and his sons by a covenant of salt? 6 Yet Jeroboam the son of Nebat, the slave of Solomon the son of David, rose up and rebelled against his master, 7 and worthless men, rascals, joined him and proved too strong for Rehoboam the son of Solomon, in as much as Rehoboam was an inexperienced and timid young man and could not hold his own against them. 8 Now you propose to resist the rule of Yahweh exercised through the sons of David because you are a vast multitude and have with you the golden calves which Jeroboam made as gods for you! 9 But have you not driven out the priests of Yahweh, the sons of Aaron, and the Levites and made for yourselves priests just as the peoples of [other] countries have

† **II Chron xiii 1–3 ‖ I Kings xv 1–2, 6; 22–23 ‖ I Kings xv 7–8.**

done? Whoever comes to consecrate himself with a young bull and seven rams may become a priest of the no-gods. 10 As for us, Yahweh is our God; we have not abandoned him, and priests who are sons of Aaron minister to Yahweh and the Levites perform his service; 11 they sacrifice burnt offerings and [offer] perfumed incense to Yahweh morning after morning and evening after evening, [set] layer bread on the clean table and light the lamps on the golden lampstand nightly. We keep the decree of Yahweh our God, but you have abandoned him. 12 Behold, God is on our side, at our head, and his priests with signal trumpets are ready to sound the alarm against you. O sons of Israel, do not fight with Yahweh God of your fathers, for you will not succeed."

The results of the campaign

13 Now Jeroboam had sent a party around to ambush them from the rear, so that they were in front of Judah and the ambush behind them. 14 When Judah turned about, behold they were attacked from both front and rear; then they cried unto Yahweh, the priests sounded the trumpets, 15 and the men of Judah raised the battle cry. When the men of Judah raised the battle cry, God routed Jeroboam and all Israel before Abijah and Judah. 16 So the sons of Israel fled before Judah, for God gave them into their hand. 17 Abijah and his people inflicted a great slaughter upon them—five hundred thousand selected men of Israel fell, slain. 18 The sons of Israel were humbled at that time while the sons of Judah prevailed because they relied upon Yahweh God of their fathers. 19 Abijah pursued Jeroboam and took away from him the cities of Bethel with its dependencies, Jeshanah with its dependencies, and Ephron with its dependencies. 20 Jeroboam could not regain strength again while Abijah lived. Finally Yahweh struck Jeroboam and he died. 21 So Abijah grew powerful; he married fourteen wives and fathered twenty-two sons and sixteen daughters.

Conclusion

22 The remainder of the history of Abijah, his exploits and his words, are recorded in the treatise of the prophet Iddo. 23 When Abijah slept with his fathers, they buried him in the city of David and Asa his son became king in his place. The land remained undisturbed in his time for ten years.

NOTES

xiii 3. Perhaps 400,000 and 800,000 are to be interpreted on the unit basis, i.e., 400 and 800 units. The number per unit is not given.

4. *Mount Zemaraim.* Somewhere in the neighborhood of Beth-el, probably slightly to the northeast. Cf. Abel, *Géographie de la Palestine,* II, p. 454. On possible location and incidental discussion of this incident see K. Koch, "Zur Lage von Şemarajim," ZDPV 78 (1962), 19–29, especially 26 ff.; cf. also Z. Kallai-Kleinmann, "The Town Lists of Judah, Simeon, Benjamin and Dan," VT 8 (1958), 134–60.

5. *eternal dominion.* This reference to the eternal dominion (kingdom) of David is independent of Samuel and of Kings, which the Chronicler usually follows and which is ambiguous; i.e., the kingdom is sometimes eternal, sometimes contingent on the behavior of the kings of the Davidic line. While this is a statement by Abijah and therefore not necessarily the same as a word from God, through a prophet, it is interesting that it should be in special Chronicles material used with approval by the Chronicler.

7. *rascals.* Literally "sons of Belial."

10. *his.* Suffix added for clarity.

12. *signal trumpets.* On the significance of trumpets see P. Humbert, *La Terou'a,* 1946. The priestly summons to battle signified Yahweh's entrance into the fray. In the face of such tremendous odds, the subsequent victory was his alone.

18. *they relied.* niš'an is parallel to "believe" or "trust" in Isa x 20, xxx 12, xxxi 1. Cf. also II Chron xiv 10, xvi 7–8.

19. *dependencies.* Literally "daughters." The chief city was called the "mother," i.e., metropolis, and the villages its "daughters."

20. *struck Jeroboam.* So for clarity. MT has "him." Two events may have been combined by the Chronicler. The last reference in Kings to Jeroboam is the death of his son. It may be that the stroke here against

Jeroboam fell upon his son. The king apparently died soon afterward and was succeeded by another son, Nadab.

22. *treatise.* The Hebrew "midrash," i.e., a study or presentation, with embellishments, of an earlier work. In the canonical books of OT, the term occurs only here and II Chron xxiv 27.

23. *in his time.* According to LXX this phrase refers to Asa. In any case, Abijah seems to have died soon after the war with Jeroboam.

COMMENT

The Chronicler's assessment of Abijah and his reign varies considerably from that of the Deuteronomist. The latter has nothing good to report about him and says that he was tolerated only for David's sake. The Deuteronomist notes the fierce struggle between him and Jeroboam which continued throughout his reign.

[Accession of Abijah, xiii 1–3]: The Chronicler obviously followed another tradition in the matter of the name of Abijah's mother. According to xi 20 and I Kings xv 2 his mother was Maacah, the daughter of Absalom (Abishalom). The problem is further complicated by the name of Asa's mother (I Kings xv 10; II Chron xv 16). To alter Micaiah to Maacah, with LXX, does not help very much in view of the family pedigree, "the daughter of Uriel from Gibeah." The problem is, whose mother was Maacah? There may have been divergent records, hardly surprising in view of the many wives, concubines, and children Rehoboam and Abijah are supposed to have had. In the present state of our knowledge, any solution can only be speculative. The following suggestions have been put forth: (a) Abijah and Asa were brothers; (b) Uriel was the husband of Tamar the daughter of Absalom; (c) the wife of Asa also bore the name of Maacah; (d) Chronicles is correct and the name of Maacah in I Kings xv 2 is secondary due to the influence of vs. 10 (Noth, US, p. 143, n. 1); (e) Maacah was the grandmother of Asa. It may be observed here that the regular formula giving the year of accession, the length of the reign and the name of the mother in the case of Asa is missing in Chronicles. Only in xv 16 is the mother of Asa referred to as Maacah. It is possible that in Kings the real name of Abijah's wife was submerged by the strong personality of his mother, Maacah. (See Montgomery and Gehman, *The Books of Kings,* pp. 274 f.; Bright, *A History of Israel,* p. 220, n. 35; Albright, ARI, pp. 158, 219, n. 105; Donner, *Festschrift Johannes Friedrich,* pp. 105–45.)

The writer speaks of war between Jeroboam and Abijah—Kings has it between Jeroboam and Rehoboam—which favored Abijah, probably because of an alliance between him and the Aramaeans of Damascus (xvi 3; I Kings xv 19). The strength of Jeroboam's forces corresponds exactly with the figures for the Northern tribes in II Sam xxiv 9. The lowering of the number by a hundred thousand for Judah is due to the desire to stress the magnitude of the victory by a force only half the size of the enemy.

[Abijah's sermon on the mount, 4–12]: Abijah's sermon on Mount Zemaraim is typical of the Chronicler. It is an excellent specimen of Levitical preaching directed at the situation prevailing at the time of the writer and illustrated by a telling example from history. Verse 5 states that God has given eternal dominion over Israel to David, which was made clear through the covenant of salt; this is another way of saying that it is Yahweh's kingdom presided over by Yahweh's king. (On the covenant of salt, see Lev ii 13 and H. C. Trumbull, *The Covenant of Salt,* 1899.) The North was thus in rebellion (vss. 6–7) against Yahweh and not simply against Rehoboam (and his successor) as a man. Despite the material advantage of Israel—a well-known fact—they could not prevail against the kingdom of Yahweh and his anointed (vs. 8). The rebels do have a cult of sorts—golden calves (the golden calves were originally pedestals for "the glory of God" and fulfilled the same function for Israel as the ark with the cherubs did for Judah. For illustrations see F. Thureau-Dangin, A. Barrois, G. Dossin, and M. Dunand, *Arslan Tash,* 1931, Pl. II, Fig. 1; *Orientalia* 15 [1946], 1–45, with plates; *Orientalia* 18 [1949], Pl. 28; Bossert, *Altsyrien,* Pls. 446, 498, 960; BA 1 [1938], 2 f.), an illegitimate priesthood in the service of no-gods—but the true cult and priesthood are in Jerusalem (vss. 10–11). There true, legitimate, acceptable sacrifices were offered regularly and the decrees of Yahweh kept properly. The writer was thinking not only of the time of Abijah, but of his own time; he thus appealed to the people of Samaria, as Abijah had appealed to Jeroboam and "all Israel," to give up their rebellion against Yahweh. The South had the true God, the true kingdom, the true cult.

Especially significant is the fact that the rebels are still referred to as "sons of Israel" (vs. 12).

[The results of the campaign, 13–21]: According to the writer, when the priests blew the alarm God intervened and routed Jeroboam and his army. The latter's strategy (vss. 13–14), however brilliant, was no match against Yahweh who fought on the side of his devotees. The victory was his. Verse 19 is certainly based on authentic information, as is shown by the inclusion of a good portion of Ephraimite territory in the Judah-Benjamin list (Josh xviii 21–27) dating from the age of Jehoshaphat. For a discussion of the problem see Cross and Wright, JBL 75 (1956) 222 f. The thrust northward by Abijah resulted in the inclusion of this territory in what the authors refer to as the eleventh administrative district of Judah in the ninth century. Cf. their sketch map on p. 213 and Van Selms, *II Kronieken* (see Selected Bibliography, Commentaries), p. 112. Bethel (modern Beitin) is ten miles north of Jerusalem; Jeshanah (Burj el-Isāneh), about four miles south of Shiloh; Ephron-Ophrah (et-Taiyibeh), about four miles northeast of Bethel. Jeroboam may not have recovered the lost territory but Baasha certainly did since Asa had to retake it later (xv 8, xvii 2; cf. GVI, II, p. 226). Kings knew nothing of a violent death for Jeroboam; the statement here is due to the Chronicler's belief that resistance to Yahweh demanded it and may have been based on the prophecy of Abijah concerning the son of Jeroboam (I Kings xiv). Reference to the wives and progeny of Abijah is the writer's way of indicating the blessing of the Lord.

[Conclusion, 22–23]: Once again the writer refers to a prophetic treatise probably included in the records at his disposal, perhaps part of a larger work used by him (cf. I Kings xv 7). After Abijah's deliverance, the land was at peace for ten years into the reign of Asa. The formula is suspiciously like that following the deliverances of the judges.

16. THE REIGN OF ASA (ca. 913–873 B.C.): THE EARLY YEARS (xiv 1–14)†

The early years

XIV 1 Asa did what was good and right in the sight of Yahweh his God. 2 He removed the foreign altars and high places, broke down the Masseboth, cut the Asherim to pieces, 3 and urged Judah to seek Yahweh God of their fathers and to observe the law and the commandment. 4 Because he removed the high places and the incense altars from all the cities of Judah, the kingdom under him was undisturbed. 5 He built fortified cities in Judah because the country was undisturbed and no one was at war with him during these years, for Yahweh had given him rest. 6 He had said to Judah, "Let us build these cities and surround them with walls, towers, gates, and bars while the land is yet at our disposal; because we sought Yahweh our God, *ᵃhe sought usᵃ* and gave us rest all around." So they built and enjoyed success. 7 Asa had an army of three hundred thousand Judeans armed with shields and spears and two hundred eighty thousand Benjaminite shield-bearers and bowmen, all of whom were mighty warriors.

The Ethiopian war

8 Zerah the Ethiopian, with an army of a million [men], in addition to three hundred chariots, went out against them and reached Mareshah. 9 Asa went out to meet him and they prepared for battle in the Valley of Zephathah near Mareshah. 10 Then Asa called to Yahweh his God and said, "O Yahweh,

† II Chron xiv 1–7 ‖ I Kings xv 11–12.

ᵃ–ᵃ *derāšānū*, with LXX. MT "we sought."

you do not take into account numbers or strength when you come to assist: help us, O Yahweh our God, for we have relied upon you and come against this multitude in your name. O Yahweh, you are our God; mortal man cannot prevail over you." 11 When Yahweh vanquished the Ethiopians before Asa and before Judah, the Ethiopians fled. 12 But Asa and his associates pursued them as far as Gerar; so many of the Ethiopians fell that they were unable to rally; they were cut to pieces before Yahweh and his army. They carried off a very great deal of booty. 13 They destroyed all the cities around Gerar—for the dread of Yahweh was upon them—and plundered all the cities because there was much booty in them. 14 They also struck down *b*those who had cattle*b* and carried away large numbers of sheep and camels when they returned to Jerusalem.

b-b Hebrew reads "tents of cattle," which probably signifies "possessors of cattle." Cf. Ar. root *'hl* "people," "possessors."

NOTES

xiv 2. *Masseboth.* Rough, unhewn stones usually set up for cultic purposes. (See Galling, BRL, cols. 368–71.)

Asherim. Cult objects of some sort, perhaps exemplifying some of the characteristics of Asherah, originally a Canaanite sea-goddess. Cf. W. F. Albright, "The High Place in Ancient Palestine," SVT: *Volume du Congrès: Strasbourg, 1956* (Strasbourg, 1957), pp. 242–58.

4. *incense altars. Ḥammānīm.* For discussion of the meaning with illustrations see H. Ingholt, "Le sens du mot Hammān," in *Mélanges Syriens offerts à Monsieur René Dussaud*, II, 1939, pp. 795–802; K. Elliger, "Chammanim=Masseben?", ZAW 57 (1939), 256–65; Albright, ARI, p. 215, n. 58.

7. On numbers see NOTE on xiii 3.

9. *Zephathah.* Place is unknown. LXX "north of." It has nothing to do with the Zephath of Judg i 17.

10. *you do not take . . . assist.* Literally "it is not with you to help between the great and the strengthless." The meaning is that the strong as well as the weak need Yahweh's assistance to gain victory.

prevail over you. For *'al* with indicative here, cf. Gray, *The Legacy of Canaan*, p. 203.

12. *unable to rally.* Literally "that no life remained to them." Cf. C. Brockelmann, *Hebräische Syntax,* 1956, p. 145a.

army. Literally "camp."

They. Asa and his followers.

13. *for the dread . . . them.* Indication of the "holy war" tradition (cf. G. von Rad, *Der heilige Krieg im alten Israel,* 1951, p. 12), which Chronicles continues (II Chron xv 1 ff., xvi 7 ff., xx 15 ff., xxxii 7 ff.), as G. von Rad has pointed out in *Studies in Deuteronomy,* 1953, pp. 45–59. The Chronicler is perhaps more consistent in his application of the theory than Kings.

COMMENT

The last verse of chapter xiii is really the incipit of the following three chapters which deal with the reign of Asa. The Chronicler has greatly expanded the account of Asa's reign both by additions of his own and material from sources not used by the Deuteronomist.

[The early years, xiv 1–7]: The peace won by Abijah's defeat of Jeroboam carried over into the reign of Asa. Here that period of rest seems to be attributed to the fervent religious activity of the new king (vss. 4–6). It was doubtless due, in large measure, to the activity of the Aramaeans inspired by Abijah (xvi 3) and the troubles that beset Israel immediately after the death of Jeroboam. Of the reforming activity of Asa there can be no doubt, though that probably did not come in the first years of his reign because he was only a boy when he became king. The chronology of Asa is rather complicated. For a discussion see W. F. Albright, BASOR 100 (December 1945); E. R. Thiele, *The Mysterious Numbers of the Hebrew Kings,* 1951, Index; Rudolph, pp. 239 ff. Just when in his reign the cities of Judah were fortified cannot be determined but that some such activity did take place cannot be doubted in view of the unsettled condition of the times (cf. I Kings xv 32; cf. ÜS, pp. 140 f.). It may have followed the Ethiopian war. It is also quite credible that Asa maintained a standing army, though the numbers are exaggerated. The proportionately large number of Benjaminites suggests that Asa held on to most of the eastern region of the tribe taken by Abijah. Several scholars have advanced the idea that the Chronicler had access to a history of the Judean army from which these notes were taken. See Junge, *Der Wiederaufbau* . . . , pp. 38 f., 77 ff.; Noth, ÜS, p. 141, n. 2.

[The Ethiopian war, 8–14]: The account of Asa's brush with Zerah can hardly be a fabrication because of the prominence of the place names involved. However, it was not so imposing as the figures indicate; they result from the writer's tendency to magnify the victory of Yahweh. How the Ethiopians got to Gerar is not known. They were probably Egyptian mercenaries with their families, though they could have been Arabs (cf. Hab iii 7; Num xii 1). That Bedouin were at least associated with them is indicated by the presence of camels (vs. 14). The Egyptian mercenaries may have been settled there by Shishak in a kind of buffer state after the campaign against Rehoboam (so W. F. Albright, JPOS 4 [1924], 146 f., and as is suggested by the combination of Ethiopians and Libyans (xvi 8); on the location of Gerar, see Y. Aharoni, "The Land of Gerar," IEJ 6 [1956], 26–32). The episode related here may have been a movement by Zerah into better pasture grounds at the expense of Judah. On the other hand, Zerah could have been inspired by his Egyptian sovereign, Osorkon I, the successor of Shishak.

The battle took place near Mareshah (Tell Sandahannah), some twenty-five miles southwest of Jerusalem. The invaders were chased back to Gerar, which was apparently the capital of their district since the surrounding cities point to outlying centers of the metropolis. There is no indication that Gerar itself was taken. Beyond those facts we cannot go. Though the account is given essentially for theological purposes, it is one more indication of the significance of many of the peculiar stories of the Chronicler. The main interest of the writer was not the presentation of the bare facts of history. The victory over Zerah was Yahweh's, a powerful illustration of what could be expected by those who relied upon him. No forces of mortal man can withstand Yahweh.

17. THE REIGN OF ASA (ca. 913–873 B.C.): THE REFORMATION
(xv 1–19)†

The sermon of Azariah

XV 1 Then the spirit of God came upon Azariah the son of Oded, 2 as he went to meet Asa and said to him, "Listen to me, Asa and all Judah and Benjamin; Yahweh will be with you so long as you are with him; if you seek him he will let himself be found by you but if you abandon him he will abandon you. 3 For a long time Israel did not have the true God, or a priest teacher, or a torah, 4 but when in their distress they turned to Yahweh God of Israel and sought after him, he let himself be found by them. 5 At that time there was no security for those who went and came, rather there was much unrest among the inhabitants of the lands. 6 Nation was crushed by nation, city by city, for God caused confusion among them by every kind of distress. 7 Be strong and do not be discouraged, for there is a reward for your work."

The reformation

8 When Asa heard these words and *the prophecy of Oded the prophet*, he took courage, removed the abominations from the whole land of Judah and Benjamin as well as from the cities he took in* Mount Ephraim and renewed the altar of Yahweh which stood before the portico of Yahweh. 9 He convoked all Judah, Benjamin, and those from Ephraim, Manasseh, and Simeon who sojourned with them—for many from Israel had deserted to him when they saw that Yahweh his God was with

† II Chron xv 8–15: cf. I Kings xv 12; 16–19 ‖ I Kings xv 13–15.

a–a Vulg. "the prophecy of Azariah the son of Oded."
b With LXX. MT "from."

him. 10 They came together at Jerusalem in the third month of
the fifteenth year of Asa's reign 11 and sacrificed to Yahweh
that day some of the booty they brought, seven hundred oxen
and seven thousand sheep. 12 Then they entered into a covenant
to seek Yahweh God of their fathers with all their minds and
with all their soul, 13 and that anyone who would not seek
Yahweh God of Israel should be put to death, whether young
or old, man or woman. 14 They swore to Yahweh with a loud
voice, with a shout of joy, with trumpets, and with rams' horns.
15 All Judah rejoiced over the oath, for they had sworn it with
all their mind and sought him with utter delight so that he let
himself be found by them; Yahweh gave them rest all around.

Removal of Maacah

16 Asa the king even removed his mother Maacah from the
status of queen mother because she had made a horrible representation of Asherah. Asa cut down her horrible representation,
smashed it and burned it in the Kidron Valley. 17 But the
high places did not disappear from Israel, though the mind of
Asa was loyal throughout his whole life. 18 He brought his
father's and his own dedicated gifts of silver, gold, and [other]
articles into the house of God. 19 There was no war up to the
thirty-fifth year of Asa's reign.

NOTES

xv 3. *a torah*. I.e., a body of instruction; better left untranslated
since "law" here is too narrow.

5. *those who went and came*. Literally "for him who went out and him
who came in"; cf. Judg v 6 f.

there was much unrest. For phrase see 1QH 3:25.

11. *some of the booty they brought*. The booty from the campaign
against Zerah (ch. xiv).

16. *queen mother*. See COMMENT on Sec. 15, xiii 1–3. The queen
mother apparently occupied a position of honor and influence, especially
in a harem where there would be numerous wives; but only the one
whose son was designated heir would be "queen." During the minority

of her son she apparently exercised considerable authority. Athaliah probably ruled as queen mother and regent during the minority of Joash. Joash was kidnaped by the priests not because his life was in danger (Athaliah may have killed others, but if she killed the last surviving son, she could not reign either), but because that was the only way to challenge her power. So long as he remained in her hands she controlled the kingship.

horrible representation. Mipleṣet only here and I Kings xv 13. Cf. Josiah's burning of Asherah, II Kings xxiii 6.

COMMENT

Verses 1–15 deal with the same situation described in xiv 1–4, where the initiative for rededication of king and people lies in the act and word of the king. Here, on the other hand, it is inspired by the preaching of Azariah.

[The sermon of Azariah, xv 1–7]: The definitive way in which the name of the prophet is set down seems to indicate its presence in the source material utilized by the writer. The sermon itself, however, is an excellent illustration of Levitical preaching (see von Rad, *Gesammelte Studien* . . . , pp. 251 f.). It is thoroughly biblical, drawing upon Judges and the prophets (see Rudolph, p. 245). It has three main points: (a) the declaration that Yahweh will be with the people so long as they are with him (vs. 2); (b) illustrations from history, especially from Judges (vss. 3–6); (c) exhortation and promise (vs. 7). The people addressed, Judah and Benjamin, are characteristic for the Chronicler.

[The reformation, 8–15]: The effectiveness of the sermon of Azariah, so far as the writer is concerned, was beyond dispute. The account of the reformation follows the notice in I Kings xv 12, which speaks of the purging of the male prostitutes (*haqqᵉdēšīm*) and the abominable objects (*haggillūlīm*) his fathers had constructed. The Chronicler says nothing of the former, but he apparently refers to the latter as *haššiqqūṣīm*, usually rendered as detestable (pagan) abominations. Along with this religious house cleaning went the renewal of the altar which had been desecrated by illicit offerings, probably at the instigation of Maacah, the queen mother. The whole movement was thoroughgoing and took in the territory of Judah and Benjamin as well as the cities Asa had taken from Ephraim. The reference to Ephraim seems to indicate that his father's conquests were of short duration; the cities mentioned in xiii 19 appear to have fallen into the hands of Baasha, perhaps during Asa's minority. Asa was supported in his reformation by all the people of Judah, Benjamin, and by those who had taken refuge there from Ephraim, Manasseh, and Simeon. Why Simeon is included is not clear. It may have been, as Beyer has suggested, that the inhabitants of Simeon (i.e., southern Judah) were forced out by the expansion of the Edomites. The Chronicler attributes the presence of the refugees in Asa's realm to their recognition that Yahweh was with him. The convocation was attended by a great sacrifice for which part of the booty taken in the campaign against Zerah was used. The entire transaction was accompanied by a covenant renewal into which the people entered wholeheartedly. That the covenant was a sovereignly imposed affair may be seen from the threat accompanying it (vs. 13). The ceremony was conducted with proper decorum and ritual, though without mention of the participation of Levitical choirs. In harmony with his theory, the writer observes that this fervent response of king and people to Yahweh brought a period of rest and peace.

[The Maacah affair, 16–19]: The deterioration of the religious situation in Judah is attributed to Maacah, the queen mother (cf. I Kings xv 13), who is said to have made a *mipleṣet,* that is, a horrible representation having something to do with the Tyrian goddess Asherah (cf. ARI, pp. 157 f.). The name Maacah is associated with pagan elements in Israel as may be seen from the fact that she came from the family of Absalom whose mother, a princess of Geshur, bore the same name. Her position enabled her to exercise a strong influence in Judah in the early years of Asa's reign. But under the pressure of such religious leaders as Azariah, the king was led to take drastic action as soon as he was in a position to do so. Maacah was removed from her commanding position and the cult object set up by her cut down and burned. But even Asa's best efforts were insufficient to eradicate the pagan practices entirely, as the Deuteronomist attests (I Kings xv 14). The deposit of Asa's and his father's dedicated gifts in the temple is obscure. The absence of war from the time of Zerah until the invasion of Baasha supports the Chronicler's contention of an era of peace; perhaps the statement that there was *no war* indicates that the Zerah affair

was no more than a skirmish and that the only major war was that
dealt with in the following chapter, despite the statement in I Kings
xv 16. There could have been border clashes from time to time
but no all-out war.

18. THE REIGN OF ASA (ca. 913–873 B.C.): THE LATER YEARS (xvi 1–14)†

Baasha moves against Asa

XVI 1 In the thirty-sixth year of Asa's reign, Baasha the king of Israel came up against Judah and fortified Ramah to prevent Asa the king of Judah from going out or coming in. 2 So Asa took out silver and gold from the storehouses of the temple and the palace, which he sent to Ben-hadad the king of Aram who resided at Damascus, with the following proposal: 3 "Let us make a treaty between me and you, like the one that existed between my father and your father; look, I have sent you silver and gold; go, renounce your treaty with Baasha the king of Israel that he may withdraw from me." 4 Ben-hadad listened to King Asa and sent the captains of his army to the cities of Israel; they destroyed Ijon, Dan, Abel-maim, and all the storage cities of Naphtali. 5 When Baasha heard about it, he stopped building operations at Ramah and suspended his work [there]. 6 Then Asa the king had all Judah carry away the stones and timber of Ramah which Baasha had used in building and fortified Geba and Mizpah with them.

The prophecy of Hanani

7 At that time Hanani the seer came to Asa the king of Judah and said to him, "Because you relied on the king of Aram and did not rely upon Yahweh your God, the army of the king of *Israel* has escaped from your hand. 8 Did not the Ethiopians

† **II Chron xvi 1–6** ‖ I Kings xv 17–22; **11–14** ‖ I Kings 23–24.

a-a With LXX^L, noted by neither Kittel (*Biblia Hebraica*, 3d ed.), nor Swete and Rahlfs. (H. B. Swete, *The Old Testament in Greek*, II, 3d ed., reprinted 1930; A. Rahlfs, *Septuaginta*, I, 3d ed., 1949.) MT "Aram." F. M. Cross, Jr., has shown that LXX^L often has better readings than other witnesses to the and Libyans have a large army, with chariots and horsemen in great abundance? But when you relied on Yahweh he gave you victory over them. 9 For the eyes of Yahweh move to and fro through all the earth to support those who are wholeheartedly committed to him. You have acted foolishly in this respect, for from now on you will have wars." 10 Asa, however, was provoked at the seer and put him in the stocks because he was angry with him about this. At the same time Asa also mistreated some of the people.

Conclusion

11 Now, the history of Asa from beginning to end is recorded in the chronicles of the kings of Judah and Israel. 12 In the thirty-ninth year of his reign Asa developed a foot disease which became very severe; yet in his illness he did not consult Yahweh but [he did consult] the physicians. 13 So Asa slept with his fathers; he died in the forty-first year of his reign. 14 They buried him in his grave chamber which he had cut out for himself in the city of David. They laid him in the crypt which was filled with perfume blended from all sorts of oils, and they made for him a very great funeral fire.

Vorlage of LXX in connection with the Samuel MS of Qumran (cf. JBL 74 [1955], 165–72; and *The Ancient Library of Qumran* [Anchor Books, revised ed.], 1961, pp. 173 ff.). Maybe the same is true here. Certainly the reading suggested by LXX[L] is required by the context.

NOTES

xvi 2. *the temple . . . the palace.* Literally "the house of Yahweh," "the house of the king."

Ben-hadad. Ben-hadad I. I Kings xv 18 "Ben-hadad, the son of Tabrimmon, the son of Hezion." See COMMENT on vss. 1–6.

4. *Ijon . . . Naphtali.* For identification of sites see Abel, *Géographie de la Palestine*, II, pp. 233, 302, 352.

8. *he . . . them.* Literally "he gave them in your hand."

9. *For . . . through all the earth.* Cf. Zech iv 10.

14. *grave chamber.* To be rendered singular, since the grave had

more than one chamber (A. Kropat, "Die Syntax des Autors der Chronik," BZAW 16 [1909], 10).

all sorts. *Zᵉnīm* in the original Hebrew text is a word borrowed from the Persian, meaning "all sorts."

COMMENT

[Baasha's hostile move toward Judah, xvi 1–6]: The only significant conflict between the rival kingdoms during this period, so far as we know, took place in the thirty-sixth (LXX, "thirty-eighth") year of Asa. On the vexed question of the date see W. F. Albright, BASOR 87 (October 1942), 27 f., and BASOR 100 (December 1945), 20, n. 14; he thinks the thirty-sixth year of Asa was ca. 879 B.C. This is another of the points at which the Chronicler has preserved authentic material, as can be seen from the famous stele of Ben-hadad treated by Albright in the above noted article. Cf. also H. L. Ginsberg, LGJV, p. 160, n. 4.

The conflict was precipitated by Baasha's fortification of Ramah, about ten miles north of Jerusalem on the main highway. The chief purpose for Baasha's action was to prevent movement of the Judahites; no one belonging to Asa was allowed to enter or leave. It appears to have been an interdiction of the roads leading north from Judah, thus cutting off trade and communication. A secondary aim may have been to prevent defection of Northerners or to cut off the stream of religious devotees going to Jerusalem to worship. Asa was not in a position to carry on offensive war with Israel and so stripped his treasuries to buy the intervention of Ben-hadad I against Baasha. The plan succeeded: Ben-hadad terminated his treaty with Baasha and invaded the northern area of Israel. While only a harassing action, it had the effect of causing Baasha to drop his fortifications at Ramah and to withdraw to Tirzah. The foray of Ben-hadad's men followed a path south between the Lebanon ranges to Ijon, then on to Abel-maim and Dan. Ijon has been connected with the Merj Ayyun, north of Abel-maim (Abel-beth-maacah in I Kings xv 20) which was some four miles west of Dan. Both the latter places were approximately 10 miles north of Huleh. For discussion see Abel, *Géographie de la Palestine*, II, pp. 233, 302, 352; W. F. Albright, AASOR 6 (1926), 16, n. 6. Apparently they moved as far as the district of Chinneroth (Galilee); cf. I Kings xv 20. The Chronicler has "store-cities" for Chinneroth which Abel (*op. cit.,* I, p. 495) says became Genneseret in the postexilic period; this explains the change by the Chronicler.

When Baasha abandoned his project at Ramah, Asa conscripted his fellow countrymen to pull down the fortifications and constructed fortifications of his own at Geba and Mizpah. Just what locations were involved is uncertain; it depends on whether Asa's reaction to Baasha's move was offensive or defensive. If the former, then Mizpah might be at Tell en-Nasbeh and Geba at Jeba; if the latter, then Mizpah could be Nebi Samwil and Geba Tell el-Ful (the Gibeah of Saul). For the former view see arguments of James Muilenberg in *Excavations at Tell en-Nasbeh,* ed. C. C. McCown, I, 1947, pp. 28–30 (see map on p. 51) and W. F. Badé in *Werden und Wesen des AT,* eds. P. Volz, F. Stummer, and J. Hempel, 1936, pp. 30–36; for the latter, W. F. Albright, AASOR 4 (1924), 38 ff. The excavations at Tell el-Ful revealed reused stones and timber and the third fortress bore evidence of hasty construction (*ibid.,* pp. 20, 39). Jeremiah xli 9 refers to a cistern made by Asa at the time "for fear of Baasha," which suggests defensive tactics on the part of the king of Judah.

[The prophecy of Hanani, 7–10]: The story of Hanani the seer (*hārō'ĕh*) is theologically motivated and follows closely the tradition of the prophets (Isa vii; Zech iv 6). The seer is represented as appearing before the king after the intervention of the Aramaeans, whose pressure upon Israel served to remove its threat against Judah. That was to the seer a direct reversal of the policy followed in the Zerah affair in which case Yahweh was besought to intervene. However, that situation was not so serious as this one; Asa faced political realities and in so doing took a leaf from Jeroboam's book. Thus, from the seer's point of view Asa acted foolishly since he took matters into his own hands when the eyes of Yahweh were scanning the earth, watching over those who were loyal to him (cf. Zech iv 10). Asa's reaction to Hanani's rebuke was swift and fateful; Hanani was put in the stocks and his partisans crushed. The reference to the persistence of wars (vs. 9) is probably a reflection of I Kings xv 16, since Asa's years were few after the Ramah affair and there was more or less peace between the kingdoms until the unwise move of Amaziah three-quarters of a century later (xxv 20 ff.).

[Conclusion, 11–14]: As has been observed by commentators generally, the writer here gives the full title of the sources he used in his work. From the materials concerning Asa said to have been taken from them, it is obvious that it is not equivalent to our book of Kings.

Asa's death was caused by a foot disease (dropsy?) which set in two years before and which may have incapacitated him. If there was a coregency for the period of his illness, nothing is said about it. The chief interest of the writer centers in the observation that he consulted physicians, rather than Yahweh, about healing. This must not be construed as a condemnation of the healing art as such; there are hints of its approval and use in the OT (Exod xxi 19; Jer viii 22; Isa xxxviii 21). In general, however, Yahweh is the healer (e.g., Ps ciii 3b). The objection here may be due to the tendency to associate magic with healing processes or to the concept that the human media alone are not enough, as the case of Asa illustrates. The point of the passage (vs. 12b) is that Asa consulted only physicians, without consulting Yahweh at all. The underlying thought is the same as that expressed in the prophecy of Hanani. Moreover, it is possible that Asa's illness may have been regarded as the result of what he did to the prophet and his friends following the rebuke administered to the king for his lack of faith. In any case, the failure to consult Yahweh pointed to a tragic lack of confidence in him, at least in the view of the writer.

The burial notice evidences the utilization of an expanded source, unknown to or unused by the Deuteronomist. Asa had prepared his own grave chamber. The festivities connected with his entombment reflect the esteem in which he was held by the people, though the expressions are those of the Chronicler.

19. THE REIGN OF JEHOSHAPHAT (873–849 B.C.): CHARACTER AND ORGANIZATION (xvii 1–19)†

Character and rule of Jehoshaphat

XVII ¹ When Jehoshaphat his son became king in his place, he proceeded to fortify himself against Israel ² by stationing troops in all the fortified cities of Judah and placing garrisons in the land of Judah and in the cities of Ephraim which Asa his father had captured. ³ Yahweh was with Jehoshaphat because he followed the earlier ways of *his father* and did not consult Baal, ⁴ but sought the God of his father, followed his commandments and did not act as Israel did. ⁵ So Yahweh firmly established the kingdom under his control, while all Judah gave gifts to Jehoshaphat until he had an abundance of wealth and honor. ⁶ His mind was so firmly set on the ways of Yahweh that he again removed the high places and the Asherim from Judah.

Teaching mission

⁷ In the third year of his reign he sent his captains, *outstanding men*—Obadiah, Zechariah, Nethanel, and Micaiah—to teach in the cities of Judah. ⁸ With them went the Levites— Shemaiah, Nethaniah, Zebadiah, Asahel, Shamiraimoth, Jehonathan, *Adonijah, and Tobiah,* the Levites; Elishama and Jehoram the priests accompanied them. ⁹ They taught in Judah, taking with them the book of the law of Yahweh; they went around to all the cities of Judah and taught the people.

† **II Chron xvii 1–6** ‖ I Kings xv 24c.

a–a So with six manuscripts and LXX. MT reads "in the ways of David his father." See NOTE.
b–b So with LXX. Others read "Ben-hail," a personal name, not occurring elsewhere.
c–c *Weṭob 'adōniyyāh* ("and Tob-adonijah") is dittography.

Tribute

10 The dread of Yahweh was upon all the kingdoms of the lands around Judah so that they did not go to war with Jehoshaphat. 11 Some of the Philistines brought gifts and a load of silver to Jehoshaphat; the Arabians also brought flocks to him—seventy-seven hundred rams and seventy-seven hundred he-goats. 12 So Jehoshaphat kept on growing greater; he built fortified towns and store-cities in Judah 13 and accumulated an abundance of supplies in the cities of Judah.

Classification of military officials at Jerusalem

He also had warriors, outstanding men, in Jerusalem. 14 This was their official classification according to their families: Over the captains of the thousands of Judah was Captain Adnah with three hundred thousand soldiers; 15 at his side was Captain Jehohanan with two hundred eighty thousand; 16 at his side was Amasiah the son of Zichri, who volunteered for Yahweh, with two hundred thousand soldiers. 17 Officer Eliada represented Benjamin with two hundred thousand men equipped with bow and shield, 18 and at his side was Jehozabad with one hundred eighty thousand men equipped for war. 19 These were the ones who were in the service of the king apart from those whom the king put in the fortified cities all over Judah.

NOTES

xvii 3. *the earlier ways of his father.* See textual note *ᵃ*. The reference must be to Asa because a distinction is made between his earlier and later practices, while the Chronicler never makes such a distinction in the case of David. I Kings xxii 43 does refer to Asa, but without the time division made by the Chronicler. Perhaps David was copied directly from the source, since it is easier to explain the dropping of the name than its insertion.

Baal. The reference is to the Baal of Canaan and not to local representations. The plural, when used of the god, is parallel to Elohim= God. Wherever the term *ba'al* is used of owner or master with the suffix, it is the plural form of the noun that is used, despite its clearly singular reference. Cf. J. M. Myers, LCQ 19 (1946), 398 f.

5. *under his control.* Literally "in his hand."

6. *again.* As his father had done.

12. *he built . . . Judah.* See F. M. Cross, Jr., and J. T. Milik, "Explorations in the Judaean Buqê'ah," BASOR 142 (1956), 5–17.

14. The numbers are doubtless to be explained on the basis of units (see NOTES on Sec. 15). Then we have a total of 1160 units, still pretty large in comparison with the Davidic census of 1100 units for all Israel. The size of the units is not given.

COMMENT

Jehoshaphat was one of the Chronicler's favorite kings of Judah, along with Hezekiah and Josiah. There is remarkably little criticism of his alliance with the Northern Kingdom; the caveat raised by Jehu, son of Hanani, is rather mild (xix 2–3).

[Character and rule of Jehoshaphat, xvii 1–6]: In view of Asa's difficulties with Baasha, the rapid movements in Israel leading to the enthronement of Omri, the soldier king, who was consolidating his position, and the uncertainties of the situation, Jehoshaphat took immediate steps to secure his position in Judah. Rudolph, pp. 249 f., thinks a source other than Kings is involved here since "Israel" in vs. 1 refers to the Southern Kingdom and "Ephraim" in vs. 2 to the Northern Kingdom, because the cities taken by Asa (xvi 6) were not in the tribal territory of Ephraim but in Benjamin. His translation then would differ somewhat from ours. "When Jehoshaphat his son became king in his place he established his authority *over* Israel. . . ." In vss. 4, 5, then, Israel refers to the Northern Kingdom and Judah to the Southern. Hence vss. 1–2 came from the source used by the Chronicler and vss. 3–6 represent his own work.

The Ephraimite cities taken by Abijah (xiii 19) and maintained, at least most of the time, by Asa (xv 8), were still in the hands of the king of Judah; they were apparently uncontested until the fiasco under Amaziah (xxv 17–24; see Cross and Wright, JBL 75 [1956], 222 f.).

The successful rule of Jehoshaphat, according to the Chronicler, was due to his loyalty to the tradition of his father in following

Yahweh and his consequent rejection of Baal. His devotion to Yahweh brought him wealth and respect—the gifts of peace and prosperity. He continued the reformation instituted by Asa, though he
had little more success than his father in completely eradicating the
high places (xx 33). The matter of reformation in Israel (Judah)
must have been one of long standing and persistent endeavor. It is
hard to believe that the reformers of the seventh century (the
Deuteronomist) were the first to institute a movement against the
high places. There must have been movements in the direction of
centralizing worship from the time of David on, sporadic efforts
made to clean out the high places by the kings mentioned, if only
for practical rather than doctrinaire reasons. Deuteronomy formulated in absolute terms a policy of long standing, generally observed
in the breach. Kings and Chronicles are thus in flat contradiction
over Asa and Jehoshaphat.

On the date of Jehoshaphat and the synchronization with the
Omri dynasty see Albright, BASOR 100 (December 1945); Thiele,
The Mysterious Numbers of the Hebrew Kings, Ch. IV.

[A teaching mission, 7–9]: This has been viewed as another version of the judicial reform reported in xix 4–11 (Albright, AMJV,
p. 82). The Chronicler refers to the mission here as an example of
Jehoshaphat's zeal for Yahweh. While some elements in the story
are obscure, the main points are clear. In view of the procedure
of the reform, there is at least a strong probability that such a
teaching mission was established to inform the people of the torah
of the Lord. The fact that laymen are mentioned first among the
participants points to a tradition older than the Chronicler, who regarded the Levites as the primary functionaries in the matter of
teaching (xxxv 3; Neh viii 7–8). In truth vs. 8 may be the Chronicler's own contribution to the story. Perhaps the position of laymen
as teachers is quite old since Hos iv 6 speaks of the priests as the
handlers of the torah. The names in vs. 7 do not prevent attributing
it to the ninth century B.C. Just what is meant here by the "book
of the torah" is not clear; the Chronicler generally refers to the
priestly work of the Pentateuch under that phrase but that can
hardly be so in this instance (cf. Rudolph, p. 251; Rehm, *Die
Bücher der Chronik* [see Selected Bibliography, Commentaries],
p. 101). Some think it was the Book of the Covenant, or an edition
of it. More plausibly it may have been a royal law code along the

lines of the Code of Hammurabi and other royal edicts. As such, it may well have been based on premonarchic sources, but for purposes of the monarchy much of the Covenant code would have been outmoded and inapplicable. Royal law is practically nonexistent in the Bible, though there must have been plenty of it to operate the kingdom successfully for so long a time. The biblical writers were not greatly interested in royal law, since their authorities were the earlier premonarchic figures with their utterances and actions. It is possible, then, that this was one of the lost law codes rather than some biblical source, though it probably contained older materials also now preserved in the Pentateuch.

[Tribute, 10–13a]: As the preceding passage was intended to illustrate the direction of the new king's piety, so this one explains the source and use of his wealth. The surrounding nations observed the strength of Jehoshaphat and recognized the presence of Yahweh with him so that they not only refrained from attacking Judah but even brought tribute to him. Their reaction toward him enhanced his prestige and power still further and enabled him to fortify Judah. The Philistines were his southwestern neighbors while the Arabians had pushed into the Negeb, where they may have been associated with the Ethiopians referred to in xiv 9 ff. (cf. xxi 16). If this is a summary assessment of Jehoshaphat's reign, other peoples or groups may have been involved too (ch. xx).

[Military arrangements in Jerusalem, 13b–19]: This interesting little pericope is meant to illustrate further the standing of Jehoshaphat because of his piety. It informs us of the military organization of Jerusalem and the arrangements for the defense of the kingdom. Jehoshaphat had a standing army in the capital as well as garrisons in the fortified cities. Doubtless we are to understand that the central command was also located at Jerusalem. The organization centered about the tribal association of Judah and Benjamin, the former directed by a chief of staff and two assistants, the latter by one chief and one assistant. This appears to be an authentic bit of information, certified by names and quite appropriate to the situation.

20. THE REIGN OF JEHOSHAPHAT (873–849 B.C.): ALLIANCE WITH THE NORTHERN KINGDOM (xviii 1–34)†

Jehoshaphat's visit with Ahab

XVIII 1 Although Jehoshaphat had wealth and great honor, he entered into a marriage alliance with Ahab. 2 So one time when he went down to Ahab at Samaria, Ahab slaughtered sheep and cattle in abundance for him and his followers to elicit his support against Ramoth-gilead. 3 Then Ahab the king of Israel said to Jehoshaphat the king of Judah, "Will you go with me to Ramoth-gilead?" He replied, "I am as you, my people as your people; I'll go to war with you!" 4 Jehoshaphat then said to the king of Israel, "Inquire first what the word of Yahweh is!" 5 So the king of Israel summoned the prophets, four hundred of them, and said to them, "Shall we go to war with Ramoth-gilead or shall I withdraw [my plan]?" "Go up," they replied, "for God has given it into the hand of the king." 6 Jehoshaphat said, "Is there no other prophet of Yahweh here, that we may inquire through him?" 7 The king of Israel said to Jehoshaphat, "Yes, there is one fellow by whom we may inquire of Yahweh, but I hate him because he never prophesies good for me, but always evil; he is Micaiah, the son of Imlah." "Let not the king speak so," replied Jehoshaphat. 8 So the king of Israel summoned a court official and ordered, "Bring quickly Micaiah the son of Imlah." 9 Now the king of Israel and Jehoshaphat the king of Judah were sitting each upon his throne, and clad in robes; they were sitting in a plaza at the entrance to the gate of Samaria where all the prophets were prophesying before them. 10 Zedekiah the son of Chenaanah had made iron horns for himself and said, "Thus, has Yahweh said, you shall gore Aram with these

† **II Chron xviii 1–34** ‖ I Kings xxii 1–36.

until they are destroyed." 11 All the other prophets prophesied similarly, saying, "Go up against Ramoth-gilead! Enjoy success, for Yahweh has given it into the hand of the king." 12 The messenger who went to summon Micaiah spoke to him as follows: "Look here, the words of the prophets are uniformly favorable to the king; so let your word be the same as theirs and speak favorably." 13 Micaiah replied, "By the life of Yahweh, I will speak just what my God tells me!" 14 When he came to the king and the king said to him, "Micah, shall we go up to Ramoth-gilead for battle or shall I withdraw [my plan]?"; he said, "Go ahead, enjoy success, for they shall be given into your hand." 15 Then the king said to him, "How many times must I adjure you to tell me only the truth in the name of Yahweh?" 16 He replied,

> "I saw all Israel
> scattered upon the mountains,
> like a flock without a shepherd.
> And Yahweh said, these have no master,
> Let them return each to his house in peace!"

17 The king of Israel said to Jehoshaphat, "Did I not tell you, he will not prophesy good for me but evil?" 18 But he said, "Listen now to the word of Yahweh. I saw Yahweh sitting on his throne with the whole host of the heavens standing on his right and his left. 19 Yahweh said, 'Who will entice Ahab, the king of Israel, to go up and fall at Ramoth-gilead?' One said this and another said that. 20 Then a spirit came forth and stood before Yahweh and said, 'I will entice him!' 'How?' said Yahweh to him. 21 He said, 'I'll go forth and be a deceiving spirit in the mouth of all his prophets.' He replied, 'You will succeed in enticing him; go and do so.' 22 Behold, now, Yahweh has put a deceiving spirit into the mouth of these your prophets, for Yahweh has really decreed evil against you." 23 Then Zedekiah the son of Chenaanah approached and struck Micaiah on the cheek and said, "Which way did the spirit of Yahweh pass from me to speak to you?" 24 "Behold you will see on that day when

you shall go from room to room to hide yourself," replied
Micaiah. 25 The king of Israel said, "Seize Micaiah and turn
him over to Amon the mayor of the city and Joash the king's
son, 26 and say, Thus has the king commanded: Imprison this
fellow and put him on meager rations of bread and water until
I return in triumph." 27 Retorted Micaiah, "If you do indeed
come back safely, Yahweh has not spoken by me." And he said,
"Listen, all peoples." 28 So the king of Israel and Jehoshaphat
the king of Judah went up to Ramoth-gilead. 29 The king of
Israel said to Jehoshaphat, "I will go into the battle in disguise,
but you keep on your robes." So the king of Israel disguised himself when they went into battle. 30 Now the king of Aram had
given orders to his chariot captains, saying, "Don't fight with
anyone, either small or great, except with the king of Israel
alone." 31 So when the chariot captains saw Jehoshaphat, they
thought he was the king of Israel and surrounded him in order
to attack [him]. But when Jehoshaphat shouted, Yahweh helped
him and God *drew them away* from him. 32 When the chariot
captains saw that he was not the king of Israel, they turned back
from pursuing him. 33 But a man drew a bow *at full
strength,* and shot the king of Israel *between the joints of the
armor.* He commanded the charioteer, "Turn around and take
me out of the turmoil of battle, for I have been wounded."
34 Because the battle raged furiously that day, the king of Israel
remained *propped up* in his chariot until evening in full view
of Aram; but at sunset he died.

a–a LXX "turned them away."
b–b LXX "with good aim." The root of the Heb. *letummō* means basically "to
be whole or full."
c–c Uncertain. Heb. "between the bands and the armor."
d–d Cf. LXX and I Kings xxii 35 where *hoph.* pt. ("he had to be held up") is
used. For syntax see *Gesenius' Hebrew Grammar*, ed. E. Kautzsch, 2d Eng.
ed. of A. E. Cowley, 1910, 116 r.

NOTES

xviii 2. *So one time.* Literally "at the end of years."

3. *Ramoth-gilead.* Tell Ramith in north Gilead. Cf. N. Glueck, BASOR 92 (December 1943), 10–16.

9. *a plaza.* For this meaning see J. Gray, VT 2 (1952), 209 f. On the basis of Aqht passage (II Aqht, col. 5, lines 6–8 in C. H. Gordon's *Ugaritic Handbook,* 1947, p. 182), Gray concludes that it means a wide plaza before the city gate rather than a threshing floor.

14. *"Go ahead, . . . your hand."* Observe the irony of the reply.

16. *master.* MT *'ᵃdōnīm,* "masters," "lords." But the parallelism appears to demand a singular. Hence this may be a case of the enclitic *mem.*

18. *standing.* The standing is technical as well as actual. They were in attendance upon the divine King, doubtless in a standing position.

23. Note the irony of the remark, as well as its insulting nature. Behind it lies the usual assumption about the powers of the prophet. Whether Zedekiah is referring to his own action, or whether the action is independent of the statement, which may refer to the same lying spirit as having passed from Zedekiah and his companions to Micaiah, is not clear. The tone of his voice may be sensed but the meaning is hard to determine.

27. *"Listen, all peoples."* Quotation from Mic i 2a, perhaps due to a confusion of names.

COMMENT

Verses 2–33 of this impressive story vary but slightly from their source, I Kings xxii. Since it deals almost exclusively with the Northern Kingdom, there must have been compelling reasons for its inclusion by the writer; these are not difficult to discover in the light of his over-all views of religion. The most obvious reason for the Chronicler's copying of the story is that it concerns itself with a prophet. He was very fond of recalling the records of prophets not mentioned elsewhere (see Introduction to *I Chronicles*) and upon which he depended for much of his information. He was doubtless led to his regard for the prophets by the Deuteronomic historian, who was strongly influenced by them. The story of Elijah-Elisha was not included in Chronicles because in no instance known to us did their activity or message impinge on Judah. In the case of Micaiah the situation is quite different. Not only did the story of Micaiah involve a king of Judah but it had some lessons to teach that were appropriate to the total message of the Chronicler.

Perhaps the outstanding significance of the whole episode to him was the fact that Micaiah unlike the official prophets of Ahab was a true prophet of Yahweh. That the king of the Davidic line insisted upon calling in this prophet of Yahweh must have made a deep impression on the writer—Micaiah the prophet of Yahweh versus "your prophets" (vs. 22). It is quite possible that he also wanted to emphasize the interest in and insistence upon the orthodox religion of Yahweh by the king of Judah as opposed to the unrecognized religion of the north.

The lesson drawn by the Chronicler is worthy of note. Jehoshaphat did not really need a marriage alliance with Ahab because he already possessed wealth and honor (vs. 1). The author follows the source in showing the involvements attendant upon the alliance. Nevertheless, Jehoshaphat was able to extricate himself from the jaws of death because, as the writer significantly asserts, "Yahweh helped him" (vs. 31). Thus, the folly of such an alliance is depicted, from which he was delivered by Yahweh and not just because of what Jehoshaphat did himself, that is, shouted to divert the attention of his pursuers.

In as much as there is no direct interest in Ahab—though the moral is apparent—the reader is given the barest outline of his misfortune and spared the gory details of his death (I Kings xxii 35b–38).

21. THE REIGN OF JEHOSHAPHAT (873–849 B.C.): GOD'S REBUKE AND JEHOSHAPHAT'S REFORMATION (xix 1–11)

Jehu rebukes Jehoshaphat

XIX 1 However, Jehoshaphat the king of Judah returned home to Jerusalem safely. 2 Jehu the son of Hanani the seer went out to meet him and said to King Jehoshaphat, "Should you help the evil or love those who hate Yahweh? Because of this, there is wrath against you from Yahweh. 3 But some good things are to your credit, for you swept the Asherahs from the land and determined in your mind to seek God."

Reform of Jehoshaphat

4 Jehoshaphat lived in Jerusalem but went about regularly among the people, from Beer-sheba to Mount Ephraim, to convert them to Yahweh God of their fathers. 5 He also appointed judges in the land, in each of the fortified cities of Judah; 6 he admonished the judges: "Be careful what you do because you are not judging for man but for Yahweh who will be*a* with you in your decisions. 7 And now may the fear of Yahweh be upon you; be careful what you do, for Yahweh our God loathes dishonesty, partiality, or bribery." 8 Jehoshaphat also appointed at Jerusalem some of the Levites, priests, and family heads of Israel to handle cases pertaining to the cult and disputes arising between the citizens*b* of Jerusalem; 9 he charged them as follows: "Thus you must do, in the fear of Yahweh, in truth, and with the utmost integrity. 10 When any case comes before you involving any of your brothers living in their cities, whether

a yhy omitted by haplography.
b So with LXX and Vulg. MT has "and they dwelt."

capital or [civil], and having to do with the interpretation of commandment, statutes, or judgments, you must warn them that they do not incur guilt before Yahweh and [his] wrath fall upon you and your brothers; thus you must do so as not to incur guilt. 11 Look now, Amariah the chief priest shall be over you in all cultic cases, Zebadiah the son of Ishmael, the leader of the house of Judah, [shall be over you] in all civil cases, and the Levites shall be your official bailiffs. Act decisively and may Yahweh be on the side of the right."

NOTES

xix 8. *cases*. Literally "matter of Yahweh."
9. Cf. 1QH 16:17 for similar expression.
10. *you must warn*. I.e., in addition to rendering the judicial decree in the case.
11. *cultic cases*. Literally "matter(s) of Yahweh."
civil cases. Literally "matter(s) of the king."
bailiffs. Cf. Albright, AMJV, p. 75, n. 56; he translates "official agent." Their duty was apparently to carry out the orders of the court and assist in the maintenance of civil order. See S. R. Driver, *A Critical and Exegetical Commentary on Deuteronomy* (in ICC), 1916, pp. 16 f.
may Yahweh . . . the right. Literally "may Yahweh be with the good."

COMMENT

[Prophetic opposition to Jehoshaphat's alliance with Ahab, xix 1–3]: Chapter xviii 1 f. already disclosed the writer's view of Jehoshaphat's marriage alliance with Ahab. The prophecy of Jehu is much more pointed, though the rebuke he administered to the king is relatively mild. The prophet is pictured as going out to meet Jehoshaphat on his way back to Jerusalem after the debacle at Ramoth-gilead. His message emphasizes two points: the judgment of Ahab—and therefore the Northern Kingdom—as evil and a hater of Yahweh, and the statement that Jehoshaphat's good deeds outweigh his mistake. Here the prophet expresses the view of the Chronicler.

[The reform of Jehoshaphat, 4–11]: But the most important portion of the chapter is the account of the judicial reform of Jehoshaphat, whose inception may have been due in part to his desire to strengthen the Southern Kingdom in view of the internal corruption and deterioration of the Northern Kingdom. The reforming activity proceeded along two lines: the teaching mission (vs. 4; cf. xvii 7–9) and the reorganization of the judiciary. Both were really two aspects of the same movement of whose general historicity there can hardly be any doubt. The Deuteronomist has little to say about the internal affairs of Judah in the reign of Jehoshaphat; they were lost sight of largely because of his main interests in Elijah and Elisha who were so deeply involved in the activities of Ahab. But the fact that Jehoshaphat's assistance was sought by Ahab (I Kings xxii) and Jehoram (II Kings iii), and the respect which Elisha is said to have had for Jehoshaphat (II Kings iii 14) add weight to the Chronicler's story about him.

The administrative organization of Solomon was continued, probably with necessary modifications, in both kingdoms (Albright, JPOS 5 [1925], 17–54, especially 36 ff., 44 ff.). The extent of Jehoshaphat's kingdom is said to be "from Beer-sheba to Mount Ephraim," which is no doubt coextensive with Judah in the story. The Solomonic structure was administrative in character, but that did not exclude the judicial function which was retained by the king, at least in Judah (I Kings iii 16 ff.). The important point here is the addition of Levites and priests, whose duty it was to preside over cultic cases coming before the court (cf. Albright, AMJV, p. 76). Jehoshaphat probably catered to local tradition in his appointment of judges from the elders or outstanding men of the community. See further, Cross and Wright, JBL 75 (1956), 202–26.

The crucial portion of the section is vss. 8–11, which deal with the situation in Jerusalem where Levites, priests, and heads of families were appointed to handle cultic and civil cases. Of particular significance is the strong religious emphasis throughout, testifying once more to the principle of social solidarity governed by the cultic interests of the writer. The Jerusalem court was thus composed of priests, civil officials (occupying the position of the elders), and Levites. For the organization of the Jerusalem court and the Egyptian parallels, see the excellent study by Albright, AMJV, especially pp. 74–82. Amariah presided over cultic and Zebadiah over civil matters. Only once in Chronicles (II Chron xxxiv 9) is the late expression *kōhēn gādōl* (great priest) used. Frequently when the chief or head priest is referred to, the term *kōhēn hā-rō'š* (head priest) is used. This appears to have been an earlier designation than the former and may have had a different meaning, that is, that of the head of a priestly family. For a discussion of the problem of the high priesthood with biblical references, see J. Morgenstern, "A Chapter in the History of the High-Priesthood," AJSL 55 (1938), 1–24, 183–97, 360–77. The Levites were the court functionaries carrying out the decisions of the court. It had specific instructions on procedure (vs. 10) and all cases were to be judged on the principle of avoiding guilt before Yahweh so as to maintain the public welfare—that is, that the wrath of Yahweh may not "fall upon you and your brothers." The ostensible reason for the reform was to avert divine wrath, which could be interpreted as foreign invasion, or internal collapse and revolt.

The pattern followed at Jerusalem was apparently adhered to also in the district courts, the reference to which was due to their inclusion in the material the Chronicler was relaying (Albright, AMJV, p. 76). These local courts were in strategic centers, "in each of the fortified cities of Judah" (vs. 5), which replaced the administrative cities in the earlier and later arrangements. The Jerusalem court was probably a high court, as well as a local court, that dealt with cases referred to it by the district courts (cf. vs. 10 —"any case . . . involving any of your brothers living in their cities").

22. THE REIGN OF JEHOSHAPHAT (873–849 B.C.): JEHOSHAPHAT'S PIETY REWARDED (xx 1–37, xxi 1)†

Jehoshaphat's great victory

XX ¹ Later when the Moabites and the Ammonites, in company with the Meunites,ᵃ had come up to make war on Jehoshaphat, ² Jehoshaphat received the following message: "A great multitude from the other side of the sea, from Edom,ᵇ is coming against you and, see, they are already at Hazazon-tamar which is En-gedi." ³ Because he was afraid, Jehoshaphat turned his attention to seeking Yahweh and proclaimed a fast throughout all Judah. ⁴ So Judah came together to implore Yahweh [for assistance]—they came from all the cities of Judah to seek Yahweh. ⁵ Then Jehoshaphat stood up in the congregation of Judah and Jerusalem in the house of Yahweh in front of the new court ⁶ and said, "O Yahweh God of our fathers, are you not God in the heavens and the ruler of all the kingdoms of the nations? Power and might are in your hand so that none can prevail over you. ⁷ Have you not, our God, dispossessed the inhabitants of this land before your people Israel and given it to the seed of Abraham, your beloved, forever. ⁸ They have lived in it and have built for you there a sanctuary for your name, saying, ⁹ "If evil, sword, flood,ᶜ pestilence or famine come upon us and we stand before this house, before you—for your name is in this house—and cry to you because of our distress, you will listen and deliver [us]. ¹⁰ Look now, the Ammonites, the Moabites, and those from Mount Seir which you did not allow Israel to enter when

---

† II Chron xx 31–34 ‖ I Kings xxii 41–47; 35–37 ‖ I Kings xxii 48–50; II Chron xxi 1 ‖ I Kings xxii 51.

ᵃ Hebrew reads "Ammonite," which is impossible here. Cf. xxvi 7.
ᵇ So for Heb. "Aram," and as found in one manuscript.
ᶜ Transposition of consonants to *štp*; Hebrew has *špwṭ*, "to judge."

they came out of the land of Egypt—they went around them and did not destroy them—11 are repaying us by coming to drive us out from your possession which you have given us. 12 O our God, will you not judge them, for we do not have the strength to cope with this great multitude which has come against us and because we do not know what to do we are looking to you [for help]." 13 All Judah, including their ᵈlittle children,ᵈ their wives, and their sons, were standing before Yahweh. 14 Then the spirit of Yahweh came upon Jahaziel, the son of Zechariah, the son of Benaiah, the son of Jeiel, the son of Mattaniah the Levite of the Asaph clan, in the midst of the congregation, 15 who replied, "Pay attention, all Judah, citizens of Jerusalem and King Jehoshaphat, thus has Yahweh said to you: Do not be afraid and do not tremble before this great multitude, for the war is not your affair but God's. 16 Tomorrow go down against them; look, they are coming up the ascent of Hassisᵉ and you will meet them at the end of the wadi in the direction of the wilderness of Jeruel. 17 You will not have to fight in this [battle]; take your stand firmly and see the salvation of Yahweh for you, O Judah and Jerusalem. Do not be afraid and do not tremble; go out toward them tomorrow, for Yahweh is with you." 18 Then Jehoshaphat knelt down with his face to the ground and all Judah and the citizens of Jerusalem fell down before Yahweh, to worship Yahweh. 19 The Levites, both of the Kehathites and of the Korahites, rose to praise Yahweh God of Israel with an exceedingly loud voice. 20 So in the morning they prepared to go out to the wilderness of Tekoa. While they were going out Jehoshaphat stood up and said, "Listen to me, O Judah and citizens of Jerusalem, believe in Yahweh your God and you will be established, believe in his prophets and you will be successful." 21 After consulting with the people, he appointed singers for Yahweh who in holy attire were to go out ahead of the troops praising [him] with:

ᵈ–ᵈ Perhaps Hebrew here means "family," of which "wives and sons [children]" is an explanatory detail.
ᵉ LXX has "Asas," "Asae"; Vulg. "Sis." For location see Abel, *Géographie de la Palestine*, I, p. 403.

Praise Yahweh,
For his devotion is everlasting.

22 The moment they began with shouting and praise, Yahweh
set ambushes against the Ammonites, the Moabites, and those
from Mount Seir who had come against Judah and they were
struck down. 23 In so doing, the Ammonites and Moabites opposed those from Mount Seir and wiped them out completely.
When they had finished off the men of Seir, they destroyed
each other. 24 When Judah came to the point overlooking the
wilderness, in quest of the horde, lo they were corpses lying on
the ground; not one had escaped. 25 When Jehoshaphat and his
people came to claim the booty they found cattle ⸢in abundance,⸣ equipment, garments,ᵍ and costly vessels beyond reckoning which they appropriated for themselves; so extensive was
[the booty] that it took them three days to claim it. 26 On the
fourth day they assembled in the valley of Beracah where they
praised Yahweh; hence they called the name of that place the
valley of Beracah as it is today. 27 Then all the men of Judah
and Jerusalem returned with Jehoshaphat at their head; they
returned to Jerusalem rejoicing because Yahweh had given them
joy over their enemies. 28 They came to Jerusalem to the house
of God with harps, zithers, and trumpets. 29 The fear of God
came upon all the kingdoms of the lands when they heard that
Yahweh had fought against the enemies of Israel. 30 Then the
reign of Jehoshaphat was peaceful, for his God gave him rest on
all sides.

Final observations on the reign of Jehoshaphat

31 And so Jehoshaphat was king over Judah. He was thirty-
five years old when he became king and he was king in Jerusalem
for twenty-five years; his mother's name was Azubah, the daughter of Shilhi. 32 He continued in the way of his father Asa, and
did not deviate from it, doing right in the sight of Yahweh;

ᶠ⁻ᶠ So with LXX for Heb. "among them."
ᵍ With some manuscripts for MT "corpses."

33 only the high places did not cease because the people had not yet set their minds intently on the God of their fathers. 34 The remainder of the history of Jehoshaphat, from beginning to end, see it is written down in the records of Jehu the son of Hanani which are recorded in the chronicles of the kings of Israel.

Abortive maritime venture of Jehoshaphat

35 Afterward Jehoshaphat the king of Judah formed a partnership with Ahaziah the king of Israel, though he acted wickedly in so doing. 36 He joined him in constructing a fleet to go to Tarshish—they constructed the ships at Ezion-geber. 37 Then Eliezer the son of Dodavahu of Mareshah prophesied against Jehoshaphat as follows: "Because you became a partner with Ahaziah Yahweh has wrecked your work." So the ships were broken and could no longer go to Tarshish.

Death of Jehoshaphat

XXI 1 When Jehoshaphat slept with his fathers, he was buried with his fathers in the city of David and Jehoram his son became king in his place.

NOTES

xx 1. *Ammonites*. Shalmaneser III (858–824 B.C.) mentions an Ammonite king, Ba'sa son of Ruhubi, who contributed soldiers to an Aramaean confederacy (ANET, p. 279).

2. *Hazazon-tamar*. Location is uncertain but has been placed near the southern end of the Dead Sea (Abel, *Géographie de la Palestine*, II, pp. 344, 475; A. Alt, PJB 30 [1934], 20–24). M. Noth ("Eine palästinische Lokalüberlieferung in 2 Chr. 20," ZDPV 66 [1944], 50–56) locates it at el-haṣāṣa, between En-gedi and Bethlehem.

5. *the new court*. The large court of iv 9. The king stood at the entrance to the priest's court while the people were assembled in the new court. The reference is to the postexilic temple.

7. Cf. Gen xviii 17–19; Isa xli 8; Prayer of Azariah xii; Jubilees xix 9.

16. *Jeruel*. Southeast of Tekoa, on the steep descent to En-gedi.

20. *they prepared*. *hškm* here means to get busy, active.

you will be established. Based on Isa vii 9, xxviii 16, etc.

23. In the confusion of the battle the enemy fought and killed each other (as in the Gideon story, Judg vii 22).

25. *beyond reckoning.* Literally "not burden," i.e., not capable of being carried away.

26. *Beracah.* "Blessing" or "praise." An etiological motive may underlie this verse; this is how the valley got its name. It may have been Wadi Berekut, between Tekoa and En-gedi.

33. *the high places did not cease.* Cf. xvii 6, where it is said that Jehoshaphat had removed the high places. This is clear indication of the stubbornness of the problem and the fact that the religious reformation was only temporarily successful.

35. *partnership.* I.e., in a trading syndicate. See W. F. Albright in *Studies Presented to David M. Robinson,* ed. G. E. Mylonas, I, 1951, p. 230. Verbal form is Aramaic.

36. The Kings parallel has "Tarshish fleet," i.e., refinery fleet, which is obviously correct. Cf. ix 21 and BASOR 83 (October 1941), 21.

37. *Dodavahu.* Perhaps to be read "Dodiyahu."

has wrecked. Prophetic perfect? As Jer xxviii 2, 4, shows, prophecy used both perfect and imperfect without clear distinction.

COMMENT

[Jehoshaphat's victory, xx 1–30]: This part of chapter xx represents another of the Chronicler's illustrations, from the history of the time, of Jehoshaphat's piety with its rewards. The essence of the story is not pure fabrication, although much of it is couched in terms drawn from the period in which the author was writing. Some older scholars (Wellhausen and Kautzsch) have seen in chapter xx a recasting of II Kings iii, a view now rejected by nearly all commentators. Benzinger refers to it as "a beautiful example of an historical midrash" (*Die Bücher der Chronik* [see Selected Bibliography, Commentaries], p. 107). Noth thinks it rests on a local tradition and not on an old historical source (ÜS, pp. 142 f., n. 3; ZDPV 66 [1944], 45–71) which the writer employed to replace the story told in II Kings iii (ÜS, p. 159). Rudolph, p. 259, believes that external circumstances of the story rest on a good tradition. Certain features have been magnified (e.g., the great multitude of vs. 2) somewhat out of proportion but that can hardly be said to invalidate the true kernel of the story, which revolves around an invasion of Judah from the south.

The invaders were Moabites, Ammonites, and Meunites. Who the Meunites were is uncertain. They are mentioned in I Chron iv 41; II Chron xxvi 7; Ezra ii 50; Neh vii 52. For suggestions see Montgomery, *Arabia and the Bible,* pp. 182 f. In the passages noted, they appear with other groups on the southern borders of Judah and may have been equated with the Minaeans, who were the dominant South Arabian traders in the period of the Chronicler. Whether the undertaking of the invaders was a razzia or a more extensive military campaign cannot be determined; but whatever it was, the attack thoroughly alarmed the authorities at Jerusalem— perhaps because of the presence of invaders at a vital center before they were aware of it. News of the invasion came from the direction of En-gedi. There is some evidence for an Iron Age road from Hebron through Nahal Seelim to the shores of the Dead Sea and on to Moab which would have been threatened by the easterners. See IEJ 11 (1961), 16. The fortress cities of Rehoboam (xi 5–10) prevented their entrance from any other direction. Invaders sometimes took to the byways to reach their objectives (cf. Isa x 27 ff.).

The effect of the news of the invasion upon Jehoshaphat was stunning. He immediately proclaimed a fast in which every man, woman, and child participated (vs. 13; cf. Joel ii 15, 16). Before the assembled congregation the king offered a solemn prayer to Yahweh—as Asa had done when he was threatened by the Ethiopians (xiv 10 f.)—recalling the requests made by Solomon at the time of the dedication of the temple (vs. 9; cf. vi 14–42; on the prayer as a confession and declaration of faith, see O. Plöger, in *Festschrift für Gunther Dehn,* 1957, pp. 46 f.). The Chronicler's reference to "a great multitude" above and in vs. 12 is justification for the intervention of Yahweh; for Judah could not, of its own strength, cope with the invaders.

The oracle of Yahweh in answer to Jehoshaphat's prayer was given by Jahaziel, an Asaphite who was reckoned among the Levites. Asaph is referred to elsewhere (xxix 30, xxxv 15) as a seer, and Jahaziel was an inspired singer. As a member of the cult personnel, he delivered an oracle of salvation (the salvation of Yahweh, vs. 17), introduced and concluded by the old formula, "Do not be afraid" (vss. 15, 17) (cf. J. Begrich, "Das priestliche Heilsorakel," ZAW 52 [1934], 83, and A. R. Johnson, *The Cultic Prophet in Ancient Israel,* 1944, pp. 61 f.). Judah would not participate in the battle, for the battle was the Lord's (cf. Exod xiv 13–14; I Sam xvii 47; Ps xci 8 f.); but they would share in the victory. Jehoshaphat and the assembled citizens of Jerusalem and Judah responded to Jahaziel's oracle of salvation with worship and praise. The following morning the host was sent off with an exhortation by the king and a religious procession. Apparently the writer viewed the whole expedition as a holy war, since cultic personnel accompanied the army and played a major role in the campaign (see von Rad, *Der Heilige Krieg im alten Israel,* pp. 80 f., and COMMENT on Sec. 16, xiv 13). The victory celebration was marked by the claiming of the booty and a service of thanksgiving in the field. The whole celebration lasted four days. Another one, presumably involving all segments of the population, took place upon the return to Jerusalem of the victorious king and his army. One of the results of the spectacular triumph of Yahweh was to strike terror into Jehoshaphat's enemies so that he remained at peace afterward.

[Final observations on Jehoshaphat's reign, 31–34]: This summary represents an adaptation of I Kings xxii 41–47. The Chronicler omits the synchronism between the reigns of Jehoshaphat of Judah and Ahab of Israel but otherwise simply reproduces his source in vs. 31. In the following verse he modifies it somewhat, for example, "he continued in the way of his father Asa" for "he continued in all the way," etc. of I Kings xxii 43. The modification may be due to the maritime alliance with Ahaziah, condemned by Eliezer (vss. 35–37). Verse 33 is altered from "the people still sacrificed and burned incense upon the high places" of I Kings xxii 44 so that the blame seems to fall upon the people rather than upon the king, which does not harmonize with their response exhibited in the first portion of the chapter. The reference to the oracles of Jehu ben-Hanani said to contain other acts of Jehoshaphat is missing in Kings. "The chronicles of the kings of Israel" equals "the chronicles of the kings of Judah" in I Kings xxii 46; hence "kings of Israel" here is probably due to the Chronicler's view that Judah is really the true Israel. Rudolph's point, p. xi, that the oracles of the various prophets mentioned in Chronicles were a part of the chronicles of the kings appears to be confirmed by this verse.

[Jehoshaphat's abortive maritime venture, 35–37]: The position of this pericope again illustrates that the Chronicler followed the Deuteronomist closely, for it appears in exactly the same place in

I Kings xxii, though in different form. The Kings narrative says simply that Jehoshaphat built a Tarshish fleet for the purpose of bringing gold from Ophir. But it never sailed because it was smashed at Ezion-geber. There is some archaeological evidence that the second period of Ezion-geber was the work of Jehoshaphat (cf. BASOR 79 [October 1940], 8 f.). It dates from the ninth century. In any case, it did not remain under Judah for long, as we learn from xxi 8 ff. The Edomites remained in control until the time of Uzziah a century later (cf. BASOR 72 [December 1938], 7 f.).

After the destruction of the Tarshish fleet, Ahaziah volunteered to join Jehoshaphat but the latter refused the offer. The Chronicler has reinterpreted the story so as to make the maritime venture a joint enterprise with Ahaziah of Israel, thus contradicting the statement by the Deuteronomist. He may have been following an independent source here (cf. Rudolph, p. 265) that suggested a much closer relationship between the two kingdoms than is generally recognized. In any case, it gave him an excellent explanation of the cause for the disaster as the prophecy of Eliezer specifically indicates. There is no reference elsewhere to this prophet.

[The death of Jehoshaphat, xxi 1]: This verse belongs with the story of Jehoshaphat; it is the regular formula that concludes the story of nearly all of the kings.

23. THE REIGN OF JEHORAM (849–842 B.C.)
(xxi 2–20)†

Removal of possible opposition

XXI ² His brothers, sons of Jehoshaphat, were Azariah, Jehiel, Zechariah, Azariah, Michael, and Shephatiah—all of them sons of Jehoshaphat the king of Israel.ᵃ ³ Their father had presented to them rich gifts of silver, gold, and other valuables along with the fortified cities of Judah, but he gave the kingdom of Judah to Jehoram because he was the first-born son. ⁴ But when Jehoram had taken over the dominion of his father and established himself firmly, he put all of his brothers to the sword, along with some officials of Israel.

Character of his reign

⁵ Jehoram was thirty-two years old when he became king and remained king in Jerusalem for eight years. ⁶ He followed the path of the kings of Israel, just as the house of Ahab did—his wife was a daughter of Ahab—and did evil in the sight of Yahweh. ⁷ But Yahweh was unwilling to destroy the house of David because he had made a covenant with David in which he had promised to provide a light for him and his sons for all time. ⁸ In his time Edom rebelled against the rule of Judah and established their own monarchy. ⁹ Then Jehoram, with his captains and all his chariots, went over and at nightfall struck down the Edomites who had encircled him and his chariot captains. ¹⁰ The Edomites have continued their rebellion against the rule

† II Chron xxi 5–11 ‖ II Kings viii 17–22; 16–20 ‖ II Kings viii 23–24.

ᵃ The Sebir, LXX, Syr., Vulg. read "Judah" here, but that may be a correction. It is more difficult to account for the presence of Israel because Jehoshaphat was the king of Judah.

of Judah to this day. Libnah also rebelled at that time against his rule because he had abandoned Yahweh God of his fathers. 11 He even made high places in the mountains of Judah, led the citizens of Jerusalem into apostasy and seduced Judah.

The Elijah document

12 Then a document of the prophet Elijah reached him with this message, "Thus has Yahweh God of your father David said, Because you have not followed the ways of Jehoshaphat your father and the ways of Asa the king of Judah 13 but have followed the way of the kings of Israel and led Judah and the citizens of Jerusalem to apostasy just as the house of Ahab led [Israel] to apostasy, and even slew your brothers, of your own father's house, who were better than you, 14 Yahweh is going to afflict your people, your sons, your wives and all your goods with a great plague, 15 and you yourself shall have a severe disease affecting your bowels so that your bowels will come out day after day because of the disease."

Last years of Jehoram

16 Then Yahweh stirred up the Philistines and the Arabs, who dwelt near the Ethiopians, against Jehoram. 17 They came up against Judah, forced their way into it, and carried away all the goods found in the king's house together with his sons and his wives so that not one of his sons was left except Jehoahaz, his youngest son. 18 After this Yahweh afflicted him in the bowels with an incurable disease. 19 In due time, at the end of about two years, his bowels protruded because of his disease and he died in severe pain. His people, however, did not provide for him a pyre like the pyre of his fathers. 20 He was thirty-two years old when he became king and reigned eight years in Jerusalem. He passed away unlamented and they buried him in the city of David, though not in the cemetery of the kings.

NOTES

xxi 4. *some officials of Israel*. May point to the presence of Israelite officials in Judah. That is quite possible considering the relationship between Judah and Israel at the time.

6. *his wife was a daughter of Ahab*. See J. Begrich, "Atalja, die Tochter Omris," ZAW 53 (1935), 78 f. and NOTE on xxii 2. Begrich thinks, on the basis of II Kings viii 26b (‖ II Chron xxii 2b), that Athaliah was the sister, not the daughter of Ahab. Cf. further H. J. Katzenstein, "Who Were the Parents of Athaliah," IEJ 5 (1955), 194–97, who holds that Athaliah was the daughter of Omri.

10. *Libnah*. Libnah has been identified with Tell es-Safi (Abel, *Géographie de la Palestine*, II, p. 85), some twenty miles southwest of Jerusalem, at the western edge of the Shephelah; and with Tell Bornaṭ (BASOR 15 [October 1924], 2–11; PJB 30 [1934], 58–63).

his . . . he . . . his. The pronoun refers to Jehoram, as the phrase "God of his fathers" shows. There is constant shifting back and forth between Judah and Jehoram in the preceding verses.

19. *a pyre like the pyre*. Literally "a burning like the burning."

COMMENT

[Removal of possible opposition, xxi 2–4]: This informative piece is found only in Chronicles and was doubtless taken from the historical records from which the writer drew his material. The matter-of-fact way in which the story is transmitted points to its basic authenticity. Jehoshaphat apparently followed the precedent established by Rehoboam (xi 23) in placing his sons in the fortified cities of Judah where he provided for them lavishly. The throne, however, was given to Jehoram, the oldest son—a rule generally, though not always, followed. As soon as Jehoram had matters well in hand, he proceeded to root out possible claimants to the throne (cf. Judg ix 5; II Kings xi 1 ‖ II Chron xxii 10), as well as the Jerusalem officials who stood in his way.

[The character of his reign, 5–11]: The writer's inclusion of the story just noted has broken the formula generally employed to introduce the reign of a king. The eight years' rule of Jehoram was a sorry one from the Chronicler's point of view. It was almost as bad as that of the monarchs of the Northern Kingdom. The one redeeming feature was the maintenance of the Davidic line (vs. 7). Jehoram was the victim of a marriage alliance with the house of Ahab whose influence was felt in Judah for some time. The main divergence from II Kings viii occurs in vs. 7 where "the house of David" replaces "Judah" (II Kings viii 19a), and "because of David his servant" is expanded to read "because he had made a covenant with David," both illustrations of his regard for the Davidic line.

Edom's revolt may have come soon after the death of Jehoshaphat, perhaps inspired by the unsettled situation in both Israel and Judah. There is some archaeological evidence at Ramet Matred (some thirty miles south of Beer-sheba) for destruction in the Negeb during either the Shishak raid or the revolt of Edom; see IEJ 10 (1960), 110. Ezion-geber probably fell victim to this Edomite expansionist movement that led to its independence (BASOR 72 [1938], 7). The notice here is somewhat contradictory, due to the confused text of the source from which the Chronicler received his information (II Kings viii 21). Verse 8 tells us that Jehoram and his army were encircled by the Edomites but broke through the latter's lines during the night. That escape the writer turns into a victory, thus carrying the assertion of the Deuteronomist a step further. But vs. 10a presents the bitter truth. Libnah also revolted. The reason given for both uprisings is stated only by the Chronicler and is naturally attributed to Judah's defection from Yahweh. Instead of removing the idolatrous objects, as his ancestors had done (xiv 2–4, xvii 6), Jehoram set about making new ones and thus seduced Judah, as Jeroboam had done in Israel (cf. vss. 12–13, below).

[The Elijah document, 12–15]: II Kings i 17 reports the accession of Jehoram of Israel in the second year of Jehoram of Judah. The former succeeded Ahaziah, who died in accordance with a prophecy of Elijah delivered at the time. Hence, it is argued, Elijah was still alive and had at least enough time to observe the blood bath following the accession of Jehoram (of Judah). But, apart from the difficulties involved in the synchronism noted above, Chronicles nowhere else mentions any prophecies of either Elijah or Elisha. In view of the Deuteronomist's high regard for the prophets, particularly Elijah, it is difficult to understand his omission of an episode that involves his favorite prophet, as this one does, if there had been the slightest hint of its existence. The only conclusion possible is that it is apocryphal. For a discussion of the various theories see Rudolph, p. 267. In a number of instances the Chronicler has prophets predicting disaster for kings before the event, for example, Shemaiah for Rehoboam (xii 5 ff.), Hanani for Asa (xvi 7 ff.), Jehu for Jehoshaphat (xix 2 f.), Zechariah for Joash (xxiv 20 ff.) and Azariah the priest for Uzziah (xxvi 17 f.). The letter could possibly have some basis in fact. In that case, the attribution to Elijah would be a mistake not uncommon in that stories and words are often shifted from a less well-known to a better known name. An interesting point here is that Elijah does not prophesy in the name of Yahweh God of Israel, but in the name of "Yahweh God of your father David."

[The last years and death of Jehoram, 16–20]: The Elijah document was the prophetic prelude to the troubles that beset Jehoram and finally brought about his end (cf. vss. 14, 15). The revolt of Edom and Libnah was successful and while it may not have encouraged others directly to take that course, it does indicate the weakness of Judah at the time. This movement was probably no more than a series of forays into the land by Philistines and Arabs from the west and southwest, a reversal of the situation prevalent in the time of Jehoshaphat (xvii 11). The Ethiopians referred to here are apparently the settlers around Gerar from the time of Shishak (cf. COMMENT on Sec. 16, xiv 8–14). The king's wives and sons may have resided in royal cities in the outlying districts of Judah and so fell into the hands of the invaders. There is no evidence of an attack upon Jerusalem at the time. It is possible that the invaders were bought off, the price being the king's wives and sons (cf. I Kings xx 5). It appears more plausible, however, that there was some resistance against the intruders, during which they lost their lives. Only Jehoahaz escaped because he was too young to participate in the fray (cf. xxii 1). That was the affliction foretold for the people in the Elijah document. The king died of a painful abdominal disease which was just what had been predicted for him. In contrast to the description of his death and burial in II Kings viii 24, Chronicles says he was buried in the city of David but not in the cemetery of the kings. The refusal of the people to accord him the customary funeral honors is noted only by our author.

The whole story appears to have been composed of legendary material and historical data, though the latter cannot be determined with finality. Certainly the reference to the Philistines and Arabs who lived in the vicinity of the Ethiopians has all the earmarks of authenticity. It is possible that the Chronicler copied the story pretty much as it stood in his source, which was independent of the account in Kings he follows most often.

24. THE REIGN OF AHAZIAH (ca. 842 B.C.)
(xxii 1–9)†

XXII 1 Then the citizens of Jerusalem made Ahaziah his youngest son king in his place, for the freebooters who came with the Arabs against the camp had slain all the older ones. Thus it was that Ahaziah the son of Jehoram king of Judah became king. 2 Ahaziah was *forty-two years old*ᵃ when he became king and reigned one year in Jerusalem. His mother's name was Athaliah, the daughter of Omri. 3 He also followed the ways of the house of Ahab, for his mother was his adviser to bring him into condemnation. 4 He did evil in the sight of Yahweh just like the house of Ahab, for they were his advisers after the death of his father and brought on his destruction. 5 He followed their advice and went with Jehoram, the son of Ahab, the king of Israel to fight against Hazael the king of Aram at Ramothgilead. When the Aramaeans wounded Joram, 6 and he returned to Jezreel to recover from the wounds they had inflicted on him at Ramah in his battle with Hazael the king of Aram, Ahaziah,ᵇ the son of Jehoram, king of Judah went down to see Jehoram the son of Ahab at Jezreel where he lay sick. 7 Now the downfall of Ahaziah when he went to Joram was God's doing, for when he arrived he went out with Jehoram to Jehu the son of Nimshi whom Yahweh had anointed to cut down the house of Ahab. 8 When Jehu was carrying out the judgment on the house of Ahab and found the captains of Judah and the sons of Ahaziah's brothers attending Ahaziah, he killed them. 9 Then he had a search made for Ahaziah and when they took him—for he was

† II Chron xxii 1–9 ‖ II Kings viii 24b–29, ix 21, 27–28.

ᵃ⁻ᵃ See NOTE.
ᵇ So with many manuscripts, LXX, Vulg. MT has "Azariah."

hiding in Samaria—they brought him to Jehu ᵉwho slew him.ᵉ But they buried him because they said, "he is the son of Jehoshaphat who sought Yahweh with his whole mind." However, there was no one left of the house of Ahaziah powerful enough to rule over the kingdom.

ᵉ⁻ᵉ So with LXX; MT "they slew him."

NOTES

xxii 2. *forty-two years old*. That makes him two years older than his father (cf. xxi 20), which is manifestly impossible. II Kings viii 26 has "22 years." The chief LXX witnesses have "20," while there is some minor support for "22," which may be due to the influence of MT of II Kings viii 26. The MT of Chronicles may represent the conflation of two traditions and exhibits a striking example of the effort to preserve two divergent traditions. Originally the numbers were kept separate, e.g., 22 or 20, and only later added together.

Athaliah. See Begrich, ZAW 53 (1935), 78 f.

3. *condemnation*. This is a legal term signifying that X has been adjudged guilty, declared to be in the wrong.

8. *the sons of Ahaziah's brothers*. Probably should be omitted since they would have been too young for such a mission at that time. Perhaps the phrase ought to be rendered "the relatives of Ahaziah."

9. *the son*. A descendant; he was a grandson of Jehoshaphat.

COMMENT

The Chronicler alone mentions that the citizens of Jerusalem put Ahaziah on the throne, which may very well have been the case since in times when the succession was in jeopardy the *'am hā-'āreṣ* intervened to stabilize the situation (xxiii 20–21, xxvi 1, xxxiii 25b, xxxvi 1). Though the phrase *'am hā-'āreṣ* does not appear here, the *yōšᵉbē yᵉrūšālaim* ("the inhabitants of Jerusalem") doubtless has the same significance. On the meaning of the former in the history of Judah see E. Würthwein, *Der 'amm ha'arez im Alten Testament*, 1936. The breakthrough of the freebooters who killed the king's sons, except for the youngest, and carried out marauding expeditions was sufficient cause for the remaining authorities to act. This reference must have come from the writer's source—the same one used in the preceding chapter—because of the appearance of the Arabs here as there. He probably chose to follow that source in preference to Kings because it supported his theory of retribution.

The rest of the story follows Kings in the main. As might be expected, the Chronicler makes Athaliah much more of an *adjutrix diaboli* than does Kings. She was responsible for the evil life of Ahaziah and her retinue became his advisers; and he was apparently a ready disciple—points stressed by the writer. Ahaziah joined Jehoram of Israel in a campaign against the Aramaeans at Ramoth-gilead where Jehoram was wounded. While recuperating at Jezreel, he was visited by Ahaziah—whether he came from the battlefield or sometime later from Jerusalem is not certain. That visit, says the Chronicler, was Yahweh's doing to bring about his overthrow. To understand the situation it is necessary to read II Kings ix 1–21, for only the part of the story involving Ahaziah directly is given here. While Ahaziah was visiting Jehoram, Jehu ben Nimshi, anointed by Elisha to purge the house of Ahab, was on the way to Jezreel to carry out the first part of his task. Both Jehoram and Ahaziah drove out in their chariots to meet Jehu. Then our story diverges from Kings, which tells of Ahaziah's flight after the shooting of Jehoram; but Jehu pursued him and dealt him a fatal blow "at the ascent of Gur near Ibleam" (II Kings ix 27). According to the Chronicler, Jehu first learned of Ahaziah's presence when he came across his attendants, whom he lost no time in dispatching. Then he turned his attention to the king of Judah who had hidden in Samaria. Jehu's police soon discovered him and brought him to Jehu, who slew him. Because of his position, he was buried, presumably at Samaria. The Kings parallel, on the other hand, says he died, of the wounds inflicted by Jehu's followers, near Megiddo but was taken to Jerusalem and sepulchered in the royal cemetery (II Kings ix 28). Benzinger, pp. 110 f., is probably right in attributing these verses to another source which the writer found more to his liking. Because Ahaziah's sons were too young to rule and all his brothers had met their doom earlier, Athaliah took over.

25. THE REIGN OF ATHALIAH (ca. 842–837 B.C.)
(xxii 10–12, xxiii 1–21)†

The murder of the royal family

XXII ¹⁰ When Athaliah the mother of Ahaziah learned that her son was dead, *she immediately exterminated* all the royal seed of the house of Judah. ¹¹ But Jehoshabeath the king's daughter took Joash, Ahaziah's son, stole him away from the midst of the king's sons who were to be slain and hid him with his nurse in the bedroom. So Jehoshabeath, the daughter of King Jehoram and the wife of Jehoiada the priest—she was the sister of Ahaziah—kept him hidden from Athaliah so that she could not kill him. ¹² He remained hidden with them in the house of God for six years while Athaliah reigned over the land.

The presentation of Joash

XXIII ¹ In the seventh year Jehoiada determined to make a pact with the commanders of the hundreds—with Azariah the son of Jeroham, Ishmael the son of Jehohanan, Azariah the son of Obed, Maaseiah the son of Adaiah, and Elishaphat the son of Zichri. ² They traveled through all Judah and summoned the Levites from all the cities of Judah and the Israelite family heads who then came to Jerusalem. ³ The whole congregation made a covenant with the king in the house of God. He*b* said

† II Chron xxii 10–12 ‖ II Kings xi 1–3; II Chron xxiii 1–11 ‖ II Kings xi 4–12; 12–21 ‖ II Kings xi 13–20.

a–a MT "she arose and spoke." II Kings xi 1 "she arose and destroyed." All the versions have "destroyed," "exterminated" here.
b I.e., Jehoiada. LXX adds "and he showed to them the son of the king." Cf. II Kings xi 4, from which the LXX addition probably came.

to them, "Behold the son of the king shall reign just as Yahweh spoke concerning the sons of David. 4 This is what you are to do now: a third of you priests and Levites who come on duty on the Sabbath shall be porters at the gates; 5 a third [shall guard] the house of the king, a third the foundation gate, while all the people [shall remain] in the courts of the house of Yahweh. 6 None must enter the house of Yahweh except the priests and the Levitical ministrants; they may enter because they are consecrated; but all the people must observe the regulations of Yahweh. 7 The Levites are to surround the king, each one with his weapons in his hand—anyone entering the house shall be put to death—and accompany the king when he enters and departs." 8 So the Levites, and all Judah, did everything Jehoiada the priest had commanded, and each one took charge of his men, those who came on as well as those who went off Sabbath duty, for Jehoiada the priest had not released [any] divisions from duty. 9 Then Jehoiada the priest delivered to the captains of the hundreds the spears, and the great and small shields of King David which were in the house of God. 10 He stationed all the people to guard the king, each with his weapon in his hand, from the south side of the house to the north side of the house and all around the altar and the house. 11 Then they brought out the son of the king, put the crown upon him, [delivered to him] the royal stipulations, and made him king. When Jehoiada and his sons had anointed him, they shouted, "Long live the king."

The reaction of Athaliah

12 When Athaliah heard the sound of the people running and praising the king, she joined the people in the house of Yahweh. 13 As she looked, behold the king was standing in his place at the entrance and the captains and trumpeters were near the king, with all the people of the land rejoicing and blowing the trumpets, and the singers with all their instruments of song giving the signals for praise. Then Athaliah tore her garments and shouted, "Treason, treason." 14 Then Jehoiada the priest brought out the captains of the hundreds who were in charge

of the army and said to them, "Bring her out from between*
the ranks, and let whoever follows her be slain with the sword!"
For the priest had declared, "Do not kill her in the house of
Yahweh." 15 So *they made way for her* and when she came to
the entrance of the horse gate of the king's house, they slew her
there.

The reformation

16 Then Jehoiada made a covenant between himself, all the
people, and the king to remain Yahweh's people. 17 All the
people then went to the house of Baal, pulled it down, smashed
its altars and its images, and killed Mattan the priest of Baal
before the altars. 18 Jehoiada placed the care of Yahweh's house
into the hands of *the priests and the Levites* whom David had
appointed over the house of Yahweh to offer the burnt offerings
of Yahweh as prescribed in the law of Moses, and with joy and
song as directed by David. 19 He also appointed porters for the
gates of the house of Yahweh so that no one who was unclean
in any way might enter. 20 Then he took the captains of the
hundreds, the nobles, the governors of the people, and all the
people of the land, and brought down the king from the house
of Yahweh: they entered the house of the king through the
upper gate and placed the king upon the royal throne. 21 So all
the people of the land rejoiced and the city was quiet although
they had slain Athaliah with the sword.

c So with Syr.
d–d So with LXX; Vulg. "they seized her." See W. Rudolph, FAB, p. 475.
e–e MT here has "Levitical priests." LXX and Vulg. have "priests and Levites."

Notes

xxii 10. *learned*. Literally "saw."
11. *the daughter . . . the priest*. Note the marriage and blood ties
between the royal and high-priestly families.
xxiii 5. *the foundation gate*. Cf. II Kings xi 6 has "Sur," the name
of a gate. Cf. Rudolph, FAB, pp. 474 f.; L. H. Vincent and A. M.
Steve, *Jerusalem de l'Ancien Testament*, 1954–55, p. 599, n. 3.

8. *those who came . . . Sabbath duty.* Literally "going on the Sabbath and going off the Sabbath."

11. *the royal stipulations.* I.e., the rules governing his position in relation to Yahweh and the people. See I Chron xxix 19. The document would signify the terms of the kingship under which the monarch would rule. There is good evidence that the covenant between king and people involved obligations for the king as well as for the people (from David's time on), and this would agree with the formula for kingship in Deuteronomy, which may be late in wording but assuredly expresses a longstanding principle of the role and subordination of the king to the word of Yahweh. Cf. Rudolph, p. 270; von Rad, TLZ 72 (1947), cols. 211 ff. Some think the term refers to bracelets (R. de Vaux, *Les Livres des Rois,* 1949, p. 166; Montgomery and Gehman, *The Books of Kings,* pp. 421, 425).

they shouted. I.e., the people.

13. *"Treason, treason."* Literally "conspiracy," "plot," and thus sedition or treason.

14. *the ranks.* Meaning is uncertain, perhaps a part of the temple.

15. *horse gate.* A gate of the temple enclosure, not the horse gate of the city. See M. Burrows, AASOR 14 (1934), 119 f. Cf. diagram of Athaliah's movements in Vincent and Steve, *op. cit.,* p. 600, Fig. 182.

16. *covenant.* The covenant confirms the prior agreement of the king; here the stress falls on the obligations of the people to Yahweh and the king.

18. *David . . . Moses . . . David.* Note the juxtaposition of David and Moses who, for the Chronicler, represent the two great personalities for the life of "all Israel."

COMMENT

[The murder of the royal family, xxii 10–12]: The actual reign of Athaliah is disposed of in few words by both Deuteronomist and Chronicler, perhaps because both wanted to forget the whole affair. It could also be because apparently no queen ruled in her own name in either Israel or Judah, though at times as regent. While Athaliah doubtless thought she was ruling in her own name—because she believed all the royal male issue had been destroyed—that was not the official view. See D. N. Freedman's remarks in G. E. Wright, *The Bible and the Ancient Near East,* 1961, p. 227, n. 40.

The one event agreed upon by both the Deuteronomist and the

Chronicler is the ruthless extermination of her own children, with the exception of Joash who was hidden by his aunt Jehoshabeath, the wife of Jehoiada the priest—a detail supplied by the Chronicler here. This little pericope is nothing more than a brief setting for the following story of the priestly and popular revolt against the atrocities of Athaliah, the maintenance of the Davidic line, and the consequences of defection from Yahweh.

[The crowning of Joash, xxiii 1–11]: The Chronicler's dependence upon II Kings xi is quite evident. But there are significant additions and omissions, in harmony with the author's religious views. For one thing, there is his concern to avoid desecration of the temple by providing ecclesiastical officials and guards rather than purely military ones as in I Kings xi (vss. 4–8). Moreover the people are kept in their proper place (vs. 5) and all "the regulations of Yahweh" with respect to the temple must be observed (vs. 6). The writer's feeling for Jerusalem and the house of Yahweh is stressed by the summoning of the leaders of the hundreds to Jerusalem and the careful handling of all movements that centered about the temple. Another concern was the perpetuation of the Davidic line, emphasized in vs. 3. Thus the two main features of the Chronicler's work stand out conspicuously—the temple and David, together with the emphasis upon the cult personnel. The latter point is illustrated, not only by the place given to priests and Levites in the coup against Athaliah, but especially in the specific statement that Jehoiada and his sons anointed the king (vs. 11).

[The reaction of Athaliah, 12–15]: This part follows the source closely, though not without significant points of emphasis. Here the noise which brought Athaliah to the scene was not simply that of officials and people but that of the people "running and praising the king"; again the king holds the center of the stage. The singers with their musical instruments also played an active role in the proceedings. The sanctity of the temple appears in the strong prohibition, "Do not kill her in the house of Yahweh" as opposed to the simple appeal in the parallel passage (II Kings xi 15). That may have been the motive for Jehoiada's provision for the safe conduct of the queen from the sacred precincts.

[The reformation, 16–21]: The first step taken by Jehoiada to restore Judah to its earlier state was the renewal of the covenant which bound all parties to remain Yahweh's people. This revival of religious leadership in Judah necessitated the uprooting of all vestiges of the Baal cult brought in under Athaliah. On the positive side it meant a return to the torah of Moses and the orders established by David. Most significantly, the claim of the Levites to an equal share with the priests in the cultic services is reaffirmed and care is taken to guard against desecration of the temple. Then the king was conducted from the house of Yahweh and enthroned in the palace. The only violence to disturb the otherwise orderly procedure was the slaying of the queen mother.

26. THE REIGN OF JOASH (ca. 837–800 B.C.)
(xxiv 1–27)†

The family relationships of Joash

XXIV 1 Joash was seven years old when he became king and reigned forty years at Jerusalem. His mother's name was Zibiah from Beer-sheba. 2 Joash did what was right in the sight of Yahweh all the days of Jehoiada the priest. 3 Jehoiada had him marry two wives and he fathered sons and daughters.

Renovation of the temple

4 Afterward Joash decided to renovate the house of Yahweh. 5 So he summoned the priests and the Levites and said to them, "Go out to the cities of Judah and collect money annually from all Israel to repair the house of your God, and you must expedite the matter." But the Levites were in no hurry. 6 Then the king called Jehoiada the chief priest and said to him, "Why have you not required the Levites to bring in from Judah and Jerusalem the tax which Moses the servant of Yahweh and the congregation of Israel [imposed] for the tent of testimony?"—7 Athaliah, that wicked woman, and her sons*a* had neglected the house of God and even had given all the sacred objects of the house of Yahweh to Baal.—8 So at the order of the king they made a chest, placed it outside the gate of the house of Yahweh, 9 and issued a proclamation to Judah and Jerusalem to bring to Yahweh the tax which Moses the servant of God [imposed] upon Israel in the wilderness. 10 Then all the captains and all

† II Chron xxiv 1–3 ‖ II Kings xii 1–4; **4–14** ‖ II Kings xii 5–16; **23–27** ‖ II Kings xii 18–22.

a Another pointing is "her builders." But MT is supported by LXX and Vulg. Her sons were Ahaziah's brothers, who may very well have been associated with her in the neglect of the temple.

the people rejoiced, brought in and deposited [their contributions] into the chest until it was full. 11 Whenever the chest was brought by the Levites for royal inspection and found to contain enough money, the royal scribe and the official of the chief priest would come and empty the chest and then take it back again to its place. They did so day after day and thus collected much money. 12 The king and Jehoiada give it to those*b* in charge of the work on the house of Yahweh who in turn hired masons and carpenters to renovate the house of Yahweh, as well as iron and brass workers to repair the house of Yahweh. 13 The workmen labored on—the repair work progressed in their hands—until they had restored the house of God to its proper state and had put it into good condition [again]. 14 When they had finished [it], they returned to the king and Jehoiada the surplus money from which they made vessels for the house of Yahweh: vessels for the service and for the burnt offering, bowls and [other] gold and silver vessels.

Reversal of the policy of Jehoiada

They offered burnt offerings continually in the house of Yahweh throughout the lifetime of Jehoiada. 15 When Jehoiada was old and well along in years he died; he was a hundred and thirty years when he died. 16 They buried him with the kings in the city of David because he had well served Israel and God and his house. 17 After the death of Jehoiada the captains of Judah came and did homage to the king. When the king yielded to them 18 they abandoned the house of Yahweh God of their fathers and served the Asherahs and the images so that wrath came upon Judah and Jerusalem for this guilt of theirs. 19 So he sent prophets among them to lead them back to Yahweh; they threatened them but they would not listen. 20 Then the spirit of God put on Zechariah the son of Jehoiada the priest who stood before the people and said to them, "Thus has God said, why have you transgressed the commandments of Yahweh so that you cannot succeed; for if you abandon Yahweh, he will

b Plural with LXX. Cf. also II Kings xii 12.

abandon you." 21 But they conspired against him and, at the command of the king, stoned him in the court of the house of Yahweh. 22 Thus Joash the king did not remember the devotion which Jehoiada his father displayed on his behalf, but murdered his son. When he died, he cried, "May Yahweh observe and requite!"

The Aramaean invasion and death of Joash

23 At the turn of the year the Aramaean army came up against him. When they came to Judah and Jerusalem, they annihilated all the captains of the people from among the people and shipped all their booty to the king at Damascus. 24 Although the Aramaean army that came was a small body of men, Yahweh delivered a very large army into their hand, because they had abandoned Yahweh God of their fathers. Therefore they executed judgment against Joash. 25 When they departed from him—for they left him with many wounds—his servants conspired against him because of the blood of ᶜthe sonᶜ of Jehoiada the priest and killed him on his bed. After he was dead, they buried him in the city of David, though they did not bury him in the cemetery of the kings. 26 These were the ones who conspired against him: Zabad the son of Shimeath the Ammonitess and Jehozabad the son of Shimrith the Moabitess. 27 [The record] of his sons, of the many oracles against him, and of the renovationᵈ of the house of God is written down in the commentary on the chronicle of the kings. Amaziah his son then became king in his place.

ᶜ⁻ᶜ Singular with LXX and Vulg.
ᵈ Heb. "foundation."

NOTES

xxiv 3. *he fathered sons and daughters.* The language here is just like that in *P*'s genealogies (cf. Gen v). The influence of *P* on the present text of Chronicles is unmistakable. Whether it was edited into the text (A. C. Welch, *The Work of the Chronicler*, 1939, pp. 78–80) or whether Chronicles is a continuation of *P* cannot be determined at present.

6. *chief priest.* Add "priest" with vs. 11. On term "chief priest" see COMMENT on Sec. 21, xix 11.

the tax . . . testimony. Cf. Exod xxx 12 ff.

7. Athaliah was accused of murdering the king's sons (i.e., Ahaziah's), her grandchildren, with the exception of Joash (xxii 10). The reference to her wanton neglect of the temple occurs only here.

11. *for royal inspection.* Literally "for the inspection of the king."

13. *its proper state.* The import of the whole verse seems to be that the temple was made as secure on its foundations as it was before. In short they restored its structural soundness and solidity.

15. *a hundred and thirty years.* Apparently a symbolic figure; older than Moses (120 years) or Aaron (123 years).

17. *did homage.* In flattery.

18. *Asherahs.* Asherah was originally a sea-goddess, the consort of El in Ugaritic mythology. In the Bible she appears as wife of Baal. The *asherahs* then were probably images of some sort or cult objects symbolizing the goddess with her peculiar function, particularly detested by the prophets (Isa xvii 8, xxvii 9; Mic v 14).

20. *the spirit of God.* For this significant expression see Judg vi 34; I Chron xii 18; Job xxix 14. See discussion of the idea by A. R. Johnson, *The One and the Many in the Israelite Conception of God,* 1942, pp. 5, 15, 33.

21. Cf. Matt xxiii 35; Luke xi 51; Josephus *Wars* IV.v.4.

22. *which his father displayed.* I.e., the *ḥesed* which he had done, the acts of devotion (or kindness) which he had done.

23. *the turn of the year.* In the spring of the year. According to J. Begrich (*Die Chronologie der Könige von Israel und Juda,* 1929, pp. 79 ff., 156 ff.), this is in accord with the Chronicler's calendrical system.

27. *the commentary.* See Sec. 15, NOTE on xiii 22.

COMMENT

This represents an augmented theological interpretation of the reign of Joash, the chief source for which is II Kings xii or a parallel source with the same story in general, though with some significant variations as will appear below.

[The family relationships of Joash, xxiv 1–3]: There is of course no co-ordination of Joash's reign with that of Jehu as in II Kings xii 2. For theological reasons and in conformity with his plan, the Chronicler modifies somewhat the characterization of Joash. He affirms that Joash did what was right so long as Jehoiada lived and then fell into apostasy. His source speaks of the king having done right all his life because of the instruction of Jehoiada and hence says nothing about his defection after the latter's death. Jehoiada, acting as regent, married him to two wives, a sort of compromise between the practice of his predecessors (e.g., David, Solomon, Abijah) and the Deuteronomic injunction (xvii 17). The reference to his sons and daughters is partly an indication of Yahweh's blessing and partly an explanation of the record (vs. 27).

[The renovation of the temple, 4–14ab]: While there may be no disagreement between Kings and Chronicles in the over-all picture of the renovation of the temple, there are significant variations in detail that illustrate the viewpoint of the Chronicler. A characteristic feature of Chronicles, the magnification of the Levites, is carried through here. Thus the Levites were summoned by the king (vs. 5) to participate along with the priests in the collection of funds for the enterprise (on provisions for the temple and its repairs see K. Galling, "Königliche und nichtkönigliche Stifter beim Temple von Jerusalem," BBLA [1950], especially pp. 134–39); indeed they appear to have been placed in charge of the operation (vss. 6, 11)— a priest, scribe, and Levite were placed in charge of the temple's treasuries by Nehemiah (xiii 13). But the observation that at first they were somewhat dilatory in the performance of their duties does not seem to be quite in line with the Chronicler's theory. Yet this indicates that he was not so biased as is sometimes suggested and that he may have drawn from another source (cf. vs. 27 and Rudolph, p. 277) than Kings for his information. It should be observed that the priests are absolved from blame here (cf. II Kings xii 6–8). The Levites appear to have been barred altogether from the actual handling of funds (vss. 11, 12), which were under the jurisdiction of the royal scribe and a representative of the chief priest and dispensed by the king and Jehoiada.

According to the writer, a special campaign was to be conducted among the cities of Judah (vs. 5) for the repair project. The appeal was to be made on the basis of the head tax decreed by Moses (Exod xxx 12–16, xxxviii 25–28) for the furnishing of the tabernacle. The tax fell into disuse, since it is specifically said to have been renewed by Nehemiah (x 32) and applied in part to temple repairs (see W. Rudolph, *Esra und Nehemiah,* 1949, pp. 177–79). It may be that this method was resorted to when the campaign for voluntary offerings failed, or that the Chronicler read back into this situation the later method adopted by Nehemiah. At any rate, there was no lack of funds after the proclamation of the summons; characteristically, there was a surplus, which was used for other purposes (vs. 14). There is no reference to a surplus in II Kings xii.

It is interesting to note that according to II Kings xii 9 the chest was placed beside the altar and the offerings were placed therein by the priests. The Chronicler has it placed "outside the gate of the house of Yahweh" (vs. 8) where all groups deposited their own contributions (vs. 10)—thus preserving the sanctity of the sacred precincts and at the same time providing for direct personal participation of the people.

[A reversal of policy, 14c–22]: The happy state of affairs during the lifetime of Jehoiada is indicated by the uninterrupted sacrifices. Thus the reformation of the cult and the preservation of the Davidic line were the product of the efforts of the chief priest, whose character and honor the Chronicler celebrated by calling attention to his long life and the place of his burial. Jehoiada's symbolic age, 130 years (see NOTE to vs. 15), indicated that he was favored by Yahweh. That he was honored by the people—the nation—is shown by his burial in the royal cemetery.

When the guiding hand of the priest was no longer present, Joash was deflected from his course by the officials—possibly holdovers from the earlier regime—and reverted to former practices. To bring them back to the ways followed by Jehoiada, Yahweh sent prophets among them but without success. Finally Zechariah, the son of Jehoiada, was used by Yahweh to remind king and people of their transgression and that to abandon Yahweh meant failure for both. Instead of showing respect for him, they rewarded him by putting him to death in the very temple where a few years before his father had brought them deliverance from the machinations of Athaliah and her minions. The dying words of the prophet were soon to find fulfillment.

[The downfall of Joash, 23–27]: While II Kings also refers to an Aramaean campaign against Judah that threatened Jerusalem, the Chronicler was dependent upon another source, as may be seen from a close comparison between the stories. He speaks of an Aramaean army making a kind of foray into Judah during which those officials responsible for misleading Joash were rooted out, and booty taken and shipped to the king (Hazael) at Damascus. Kings, on the other hand, tells of an invasion of Judah during which Gath was captured and Jerusalem threatened by the Aramaean king and his army. To spare the capital, Joash stripped the temple and palace of the votive gifts accumulated during the preceding three reigns. Kings knows nothing of the wounding of Joash in the fray, because there was actually no attack upon Jerusalem according to the Deuteronomist. There is agreement on the conspiracy against Joash in which he was murdered and there is some evidence that even the names are the same (manuscript variation on the name "Zabad" can be found in II Kings xii 21, where MT has "Jozabad," but some manuscripts of LXX have "Jozakar"). According to Kings, Joash was buried "with his fathers," which the Chronicler denies—he was not buried in the cemetery of the kings.

The Chronicler's version of the episode was probably taken from the treatise (midrash) he mentions in vs. 27. Unless these materials are regarded as largely fictitious and fabricated, like the vast body of intertestamental pious literature (cf. also the "Words of Moses" and the "Psalms of Joshua" from the Qumran caves), then the Chronicler must have had at his disposal extensive sources in addition to canonical Samuel and Kings. The religious motives were uppermost in his mind and must have been more apparent in his source than in the Deuteronomic parallel. The officials who misled Joash were rooted out, the small Aramaean band overcame a much larger force because of their defection, and Joash himself was the victim of a conspiracy because of his guilt in the death of Zechariah.

27. THE REIGN OF AMAZIAH (ca. 800–783 B.C.)
(xxv 1–28)†

Accession of Amaziah

XXV ¹ Amaziah was twenty-five years old when he became king and reigned twenty-nine years at Jerusalem. His mother's name was Jehoaddan from Jerusalem. ² He did what was right in the sight of Yahweh, only not wholeheartedly. ³ When the kingdom was securely established under him, he slew his servants who had struck down the king, his father. ⁴ However he did not put their sons to death, because it is written in the law—in the book of Moses—which Yahweh commanded, saying, "The fathers shall not die for the sons nor shall the sons die for the fathers, but each one shall die for his own sin."

Campaign against Edom

⁵ Amaziah convoked Judah and classified all Judah and Benjamin, according to families, to captains of thousands and captains of hundreds. He also registered them from twenty years old and upward and found that there were three hundred thousand select men, ready for service and capable of wielding spear and shield. ⁶ Moreover he hired one hundred thousand warriors from Israel for a hundred talents of silver. ⁷ Then a man of God came to him, saying, "O king, let not the Israelite army go with you for Yahweh is not with Israel, or with any of the Ephraimites. ⁸ Though you might appear to gain support from them for war, God will overturn you before the enemy, for God has the power to help or to cast down." ⁹ Amaziah said to the man of God, "But what is to be done about the hundred talents I have

† **II Chron xxv 1–4** ‖ II Kings xiv 2–6; **5–16** ‖ II Kings xiv 7; **17–28** ‖ II Kings xiv 8–20.

paid for the troops of Israel?" "God is able to give you more than that," said the man of God. 10 Then Amaziah released the troops that had come to him from Ephraim so they could go home again. They were very angry with Judah and returned home full of wrath. 11 However, Amaziah took courage, led out his people, went to the Valley of Salt, and struck down ten thousand men of Seir. 12 The men of Judah took ten thousand more alive, brought them to the top of the Rock and cast them down from the top of the Rock so that they were all dashed to pieces. 13 The troops whom Amaziah sent back from accompanying him to battle, plundered the cities of Judah from Samaria to Beth-horon, struck down three thousand of their people and took a large quantity of booty. 14 When Amaziah returned from the destruction of the Edomites, he brought along the gods of the men of Seir, set them up as his gods, bowed down before them, and burned incense to them. 15 The anger of Yahweh blazed against Amaziah and he sent a prophet to him who said to him, "Why do you inquire of the gods of the people who could not even deliver their own people from your hand?" 16 While he was still speaking to him, he said, "Have we made you a royal adviser? Stop, or you will be struck down!" So the prophet ceased with the retort, "I know that God has resolved to destroy you because you did this and did not listen to my advice."

War with Joash of Israel

17 Then Amaziah the king of Judah resolved to send the following message to Joash, the son of Jehoahaz, the son of Jehu the king of Israel: "Come, let us meet face to face!"*a* 18 Joash the king of Israel sent the following reply to Amaziah the king of Judah: "The briar of Lebanon sent the following message to the cedar of Lebanon: Give your daughter as a wife for my son, but a wild animal of Lebanon ran over and trampled down the briar. 19 You thought, 'Behold I have struck down Edom' and your ego has been inflated to seek even greater glory. Now, stay in your own place; why should you engage in disaster, since both

a LXX*B* omits, by homoioteleuton, all of the verse except "Amaziah resolved."

you and Judah will perish?" [20] But Amaziah refused to listen, for it was an act of God to give them [b]into the hand of Joash[b] because he inquired of the gods of Edom. [21] So Joash the king of Israel came up and he and Amaziah the king of Judah met face to face at Beth-shemesh which belonged to Judah. [22] Judah was routed before Israel and each man fled to his tent. [23] But Joash the king of Israel seized Amaziah the king of Judah, the son of Joash the son of Ahaziah[c] at Beth-shemesh, brought him to Jerusalem, and then broke down four hundred cubits of the wall of Jerusalem between the gate of Ephraim and the corner gate. [24] He took along back to Samaria all the gold and silver, all the vessels found in the house of God in charge of Obed-edom, the treasures of the king's house, and the hostages. [25] Amaziah, the son of Joash, the king of Judah lived for fifteen years after the death of Joash, the son of Jehoahaz, the king of Israel. [26] The remainder of the history of Amaziah, from beginning to end, is it not recorded in the chronicle of the kings of Judah and Israel? [27] From the time that Amaziah defected from Yahweh, they raised a conspiracy against him in Jerusalem so that he fled to Lachish. But they sent to Lachish after him and killed him there. [28] Then they transported him on horses and buried him with his fathers in the city of Judah.

[b-b] MT "into a hand." Targ. "in his hand." Reading here is that of LXX[L].
[c] So with II Kings xiv 13; MT "Jehoahaz."

NOTES

xxv 1. *reigned . . . Jerusalem*. On the vexing problem of chronology see Albright, BASOR 100 (December 1945), p. 21, n. 21.

2. *wholeheartedly*. Literally "with his whole heart."

4. *"The fathers . . . own sin."* Law of Deut xxiv 16. Cf. M. Greenberg, who discusses the significance of this law and its observance in connection with the Ten Commandments and other indications of family punishment (*Yehezkel Kaufmann Jubilee Volume*, 1960, pp. 21 f.). The difference between individual and family punishment for transgressions would presumably be in the nature of the crime or sin; also the law, while doubtless old, was often disregarded by kings and usurpers for

whom it would be a matter of course to wipe out the family of those involved. Here the procedure was dictated on the one hand by practical considerations, and on the other (in the case of prophetically inspired purges) by the overriding will of God. As in the case of Achan, certain crimes merited punishment for the whole family. Divine judgment involved taint but human judgment was forbidden to extend beyond the guilty individual.

5. *three hundred thousand.* On the unit basis (*eleph*=one unit), there would be 300 (and 100 in vs. 6) units.

6. *a hundred talents of silver.* About 3¼ tons.

11. *the Valley of Salt.* Identified with Wadi el-milḫ, east of Beer-sheba, by Abel, *Géographie de la Palestine*, I, p. 407; with the Araba, south of the Dead Sea by Grollenberg and the older geographers.

12. *the Rock.* Play on the word Selaʻ of II Kings xiv 7; Selaʻ is now identified with Umm el Biyārah (AASOR 14 [1934], 77; AASOR 15 [1935], 49).

13. *Samaria.* Samaria is doubtful here because it is difficult to understand why the Ephraimites would have plundered their own territory, unless they began their raid from that point. It may be a mistake for some Judean town. Rudolph, pp. 278 f., suggests Migron (I Sam xiv 2; Isa x 28). Cf. G. Dalman, PJB 12 (1916), 44.

Beth-horon. Beth-horon was in the Valley of Aijalon, some ten miles west-northwest of Jerusalem, on the border between Ephraim and Benjamin. See COMMENT on Sec. 9, viii 5. Earlier it belonged to Ephraim (I Chron vii 24).

14. *the gods . . . Seir.* I.e., the gods were images.

16. *Stop, . . . down.* Literally "Cease, why should they strike you."

resolved. Implies that consultation had taken place, perhaps with advisers.

17. *"Come, . . . to face!"* An English equivalent might be, "Come, let us look each other in the eye."

21. *Beth-shemesh.* About fifteen miles southwest of Jerusalem, on the border between Judah and Dan (Josh xv 10).

23. *four hundred cubits.* About six hundred feet.

the gate of Ephraim and the corner gate. Cf. Vincent and Steve, *Jerusalem de l'Ancien Testament*, pp. 93 f.; M. Avi-yonah, *Sepher Yerushalayim*, I, 1956, opposite p. 160, Map 9, according to which the Ephraim gate was located at the northwest corner of the city and the corner gate (cf. Neh iii 31) at the northeast corner.

24. *He took.* With II Kings xiv 14.

in charge of Obed-edom. Cf. I Chron xxvi 15; i.e., those in that part of the house of God in his care.

hostages. Term and idea occur only here and in the parallel in II Kings xiv 14.

28. *Judah.* II Kings xiv 20 has "David." But the Chronicler's phrase is equally correct for his time, since Jerusalem is referred to in the Babylonian Chronicle as *al ia-a-ḫu-du* "city of Judah" (see D. J. Wiseman, *Chronicles of Chaldaean Kings (626–556 BC) in the British Museum,* 1956, p. 73).

COMMENT

[Accession of Amaziah, xxv 1–4]: The Chronicler omits any reference to the synchronism with the Northern Kingdom (II Kings xiv 1), confining himself to a simple statement as to Amaziah's age when he became king and the length of his reign. Defining his character, he says only that he did right, though not with his whole heart. There is no comparison with David and Joash his father as in II Kings xiv 3bc. The Deuteronomic law specified that only the guilty and not their families were to be put to death for crimes.

[The Edomite campaign, 5–16]: Only one verse is devoted to this episode in II Kings xiv 7; the Chronicler has a considerably expanded account which he obviously took from one of his other sources because of the religious interests involved. In preparation for the campaign, the army was reorganized and a military census, like the one undertaken by David (I Chron xxi), Asa (II Chron xiv 8), and Jehoshaphat (II Chron xvii 14–19), was taken to discover the available manpower (see Junge, *Der Wiederaufbau . . . ,* pp. 41–42). Amaziah also enlisted a hundred thousand men from Israel to achieve the required strength. These men were free lances, enlisted privately from the border territory. In addition to the stipend given them by Amaziah, they were to share in the booty; when they were sent home on the advice of the prophet, they made up their loss by raiding Judean communities while the king and his army were in Edom (vs. 13).

One of the religious interests of the Chronicler is evident in his explanation of why the recruits from Israel were refused permission to assist in the campaign—because Yahweh was not with Israel, or any Ephraimite. To go through with Amaziah's original plan would therefore have meant defeat. Moreover, Yahweh was not

dependent upon numbers to achieve victory (cf. xiii 3–18). Thus
with prophetic assurance the campaign was undertaken and proved
successful. A large number of Edomites were slain—the numbers
here, as elsewhere in Chronicles, are greatly exaggerated—and an
equal number were thrown down from the Rock. As indicated in
the NOTE on vs. 12, this was probably Sela' in Petra itself. It was
accessible only by a very difficult trail (AASOR 15 [1935], 82;
the best description of the acropolis is that of W. H. Morton, BA 19
[1956], 27–28, and for a view see Grollenberg, *Atlas of the Bible*,
p. 111, Fig. 311). The success of the campaign was doubtless
Amaziah's reward for giving heed to the word of the prophet.

Of equal theological significance for the writer was the sequel to
the Edomite campaign, vss. 14–16. Amaziah acted like one of the
great oriental kings who frequently transported the gods of conquered people to their capitals for various reasons. But nowhere else
is a Hebrew king reported to have done so. Of course, the Chronicler's attempt to find a reason for Amaziah's defeat at the hands of
Joash of Israel provides the occasion for the story. Again a prophet
intervenes with the reminder of the impotence of the gods of Edom,
as the king's victory had just demonstrated. The silencing of the
prophet by the authorities led him to retort "God has resolved to
destroy you"; and for two reasons, (a) because he harbored and
paid homage to the gods of Edom and (b) because he rejected the
advice of the prophet.

[War with Joash of Israel, 17–28]: The Chronicler's account of
the war between Amaziah and Joash follows the parallel in II Kings
xiv 8–20 with only minor deviations. The boldness of the former was
inspired by his success in the campaign against Edom. In replying
to the presumptuous message of Amaziah, Joash reacted firmly,
though gentlemanly. But Amaziah was not to be deflected from his
purpose because, as the writer adds, "it was an act of God" to bring
punishment upon him for his invocation of the gods of Edom (vs.
20). The result was just as the prophet had predicted (vs. 16):
Amaziah was defeated, his army put to flight, the king humiliated
before his people in his own capital, the house of God and the
treasuries of the king stripped, hostages taken, and a portion of the
walls of the city broken down. Amaziah may have been personally
so shaken as to be ineffective as ruler. In any case, a conspiracy was
raised against him after some years and he fled to Lachish, where he

was slain. The Chronicler's observation that the conspiracy took place after his religious defection may refer only to the opposition of the religious authorities such as the prophet referred to in vss. 15–16, which was ultimately to issue in a full-blown rebellion.

28. THE REIGN OF UZZIAH (ca. 783–742 B.C.)
(xxvi 1–23)†

General observations

XXVI 1 Then all the people of Judah took Uzziah, who was sixteen years old, and made him king in the place of his father Amaziah. 2 He [re]built Eloth and restored it to Judah after the king slept with his fathers. 3 Uzziah was sixteen years old when he became king and reigned for fifty-two years at Jerusalem. His mother's name was Jecoliah from Jerusalem. 4 He did what was right in the sight of Yahweh, just as Amaziah his father had done. 5 He inquired of God so long as Zechariah, who instructed him *in the fear of God,*ª lived, and so long as he inquired of Yahweh, God gave him success.

Campaigns

6 He went out and fought with the Philistines, breaking down the wall of Gath, the wall of Jabneh, and the wall of Ashdod. He also built cities [in the region of] Ashdod and in [the other territory of] the Philistines. 7 God assisted him against the Philistines, the Arabs who lived at Gur-baal, and the Meunites. 8 The Meunitesᵇ paid tribute to Uzziah and his fame extended as far as Egypt, for he grew increasingly stronger.

Internal developments

9 Uzziah erected towers in Jerusalem, at the corner gate, at the valley gate, and at the corner and fortified them. 10 He also erected towers in the wilderness and carved out many cisterns

† **II Chron xxvi 1–5** ‖ II Kings xiv 21–xv 4; **16–23** ‖ II Kings xv 5–7.

ª–ª So with LXX and a number of Hebrew manuscripts. MT "in seeing God."
ᵇ So for MT "Ammonites," with LXX.

because he had many cattle both in the Shephelah and in the plains, and farmers and vinedressers in the mountains and the fertile areas, for he loved the land. 11 Moreover Uzziah had an army ready for military service organized in companies according to the number of their complement by Jeiel the scribe and Maaseiah the officer and under the direction of Hananiah, one of the king's captains. 12 The entire register of family heads of the mighty men numbered twenty-six hundred. 13 Under them was an army of three hundred and seven thousand, five hundred men ready for war, a powerful enough force to support the king against the enemy. 14 Uzziah provided shields, spears, helmets, armor, bows, and slingstones for the entire army. 15 He also set up skillfully contrived devices on the towers and corners of Jerusalem [from which] to shoot arrows and [hurl] large stones. Hence his fame spread far and wide for he was miraculously assisted until he became strong.

Pride and downfall of Uzziah

16 But when he was strong, his arrogance was so great that it led to his downfall; he was disobedient toward Yahweh his God when he entered the temple of Yahweh to burn incense upon the incense altar. 17 Azariah the priest accompanied by eighty valiant priests of Yahweh went in after him; 18 They confronted Uzziah the king and said to him, "It is not permissible for you, Uzziah, to burn incense to Yahweh; only the Aaronite priests consecrated for the purpose may burn incense. Leave the sanctuary, for you have disobeyed and will have no honor from Yahweh God." 19 But Uzziah, who already had a censer in his hand to burn incense, became so angry that in the altercation with the priests a lesion broke out on the skin of his forehead before the priests in the house of Yahweh near the incense altar. 20 So when Azariah the chief priest and all the priests turned toward him, behold leprosy was on his forehead and they hurried him out of there; and he also was anxious to get out because Yahweh had afflicted him. 21 Uzziah the king was thus a leper to the day of his death and lived in house

of quarantine as a leper because he was excluded from the house of Yahweh. Jotham his son, who was in charge of the royal palace governed the people of the land. 22 The remainder of the history of Uzziah, from beginning to end, Isaiah the prophet, the son of Amoz has written down. 23 So Uzziah slept with his fathers and they buried him with his fathers in the field [beside] the cemetery of the kings because they said, "he is a leper." Then Jotham his son became king in his place.

NOTES

xxvi 1. *Uzziah*. Frequently referred to as "Azariah," which was apparently the personal name, "Uzziah" the throne name. (Cf. A. M. Honeyman, JBL 67 [1948], 20–22.) May have been avoided by the Chronicler because of the name of the high priest (vss. 17, 20).

sixteen years old. Cf. Albright, BASOR 100 (December 1945), 21. But see also H. Tadmor, *Scripta Hierosolymitana*, VIII: *Studies in the Bible*, 1961, p. 232, n. 1.

2. *Eloth*. The seaport constructed by Solomon at the head of the Gulf of Aqaba (viii 17, 18; I Kings ix 26–28), which Uzziah reactivated.

3. *reigned . . . Jerusalem*. See second NOTE on vs. 1.

5. *inquired of God*. A technical term meaning "to seek an oracle" or "to worship."

6. *Gath*. One of the Philistine cities, some twenty-five miles southwest of Jerusalem though it could have been Gittaim, a few miles north of Gezer. Cf. B. Mazar, "Gath and Gittaim," IEJ 4 (1954), 227–35, especially p. 231. But Gath was destroyed before the time of Amos (i 6–8, vi 2), possibly by Uzziah as indicated here. On the location, see S. Bülow and R. A. Mitchell, "An Iron Age II Fortress on Tell Nagila," IEJ 11 (1961), 101–10.

Jabneh. A city on the border of Judah (Josh xv 11), approximately 30 miles west of Jerusalem, later Jamnia (I Maccabees iv 15), present-day Yebna.

Ashdod. Near the coast twelve miles north of Gath.

7. *Gur-baal*. Unknown. "Gerar" may be meant. The consonantal text would then have been *bgrr (w) 'l hm'wnym* "at Gerar (and) against the Meunites." But see A. Alt, JPOS 12 (1932), 135, n. 4, and Abel, *Géographie de la Palestine*, II, p. 340.

Meunites. See COMMENT on Sec. 22, xx 1–30.

9. *the corner gate . . . the valley gate . . . the corner*. For the loca-

tion of these points, see references listed in the second NOTE on xxv 23, Sec. 27, and especially the topographical map in Avi-yonah, *Sepher Yerushalayim*, I, opposite p. 160.

10. *farmers*. For an interpretation of the term see BASOR 167 (October 1962), 34.

12. *twenty-six hundred*. A slightly different pointing of *'lpm* as *'allūpīm* ("chiefs") would mean there were six hundred chiefs.

13. This figure, 307,500 men, looks like the sort that G. E. Mendenhall (JBL 77 [1958], 52–66) has successfully resolved. The 300 units (*'ᵃlāpīm*) consist of 7500 men, which would be a rather large army, though not impossible. The preceding verse (see NOTE) would indicate that there were 600 chiefs for the 7500 men in 300 units. The distribution does not quite fit the usual Israelite groupings of 10s, 50s, 100s, 1000s. But the general scope of the numbers is reasonable for the official standing army, including those on active duty and the ready reserves.

14. *helmets*. For a discussion of the term see E. A. Speiser, JAOS 70 (1950), 47–49.

15. *skillfully contrived devices*. On the defensive character of these devices, see Y. Sukenik, "Engines Invented by Cunning Men," BJPES 13 (1946/47), 19–24. Catapulting devices were unknown then; the defenses of Lachish illustrate the nature of the constructions of Uzziah (ANEP, pp. 130–31). They were thus protective or shielding devices from which the defenders could shoot arrows and hurl stones at the attackers. For the possibility of the Assyrians having catapults, see B. Meissner, *Babylonien und Assyrien*, I, 1920, p. 110; Galling, BRL, col. 95; E. Unger, "Belagerungsmaschinen," *Reallexikon der Assyriologie*, I, pp. 471 f.

18. *only . . . incense*. For the priestly regulations see Exod xxx 7–10; Num xviii 1–7. Cf. M. Haran, "The Uses of Incense in the Ancient Israelite Ritual," VT 10 (1960), 113–29.

20. *the chief priest*. Note the use of *kōhēn hā-rō's* here for the more widely used *hak-kōhēn* in vs. 17. See COMMENT on Sec. 21, xix 4–11.

leprosy. In the biblical sense a generic term under which were included all kinds of skin ailments. Only one group of these would correspond to modern leprosy. Actually, we don't know what Uzziah had but it must have been a loathsome disease. Unless it had happened under extraordinary circumstances, or was especially disabling, it is hard to see why he withdrew from active service. Naaman, who had a similar disease, apparently continued as commander in chief. Uzziah must have retired for cultic reasons (Jotham took over official duties while Uzziah apparently continued in charge of foreign policy) or else he must have been very ill indeed.

21. *house of quarantine. Bēt haḥopšīt.* Term occurs in Ugaritic texts as *btḥptt* "the house of pollution." Cf. Gray, *The Legacy of Canaan*, p. 46, n. 1.

who . . . palace. For significance of the phrase see H. J. Katzenstein, IEJ 10 (1960), 149–54, especially p. 152.

COMMENT

[Summary observations on the reign of Uzziah, xxvi 1–5]: With a few variations due to the special interests of the writer, this summation corresponds with the Deuteronomic account in II Kings xiv 21–xv 4. The chief differences are: (a) the Chronicler's omission of the reference to Uzziah's failure to remove the high places (II Kings xv 4) and (b) his statement that the king sought the Lord so long as his religious mentor lived (cf. the situation of Joash [xxiv 2, 17–22]). In line with his theology, he notes that so long as Uzziah "inquired of Yahweh" he was successful. At the same time, he prepares for the subsequent story of the king's downfall. One of Uzziah's significant contributions was the reconquest of Ezion-geber (Elath), lost to Judah in the reign of Jehoram (xxi 8–10) and the reconstruction of the city. The excavations of Nelson Glueck reflect three periods in the history of Ezion-geber before the Judean exile. The first period was that covering the activity of Solomon, the second that of Jehoshaphat, and the third that of Uzziah (BA 3 [1940], 54). The third period belongs to the eighth century B.C. (BASOR 79 [October 1940], 12 f.). The city remained in the hands of the kings of Judah until ca. 735 when it was retaken by the Edomites. The famous seal of Jotham (BASOR 79 [October 1940], 13 ff., Figs. 8, 9, and note by Albright, p. 15), which was used in official transactions, indicates that Ezion-geber was an important center in the time of Uzziah and Jotham.

[Conquests, 6–8]: The writer, relying upon another source of information, refers to significant conquests of Uzziah directed against the Philistines and the Arabs residing on the southwestern borders of Judah. For pertinent remarks on the conquests of Azariah, notably that of the Philistine cities, see G. Rinaldi, "Quelques remarques sur la politique d'Azarias (Ozias) de Juda en Philistie (2 Chron. 26:6 ss)," in SVT: *Congress Volume* (Bonn, 1962), pp.

225–35. Following the conquests, Uzziah lost no time in strengthening his hold upon the territory in question. He constructed cities (probably fortresses) in the conquered territory. The fortress at Tell Mor near Ashdod may have been the work of Uzziah (cf. IEJ 9 [1959], 271 f.; 10 [1960], 124; RB 67 [1960], 397). Tadmor argues strongly for an expansionist movement under Uzziah after the death of Jeroboam II (see *Scripta Hierosolymitana*, VIII, pp. 232–71). Since there was no possibility of extending his rule northward, where Jeroboam II was in undisputed control, he could only move toward the west and south. It was noted above that Uzziah turned his attention to Elath; he also moved westward from there (see COMMENT on Sec. 16, xiv 8–14) and subdued the Meunites associated with Edom and the Arabs around Gerar both of whom doubtless had taken advantage of the unsettled conditions in Judah prevailing since the time of Ahaziah.

[Internal developments, 9–15]: Archaeological explorations confirm the building and agricultural activity here attributed to Uzziah. It was a period of progress in many directions. Apart from the fortifications of Jerusalem, there is additional clear evidence of the hand of the great king, as our author maintains (vs. 10). For example, the *migdal* (tower) IIIB at Gibeah may date from this period (AASOR 4 [1924], 52 f.); so may the prosperous stratum at Tell Abu Selimeh (C. C. McCown, *The Ladder of Progress in Palestine*, 1943, p. 131). Father de Vaux also points out the evidences for early buildings and cisterns at Qumran and Ain Feshkha in the time of Uzziah (RB 63 [1956], 535–38, 575; note especially the cistern at Qumran). There are evidences of activity in this period also in the Nahal Seelim area—at Hasron and two locations above the north branch of Nahal Hardof (see IEJ 11 [1961], 15–16). But perhaps the most striking confirmation of the Chronicler's report is found in the recent discoveries in the Negeb of Judah around Beersheba, where fortifications, cisterns, farms, etc., have been located, as for instance, at Khirbet al-Gharra and Hurvat Uzzah (cf. IEJ 8 [1958], 33–38; Glueck, *Rivers in the Desert*, pp. 174–79) and other sites in the vicinity. See also the article by R. L. Schiffer, "The Farms of King Uzziah," *The Reporter*, September 1, 1960, pp. 34–38, which describes the excavation of a farmhouse in the Negeb, dated by Aharoni and Evenari in Iron Age II (ninth-eighth centuries B.C.); also nearby were cisterns and well-developed drainage channels. This is an excellent illustration of the Chronicler's remark that Uzziah loved agriculture (the land). The importance of Uzziah in his time may be seen from the fact that important persons identified themselves as his servants (cf. seals of Abiyau servant of Uzziah and Shebanyau servant of Uzziah [D. Diringer, *Le iscrizioni antico-ebraiche Palestinesi*, 1934, pp. 221 f., 223 f.; M. Lidzbarski, *Altsemitische Texte*, 1907, pp. 10 f.] and also the Uzziah or Azariah seal found in a cistern at Tell Beit Mirsim [AASOR 21–22 (1943), 63 f., 73]).

The conquests of Uzziah naturally demanded a strong, well-organized army under the leadership of a single head. Apparently each company had some 116+ men, though the numbers themselves are probably exaggerated; the ratio of officers to men is doubtless fairly accurate. It is interesting to note that no longer did the soldiers supply their own arms but were armed by the king. The latest equipment was evidently kept in the local fortress ready for immediate use in case of attack. The respect in which Uzziah's army was held is indicated by the part it took in a coalition against Assyria in the time of Tilgath-pilneser III (see ANET, p. 282. For a discussion of the reference see Thiele, *The Mysterious Numbers of the Hebrew Kings*, pp. 78–98; Albright, BASOR 100 [December 1945], 18, n. 8, and JBL 71 [1952], 251). The great strength and prosperity of Uzziah was attributed by the Chronicler to Yahweh, because he did right in his sight.

[The downfall of Uzziah, 16–23]: Too much prosperity was Uzziah's undoing, according to the Chronicler, because it made him proud and led him to overstep his bounds as a layman. (Note the use of the unqualified "Uzziah" by Azariah the priest in addressing the king in vs. 18.) The misfortune that befell the king—his leprosy and consequent isolation—was due directly to a violation of the priestly prerogatives set up by the P code (on the sin of Uzziah, see J. Morgenstern, HUCA 21–22 [1937–38], 1 ff.; for later speculation on its effect see Josephus *Antiquities* IX.x). The Deuteronomist (II Kings xv 5) speaks of Yahweh's afflicting Uzziah with leprosy but naturally does not go into the reason for it. It was earlier recognized as legitimate for the king to officiate at the altar (cf. David and Solomon); nor was Ahaz condemned by him for offering sacrifice upon his new altar (II Kings xvi 12–13). Nevertheless, the Chronicler credits the king with speedy recognition of his situation and co-operation with the priests in getting away from the house of Yahweh. Jotham then assumed control of affairs as regent for his father, who was living in quarantine. How long the coregency lasted is not certain; Albright (BASOR 100 [December 1945]) thinks it was about eight years, from 750–742 B.C.

The final observations by the writer, that his source also contained the record of Isaiah, who was a younger contemporary of the king, and that he was interred in the field beside the cemetery of the kings, are doubtless based on factual materials. Both Amos (i 1) and Zechariah (xiv 5) refer to the earthquake in the reign of Uzziah. Isaiah (vi 1) received his call the year Uzziah died. The Uzziah tomb inscription from the first century B.C. appears to confirm the burial of the king outside the royal burial ground (cf. Galling, BRL, col. 405).

29. THE REIGN OF JOTHAM (ca. 750–735 B.C.)
(xxvii 1–9)†

XXVII 1 Jotham was twenty-five years old when he became king and reigned sixteen years at Jerusalem. His mother's name was Jerushah the daughter of Zadok. 2 He did what was right in the sight of Yahweh just as Uzziah his father had done, only he did not come to the temple of Yahweh. But the people continued to do wrong. 3 He built the upper gate of the house of Yahweh and greatly extended the wall of the Ophel. 4 He also built cities in the highland of Judah and in the wooded areas he constructed fortified places and towers. 5 He fought against the king of the Ammonites and prevailed over them so that the Ammonites gave him a hundred talents of silver, ten thousand kors of wheat, and ten thousand kors of barley that year. This amount the Ammonites delivered to him the second and third years. 6 Jotham became strong because he continued unflinchingly in his ways before Yahweh his God. 7 The remainder of the history of Jotham, together with all his wars and exploits, behold they are recorded in the chronicle of the kings of Israel and Judah. 8 He was twenty-five years old when he became king and reigned for sixteen years at Jerusalem. 9 Then Jotham slept with his fathers and they buried him in the city of David while Ahaz his son became king in his place.

† II Chron xxvii 1–9 ‖ II Kings xv 32–38.

NOTES

xxvii 3. *the upper gate.* Located at the north entrance to the temple enclosure (see Avi-yonah, *Sepher Yerushalayim,* I, map opposite p. 160).
the Ophel. For the location of Ophel see map *ibid.* and sketches of other views on p. 160.
5. *a hundred talents of silver.* About 3¼ tons.
ten thousand kors of wheat. About sixty-five thousand bushels.

COMMENT

[General observations, xxvii 1–2]: As might be expected, Jotham continued the attitude and policies of his father, for which he received the commendation of the writer. The discovery of the seal of Jotham at Ezion-geber reflects the continuity of administrative activity at the Aqabah seaport (BASOR 79 [October 1940], 13 ff.; BASOR 163 [October 1961], 18–22). Yadin thinks it was a signet ring used by Jotham, not as king but as minister, since the bellows on it indicates "a limited and specific authority" rather than that of a sovereign. Jotham's only caveat, if it be such, was that he did not enter the temple of Yahweh. For what reason we do not know. This remark may actually be an expression of approval on the part of the Chronicler indicating that Joham observed his status as a layman and did not violate the sacred precincts as his father had done. However, the introductory word in Hebrew (*raq*) appears to indicate an exception (cf. II Kings xv 35). If that is the case, some other reason must have dictated the action of the king in this respect. We can only guess at what it may have been. Cf. remarks by Cazelles, p. 202, n. d. The writer summarizes the observation of the Deuteronomist (II Kings xv 35ab) by saying that the people continued to do wrong.

[Building activity, 3–4]: Nothing is said of Uzziah's local building activity in Jerusalem, except in connection with the defense devices made for the towers and corners of the city (xxvi 15). That Uzziah made the necessary repairs after the fiasco of Amaziah may be taken for granted. Jotham built the upper gate of the house of Yahweh and extended the walls of Ophel. His efforts to continue the progressive program of his father did not stop there; he constructed cities in the highlands of Judah probably as lines of defense to fall back upon in case of invasion. He erected towers and fortifications in the wooded areas; hidden in this word may be another of Uzziah's activities, that is, a program of reforestation (cf. Akk. *ḫarāšu* "to plant trees"). Jotham had learned much from his experience as coregent.

[Campaign against the Ammonites, 5–6]: Verses 3b–6 were taken from a source other than Kings where there is no mention of the achievements involved. But, as in the case of Uzziah's progressive undertakings, there is no reason to doubt the substantial accuracy of these reports. It has been affirmed that there could have been no war between Judah and Ammon since their borders were not contiguous at the time. But Israel was rapidly losing prestige and power after the death of Jeroboam II, in the wake of which the border peoples spilled over, as they always did, into the territory where the power vacuum existed. Moreover the Syro-Ephraimitic wars, which would have offered ample opportunity for Ammonite expansion, may already have been in progress. It was doubtless such a movement that brought Jotham into conflict with them (cf. Noth, ÜS, p. 142, n. 2). The enormous amount of tribute is probably an exaggeration. The king's success is attributed to his loyalty to the ways of Yahweh.

[Obituary, 7–9]: Verse 8 repeats the first half of vs. 1. The other two verses (7, 9) refer to the achievements of Jotham, the annals where they are recorded, the death and burial of the king, and the succession to the throne of his son Ahaz.

30. THE REIGN OF AHAZ (735–715 B.C.)
(xxviii 1–27)†

Character of Ahaz

XXVIII ¹ Ahaz was twenty years old when he became king and reigned sixteen years at Jerusalem. He did not do what was right in the sight of Yahweh as David his father had done. ² He followed the ways of the kings of Israel and even made molten images for Baal. ³ He burned incense in the valley of Ben-hinnom and burned his sons in the fire in accordance with the abominations of the nations whom Yahweh expelled before the Israelites, ⁴ and he sacrificed and burned incense on the high places, on the hills, and under every green tree.

Syro-Ephraimitic war

⁵ So Yahweh his God delivered him into the hand of the king of Aram; they defeated him and took a large number of them as captives whom they brought to Damascus. He also delivered him into the hand of the king of Israel who inflicted a great slaughter upon him. ⁶ Pekah the son of Remaliah killed one hundred and twenty thousand in Judah in a single day, all of them prominent men, because they abandoned Yahweh God of their fathers. ⁷ Zichri, an Ephraimite hero, slew Maaseiah the king's son, Azrikam the chief of the house, and Elkanah the second to the king. ⁸ The Israelites took captive two hundred thousand women, sons, and daughters of their brothers; they also took from them a large quantity of booty which they carried to Samaria.

† **II Chron xxviii 1–4** ‖ II Kings xvi 1–4; **5–8** ‖ II Kings xvi 5; **16–21** ‖ II Kings xvi 7–9.

Prophecy of Oded

9 Now there was at that place a prophet of Yahweh by the name of Oded who appeared before the army when it entered Samaria and said to them, "Behold, because Yahweh God of your fathers was angry with Judah, he delivered them into your hand, but you slew them in a rage that reaches to heaven, 10 and now you plan to subjugate the Judeans and Jerusalemites as your male and female slaves—have you not yourselves committed sins against Yahweh your God? 11 Listen to me now and return the captives you took from your brothers, otherwise the violent wrath of God will fall upon you." 12 Then some of the chiefs of the Ephraimites—Azariah the son of Jehohanan, Berechiah the son of Meshillemoth, Jehizkiah the son of Shallum, and Amasa the son of Hadlai—rose up against those of the army who had returned 13 and said to them, "You must not bring the captives here, for we have already sinned against Yahweh and you propose to multiply our sin and our guilt although our guilt is now sufficient to bring violent wrath upon Israel." 14 So the soldiers left the captives and the booty before the captains and the whole congregation. 15 Then the men who were designated by name took the captives and clothed all the naked with the booty; they clothed them, put sandals on them, fed them, gave them drink, poured oil upon them, transported on donkeys all the weak and brought them to Jericho, the city of palms, to their brothers; then they returned to Samaria.

Appeal of Ahaz to Assyria

16 At that time King Ahaz had sent to the king of Assyria for assistance for himself 17 because the Edomites had come again, beaten Judah and taken captives; 18 at the same time the Philistines raided the cities of the Shephelah and the Negeb of Judah, captured Beth-shemesh, Aijalon, Gederoth, Soco, and its dependencies, Timnah and its dependencies, and Gimzo and its dependencies, and settled down there. 19 For Yahweh

had humbled Judah because of Ahaz the king of Israel[a] who
had exercised no restraint in Judah and greatly wronged
Yahweh. 20 But Tilgath-pilneser the king of Assyria came up
against him and oppressed him; he did not support him. 21 Although Ahaz robbed the house of Yahweh, the house of the king
and the captains and gave [the proceeds] to the king of Assyria,
he received no support from him.

Apostasy and death of Ahaz

22 Thus at the very time he was oppressed, he continued to
wrong Yahweh; that was King Ahaz! 23 He offered sacrifice to
the gods of Damascus who had beaten him for he thought,
"Because the gods of the kings of Aram supported them I will
offer sacrifice to them, perhaps they will help me too." But
they served only to ruin him and all Israel. 24 Then Ahaz collected all the equipment of the house of God, cut up in frag-
ments the equipment of the house of God, sealed up the doors
of the house of Yahweh and made altars for himself in every
corner of Jerusalem. 25 In every city of Judah he made high
places to burn incense to other gods and thus provoked to anger
Yahweh God of his fathers. 26 The remainder of his history and
all his acts, from beginning to end, behold they are recorded in
the chronicle of the kings of Judah and Israel. 27 When Ahaz
slept with his fathers, they buried him in the city of Jerusalem
but they did not bring him to the cemetery of the kings of
Israel. Hezekiah[b] his son became king in his place.

[a] Some manuscripts and Vrs. read "Judah," obviously a correction. May be
due to source or a tendentious reference to Ahaz, who acted like a king of
Israel, depending on man rather than on God.
[b] Hebrew reads "Jehizkiah," but context indicates that "Hezekiah" is meant.

Notes

xxviii 2. *Baal.* Cf. second Note on xvii 3, Sec. 19.

3. *the valley of Ben-hinnom.* On the south side of Jerusalem, joining
the Kidron Valley at the southeast corner of the city. In Jeremiah's
day there was a *tōpet* there (vii 31–32) where children were sacrificed

(cf. II Kings xxiii 10). Later the *gē-ben-hinnōm* "valley of the son of
Hinnom" was corrupted to *gē-hinnōm* "Gehenna."

abominations . . . expelled. The spelling of these words is significant.
Neither of them indicate the contracted diphthong (aw>ô) by the *waw.*
Here we have *kt'bwt,* "abominations" for *ktw'bwt* and *hryš,* "expelled"
for *hwryš.* The Chronicler normally has very full spelling; here he may
have copied directly from an early (Northern?) source. The Kings parallel supplies the *waw* in *hwryš,* in accordance with typical Judahite or-
thography, while preserving the defective spelling in the other word.

7. *second to the king.* Phrase occurs only here and Esther x 3.

15. *the men . . . designated by name.* Not those named in vs. 12 (since
four would hardly have been sufficient for the task) but men appointed
by the assembly to act for it.

16. *At that time.* Refers to the events related in vs. 5.

18. *the cities . . . Gimzo and its dependencies.* All cities to the west
of Jerusalem, on the border of the hill country; Gimzo was in the
territory of Israel.

20. *Tilgath-pilneser.* Tiglath-pileser III (ca. 744–727 B.C.).

24. *the equipment.* Includes furnishings of all kinds—vessels, utensils,
tools, etc.

27. *the cemetery . . . Israel.* Kings of Judah, since no monarchs of
the Northern Kingdom were buried in Jerusalem. This is probably another of the writer's predilections for the Davidic line as the legitimate
one in "Israel." But see Rudolph, p. 293. Ahaz, because of his apostasy,
was unworthy to occupy a place in the cemetery of the ancestors.

COMMENT

[Characterization of Ahaz, xxviii 1–4]: The name of Ahaz is surrounded by infamy as may be seen from this evaluation but even
more clearly from the references to him by Isaiah (Isa vii). It is
striking that the name of his mother is not given. The Chronicler
has taken his cue from the Kings story with a few additions, some
of which may have been drawn from Isaiah; for example, the
reference to images (cf. Isa ii 8–13, 20) and the illicit worship in
the valley of Hinnom which may be simply a conjecture based on
the following statement regarding the sacrifice by Ahaz of his sons
but which was severely condemned by the prophets (Mic vi 7; Jer vii
31). The worst epithet that could be applied to a king of Judah,

from the viewpoint of both the Deuteronomist and the Chronicler, was that "he followed the ways of the kings of Israel."

The name of Ahaz occurs on a seal in the Newell collection. The inscription reads: *l'šn' 'bd 'hz* "to Ušna the servant of Ahaz" (cf. BASOR 79 [October 1940], 27 f.; BASOR 82 [April 1941], 16 f.; BASOR 84 [December 1941], 17).

[The Syro-Ephraimitic war, 5–8]: The background for this story is II Kings xv 37, xvi 5; Isa vii; Hos v 8–vi 6 (see article by Alt, KS, II, pp. 163–87). The Chronicler was probably drawing upon a different source than Kings from which he derived his assessment of the character of Ahaz (Rudolph, p. 289, suggests that the source used by the writer contained separate accounts of the loss inflicted upon Judah by each member of the coalition). His objective must be kept in mind: it was to set forth the divine judgment upon the defection of Ahaz. Only vs. 5 reveals the true situation: that the invasion of Judah was due to the alliance between Pekah and Rezin, who were jointly responsible for it. According to II Kings xvi 5, Judah was invaded and Jerusalem attacked but without success. However, it is not stated here that Jerusalem was breached or even attacked; only the loss sustained at the hands of Israel is recounted, possibly as an introduction to the episode centering about the prophecy of Oded. The figures are grossly exaggerated, but that there was something to the invasion can hardly be doubted as the names of the important persons slain indicate. While nothing is known of these persons beyond what is said here, the names are common in postexilic times, though Elkanah and Maaseiah and possibly Zichri occur earlier.

[The prophecy of Oded, 9–15]: Injected into the account of Ahaz's troubles with Ephraim-Syria and the ensuing revolts all around is the sequel to the story of Judah's defeat at the hands of Israel. This is, in many respects, a remarkable passage whose essentials the writer found in his sources, because it runs counter to his otherwise strong emphasis on the separation of the two kingdoms, only one of which was legitimate. The prophet Oded is mentioned nowhere else but, like Elijah and Hosea, he was a Northerner. He does not question the execution of judgment upon Judah by Israel— it was the doing of Yahweh—but sternly rebukes Israel for venting its own wrath upon brethren. Israel was simply the instrument in the hands of Yahweh. Of special import is the Chronicler's allowing the word "brothers" to stand. They had gone too far. The Ephraimite chiefs were impressed by the prophet and appealed to the army to relent. The reaction of these men from Ephraim (vs. 15) illustrates the effectiveness of prophecy and the working of the mercy of Yahweh, even in judgment.

[Appeal to Assyria, 16–21]: The Syro-Ephraimite invasion was fraught with dire consequences for Judah. Despite the advice of Isaiah (see Isa vii), Ahaz appealed to Assyria for help—to man rather than to God. How serious the situation was is clear from vss. 17–18. According to II Kings xvi 6, Elath was taken from Judah never to be regained; the Philistines reclaimed what had been lost to them by the movements of Uzziah and even spilled over into the Negeb. It now appears that Ahaz's appeal for help was against Edom and Philistia rather than against Aram and Israel (cf. J. Gray, "The Period and Office of the Prophet Isaiah in the Light of a New Assyrian Tablet," *The Expository Times*, vol. 63, June 1952, pp. 263–65; and D. J. Wiseman, *Iraq* 13 [1951], 21–24). The new tablet records Tiglath-pileser's campaign against Philistia in the course of which his victory stele was set up at *Naḫalmuṣir*, the river of Egypt; and an Assyrian province (Du'ru) might also have been established at that time. Cf. Alt, "Tiglathpilesers III. erster Feldzug nach Palästina," KS, II, pp. 150–62. A Nimrud letter reflects this unrest in Palestine at the time (H. W. F. Saggs, *Iraq* 17 [1955], 131 f., 149–53) and indicates that the Chronicler utilized other sources besides Kings. In any case, Tiglath-pileser did come to the west and overran the Philistine territory as shown by the Nimrud fragment. But, as the Chronicler says, "He did not support him," for later in his reign the Assyrian king records tribute received from Ahaz (ANET, p. 282, where the full name of the Judean king appears *ia-u-ḫa-zi ia-u-da-a-a* "Jehoahaz of Judah"), just as from the Philistine states, Edom, Ammon and Moab. What the writer means is that though the rebellions were put down, the states involved were not returned to Judah but organized into Assyrian provinces. The tribute referred to in the inscriptions was in all probability ransom money. The resources of Judah were depleted to no avail. All this was due to the wrongdoing of Ahaz (vs. 19), according to our author, and not to the conspiracy of world politics at the time.

[Apostasy and death of Ahaz, 22–27]: The political situation forced upon Ahaz recognition of Assyrian hegemony in religious matters also, though he may not have been too reluctant in so doing. To judge from the complaints of Isaiah (vii–ix), the Chronicler may not be too far wrong in his assessment of the king's religious activities. The Kings narrative speaks only of an altar pattern imported from Damascus; this importation becomes for our author a worship of the gods of Aram because of their apparent superiority over the God of Israel. The removal of the furniture of the temple that was offensive to the king of Assyria (II Kings xvi 18) has been reinterpreted, probably under the influence of its destruction by the Babylonians, into a wholesale iconoclasm and padlocking of the temple itself. Thus Ahaz was guilty of apostatizing to the Baal of Israel and now to the gods of Aram. The whole land was made into a hotbed of foreign cultic practices. While he did not meet a violent death as punishment for his defection, he was, according to the Chronicler, buried outside the cemetery of the kings (cf., however, II Kings xvi 20).

31. THE REIGN OF HEZEKIAH (ca. 715–687 B.C.): REHABILITATION OF THE TEMPLE
(xxix 1–36)†

Introductory observations

XXIX 1 Hezekiah[a] became king when he was twenty-five years old and remained king at Jerusalem for twenty-nine years. The name of his mother was Abijah[b] the daughter of Zechariah. 2 He did what was right in the sight of Yahweh just as David his father had done.

Cleansing of the temple

3 In the first month of the first year of his reign he opened the doors of the house of Yahweh, having repaired them. 4 He brought the priests and the Levites together on the east plaza 5 and said to them, "Listen to me, O Levites: now consecrate yourselves and consecrate the house of Yahweh God of your fathers and remove the impurities from the sanctuary. 6 For our fathers were untrue and did evil in the sight of Yahweh our God, since they abandoned him, turned their faces away from the dwelling place of Yahweh and turned their back [on him]. 7 They even closed the doors of the portico, extinguished the lamps, failed to burn incense and offer burnt offerings in the sanctuary to the God of Israel. 8 Therefore the wrath of Yahweh fell upon Judah and Jerusalem and he made them a terror, a horror, and a mockery as you can see with your own eyes. 9 Behold, our fathers fell by the sword and our sons, our daughters, and our wives were taken captives because of it. 10 Now I firmly intend to make a covenant with Yahweh God of Israel that his violent anger may turn away from us. 11 My sons, now do not

† II **Chron xxix 1–2:** cf. II Kings xviii 1–3.

[a] Hebrew reads "Jehizkiah," but context indicates that "Hezekiah" is meant.
[b] II Kings xviii 1 "Abi." LXX "Abba" here and "Abou" in II Kings.

be remiss, for Yahweh has chosen you to stand before him in order to serve him as his ministers and incense burners." 12 Then the Levites arose—Mahath the son of Amasai and Joel the son of Azariah, from the Kehathites; Kish the son of Abdi and Azariah the son of Jehallelel, from the Merarites; Joah the son of Zimmah and Eden the son of Joah, from the Gershunnites; 13 Shimri and Jeuel, of the sons of Elizaphan; Zechariah and Mattaniah, of the sons of Asaph; 14 Jehiel and Shimei, of the sons of Heman; Shemaiah and Uzziel, of the sons of Jeduthun —15 and assembled their brothers and consecrated themselves and came to cleanse the house of Yahweh in accordance with the command of the king in harmony with the words of Yahweh. 16 So the priests entered the innermost part of the house of Yahweh to cleanse it and brought out all the unclean things they found in the temple of Yahweh to the court of the house of Yahweh where the Levites received it to remove it outside to the Kidron Valley. 17 They began the consecration on the first day of the first month and by the eighth day of the month they had reached the portico of Yahweh, so that in eight days they had consecrated the house of Yahweh and by the sixteenth day of the first month they had finished [the work].

Rededication of the temple

18 Then they went in to Hezekiah the king and said, "We have cleansed the whole house of Yahweh together with the altar of burnt offering with all its vessels and the table of layer bread with all its vessels. 19 We have also prepared and consecrated all the vessels which King Ahaz during his reign had removed in his defection. Behold they are before the altar of Yahweh." 20 So Hezekiah*a* the king went to work and assembled the chiefs of the city and went up to the house of Yahweh. 21 They brought seven bulls, seven rams, seven lambs, and seven he-goats as a sin offering for *e*the royal house,*e* for the

c–c So with Rudolph, p. 296, since Judah is mentioned later. MT reads *h-mmlkh* (usually meaning "kingdom"), which here means the royal family. Cf. Phoen., *mmlkt.*

sanctuary, and for Judah, and he told the Aaronite priests to offer them on the altar of Yahweh. 22 So they slaughtered the bulls and the priests took the blood and sprinkled it toward the altar; they slaughtered the rams and sprinkled the blood toward the altar, and they slaughtered the lambs and sprinkled the blood toward the altar. 23 Then they brought the goats for the sin offering before the king and the congregation and laid their hands upon them. 24 The priests slaughtered them and made a sin offering with their blood at the altar to atone for all Israel because the king had ordered a burnt offering and a sin offering for all Israel. 25 He stationed the Levites in the house of Yahweh with cymbals, harps, and zithers in accordance with the order of David, Gad the king's seer, and Nathan the prophet, for such was the command of Yahweh through his prophets. 26 The Levites stood there with the [musical] instruments of David, while the priests had the trumpets. 27 Then Hezekiah ordered the burnt offering to be offered on the altar and at the same time the burnt offering began, the song of Yahweh and the trumpets also began, to the accompaniment of the instruments of David the king of Israel 28 while the whole congregation worshiped. So the singers sang and the trumpeters sounded the trumpets, all continuing until the completion of the burnt offering. 29 When the sacrifice was completed, the king and all who were present with him knelt down and worshiped. 30 Then Hezekiah[a] the king and the chiefs ordered the Levites to praise Yahweh with the words of David and Asaph the seer; so they sang their praises with joy and knelt in worship.

Offerings brought for the occasion

31 Hezekiah[a] replied, "Now that you have consecrated yourselves to Yahweh, draw near and bring sacrifices for thank offerings to the house of Yahweh." Then the congregation brought sacrifices for thank offerings and those with generous spirits [brought] burnt offerings. 32 The number of burnt offerings which the congregation brought was as follows: seventy bulls, a hundred rams, and two hundred lambs; all these were for burnt

offerings for Yahweh. [33] The consecrated gifts amounted to six
hundred bulls and three thousand sheep. [34] But unfortunately
there were not enough priests; they were unable to slaughter all
the burnt offerings so their brothers, the Levites, helped them
until the work was finished or until [other] priests had consecrated themselves; for the Levites were more conscientious
in consecrating themselves than the priests. [35] In addition to
the abundance of burnt offerings, there were also the choice
pieces for the peace offerings and the libations for the burnt
offerings. Thus the service of the house of Yahweh was rein-
stituted. [36] Then Hezekiah[a] and all the people rejoiced over
what God had provided for the people because the thing had
been carried out so quickly.

Notes

xxix 1. Exactly the same figures are given for Amaziah (xxv 1 and
II Kings xiv) as Hezekiah, both as to age and length of life. Hezekiah's
appears to be about right; Amaziah's reign of twenty-nine years is difficult to fit into the scheme of history: it is too long. (Cf. Albright,
BASOR 100 [December 1945].)

3. *having repaired.* The use of the verb *ḥzq*, "strengthen," "repair,"
may be a play on the name of Hezekiah.

4. *the east plaza.* Hardly the plaza of the temple (Ezra x 9) because
it was still unclean, but rather an assembly place like the one referred
to in Neh viii 1, 3 (cf. Rudolph, p. 292).

6. *our fathers were untrue.* Cf. *ma'al 'ᵃbōtay* "the unfaithfulness of
my fathers" in 1QH 4:34.

20. *went to work.* See first Note on xx 20, Sec. 22.

21. *the Aaronite priests.* Cf. xxxi 19; Josh xxi 19; 1QSa 1:15 f., 2:13.

23. See Lev iv for atonement offering ritual.

24. *all Israel.* "All Israel" is meant to include every group and stands
for the whole nation as the Chronicler understood it (cf. Ezra vi 17,
viii 35).

25. *his prophets.* David is not meant to be included among the prophets. The command of Yahweh was delivered by his prophets to David,
who issued the order. Nathan and Gad are mentioned only here in this
connection.

26. *[musical] instruments of David.* Cf. Amos vi 5.

27. *the song of Yahweh*. Technical expression for the anthem or hymn.

the instruments of David. Cf. Brockelmann, *Hebräische Syntax*, Sec. 110 i.

30. *to praise . . . Asaph*. Points to the use of a hymnal or psalter, perhaps somewhat like the canonical book of Psalms.

31. *Now . . . yourselves*. Literally "you have filled your hand," a technical term for consecration of the priests. Thus Hezekiah was addressing the priests, exhorting them to carry on their functions now that the temple was dedicated.

sacrifices for. Hebrew has "sacrifices and thank offerings" but the *w* ("and") before *tōdōt* ("thank offerings") is here taken as epexegetical.

COMMENT

The Hezekiah material must be evaluated in the light of the Chronicler's theology, since he departs rather widely from the presentation in II Kings. For a brief discussion see Introduction. The real question is the degree to which the Chronicler may be more correct in his portrait of Hezekiah than the author of Kings, who was also biased, though in a different direction. For the Deuteronomist (Kings), Josiah is the Davidic king par excellence, and he may be responsible for the only notable *vaticinium ex eventu* in the whole complex of his work, that is, the Josiah prophecy in I Kings xiii 2. Kings was written under the spell of the Deuteronomic reform set in motion by Josiah, and the writer was charmed by his early achievements. The Chronicler, on the other hand, was under no historical illusions about any of the Davidic kings. While there were many good kings, some of whom he might want to glorify in a special way, his great concern was for the present and how its problems could be met. His aim is predominantly to present the religious situation with a view toward the orientation of the nation in his own day. Hence he severely limits the historicopolitical details and stresses the points appropriate to his purpose. The historical data bearing on the religious situation are presented in homiletic fashion.

[Introduction, xxix 1–2]: Only the barest facts on the accession of Hezekiah are given—his age upon assuming the throne, the length of his reign, and his mother's name. On the important matter of dates see Albright, BASOR 100 (December 1945), 22. Hezekiah became king in 715 B.C. and died in 687. The date of accession is certain since it can be controlled by other sources; the date of his death is almost as sure (cf. H. H. Rowley, BJRL 44 [1961/62], 409 ff.). It was a welcome task to observe the well-doing of this king after the record of events that transpired under his father.

[The cleansing of the temple, 3–17]: According to the Chronicler, Ahaz had closed the temple (xxviii 24), perhaps only temporarily, and on some excuse. The first official move of Hezekiah in inaugurating his reformation was to restore the temple service. On the matter of official date of the beginning of his reign—whether postdating or antedating applied—see Albright, BASOR 100 (December 1945), 22, n. 29.

No time is lost or effort spared in placing the blame for the politico-religious conditions. The fathers had been untrue to Yahweh as shown by their evil deeds—abandoning Yahweh, closing the entrance to the temple, putting out the lamps, and failing to have formal services in the temple. No one could deny the calamities; they were apparent to everyone with eyes to see. Hezekiah wanted to return to the good old days. The nation's relationship to Yahweh was sustained by the covenant and that is precisely what Hezekiah determined to renew. Part of that renewal, the reinstitution of proper formal services in the temple could be done only after a thorough cleansing of the sacred precincts, which in turn required that the religious officials—the Levites—respond and fulfill their obligations as determined by David. This they did by first consecrating themselves and then performing the task of cleansing the polluted house of Yahweh. The work was completed in record time.

M. Buttenwieser (*The Psalms,* 1938, pp. 135–38) connects Psalm lxxviii with the cultic reformation of Hezekiah, which he thinks took place after Sennacherib's withdrawal from Jerusalem in 701 B.C. It was then that the religious leaders saw that God had destroyed Samaria and Ephraim by the Assyrian armies, but that he saved Jerusalem and Judah.

Note the full complement of Levitical officials (vss. 12–14), though not in the same order as earlier. The following lists are interesting:

I Chron vi 1–15	*I Chron vi 16–32*	*Here*
Gershon	Kehath	Kehath
Kehath	Gershon	Merari
Merari	Merari	Gershon

The Aaronites are included here with the Levites, in accordance
with the Chronicler's high regard for the latter. While he has drawn
upon materials included earlier, the situation appears somewhat
confused (cf. K. Möhlenbrink, ZAW 52 [1934], 213). The expansion of the list by the addition of Elizaphan (cf. I Chron xv 8)
indicates the incorporation of secondary elements and the fluid character of the situation. The inclusion of the Levitical singers is perfectly good tradition.

[Rededication of the temple, 18–30]: The fulfillment of the covenant proceeded in three steps. The first was the cleansing of the
temple—its reconsecration which itself began through a reconsecration of officials. The second was the rededication of the reconse-
crated house. The ceremony was inaugurated by a notification to the
king that his order for reconsecration had been carried out according to plan and in all essentials. Hezekiah and the officials went to
the sanctuary the next day. They brought the proper offerings for
the atonement of the royal house, the sanctuary and the nation.
All these stood in special need of it. The slaughtering was done
properly and the blood handled according to prescription (Lev xvii
6; Num xviii 17). The Levites played their instruments (I Chron
xxiii 5, xxv 1–7) and the priests the trumpets (I Chron xv 24, xvi 6;
Ezra iii 10). The congregational act of worship (prostration before
Yahweh) took place at the beginning and at the end of the offering—doubtless the procedure was characteristic of the writer's
own time. At the direction of the king and officials, there was a
concluding service at the end of the formal offering during which
praises were sung and further worship ensued.

[Congregational offerings, 31–36]: When the dedicatory ceremonies were completed and the temple ready for use, Hezekiah
called upon the people to present their offerings. The response was
enthusiastic, as may be seen from the numbers of animals involved.
While burnt offerings were presented in connection with the rededication, the people now offered some of their own—this may account

for the smaller number here. For the law for burnt offerings, see Lev i. Nothing of this offering was for human consumption; it designated a particular zeal for Yahweh on the part of the worshiper. But along with the burnt offerings were the peace offerings— the thanksgiving offerings were types of peace offerings (cf. Lev vii 11 ff.). Portions of this offering were consumed on the altar and the remainder by the worshiper (cf. Lev iii). There were also libations for the burnt offering (Exod xxix 40; Num xv 1–10). The proceedings were somewhat marred by the shortage of priests. The circumstance was used by the writer to observe that the Levites were more conscientious than the priests and that on certain occasions the former could perform priestly functions. This could be a reflection of the Chronicler's own time when the priests were not so conscientious as the Levites and perhaps a certain cleavage between them existed. On the other hand, the rivalry may have been present in his sources. With these offerings, the temple cult was functioning again.

32. THE REIGN OF HEZEKIAH (ca. 715–687 B.C.):
THE PASSOVER
(xxx 1–27)

Preparations

XXX 1 Then Hezekiah[a] sent to all Israel and Judah and also wrote letters to Ephraim and Manasseh [inviting them] to come to the house of Yahweh at Jerusalem to celebrate the passover to Yahweh God of Israel, 2 for the king, his officials and the whole congregation at Jerusalem had agreed to celebrate the passover in the second month. 3 They had been unable to celebrate it at the proper time because the priests had not consecrated themselves in sufficient numbers and the people were not assembled at Jerusalem. 4 Therefore, since the plan pleased the king and the people, 5 they resolved to issue an invitation to all Israel from Beer-sheba to Dan to come to celebrate a passover at Jerusalem to Yahweh God of Israel, for they had not celebrated [it] en masse as prescribed. 6 Then, by order of the king, couriers delivered letters from the king and the officials throughout all Israel and Judah with the following message, "O Israelites return to Yahweh God of Abraham, Isaac and Israel and [b]he will return to your remnant[b] that has escaped from the hand of the kings of Assyria. 7 Do not be like your fathers and your brothers who wronged Yahweh God of their fathers; he brought them to desolation as you can see. 8 Do not be as obstinate as your fathers were, [c]submit to Yahweh,[c] come to his sanctuary which he has consecrated forever and serve Yahweh your God that his violent anger may depart from you. 9 If you

---

[a] Hebrew reads "Jehizkiah," but context indicates that "Hezekiah" is meant.
[b-b] There is some LXX support for "he will restore the remnant . . . ." But cf. Zech i 3.
[c-c] LXX "give glory to Yahweh God." See NOTE.

return to Yahweh, your brothers and your sons will be dealt with mercifully by their captors and permitted to return to this land, for Yahweh your God is gracious and merciful and he will not turn his face from you, if you return unto him." 10 So the couriers went from city to city in the land of Ephraim and Manasseh as far as Zebulun, but they laughed at them and ridiculed them. 11 Nonetheless some from Asher, Manasseh, and Zebulun humbled themselves and came to Jerusalem. 12 The hand of God was also at work in Judah to give them a common mind to obey the command of the king and the officials, consistent with the word of Yahweh.

Celebration

13 A huge crowd of people assembled at Jerusalem to celebrate the festival of unleavened bread in the second month—it was a very numerous congregation. 14 So they arose and removed the altars that were in Jerusalem; they also removed the incense altars and cast them into the Kidron Valley. 15 They slaughtered the passover [lambs] on the fourteenth day of the second month. Meanwhile the priests and the Levites had become ashamed of themselves and consecrated themselves and brought burnt offerings to the house of Yahweh. 16 So they now stood at their stations according to their custom prescribed in the law of Moses the man of God; the priests sprinkled the blood which they received from the hand of the Levites. 17 Because many of the congregation had not consecrated themselves, the Levites took care of the slaughter of the passover lambs so as to consecrate [them] to Yahweh for all who were not clean. 18 There were many people, especially from Ephraim, Manasseh, Issachar, and Zebulun, who had not purified themselves, for they did not eat the passover as prescribed. But Hezekiah[a] prayed for them as follows: "May the good Yahweh pardon 19 everyone whose heart is ready to seek God, Yahweh God of his fathers, though [he is not cleansed] according to the [ceremonial] purification of the sanctuary." 20 Yahweh listened to Hezekiah[a] and healed the people. 21 The Israelites present in

Jerusalem celebrated the festival of unleavened bread for seven days with great joy; the Levites and the priests praised Yahweh day after day with the mighty instruments of Yahweh. 22 Then Hezekiah*a* congratulated the Levites who had exhibited such excellent skill [in the conduct of the service] of Yahweh.

The second seven days

*a*After they had concluded*a* the seven-day festival during which they sacrificed peace offerings and praised Yahweh God of their fathers, 23 the whole congregation resolved to celebrate for another seven days. So they celebrated [another] seven days with joy, 24 for Hezekiah the king of Judah contributed a thousand bulls and seven thousand sheep for the congregation and the officials contributed a thousand bulls and ten thousand sheep for the congregation; a large number of priests consecrated themselves. 25 So the whole congregation of Judah, the priests and the Levites, the whole congregation that came from Israel, and the resident aliens who came from the land of Israel as well as those who lived in Judah rejoiced. 26 There was great joy in Jerusalem; nothing like this had taken place in Jerusalem since the days of Solomon the son of David, the king of Israel. 27 Then the priests and the Levites arose and blessed the people and Yahweh*e* listened to their cry and their prayer came to his holy dwelling place, to the heavens.

a–a LXX. Heb. "After they had eaten."
e Insert with Syr. because of suffix in next clause.

NOTES

xxx 3. *at the proper time.* I.e., at the time when the ceremonies recorded in the preceding chapter took place.

8. *submit to Yahweh.* Literally "give the hand to the Lord," a covenantal expression. (Cf. R. Kraetzchmar, *Die Bundesvorstellung im Alten Testament*, 1896, p. 47; and for the giving of the hand in oaths see J. Wellhausen, *Reste aräbischen Heidentums*, 1897, p. 186.)

14. *the altars . . . Jerusalem.* Cf. xxviii 24 f.

incense altars. A hapax legomenon but to be explained on the basis of xxviii 25.

18. *the good Yahweh.* Phrase occurs only here in the Bible.

21. *praised Yahweh . . . Yahweh.* M. Buttenwieser (JBL 45 [1926], 156–58) thinks *biklê* means "song" and *'ōz la'ᵃdōnai* are the initial words of the song.

27. *the priests and the Levites.* May be Levitical priests here because the giving of the blessing was a priestly function (cf. Lev ix 22; Num vi 22).

COMMENT

[Preparations for the passover, xxx 1–12]: That some sort of religious celebration, apart from the rededication of the temple, took place soon after the accession of Hezekiah is extremely likely, especially in view of the character and ambitions of the king (cf. II Kings xviii 4–6). It is usually held that the Chronicler transferred to Hezekiah some of the religious celebrations of Josiah, notably this one. See the commentaries on Kings and Chronicles for details. It must not be forgotten that the Josiah story is Deuteronomic. On the case for a reform in the time of Hezekiah see BJRL 44 (1961/ 62), 425–31. While the Chronicler may have used some of the language and ideas employed by the Deuteronomist (particularly in vss. 6–9), there is no reason to believe that he invented the story itself. There is good reason to believe that Josiah followed, at least to some extent, the policies of Hezekiah. The political and religious exigencies demanded resolute action. The Northern Kingdom had fallen, the heavy hand of Assyria was laid to the throat of the west, and only Yahweh could deliver Judah, as Isaiah had indicated. Ahaz had tried co-operation and failed. With his death the stage was set for religious reformation, which was prosecuted with vigor (II Kings xviii 4 ff.) and an attempt made to reclaim some of the territory won by Uzziah and lost under Ahaz (II Kings xviii 8). Thus Hezekiah had political ambitions that could be realized only with the help of the religious officials, who apparently had the upper hand at the time. The debacle at Samaria strengthened the hand of the reform groups who naturally supported the king, but perhaps for different reasons. Indeed it appears that the reform activities of Hezekiah and their partial success formed the

pattern upon which the Deuteronomic movement later proceeded
with the same purpose—to save the nation. (Cf. BP, p. 42.) In
short, Deuteronomy's legislation may have been based, in part, on a
Hezekian precedent, in which case the D code may have been
formulated in connection with Hezekiah's attempt to unify the nation
in the worship of Jerusalem; and it is possible that D was to some
extent discovered in the temple, having been lost during the reaction under Manasseh. Hezekiah plausibly appropriated the
northern traditions of both E and D partly to further his objective.
See also Elmslie (Selected Bibliography, Commentaries), pp. 524,
541.

It must be remembered that this is a sermon for the time of the
Chronicler but based squarely on broad historical precedents and
therefore later details may easily have intruded themselves as the
preacher made his point. The fact that the initiative was taken
so early in the reign of Hezekiah indicates that the advisers of the
king had thought through their plans pretty well. Of course not all
elements were sympathetic, at least not wholly so as is demonstrated by the dilatoriness of the priests (vs. 3).

The national significance of the passover lent itself admirably to
the purposes of king and officials. Refugees from the north had doubtless found their way to Judah in the wake of the Assyrian conquest
of Samaria. Bethel had been refurbished as a center of religion
(II Kings xvii 28) and syncretism was rampant (II Kings xvii
29–34) throughout the Assyrian province of Samaria. Now was the
time to appeal to the true followers of Yahweh in Israel. The
language of the decision to issue the invitation and its wording are
couched in the writer's own ideas and were quite obviously meant
to apply also to his own situation, but the underlying framework
is historical. How else is one to account for the fact that the wives
of Manasseh and Josiah came from Galilee (cf. W. F. Albright's
review of Abel's *Géographie de la Palestine* in JBL 58 [1939],
185; but see H. L. Ginsberg, in AMJV, pp. 350 f.). A further
indication of Hezekiah's interest in the north is that he named his
heir after a Northern tribe and eponymous hero. Politically the situation in the early years of Hezekiah's reign was quite opportune for
such a religious appeal. Sargon II was occupied with northern and
eastern areas from the sixth to the tenth years of his reign (ca.

716–712 B.C.) as we know from his annals (cf. ARAB, II, pp. 4–13).

A mission was sent throughout the territory of the old Northern Kingdom with a strong appeal to the people to rejoin their brethren at Jerusalem. There was some response from the Galilean area and Manasseh but none from Ephraim, possibly because the true followers of Yahweh had already withdrawn to Judah while the remainder cared little about the matter or because the people there were afraid to go because of the political implications involved— and the Assyrian officials probably kept close watch over Ephraim for any sign of rebellion.

[Celebration of the passover, 13–22a]: As already remarked, certain Deuteronomic prescriptions were woven into the Chronicler's narrative (vss. 5, 12) but that does not necessarily mean that he invented the whole story. At least some of the details have no meaning apart from the time of Hezekiah. It is important to observe that there were two deviations from general practice in this celebration of the passover: (a) the time of its celebration (on the fourteenth day of the second month), and (b) the exemption of Israelites from ritual prescriptions. Verses 18–19 are exceedingly illuminating since they portray the writer as no thoroughgoing ritualist. In cases of necessity, ritual could be set aside in favor of the worship of the broken and contrite heart. His belief in the efficacy of prayer should not be overlooked. On the matter of date of passover see H. J. Kraus, *Evangelische Theologie* 18 (1958), 47–67; S. Talmon, VT 8 (1958), 48–74. The shift in calendar reflects Hezekiah's desire to accommodate the Northerners who had been celebrating this feast a month later (to correspond with their autumn festival held in the eighth month). Observe the difference in approach between Hezekiah and Josiah (II Kings xxiii 15 f.), who destroyed the altar at Bethel.

Of course the writer's enthusiasm is evident through his reference to the very large congregation. A further reformation took place, this time in the city from which all foreign accouterments of worship were removed and cast into the refuse place in the Kidron Valley. The response of the people inspired the priests and Levites to consecrate themselves so that they occupied their stations for the service. Hence they could also step in to slay the passover lambs for those who could not meet ritual prescriptions. (This was probably a misunderstanding, as Rudolph, p. 301, thinks, as according to the law [Exod xii 6; Deut xvi 6] the family heads were to slay the lambs. The Levites probably did act for those from Israel who were not ritually capable of doing so.) The whole combination of festivities—festival of unleavened bread, passover, and peace offerings—continued for a full seven days after which the Levites were congratulated by the king—another indication of the esteem in which they were held by the Chronicler. The story probably had some homiletic application for the writer.

[A second period of festival, 22b–27]: Hezekiah appears like a second Solomon, who celebrated two weeks when the temple was dedicated (vii 8–9). The king and his officials contributed the sacrificial animals. The priests too had caught the spirit of joy and consecrated themselves. The festivities were shared by Judah, the Israelites who had come as pilgrims or refugees, the resident aliens, and the priests and Levites. No celebration like this (it is not referred to as any special feast) had taken place since the days of Solomon. It was concluded by the priestly blessing (cf. Num vi 22–27).

33. THE REIGN OF HEZEKIAH (ca. 715–687 B.C.): REFORM ACTIVITIES
(xxxi 1–21)†

Cleansing of the land

XXXI ¹ After all this was over, all Israel present went out to the cities of Judah, broke the pillars, cut to pieces the Asherahs, and wrecked completely the high places and the altars from all Judah, Benjamin, Ephraim, and Manasseh. Then all the Israelites returned to their cities, each one to his property.

Assignments of priests and Levites

² Hezekiah*ᵃ* assigned the divisions of the priests and Levites according to their divisions, each one of the priests and Levites for his service, to offer burnt offerings and peace offerings, to minister and to give thanks and praise *ᵇ*in the gates of Yahweh's camp.*ᵇ*

Assignment for offerings

³ [He also assigned] the king's portion from his possessions for the burnt offering, the [regular] morning and evening burnt offerings and the burnt offerings for the Sabbaths, the new moons, and the festivals as prescribed in the law of Yahweh.

Provision for support of religious officials

⁴ Moreover, he requested the people who lived in Jerusalem to present the portion of the priests and Levites *ᶜ*that they might occupy themselves [unreservedly] with the law of Yahweh.*ᶜ*

† **II Chron xxxi 1:** cf. II Kings xviii 4.

ᵃ Hebrew reads "Jehizkiah," but context indicates that "Hezekiah" is meant.
ᵇ⁻ᵇ MT "camps." Vulg. follows MT. LXX "in the courts of the house of the Lord"; Syr. omits "house." See NOTE.
ᶜ⁻ᶜ LXX "that they excel in the service of the house of the Lord."

5 As soon as the order was proclaimed, the Israelites provided
the first fruits of grain, must, oil, honey, and all the produce of
the field in abundance; they brought in the tithe of everything
in great quantities. 6 The Israelites and Judeans who lived in
the cities of Judah also brought in the *tithe of cattle,*[a] sheep,
and the sacred gifts consecrated to Yahweh their God and
placed them on piles. 7 They began to accumulate the piles in
the third month and by the seventh month had finished [them].
8 When Hezekiah[a] and the chiefs came and saw the piles they
praised Yahweh and his people Israel. 9 When Hezekiah[a] consulted with the priests and Levites about the piles, 10 Azariah
the chief priest of the house of Zadok answered him as follows:
"Since they began to bring the contributions to the house of
Yahweh there has been enough to eat and an enormous surplus,
for Yahweh has blessed his people, and so we have this great
quantity." 11 Then Hezekiah[a] ordered [them] to prepare store-
rooms in the house of Yahweh and, when they had prepared
[them], 12 they conscientiously brought in the contributions,
the tithes, and consecrated gifts and they placed Conaniah the
Levite in charge of them with Shimei his brother as assistant;
13 Jehiel, Azaziah, Nahath, Asahel, Jerimoth, Jozabad, Eliel,
Ismachiah, Mahath, and Benaiah were overseers under Conaniah
and Shimei his brother in accordance with the order of Hezekiah[a]
the king and Azariah the chief of the house of God. 14 Kore
the son of Imnah the Levite and porter of the east [gate] was
in charge of the freewill offerings of God and the distribution of
the contributions of Yahweh and the consecrated gifts. 15 Supporting him loyally in the priestly cities were Eden, Minjamin,
Jeshua, Shemaiah, Amariah, and Shecaniah who distributed to
their brothers according to their divisions, whether old or young,
16 irrespective of their official genealogy, to the males from
thirty[e] years old and upward—to every one [of them] who entered the house of Yahweh to fulfill his daily obligations—for

a–a LXX "tithes of goats."
e So for Heb. *šlwš* ("three"). Vulg. *tribus*, "third," or "tribe." See NOTE.

their work in their ministrations according to their divisions:
17 both the officially registered priests according to their families
and the Levites from twenty years old and upward according
to their services in their divisions. 18 And the official genealogy
included all their small children, their wives, their sons, and
their daughters, for the whole congregation, because they kept
dedicating themselves in their devotion. 19 The Aaronites, the
priests who lived on the pasture lands belonging to their cities,
had men of renown in every city ready to distribute portions to
every male among the priests and to everyone included in the
official genealogy of the Levites.

Characterization of Hezekiah

20 Hezekiah*a* did so throughout all Judah; he did what was
good, right, and true before Yahweh his God. 21 Every work
which he undertook, whether in the service of the house of God
or in the law or in the commandments, he carried out with
utter devotion in the worship of his God, and so succeeded.

NOTES

xxxi 2. *in the gates of Yahweh's camp.* Cf. I Chron ix 18, 19, where
the camps (plural) of the Levites are mentioned in connection with
their service at the tent as their fathers had served the camp (singular)
of Yahweh. The writer was doubtless influenced by *P*'s wilderness tradition. There is probably no relation to an eschatological conception found
later in 1QM 4:9.

5. *the Israelites.* Refers to the dwellers in Jerusalem, not North Israelites.

honey. Honey could not be used with the burnt offering (Lev ii 11),
though it may have been acceptable as a cereal offering.

6. *The Israelites.* The refugees from Israel living in the cities of
Judah.

the tithe of cattle . . . sacred gifts. This does not appear in the law
of Moses (but cf. Neh x 38).

13. *the chief. nāḡīd* (cf. I Chron ix 11; Neh xi 11).

16. *thirty years old.* MT "three." Must be "thirty" because they came
to work (cf. I Chron xxiii 3).

COMMENT

[Cleansing of the land, xxxi 1]: The compression of reform activity into two chapters (xxx and xxxi) represents a schematization of the reforms characteristic of the whole reign of Hezekiah, which was influenced greatly by the preaching of Micah and Isaiah (cf. Bright, *A History of Israel,* pp. 261–67).

Just as Jerusalem had been cleansed (xxx 14) before the festival of unleavened bread and passover, the whole land was swept clean of impurities left over from the days of Ahaz. The two verses belong together and are an expansion of II Kings xviii 4, except that nothing is said here about the destruction of the bronze serpent. No specific extent of the reformation is recorded in II Kings, but it probably pertained to Judah. How far it went beyond that is uncertain, though there may have been some such activities in local situations conducted by those who had participated in the Jerusalem festivities.

[Priestly and Levitical assignments, 2]: The background for this verse is viii 14 which itself refers to I Chron xxiii 26. Hezekiah reaffirmed the old order established by Solomon in accordance with the command of David. The priests were in charge of the offerings and the Levites supervised and carried out their functions of music at the established posts and time.

[Provision for offerings, 3]: According to viii 12–13, Solomon provided burnt offerings regularly for the temple services. Hezekiah followed the precedent of Solomon—the Chronicler looks upon him as a kind of second Solomon (cf. ii 4). The provisions for these offerings are enumerated in Num xxviii–xxix.

[Provision for the religious personnel, 4–19]: The zeal for the reformation can be judged by the popular and royal provision for temple services. When the royal decree was issued for provision for religious personnel, the response was overwhelming, both from Jerusalem and from the cities of Judah—much to the surprise of the king. The contributions consisted of the best gifts (*rē'šīt*) and the tithe. According to Num xviii, the gifts were for the priests (vs. 12) and the tithe for the Levites (vs. 21). In his colloquy with the religious leaders, the chief priest Azariah informed him that the huge stock piles were due to the generosity of the people and the blessing of Yahweh. At the command of the king storage rooms were readied in the temple for the tithes (cf. I Chron ix 26, xxvi 20–28, xxviii 12). Twelve Levites were placed in charge of the collections (cf. I Chron xxvi 26–28). As in the case of Joash and Jehoiada (xxiv 12), Hezekiah and Azariah co-operated closely in this project. Kore, the Levitical porter of the east gate, had charge of the voluntary offerings and the distribution of contributions and gifts, a very important function. To assist him in the proper discharge of his duties was a corps of priests in the various cities of Judah, so that proper care was taken of the families of those religious officials who were performing their duties. The register of priests was according to families, that of Levites according to functon (divisions); (cf. the organization of David, I Chron xxiii–xxvi). The landed priests too were included in the scheme of service and were thus eligible to share in the contributions. Much of this material doubtless reflects the practice obtaining in the time of the writer, though there may have been such an order carried out under the reformation of the period of Hezekiah.

[Evaluation of Hezekiah, 20–21]: This little pericope is based on II Kings xviii 5–7a and emphasizes his activity for his entire kingdom, his utter devotion to Yahweh in all he undertook and hence his success. But the Chronicler, despite his obvious bias for Hezekiah, does not go so far as the Deuteronomist in declaring him to have been the best king ever (II Kings xviii 5).

34. THE REIGN OF HEZEKIAH (ca. 715–687 B.C.): THE ASSYRIAN INVASION (xxxii 1–23)†

XXXII 1 After these faithful acts, Sennacherib the king of Assyria came and invaded Judah, and laid siege to the fortified cities with the thought of conquering them. 2 When Hezekiah*a* saw that Sennacherib had come with the main purpose of making war on Jerusalem, 3 he consulted with his chiefs and warriors about closing up the water courses outside the city; they supported him. 4 A large number of people were brought together to stop up all the springs and the brook that ran *b*through the midst of the land,*b* saying, "Why should the kings of Assyria find abundant water when they come." 5 He also went to work with determination and repaired every section of the wall that was damaged, erected towers upon it, [constructed] another wall on the outside, strengthened the Millo of the city of David, and made a large quantity of spears and shields. 6 He placed military officers in charge of the people, summoned them to himself on the plaza at the city gate, and spoke directly to them as follows: 7 "Be strong and courageous, do not be afraid or tremble before the king of Assyria and all the multitude accompanying him, for those with us are more than those with him. 8 He has only *c*human power*c* but we have Yahweh our God to help us and to fight our battle." The people were encouraged by the words of Hezekiah*a* the king of Judah. 9 After this, while he and all his command were at Lachish, Sennacherib sent his servants to Jerusalem, to Hezekiah*a* and all Judah at

† II Chron xxxii 1–23 ‖ II Kings xviii 13–37, xix 14–19, 35–37, Isa xxxvi 1–22, xxxvii 14–19, 36–38.

a Hebrew reads "Jehizkiah," but context indicates that "Hezekiah" is meant.
b–b LXX "through the city." See NOTE.
c–c MT "arm of flesh." For expression, see Jer xvii 5; cf. also Isa xxxi 3.

Jerusalem with the following message: 10 "Thus has Sennacherib the king of Assyria said: In what do you put your confidence, you who sit in the fortress of Jerusalem? 11 Is not Hezekiah*a* deluding you in order to deliver you to death by famine and thirst when he says, 'Yahweh our God will save us from the hand of the king of Assyria'? 12 Is Hezekiah*a* not the one who removed his high places and his altars and said to Judah and Jerusalem, 'Before one altar you must worship and upon it burn incense'? 13 Don't you know what I and my fathers did to all the peoples of the lands? Were the gods of the nations of the lands able at all to deliver their land from my hand? 14 Who among all the gods of these nations whom my fathers devoted to destruction was able to deliver his people from my hand, that your God should be able to deliver you from my hand? 15 Now, do not let Hezekiah*a* mislead you; do not let him delude you like this; do not believe him. No god of any nation or kingdom was able to deliver his people from my hand or the hand of my fathers, how much less can your God deliver you from my hand?" 16 His servants spoke still further against Yahweh God and Hezekiah*a* his servant. 17 He also wrote letters to insult Yahweh God of Israel and spoke against him, saying, "As the gods of the nations of the lands could not deliver their people from my hand, so the God of Hezekiah*a* cannot deliver his people from my hand." 18 Then they shouted with a loud voice in the Jewish language to the people of Jerusalem who stood on the wall to frighten and terrify them, hoping to capture the city. 19 They spoke against*d* the God of Jerusalem as [they had] against the gods of the peoples of the earth which were the product of men's hands. 20 Then Hezekiah*a* the king and Isaiah the prophet, the son of Amoz, prayed about this and cried to the heavens. 21 Then Yahweh sent a messenger who destroyed every mighty man, leader and captain in the camp of the king of Assyria; so he had to return to his country shame-facedly and when he entered the house of his god his own offspring there struck him down with the sword. 22 So Yahweh

d So for Heb. "to."

saved Hezekiah[a] and the citizens of Jerusalem from the hand of Sennacherib the king of Assyria and from the hand of all [others] and [e]gave them peace[e] on every side. [23] Then many brought gifts to Yahweh at Jerusalem and costly presents to Hezekiah[a] the king of Judah; from then on he was exalted in the estimation of all the nations.

[e-e] So with LXX and Vulg. for Heb. "and he led them." Cf. also Josh xxi 42; II Chron xiv 6, xv 15, xx 30.

NOTES

xxxii 1. On the campaigns of Sennacherib in Palestine see Bright, *A History of Israel*, pp. 282–87, and the references there listed.

3. *the water courses.* I.e., the springs, wells, and conduits.

4. *all the springs.* Thought to have been Gihon and En-rogel. Rudolph, p. 311, thinks the Dragon's fountain may also have been involved.

the brook . . . land. May refer to open conduits that carried the water to a pool within the city (Isa vii 3). See Vincent and Steve, *Jerusalem de l'Ancien Testament*, Pt. I, pp. 280, 289–97. Hezekiah later replaced these open water channels with the Siloam tunnel; see xxxii 30, next section.

5. *another wall on the outside.* On the location of the second wall see Avi-yonah, *Sepher Yerushalayim*, I, pp. 157 f., and map opposite p. 160; Galling, BRL, 301–4; Vincent and Steve, *op. cit.*, Pt. III, p. 647.

6. *and spoke directly.* Specifically and directly, to encourage them.

7. *Be strong . . . tremble.* Cf. Deut xxxi 6; Josh x 25.

those with us . . . him. Cf. II Kings vi 16, words of Elisha to his servant. There may be some connection with Isa vii 14 here (Immanuel= God with us), just as in Isaiah there is a connection between Immanuel and Hezekiah, which was accepted by the Chronicler. While this is explicit only later in Rabbinic sources, it has a long history, going back at least to the Chronicler, if not to Isaiah himself. The royal prophecies belong to the early period of the prophet and refer originally and essentially to the hopes in the royal house, and presumably to Hezekiah. The latter's boldness, and his close association with the prophet, could be understood in this light, even though neither Hezekiah nor any other king could completely fulfill the hopes of the poet-prophet.

12. The play on the resentment of the people about the highhanded reform reflects the writer's view that Hezekiah carried out a Deuteronomic reform.

13. *Don't you know . . . the peoples of the lands?* Cf. 1QH 4:26.

19. *the God of Jerusalem.* Phrase found scratched on the wall of a cave near Lachish. *Land of the Bible: Newsletter,* Vol. 3, No 26 (April/May 1962), 1.

21. *struck . . . sword.* For discussions on the problem of the strange death of Sennacherib, see references in ANET, p. 288.

COMMENT

Comparison with II Kings xviii–xx shows that the Chronicler reversed the emphasis: he stressed the religious activities of Hezekiah to which he devoted two chapters. The Deuteronomist dismissed the reformation with only four verses (II Kings xviii 3–6). But the Chronicler did not deal so curtly with the political events as his predecessor had done with Hezekiah's reformation. However, the political involvements of the period as presented by the writer are so telescoped that they cannot be understood without the records of Kings, the references in Isaiah, and the Assyrian inscriptions.

[Countermeasures of Hezekiah, xxxii 1–8]: According to II Kings xviii 13 (cf. Isa xxxvi 1), Sennacherib invaded Judah in the fourteenth year of Hezekiah (ca. 701 B.C.). The Chronicler tells only of the Assyrian king's *thought* of conquering the fortified cities of Judah; he does not say that they were actually taken. According to the Taylor Prism, Sennacherib took forty-six cities and a huge number of prisoners, gave some of Hezekiah's territory to the neighboring kings of Ashdod, Ekron, and Gaza, and laid a heavy tribute upon him (ANET, pp. 287 f.). For results of excavations of Lachish and Tell Beit Mirsim reflecting this period see Wright, *Biblical Archaeology,* pp. 164–72. Hezekiah took three measures in preparation for meeting the invaders—all with reference not to the outlying areas of Judah which were probably already as good as lost but to Jerusalem, where the last stand was to be made. The first had to do with the water problem, which was tackled from both a defensive and offensive point of view. The springs and wells outside the city were stopped up to prevent the enemy from using them—a powerfully offensive weapon in a water-famished region. Steps were taken at the same time to use the available supply for the defenders of the city. The second was the strengthening of the fortifications of the city: repairing the weak spots in the wall, erection of towers, construction of an outside wall, and building up the Millo (cf. Isa xxii 9–10; for the Millo, see my *I Chronicles*, COMMENT on Sec. 15). Finally, Hezekiah reorganized the army, placed the nation on a wartime footing, and supplied his forces with weapons of war (cf. Isa xxii 8b).

The Chronicler attempts to clear Hezekiah of failure to consult Yahweh, as charged by Isaiah (xxii 11), by having him exhort the military and people to trust in Yahweh who will fight their battle. With him on their side there is no need to fear or tremble before an arm of flesh.

[Sennacherib's message, 9–19]: During the siege of Lachish, Sennacherib sent envoys to Jerusalem with a message for Hezekiah and the people of Jerusalem with the hope of throwing them into panic (see ANET; for a reproduction of the Assyrian relief showing the siege and capture of Lachish see ANEP, pp. 372–73). There is no mention of the army sent with the envoys (II Kings xviii 17). The message spoken of here is composed of the communication of Sennacherib (II Kings xix 10–13) and the speech of the Rabshakeh (II Kings xviii 19–35); more precisely, the sources of the verses here are: vs. 10 || II Kings xviii 19, 20b; vs. 11 || II Kings xviii 32b; vs. 12 || II Kings xviii 22b; vs. 13 || II Kings xix 11 and xviii 33; vs. 14 || II Kings xviii 35; and vs. 15 || II Kings xviii 29. The Chronicler has composed Sennacherib's message in accordance with his own views, choosing to omit the well-known references by the writer of II Kings to the strength of Hezekiah and the Egyptian alliance (xviii 19–25). He takes up the religious argument propounded by the Rabshakeh in II Kings xviii 28–35 which follows quite logically after Hezekiah's address to his people to inspire them with confidence. Verse 18 refers to the speech of the Rabshakeh.

[Hezekiah's deliverance, 20–23]: For a fuller description of Hezekiah's reaction to the appeal of the Assyrian commander see II Kings xix. Here he is said to have been joined in prayer by Isaiah, probably on the basis of II Kings xix 20. Both the prayer of Hezekiah and the response of Yahweh through the prophet are omitted by the Chronicler (cf. II Kings xix 15–19, 21–34) because he is more concerned about the reward of faithfulness and doing right (cf. James v 16). Our author and the Deuteronomist are agreed on the deliverance of Hezekiah and Jerusalem, though it was not without a tremendous price (see ANET, p. 287) and after Jerusalem was actually laid under siege (cf. II Kings xviii 17, xix 35). Not only was Jerusalem spared but Hezekiah's stature rose tremendously, and countless offerings were brought to Yahweh as thank offerings for his goodness and mercy. On the whole matter of Sennacherib's campaigns to the west, see NOTE on vs. 1 and Rowley, BJRL 44 (1961/62), 395 ff.

35. THE REIGN OF HEZEKIAH (ca. 715–687 B.C.): THE LATER YEARS (xxxii 24–33)†

Hezekiah's illness

XXXII ²⁴At that time Hezekiah^a became mortally sick and when he prayed to Yahweh, he responded and gave him a token.

The pride of Hezekiah

²⁵But Hezekiah^a did not repay the benefit received by him; rather he became proud so that wrath would fall upon him and upon Judah and Jerusalem. ²⁶However, when Hezekiah^a, with the citizens of Jerusalem, humbled himself in respect to his pride, the wrath of Yahweh did not come upon them in the time of Hezekiah.^a

Wealth and honor of Hezekiah

²⁷Hezekiah^a became very rich and respected; he provided for himself treasure houses for his silver, gold, precious stones, spices, shields, and all kinds of desirable articles, ²⁸as well as storage places for the produce of grain, must, and oil, and stalls for all kinds of cattle and pens for the flocks. ²⁹He also provided cities for himself, in addition to an abundance of wealth in the form of sheep and cattle, because God gave him a very great abundance of wealth. ³⁰Hezekiah^a also was the one who closed the upper outlet of the waters of Gihon and channeled them straight down on the west side of the city of David. Hezekiah^a was successful in all his undertakings. ³¹But when the

† **II Chron xxxii 24** ‖ II Kings xx 1–3, Isa xxxviii 1–3; **25–26** ‖ II Kings xx 12–19, Isa xxxix 1–8; **32–33** ‖ II Kings xx 20–21.

^a Hebrew reads "Jehizkiah," but context indicates that "Hezekiah" is meant.

representatives of the chiefs of Babylon were sent to him to inquire about the sign that was done in the land, God left him alone to test him so that he might know his mind fully.

Conclusion

32 The remainder of the history of Hezekiah*a* and his devoted acts, behold they are written down in the vision of Isaiah, the son of Amoz, the prophet in the chronicle of the kings of Judah and Israel. 33 When Hezekiah*a* slept with his fathers, they buried him in the upper section of the graves of the sons of David; so all Judah and Jerusalem honored him at his death. Manasseh his son then became king in his place.

NOTES

xxxii 27. *shields.* May have been ornamental shields.

33. *the upper section.* Cf., however, A. B. Ehrlich, *Randglossen zur hebräischen Bibel,* VII, 1914, p. 381, and Rudolph, *in loco,* who suggest "prominent or honored place."

COMMENT

[Hezekiah's illness, xxxii 24]: A simple statement of the fact without details illustrates the writer's method of utilizing well-known episodes to strengthen his argument in a given case. His audience required no more. The token refers to the sundial (II Kings xx 8–11).

[The pride of Hezekiah, 25–26]: These verses must manifestly be interpreted in the light of the story of the visit of the representatives of Merodach-baladan (II Kings xx 12–19; Isa xxxix 1–8) during which Hezekiah proudly displayed *his* treasures. His pride was bound to lead to disaster, as the prophet Isaiah declared. Though only the royal house stood under judgment, the Chronicler brings Judah and Jerusalem into the picture because he was aware of the wider consequences of such action—the deeds of leaders always involve those they lead. The response of Hezekiah to the rebuke of

Isaiah averted trouble for the time being (cf. II Kings xx 19).

[Wealth and honor of Hezekiah, 27–31]: This catalogue of achievements is meant to demonstrate the blessings of God upon the king who did good in his sight (cf. vs. 29b). While the list is too indefinite for purposes of specific comparison, certain archaeological discoveries tend to support the over-all features of a rather prosperous reign. A seal found at Tell Beit Mirsim with Hezekiah's name dates from around 700 B.C. (*l-ḥzq* [*yw*]; cf. AASOR 12 [1932], 78). The *l-mlk* jar-handle stamps may have originated in the period of Hezekiah (Albright dates class 1 to this period [AASOR 21–22 (1943), 73–75]; cf. also D. Diringer's study in BA 12 [1949], 70–86, especially pp. 84–86). The famous Siloam inscription appears to come from the same age. For the history of the discovery, illustrations, and translation of the inscription, cf. Wright, *Biblical Archaeology*, pp. 169–72. Another interesting and significant item is the Great Shaft uncovered at Lachish; Hezekiah may have had something to do with its construction (see Tufnell, *Lachish III: The Iron Age*, pp. 158–63). For a study of the water courses in the period of Ahaz and Hezekiah, see M. Burrows, "The Conduit of the Upper Pool," ZAW 70 (1958), 221–27.

According to the Chronicler the Babylonian officials came to Jerusalem to study "the sign that was done in the land," that is, the token of the sundial (II Kings xx 9–11). The Babylonians had developed astrological interests long before this time.

While it seems clear that behind the writer's story of the visit of the delegation from Babylon lies that of the mission of the representatives of Merodach-baladan reported in Kings, Chronicles says nothing about Hezekiah's display of his treasures to the Babylonians. The Chronicler chooses rather to connect the mission with an inquiry about the sign of the sundial. The coming of the delegation was nevertheless interpreted by him as a test for the king and in which he was left to himself. Traditionally, in time of testing, God was thought to have abandoned the one being tested (cf. Abraham, Job, and, in part, Israel in the wilderness). The purpose of the test was to establish Hezekiah's devotion to Yahweh, demonstrated in part by his prayer (vs. 24) but rendered uncertain by his subsequent pride (vs. 25). He had indeed repented after experiencing the divine displeasure but this test was to show if his devotion was now wholehearted.

[Conclusion, 32–33]: Follows the general pattern but lays special stress on "his devoted acts" and the source in "the vision of Isaiah" recorded in the history of the kings of Judah and Israel. It should not be overlooked that other activities may have taken place in the time of Hezekiah, notably that of wise men (Prov xxv–xxix). See O. Eissfeldt, *Einleitung in das Alte Testament,* 3d ed., 1964, pp. 641 ff.

36. THE REIGN OF MANASSEH (687–642 B.C.)
(xxxiii 1–20)†

Relapse

XXXIII 1 Manasseh was twelve years old when he became king and remained king at Jerusalem for fifty-five years. 2 He did evil in the sight of Yahweh, following the abominations of the nations whom Yahweh dispossessed before the Israelites. 3 He rebuilt the high places which Hezekiah*a* his father had smashed, he erected altars for Baal, made Asherahs, and worshiped all the host of the heavens and served them. 4 He built altars in the house of Yahweh of which Yahweh himself had said, "My name shall remain in Jerusalem forever." 5 He built altars for all the host of the heavens in both courts of the house of Yahweh. 6 He made his sons to pass through the fire in the valley of Ben-hinnom, practiced soothsaying, divination, and sorcery, and dealt in necromancy and familiar spirits; he did so much evil in the sight of Yahweh, inciting him to anger. 7 He also set up the slab-image which he had made, in the house of God of which God had said to David and to Solomon his son, "I will put my name forever in this house and in Jerusalem which I selected from all the tribes of Israel. 8 I will not again remove the foot of Israel from the ground upon which I permitted your fathers to stand so long as they are careful to observe all that I commanded them with respect to all the law, the statutes and the judgments [given] through Moses." 9 But Manasseh misled Judah and the citizens of Jerusalem into doing

† II Chron xxxiii 1–10 ‖ II Kings xxi 1–10; 18–20 ‖ II Kings xxi 17–18.

a Hebrew reads "Jehizkiah," but context indicates that "Hezekiah" is meant.

greater evil than the nations whom Yahweh destroyed before the Israelites. 10 When Yahweh spoke to Manasseh and his people, they paid no attention [to him].

Conversion of Manasseh

11 Then Yahweh brought against them the captains of the army of the king of Assyria who captured Manasseh with hooks, bound him with bronze chains, and took him to Babylon. 12 When he was in distress, he placated Yahweh his God and humbled himself greatly before the God of his fathers. 13 When he prayed to him, he was moved by his entreaties, listened to supplication for favor, and brought him back to Jerusalem to his kingdom. Then Manasseh knew that Yahweh is God. 14 Afterwards Manasseh built the outer wall of the city of David on the west side of Gihon, in the valley, to the fish gate and around the Ophel and made it very much higher. Then he stationed army captains in all the fortified cities of Judah. 15 He also removed the foreign gods and the idol from the house of Yahweh as well as all the altars he had erected on the mountain of the house of Yahweh and in Jerusalem and threw them outside the city. 16 He repaired*b* the altar of Yahweh, sacrificed peace offerings and thank offerings upon it, and commanded Judah to serve Yahweh God of Israel. 17 Nevertheless, the people continued to sacrifice at the high places, only to Yahweh their God.

Concluding observations

18 The remainder of the history of Manasseh, his prayer to his God and the oracles of the seers who spoke to him in the name of Yahweh God of Israel—they are in the records of the kings of Israel. 19 His prayer, [how God] was moved by his entreaties, all his sins, his wrongdoing, the locations where he built high places, his setting up of Asherahs and images before he humbled himself are written down in the records of his seers.

b So with LXX and Vulg., for Heb. "prepared."

20 When Manasseh slept with his fathers, they buried him °in his house°. Amon his son became king in his place.

°–°LXX "garden of his house," following the parallel in II Kings xxi 18, where it is further defined as the garden of Uzza, not otherwise identified except as the burial place of Amon (II Kings xxi 26).

NOTES

xxxiii 1. *fifty-five years*. For chronology see Albright, BASOR 100 (December 1945), 22. He reduces the length of Manasseh's reign to forty-five years.

3. *the host of the heavens*. Astral cults pointing to subservience to Assyria.

6. *the valley of Ben-hinnom*. See NOTE on xxviii 3 in Sec. 30.

soothsaying . . . spirits. Assyria was deeply involved in the occult at the time. (Cf. F. M. Th. de Liagre Böhl, *Opera Minora*, 1953, pp. 384–422.) None of the terms used here are very clear. They cover the whole field of magic and divination.

7. *slab-image*. This meaning of *semel* is Albright's (ARI, p. 221, n. 121). According to II Kings xxi 7, it was an image of Ashera which would have been particularly offensive to Yahwists.

19. *his seers*. So instead of "my seers." The *w* of the third person masculine singular suffix of the plural noun was omitted by haplography.

COMMENT

The Chronicler devotes one more verse than the Deuteronomist to Manasseh, but the evaluation of his reign is vastly different.

[Relapse under Manasseh, xxxiii 1–10]: The first passage is almost identical with its parallel and source (II Kings xxi 1–10). For one thing, our writer curiously omits the name of the king's mother, a practice he generally follows elsewhere, with the exceptions of Joram and Ahaz earlier, and does not name the king's mother's again in Chronicles. It is not difficult to understand why he does not refer to Ahab, king of Israel in comparison with Manasseh—no king of Judah could be that bad, for all of them were of the Davidic line. There are also a few additions such as "in the valley of Ben-hinnom" (6), "the statutes and the judgments" (8) interpreting the content of the law of Moses, and "Judah and the citizens of Jerusalem" (9), a characteristic expression, which spells out more clearly the objects of Manasseh's seduction.

The relapse under Manasseh was, no doubt, due to the conditions which prevailed in his day, as in the time of Ahaz. The climax of Assyrian intervention in the west came in this period, for the most part because of the protracted crises in Egypt which occupied much of the time of Esarhaddon (680–669). Manasseh's name occurs in the list of twenty-two kings of Hatti, the seashore and the islands, who were summoned to Nineveh (ANET, p. 291). The inscriptions of both Esarhaddon and Asshurbanipal are full of references to Egypt and the Palestinian states, indicative of their activity in these regions. As Ahaz before him, Manasseh was doubtless caught in the stream of world politics and had perforce to become subservient to Assyria. That meant, in part, the adoption of Assyrian religion which in turn compelled the nullification of the achievements of his father and earned for the king the enmity and violent opposition of prophets and religious officials, many of whom worked underground. Manasseh was, in all probability, not an unwilling tool —though certainly not at first—in the hands of the Assyrian kings. Prophecy was not altogether quiescent, as can be inferred from vs. 10 (cf. II Kings xxi 10), but its message availed little and was even met with violence (II Kings xxi 16).

[Conversion of Manasseh, 11–17]: That Manasseh found himself in the presence of the Assyrian king is quite probable in view of the vassal-treaties of Esarhaddon (see D. J. Wiseman, "The Vassal-Treaties of Esarhaddon," Iraq 20 [1958], 1–99). These treaties are dated in the year 672 and center around the ceremony of induction of the crown prince Asshurbanipal. Representatives of all the lands under Assyrian hegemony were gathered at the royal palace, where in special ceremony they were bound with fearful oaths to support the crown prince after the death of his father. Among other things, they were sworn not to arouse the ire of the gods or goddesses against him (line 265) and to serve Ashur as their own god (line 409). The interest and activity of both Esarhaddon and Asshurbanipal in the west could well have forced compliance with their demands in Judah, though undoubtedly opportunities were not missed to deviate from them or even to rebel. Possibilities for rebellion existed in connection with the activities of Psammeticus I and perhaps at the time of difficulty with Shamash-shum-ukin (see Bright, *A History of Israel,* pp. 291–93). The occurrence of the name of Manasseh in the inscriptions of both points in that direction. It may be taken for granted that the vassal kings were allowed to return to their countries after having been placed under the threat of divine retribution with its fearful consequences. However, if such was the case, the Chronicler interprets it as due to a change of heart on the part of Manasseh, who prayed to Yahweh who brought him back to Jerusalem. The ensuing reformation does not coincide with the Kings sources or with Jeremiah (xv 4), all of which agree that the sin of Manasseh remained. It is possible that the long life of the king, on the theory of the Chronicler, was the ultimate source for the story, which continued to grow as may be seen from the apocryphal prayer of Manasseh based on vs. 13 (see E. J. Goodspeed, *The Apocrypha,* 1938, pp. 369–72). At any rate, the writer himself says that Amon followed in the footsteps of his father (vs. 22) and that the abominations were removed by Josiah. There may be a historical kernel in vs. 14; if so, the fortification of Jerusalem would not have been against Assyria but against the renascent power of Egypt under Psammeticus I, Judah figuring as a buffer state between Egypt and the Palestinian provinces of Assyria (cf. Rudolph, p. 317, but see A. Malamat, "The Last Wars of the Kingdom of Judah," JNES 9 [1950], 226, n. 30).

[Conclusion, 18–20]: This is simply a summary of the supposed activities of Manasseh by way of indicating the sources where they have been recorded. It is interesting to note the mention of the oracles of his seers!

37. THE REIGN OF AMON (642–640 B.C.)
(xxxiii 21–25)†

XXXIII 21 Amon was twenty-two years old when he became king and reigned at Jerusalem for two years. 22 He did evil in the sight of Yahweh as Manasseh his father had done; Amon sacrificed to the images which Manasseh had made and served them. 23 He did not humble himself before Yahweh as Manasseh his father had humbled himself; but he, [that one] Amon, rather increased his guilt. 24 Finally his servants conspired against him and killed him in his own house. 25 Then the people of the land slew those who conspired against King Amon, and the people of the land made Josiah his son king in his place.

† II Chron xxxiii 21–25 ‖ II Kings xxi 19–24.

COMMENT

The short reign of Amon is a repetition of that of Manasseh with its evils and apostasy. The story here follows closely that in II Kings xxi, with the addition of vs. 23 based on the story of the conversion of Manasseh. The palace revolt issuing in the death of Amon was put down by the 'am hā-'āreṣ, "people of the land," the free landholders of Judah who always acted decisively in times of crises to see that the Davidic dynasty was perpetuated (see Würthwein, Der 'amm . . . , especially pp. 30 ff.). A. Malamat ("The Historical Background of the Assassination of Amon, King of Judah," IEJ 3 [1953], 26–29) thinks Amon was slain by anti-Assyrian opponents of his foreign policy who were, in turn, ousted by the 'am hā-'āreṣ to avoid a direct collision with Assyria. Nothing is said of his burial (cf. II Kings xxi 26).

38. THE REIGN OF JOSIAH (640–609 B.C.): DISCOVERY OF THE LAWBOOK OF MOSES (xxxiv 1–33)†

Introductory statement

XXXIV 1 Josiah was eight years old when he became king and reigned at Jerusalem for thirty-one years. 2 He did what was right in the sight of Yahweh, following the ways of David his father and turning neither to the right nor to the left.

First steps in reformation

3 During the eighth year of his reign, while he was still a youth, he began to seek the God of David his father and in the twelfth year he began to purge from Judah and Jerusalem the high places, the Asherahs, and the carved and molten images. 4 He smashed the altars of Baal in his presence, cut to pieces the incense altars that were above them, broke up and pulverized the Asherahs and the carved and molten images, and strewed [the dust] before the graves of those who sacrificed to them. 5 He burned the bones of their priests upon their altars and thus cleansed Judah and Jerusalem. 6 And in the cities of Manasseh, Ephraim, and Simeon, as far as Naphtali, and around their plazas, 7 he smashed the altars and the Asherahs, reduced to dust the carved images, and cut to pieces all the incense altars in all the land of Israel. Then he returned to Jerusalem.

Repairs for the temple

8 In the eighteenth year of his reign, after purging the land and the temple, he sent Shaphan the son of Azaliah, Maaseiah the mayor of the city, and Joah, the son of Jehoahaz, the

† II Chron xxxiv 1–2 ‖ II Kings xxii 1–2; 8–13 ‖ II Kings xxii 3–7; 14–21 ‖ II Kings xxii 8–13; 22–28 ‖ II Kings xxii 14–20; 29–33 ‖ II Kings xxiii 1–3.

speaker to refurbish the house of Yahweh his God. 9 When they came to Hilkiah the high priest, they delivered the money brought to the house of God and collected by the Levitical porters from Manasseh and Ephraim, from all the remainder of Israel, from all Judah and Benjamin, and from ªthe citizensª of Jerusalem. 10 They delivered [it] to the workmen, who were commissioned, for the house of Yahweh and the workmen delivered it to those who worked on the house of Yahweh for repairing and refurbishing the temple—11 they delivered it to the craftsmen and builders for the purchase of hewn stones and lumber for beams to undergird the buildings which the kings of Judah had allowed to decay. 12 The men did the work faithfully; their foremen were Jahath and Obadiah, the Levites of the Merarite line and Zechariah and Meshullam, of the Kehathite line, who exercised supervision. The Levites—all of whom were expert with musical instruments—13 had charge of the burden-bearers and supervised all the workmen from job to job. Some of the Levites also served as scribes, officials, and porters.

Discovery of the lawbook

14 In the course of bringing out the money that had been contributed for the house of Yahweh, Hilkiah the priest found the book of the law of Yahweh given by Moses. 15 Hilkiah spoke as follows to Shaphan the scribe, "I have found the book of the law in the house of Yahweh"; then Hilkiah gave the book to Shaphan, 16 and Shaphan brought the book to the king and also gave him the further report: "Everything that has been entrusted to your servants they have done. 17 They have poured out the money that was found in the house of Yahweh and placed it in the hands of the supervisors and in the hands of the workmen." 18 Shaphan also told the king, "Hilkiah the priest gave me a book." Shaphan then read from it in the presence of the king. 19 When the king heard the words of the law, he tore his garments. 20 Then the king gave the following order

ª-ª MT, Qere "and they returned"; Kethib "citizens"; so also LXX and Vulg.

to Hilkiah, Ahikam the son of Shaphan, Abdon the son of
Micah, Shaphan the scribe, and Asaiah the king's minister:
21 "Go and inquire of Yahweh on my behalf and on behalf of
the remnant of Israel and of Judah about the words of the book
that has been discovered; for great is the wrath of Yahweh which
has been poured out upon us because our fathers did not observe the word of Yahweh by acting in harmony with everything
prescribed in this book."

Prophecy of Huldah

22 So Hilkiah and those whom the king *had designated*
went to Huldah the prophetess, the wife of Shallum, the son
of Tokhath, the son of Hasrah the keeper of the wardrobe, who
lived in the second quarter of Jerusalem and spoke to her about
this. 23 She replied to them, "Thus has Yahweh God of Israel
said: Tell the man who sent you to me, 24 Thus has Yahweh
said: Behold I am going to bring evil upon this place and all its
citizens, all the curses recorded in the book which they have
read in the presence of the king of Judah; 25 because they have
abandoned me and burnt incense to other gods so as to provoke
me to anger by all the works of their hands, my wrath shall be
poured out on this place and it cannot be quenched. 26 And as
for the king of Judah who sent you to inquire of Yahweh, thus
shall you say to him: Thus has Yahweh God of Israel said, As
for the words which you heard—27 because your heart has become tender and you humbled yourself before God when you
heard his words concerning this place and its citizens, and you
humbled yourself before me, tore your garments and wept before me, I have taken cognizance: the oracle of Yahweh. 28 Behold when I gather you to your fathers, you shall be gathered
to your grave in peace so that your eyes shall not look upon all
the evil which I am going to bring upon this place and its citizens." Then they brought back the report to the king.

b-b Add with LXX.

Response of king and people

29 So the king called together all the elders of Judah and Jerusalem. 30 Then the king, together with all the men of Judah, the citizens of Jerusalem, the priests, the Levites, and all the [other] people, great and small, went up to the house of Yahweh where he read in their hearing all the words of the book of the covenant discovered in the house of Yahweh. 31 The king standing in his place then entered into the covenant before Yahweh to follow Yahweh, to observe his commandments, testimonies and statutes with all his mind and soul and to carry out the terms of the covenant as prescribed in this book. 32 He made all those present at Jerusalem, and Benjamin, stand [by it]; the citizens of Jerusalem acted in accordance with the covenant of God, the God of their fathers. 33 Josiah removed all the abominations from all the territories belonging to the Israelites and required all present in Israel to serve Yahweh their God; throughout his life they did not deviate from following Yahweh God of their fathers.

NOTES

xxxiv 3. *in the twelfth year.* Ca. 628 B.C.

6. *their plazas.* Reading *birḥōbōtēhem* for *bᵉḥar bōtēhem.*

8. *the mayor.* Literally "captain of the city."

the speaker. See my *I Chronicles,* Sec. 20, NOTE on xviii 15 f.

9. *delivered.* Rudolph reads "poured out," as in vs. 17.

10. *the workmen.* I.e., the building committee.

14–15. For examples of the book of the law, see ANET, p. 495a.

20. *Abdon the son of Micah.* II Kings xxii 12 reads "Achbor son of Micaiah."

21. *the remnant.* The situation in the time of the Chronicler. See parallel in II Kings xxii 13.

22. *Tokhath, the son of Hasrah.* II Kings xxii 14 reads "Tikvah son of Ḥarḥas" (perhaps a non-Semitic name). Chronicles is to be preferred here. Cf. Noth, IPN, p. 260.

the second quarter. Usually regarded as the northern extension of

the city. See M. Burrows, JBL 54 (1935), 37 f. for possible connection
with yᵉšānāh gate of Neh iii 6.

31. *in his place.* Cf. xxiii 13—the cultic place of the king in the
temple.

32. *and Benjamin.* Rudolph reads "by the covenant" for Benjamin,
but without any textual evidence in either MT or the versions. The
idea of "standing" has a double significance—to stand in their cultic
position (cf. xxxv 5) and to stand by the covenant.

COMMENT

[Introductory statement, xxxiv 1–2]: With the exception of the
omission of Josiah's mother's name, this passage follows almost
exactly the parallel in II Kings xxii 1–2.

[Removal of offenses, 3–7]: This important pericope has hitherto
been viewed with unwarranted skepticism, partly because there is
no reference to it elsewhere and partly because it appears to follow
the regular pattern of reform movements taking place in the earlier
reigns of Asa (xv 8–15) and Hezekiah (xxix). While there is some
schematization here, there is no reason to suspect the basic elements
involved. Since the writer was concerned primarily with religious
matters, he naturally stresses the removal of foreign cult objects
and the institution of regular, authentic rites—all of which took
some time, though they tend to be telescoped. The chronological
data is so reasonable in itself that it is difficult to see how the
episode can be seriously questioned. During the early years of Josiah,
the kingdom was under a regency, which must have been characterized by moderation, to judge from the action of the people of
the land after the death of Amon. If the preaching of Zephaniah is
connected with events dating between 630–625 B.C., Josiah's early
piety (at the age of sixteen) is quite credible (Eissfeldt, *Einleitung
in das Alte Testament,* p. 572; C. Kuhl, *The Prophets of Israel*
[1960], p. 95; cf. Bright, *A History of Israel,* pp. 297–300, for an
excellent description of the situation). The first overt move began four
years later (ca. 628 B.C.) when there was a noticeable decline in the
fortunes of Assyria during the last years of Asshurbanipal. For a
discussion of the political conditions, see F. M. Cross, Jr., and D.
N. Freedman, "Josiah's Revolt against Assyria," JNES 12 (1953),

56–58. The chronology needs some revision, but the basic arguments remain. Asshurbanipal died in 627/26 B.C. See C. J. Gadd in *Anatolian Studies,* VIII, 1958, pp. 70 f. There was probably no immediate effort to extend his purge of the high places beyond Judah, that is, before the death of Asshurbanipal. But soon after that event, Josiah apparently assumed the obligation of caretaker of the territory of Israel, perhaps at first as a vassal for Assyria. As a loyal and patriotic son of Israel his ambition was to claim his people for Yahweh, and perhaps to be a second David. Hezekiah had interested himself in the religion of the people of the north; Josiah followed in his footsteps but with far more propitious times in his favor. (On Josiah's Northern reformation with its political overtones, see *Studies in Old Testament Prophecy,* ed. H. H. Rowley, 1950, p. 165.) The first steps toward restoration of the land to Yahweh were taken in Judah and Jerusalem, where Josiah was in complete control. This is a sure indication that there was no effective reformation under Manasseh, as the Chronicler asserts. Then he extended his command into the territory of the former Northern Kingdom—as far as Naphtali, that is, to the northern border of the land. The Hebrew inscriptions found near Yavneh-yam, dating from the seventh century B.C., point to Judean control in the area at the time and help to substantiate the biblical witness to Josiah's political activities. (See J. Naveh, "A Hebrew Letter from the Seventh Century B.C.," IEJ 10 [1960], 129–39.) The destruction of the Bethel cult, long a rival of Jerusalem, must have been one of the aims of the young king (II Kings xxiii 15).

[Temple repairs, 8–13]: Six years later Josiah undertook a temple reconstruction program, necessary according to the Chronicler because it had fallen upon lean times under Manasseh and Amon. A similar program followed the reign of Ahaz (xxix 3). The king took the initiative in the temple work, as David had done in the plans for the original building; he sent the three top officials to negotiate with the religious authorities and to deliver the funds for the enterprise. Compare the view of the Deuteronomist in II Kings xxii 4 ff. The royal officials were sent to supervise the emptying of the offering chest (cf. II Kings xii 11; II Chron xxiv 11). According to II Kings xxii 3 Shaphan was the royal secretary. II Kings xxiii 8 speaks of a Jehoshua as the mayor of the city. However, in the II Kings parallel passage only Shaphan is mentioned. For a discussion of the functions of these officials, see NOTE on I Chron xviii 15 f. and R. de Vaux, *Les Institutions de l'Ancien Testament,* I, 1958, pp. 201–3, 211 f.

Since the kings of Judah had permitted the deterioration of the temple (vs. 11), Josiah now took the necessary steps to repair the damage. II Kings xxii 4 asserts that the money had been collected by the porters at the temple's gates. The Chronicler, on the other hand, speaks of the Levites collecting the funds from Manasseh, Ephraim, all the rest of Israel, Judah, and Benjamin and the citizens of Jerusalem. Perhaps he thinks of them as accompanying Josiah on his mission of purification and collecting as they proceeded. It may be that he is sermonizing here, stressing his favorite theme of all Israel having a share in the temple as the true center of worship for the entire nation. The whole project, as the organization shows, was well planned in advance. The Levites were the chief functionaries, though only two classes appear here, the Merarites and Kehathites. The Gershunnites are not mentioned. (For the reasons, see Möhlenbrink, ZAW 52 [1934], 213, and Rudolph, pp. 322 f. For references to musical accompaniment in building, see Rudolph, p. 323.)

[Discovery of the lawbook, 14–21]: More nearly in line with the story of II Kings, the Chronicler now connects the discovery of the lawbook with the emptying of the money chests. From vss. 15–33 he follows the Deuteronomist closely. Verse 18 says that Shaphan read from only part of a larger book (see Goettsberger, p. 376), whereas II Kings xxii 10 apparently reflects a more accurate view: the whole book was read to the king. Verse 21 reflects the period of the writer rather than that of Josiah.

[Prophecy of Huldah, 22–28]: For the names of those who accompanied Hilkiah see II Kings xxii 14. The prophecy delivered by Huldah was an uncomfortable one as may be seen from the substitution of "all the curses" for "all the words"; this may be a more specific application of Deut xxvii, xxix 20. The prophecy concerning the peaceful end of Josiah was not fulfilled (xxxv 23 f.). Yet the Chronicler did not revise the prophecy. There were, however, two aspects to it, and one was realized: that he would not see the destruction of the city and nation. It is rather remarkable that prophecies were faithfully preserved intact regardless of conformity in detail to what was known to have happened.

[Response of king and people, 29–33]: The response of the

king was to summon the elders of Judah and Jerusalem for consultation, the outcome of which was the decision to renew the covenant. The Chronicler here follows quite closely the Deuteronomic source, which limits the participants, with the officials, to the men of Judah and Jerusalem. Only one significant variant occurs—in vs. 30 when the Levites replace the prophets of II Kings xxiii 2. A. R. Johnson thinks this reflects the time of the writer when the cult prophets were the singers who in turn were merged with the Levites (*The Cultic Prophet in Ancient Israel*, pp. 60 f., and note on p. 64). The ceremony of covenant renewal was cultic in character and consisted of a procession to the temple, the reading of the terms of the covenant and the solemn oath taken by the king in the presence of the people. Following the king's covenanting, the people were pledged also to stand by it. Cazelles, p. 234, n. b., points out the cultic aspects involved in this statement, that is, the liturgical position (standing in their place as the king stood in his) of the people. The last part of vs. 32 and all of vs. 33 is a typical expansion of the writer in which he particularly makes the covenant apply to all Israel.

39. THE REIGN OF JOSIAH (640–609 B.C.): THE PASSOVER
(xxxv 1–19)†

XXXV ¹ Then Josiah celebrated a passover to Yahweh at Jerusalem. They slaughtered the passover on the fourteenth day of the first month. ² He assigned the priests to their posts and encouraged them in the service of the house of Yahweh. ³ He also said to the Levites who were the instructors of all Israel [and] were dedicated to Yahweh: "Put the sacred ark in the house which Solomon, the son of David, the king of Israel constructed; you need no longer carry it around on your shoulders. Now serve Yahweh your God and his people Israel! ⁴ Prepare yourselves by families in accordance with your divisions and in harmony with the decree of David the king of Israel and the decree of Solomon his son. ⁵ Stand in the sanctuary according to the family divisions of your brothers, the laity, *so that for each family division there may be Levites.* ⁶ Slaughter the passover, consecrate yourselves and prepare [it] so that your brothers may observe it in accordance with the word of Yahweh through Moses." ⁷ Josiah contributed for the laity sheep, lambs, and young goats—everything for the passover for those present—to the number of thirty thousand, together with three thousand head of cattle; these came from the king's property. ⁸ His officials also contributed voluntarily for the people, the priests and the Levites; and Hilkiah, Zechariah, and Jehiel, the chiefs of the house of God, gave two thousand six hundred [lambs] and three hundred head of cattle to the priests for the passover offerings. ⁹ Conaniah, Shemaiah, Nethanel his brother, Hashabiah, Jeiel, and Jozabad, the Levitical chiefs, contributed five thou-

† **II Chron xxxv 1–19** ‖ II Kings xxiii 21–23.

a–a MT is difficult, but this appears to be the meaning.

sand [lambs] and five hundred head of cattle to the Levites for the passover offerings. 10 So the service was prepared and the priests took their place and the Levites [occupied] their divisions in accordance with the command of the king. 11 Then they slaughtered the passover and while the priests sprinkled some of the blood[b] received from them, the Levites did the skinning. 12 Next they put aside the burnt offering for presentation to the family divisions of the laity that they might offer it to Yahweh in accordance with the prescription of the book of Moses; they did the same with the cattle. 13 They roasted the passover on fire in accordance with the regulation and boiled the consecrated offerings in pots, kettles,[c] and pans and brought them speedily to all the laity. 14 Afterwards they provided for themselves and the priests, for the Aaronite priests were engaged in offering burnt offerings and fat until night; thus did the Levites provide for themselves and for the Aaronite priests. 15 The Asaphite singers occupied their place according to the command of David and Asaph, Heman and Jeduthun, the king's seer; so did the porters at each gate; because they could not leave their duties, their brothers the Levites provided for them. 16 So all the service of Yahweh was prepared that day for the celebration of the passover and the offering of the burnt offering on the altar of Yahweh as King Josiah had commanded. 17 At that time the Israelites who were present celebrated the passover and the festival of unleavened bread for seven days. 18 There was not celebrated a passover like it in Israel since the days of Samuel the prophet, nor did any of the kings celebrate such a passover as Josiah, the priests, the Levites, all Judah and Israel who were present, and the citizens of Jerusalem celebrated. 19 This passover was celebrated in the eighteenth year of Josiah's reign.[d]

[b] Added with LXX.
[c] Heb. *dwd*—see PEQ (1939), 80 f.
[d] LXX inserts here II Kings xxiii 24–27. Cf. also I Esdras i 23–24. For discussion see Rudolph, pp. 329–31.

Notes

xxxv 1. I Esdras begins its history with Josiah's passover. See Rudolph, *Esra und Nehemia*, p. XIV.

3. *you . . . shoulders.* The meaning is that since the ark had been deposited in the temple (I Chron xxiii 25 f.) the Levites no longer functioned as gatekeepers (I Chron xv 15, xxiii 28 f.) but as assistants to the priests with regularly assigned duties. For rendering, see Rudolph, Galling (*Die Bucher der Chronik, Esra, Nehemia* [see Selected Bibliography, Commentaries]), Rehm, and Ehrlich (*Randglossen zur hebräischen Bibel*, VII)—"Since the sacred ark has been placed . . . you need no longer. . . . Now therefore. . . ."

8. *Hilkiah, . . . God.* Three persons share the title *nāgīd*, "chief" of the house of God. Cf. I Chron ix 11; II Chron xxxi 13; Neh xi 11, where only one person bears it.

9. The names "Conaniah" and "Jozabad" occur also in xxxi 12–13, though not of the same persons.

11. *they.* I.e., the Levites.

13. *roasted.* Literally "boil in the fire." A conflation of Exod xii 8 f., which requires roasting, and Deut xvi 7, which requires boiling.

Comment

Verse 1 is based on the tradition transmitted in II Kings xxiii 21, though it is rewritten. Here the king acts for the nation, whereas in Kings he gives the command to his officials and the people. The Chronicler specifies the proper time (Lev xxiii 5), rather than the exceptions made by Hezekiah (xxx 2 f.). Like the latter's celebration, the passover was held at Jerusalem in accordance with the general interpretation of Deuteronomy (xvi 5 f.). No reference is made to "the book of this covenant" (II Kings xxiii 21) because the Chronicler regards Josiah's passover as following the pattern established by Hezekiah and hence is nothing new.

Verses 2–19, absent in Kings, offer a description of this great event (cf. II Kings xxiii 22). As in the case of Hezekiah, appointment and encouragement of religious officials precedes the actual ceremony. The priests were assigned to their posts (i.e., their cultic positions) and exhorted specially to carry out their service in connection with the temple. The priests required special urging, as noted elsewhere (xxix 34, xxx 3); for the Chronicler, who is not very well inclined toward them, this was an important point.

The Levites, too, were assigned their functions. But, as the text now stands, they went about their job of instructing the people— for the Chronicler, one of the duties of the Levites was to teach the people (cf. xvii 8; Neh viii 7 f.) out of the torah, a function earlier devolving upon the priests (cf. Hos iv 6; Jer v 31, xviii 18) —and were dedicated (I Esdras i 3 has the imperative here); this is another illustration of the Chronicler's favoritism. But the Levites had other duties since the time of David (I Chron xvi 4, 41, vi 16 f. [vi 31E f.]; xxiii 4 ff.). Their obligations are then enumerated: they are to arrange themselves by families into appointed divisions according to the decrees of David and Solomon (cf. viii 14) and be ready in the court of the temple to render their service to the laity as the situation required. Their service was to kill the passover lamb and prepare it for the people while the priests took care of the blood. Rudolph, p. 325, is doubtless correct in saying that the emergency functions carried out by the Levites in the time of Hezekiah (xxx 17) were now normalized. The Levitical regulations here set forth obtained beyond the Josiah passover (see Goettsberger, p. 381, as opposed to von Rad, *Gesammelte Studien* . . . , pp. 248 f.). In any case, the Chronicler's conception of the Levitical service was not a degradation as in Ezek xliv 10–14.

An important phase in the preparation for the passover was the provision of sacrificial animals. The enormous number (highly exaggerated) is intended to suggest the liberality of the providers and possibly the great concourse of people participating in the ceremonies. For the figures, see references in Rudolph, pp. 326 f. The fact that sheep, lambs, goats, and cattle were provided seems to indicate that provision was made for both passover and peace offerings. The proportion of small cattle to large cattle is interesting— ten to one, except for the animals provided by the chiefs of the house of God.

The preparation began with the priests and Levites occupying their stations—the former at the altar, the latter in the court at the service of the families participating in the passover. The Levites slaughtered the passover animals and then passed the blood to the priests who sprinkled it upon the altar. The blood could no longer be disposed of in the customary way (Exod xii 7), since the Deuteronomic centralization law required the passover to be eaten at the sanctuary. Meanwhile the Levites did the skinning and the separation of the portions (of the cattle) for the burnt offering (vs. 14). Apparently both the paschal animals and the cattle were slaughtered at the same time (cf. vs. 16; the sprinkling of the blood and the burning of the fat pieces is characteristic of the burnt offering). While the passover was roasting, the consecrated offerings were boiled; the Levites seem to have been active in that task. The priests were occupied with the burnt offerings; hence the provision for both priests and Levites was set aside until their tasks were completed. Moreover, the musicians and porters were occupied at their respective posts so that the Levites had to provide for them too. All in all, there can be no doubt about the writer's feeling for the Levites—they were present everywhere and played a significant role in every phase of the celebration. This really is the new emphasis the Chronicler brings to the celebration. Another noticeable feature is the combination of the passover with the burnt offering.

Verse 18 is a somewhat altered version of II Kings xxiii 22, with additions, and the substitution of Samuel for the judges. The writer may have had in mind Josh v 10 after which the passover remained a family rite, until this time. Evidently the meaning of the verse is that precedents antedate the foundation of the kingdom. De Vaux (*Les Institutions de l'Ancien Testament,* II, 1960, p. 388) thinks there may have been such celebrations at a central cult shrine in premonarchial times. Certain features of the Chronicler's treatment stand out: (a) the command of the king (vss. 10, 16); (b) the decrees of David and Solomon; (c) reference to Moses (twice). He has combined the commands of Moses dealing with the passover and burnt offering and the Davidic and Solomonic decrees relating to the Levites. For further discussion see Rudolph, p. 329.

The final verse of the section parallels II Kings xxiii 23, though a portion of the latter, "in Jerusalem," was transferred to vs. 1.

40. THE REIGN OF JOSIAH (640–609 B.C.):
THE LATER YEARS
(xxxv 20–27)†

XXXV 20 After all this, when Josiah had provided for the house, Neco the king of Egypt came up to fight at Carchemish on the Euphrates and Josiah went out to engage him. 21 But he sent messengers to him, saying, "What have we to do with each other, O king of Judah; *a*I am not coming*a* against you today but against the house with which I am carrying on war. God has commanded me to move quickly, so forbear for your own sake from interfering with God who is on my side, lest he destroy you." 22 However, Josiah did not turn away but determined*b* to fight him; so he would not listen to the words of Neco which issued from the mouth of God but went to fight on the plain of Megiddo. 23 The archers shot King Josiah. Then the king said to his servants, "Take me away for I am seriously wounded." 24 So his servants took him out of his chariot and laid him on a second chariot which he had and brought him to Jerusalem where he died and was buried in the cemetery of his fathers. All Judah and Jerusalem held mourning rites for Josiah. 25 Jeremiah composed a lamentation for Josiah, and all the male and female singers lament for Josiah in their dirges to this day and chant*c* them according to established custom throughout Israel; they are recorded in the Lamentations. 26 The remainder of the history of Josiah and his acts of devotion as

† II Chron xxxv 20–27 ‖ II Kings xxiii 28–30.

a–a Reading *'anī 'ōteh*, with LXX, Vulg.
b MT "he disguised himself." LXX "he was determined"; I Esdras i 26 "he attacked him"; Vulg. "he had prepared for war against him."
c The root here is *tnh* (piel=*yᵉtannūm*), not *ntn* as MT. Cf. Judg xi 40; Ps viii 2 (Ps viii 1E).

recorded in the law of Yahweh, [27] along with his acts from beginning to end, are recorded in the chronicle of the kings of Israel and Judah.

NOTES

xxxv 20. *the house.* I.e., the temple.

Neco . . . Euphrates. The parallel passage in Kings is not clear; "Carchemish" is omitted (but cf. Jer xlvi 2, dated in the reign of Jehoiakim). Carchemish was the main military base of the Egyptians during the period of control over Syria-Palestine. See also Josephus *Antiquities* X.v.1. Cf. M. Noth, "Die Einnahme von Jerusalem im Jahre 597 v. Chr.," ZDPV 74 (1958), 143 f. Verses 20–24 appear more reliable than II Kings xxiii 28–30—Malamat, JNES 9 (1950), 220, n. 14.

21. *the house. Bēt milḥamtī* has never been satisfactorily explained. I Esdras i 25 has *Perath,* "Euphrates." J. Lewy ("Forschungen zur alten Geschichte Vorderasiens," MVAG 29 [1925], 21) thinks it refers to the permanent encampment of the pharaoh in Syria, or his front line position. B. Alfrink ("Die Schlacht bei Megiddo und der Tod Josias," *Biblica* 15 [1934]) renders "Kriegsstadt, Garnisonsstadt, Festungsstadt."

24. *a second chariot.* Doubtless a chariot carrying supplies.

COMMENT

We know next to nothing about Josiah's movements between the reformation and the time of his death. It seems fairly certain that he organized and strengthened the administration, to judge from the extensive use of the scroll-type stamps. Cf. Diringer, BA 12 (1949), 74–76; Tufnell, *Lachish III: The Iron Age,* tables on pp. 346 f.— 161 out of a total of 492 of these stamps belong to this type, to which must be added the 68 from el-Jib (*Hebrew Inscriptions and Stamps from Gibeon,* ed. J. B. Pritchard, 1959, pp. 18 ff.). The battle at Megiddo in which he was mortally wounded took place in 609 B.C. (cf. W. F. Albright, BASOR 143 [1956], 31 f.). That a battle took place as implied by the Chronicler seems to be indicated by the excavations at Megiddo where stratum II suffered some destruction (Lamon and Shipton, *Megiddo,* I, p. 87; W. F. Albright, *The Archaeology of Palestine* [Penguin Books, revised and reprinted, 1960], p. 130). Cf. D. N. Freedman, BA 19 (1956), 53, n. 10. For date see also H. Tadmor, JNES 15 (1956), 228.

According to the Chronicler, Pharaoh Neco was on an urgent mission to assist the Assyrians, whose forces were poised to recross the Euphrates in an attempt to retake Harran (Wiseman, *Chronicles of Chaldaean Kings*, p. 19; cf. A. Dupont-Sommer, *Semitica* 1 [1948], 55 ff.). There was an Egyptian garrison at Carchemish which withstood the Babylonians until 605 B.C. Neco was thus going to Carchemish (the Chronicler has correctly transmitted the course of events) to reinforce his garrison and assist the Assyrians. Josiah was apparently an ally of the Babylonians and thus attempted to impede the march of Neco and he may have succeeded better than he knew, for the Assyro-Egyptian forces were thwarted in their endeavor to retake Harran (Wiseman, *loc. cit.,* and p. 63).

Neco was on a divine mission, that is, of his god, for he certainly did not recognize Yahweh (Rudolph, pp. 331 f.; B. Couroyer, RB 55 [1948], 388 ff.). However, the Chronicler probably understands the meaning to be Yahweh (as I Esdras i 27 f.). If an Egyptian deity was involved, Josiah rightly refused to listen, but Yahweh sometimes used foreign rulers to carry out his plans (cf. Isa xlv 1; Jer xxvii 6) and the author of I Esdras i 28 interprets the warning as coming from Jeremiah. Verse 22 is quite definite —the words of Neco issued from the mouth of God, that is, Yahweh. Josiah failed to heed the warning and thus lost his life. His death evoked profound sorrow throughout the nation and was the occasion for an extended period of mourning. The lamentation said to have been composed by Jeremiah is no longer extant. The mention of Lamentations in vs. 25b in all probability is meant to suggest that it was included in our Book of Lamentations, which may indeed have been part of a collection of such dirges. But that work does not now have it nor is it to be found in the Book of Jeremiah. According to I Esdras i 33 it was preserved in the official history of the kings of Judah. The death of Josiah is said to have been celebrated regularly in a memorial service.

41. THE REIGNS OF JEHOAHAZ (609 B.C.), JEHOIAKIM (609–598 B.C.), AND JEHOIACHIN (598 B.C.) (xxxvi 1–10)†

The reign of Jehoahaz

XXXVI 1 Then the people of the land took Jehoahaz the son of Josiah and made him king at Jerusalem in place of his father. 2 Jehoahaz was twenty-three years old when he became king and he reigned three months at Jerusalem.ᵃ 3 The king of Egypt deposed him at Jerusalem and laid the land under [tribute to the extent of] a hundred talents of silver and a talent of gold.

The reign of Jehoiakim

4 The king of Egypt then made Eliakim his brother king over Judah and Jerusalem and changed his name to Jehoiakim; but Neco took along Jehoahaz his brother and brought him to Egypt.ᵇ 5 Jehoiakim was twenty-five years old when he became king and reigned eleven years at Jerusalem. He did what was evil in the sight of Yahweh his God. 6 Nebuchadnezzar the king of Babylon came up against him and bound him in bronze chains to bring him to Babylon. 7 Nebuchadnezzar also brought some of the articles of the house of Yahweh to Babylon and put them in his palace at Babylon. 8 The remainder of the history of Jehoiakim, the abominations of which he was guilty, and what happened to him [because of them] are recorded in the chronicle of the kings of Israel and Judah. Jehoiachin his son became king in his place.

† II Chron xxxvi 1–3 ‖ II Kings xxiii 30b–33; 4–8 ‖ II Kings xxiii 34–xxiv 7; 9–10 ‖ II Kings xxiv 8–17.

ᵃ LXX inserts II Kings xxiii 31b–33a here.
ᵇ LXX, on the basis of the Kings parallel, adds "and he died there." Between verses 4 and 5 it inserts a version of II Kings xxiii 35.

The reign of Jehoiachin

9 Jehoiachin was eight years° old when he became king and reigned for three months and ten days at Jerusalem. He also did what was evil in the sight of Yahweh. 10 At the turn of the year King Nebuchadnezzar sent and brought him to Babylon together with the costly articles of the house of Yahweh, and made Zedekiah his brother king over Judah and Jerusalem.

° LXX and II Kings xxiv 8 read "eighteen years," obviously correct. See NOTE.

NOTES

xxxvi 3. *a hundred talents of silver.* About 3¾ tons.

a talent of gold. About 75½ lbs.

4. *changed his name to Jehoiakim.* On double name, see NOTE on xxvi 1, Sec. 28.

6. This must be the episode referred to in Dan i 1 f. The Chronicler's reference is independent and certainly much older than Daniel. Perhaps there is some historical foundation to the story after all. Neither story is clear about what actually happened to Jehoiakim. Both distinctly indicate that the temple vessels were brought to Babylon, but they do not say explicitly that Jehoiakim was taken to Babylon. He may only have been threatened by Nebuchadnezzar and frightened into submission by being put into chains. See Rudolph, p. 335.

8. *what . . . him.* Literally "what was found against him."

9. *eight years old.* See textual note °. Jehoiachin already had five sons in 592 B.C. (E. Weidner, *Mélanges Syriens offert à Monsieur René Dussaud,* II, pp. 925 f.) which means that at least one of them was born in Jerusalem before 597 B.C., unless he had more than one wife (cf. W. F. Albright, "King Jehoiachin in Exile," BA 5 [1942], 53; and II Kings xxiv 15).

10. *At . . . year.* II Kings xxiv 10 reads "at that time," a much less definite phrase.

brother. II Kings xxiv 17, "uncle," is correct (cf. Jer xxxvii 1). He was perhaps chosen because Jehoiachin had no available sons at the time (cf. II Kings xxiv 15; Jer xxii 30).

COMMENT

[The reign of Jehoahaz, xxxvi 1–3]: After the untimely death of Josiah, the 'am hā-'āreṣ (see Würthwein, Der 'amm . . . , pp. 33–36) acted quickly to fill the vacancy by putting Jehoahaz on the throne. The Chronicler does not give the name of his mother nor any characterization of him. There is no reference to his being put in chains at Riblah, though there is to his exile in Egypt (vs. 4b). The heavy tribute laid upon the land is mentioned but not the method by which it was collected or from whom (cf. II Kings xxiii 35). It should be noted that Jehoahaz was the last king of Judah invested by the people. Henceforth Egypt and Babylon appointed the kings, though the Davidic line remained intact until after the final siege of Jerusalem. Jehoiakim was probably regarded as regent for the captive king until his death.

[The reign of Jehoiakim, 4–8]: Josiah, like Hezekiah before him, was beholden to the Babylonians. Jehoiakim began as an Egyptian vassal and remained so until after the battle of Carchemish in 605 B.C. (for an idea of conditions in Judah in the interim, see Jer xxiii 13–19). A year later Nebuchadnezzar's army appeared at Ashkelon, where a severe engagement took place that resulted in the devastation of the city (Wiseman, Chronicles of Chaldaean Kings, p. 69) and the deportation of its inhabitants. Cf. an Aramaic letter to the pharaoh, which may have come from the king of Ashkelon (H. L. Ginsberg, BASOR 111 [October 1948], 24–27; Dupont-Sommer, Semitica 1 [1948], 43–68). Possibly in connection with that invasion, Jehoiakim shifted his allegiance to Babylon. Whether Nebuchadnezzar actually invaded Judah is uncertain; perhaps the news of his treatment of Ashkelon was enough (cf. Jer xlvi, but see Albright, BASOR 143 [1956], 31). Wiseman (Chronicles of Chaldaean Kings, pp. 28, 69) thinks Jehoiakim may have been one of the Hatti-land kings who appeared and paid tribute to Nebuchadnezzar in the first year of his reign. However, the Chronicler speaks here of an invasion during which Jehoiakim was thrown into chains and threatened with deportation. That was not the invasion of 598/97 since Jehoiakim was dead a hundred days before the capture of Jerusalem (vs. 9). Jehoiakim remained loyal to Babylon

only so long as there was no chance of desertion, but after the
Egyptians had fought Nebuchadnezzar to a draw in 601, he with-
held tribute. The great king revamped and strengthened his army
and returned in 598, laid the city under siege and captured it on
the second of Adar, 597, 15/16 of March by our calendar (Wiseman, *op. cit.*, p. 73—from the Babylonian Chronicle). The Chronicler's assessment of Jehoiakim coincides with that of Kings and
Jeremiah. There is no reference to his death and burial (cf. Jer
xxii 19, xxxvi 30).

[The reign of Jehoiachin, 9–10]: While the Chronicler omits
some of the details about Jehoiachin—his mother's name, the
given name of Zedekiah-Mattaniah, and the catalogue of classes
exiled—he presents others with great accuracy. The list of Jehoiachin's seven sons is given in I Chron iii 17–18. The Weidner texts
report five. The phrase "at the turn of the year" corresponds with
the new data given in the Babylonian Chronicle; the "heavy
tribute" of the latter supports the reference to the costly articles of
the house of God; and the Babylonian Chronicle's "king of his own
choice" is in line with the statement about Nebuchadnezzar's in-
vesting of Zedekiah as his vassal king over Jerusalem and Judah.
Jehoiachin was deported to Babylon, where he was apparently well
treated and finally released from custody (Jer lii 31–34).

On the Babylonian Chronicle, cf. Wiseman, *Chronicles of Chaldaean Kings,* pp. 34, 73; Noth, ZDPV 74 (1958), 133–57; F. X.
Kugler, *Von Moses bis Paulus,* 1922, pp. 147–50; A. Parrot, *Babylon and the Old Testament,* 1958, pp. 89 f.; Albright, BA 5 (1942),
49–55. Incidentally, the royal treatment received by Jehoiachin in
captivity encouraged the people of Judah to hope for his return to
power (Jer xxviii 4) and they probably looked on Zedekiah as
merely a regent. The seals bearing the inscription "Eliakim steward
of Yaukin" may refer to King Jehoiachin and thus indicate that the
royal property remained intact, administered for him by Eliakim.
Cf. W. F. Albright, JBL 51 (1932), 77–106 and BA 5 (1942),
50 f. Another seal with the same inscription impressed on a jar handle
has turned up at Ramat Rahel (*The Israel Digest,* Vol. 4, No. 18,
September 1, 1961, p. 8).

42. THE REIGN OF ZEDEKIAH (598–587 B.C.). THE EXILE
(xxxvi 11–21)†

XXXVI ¹¹ Zedekiah was twenty-one years old when he became king and he reigned eleven years at Jerusalem. ¹² He too did what was evil in the sight of Yahweh his God; he did not humble himself before the prophet Jeremiah who spoke for Yahweh. ¹³ Furthermore, he rebelled against King Nebuchadnezzar who had compelled him to swear [loyalty] by God. He became stubborn and set his mind resolutely against returning to Yahweh God of Israel. ¹⁴ Even the chiefs of ᵃJudah,ᵃ the priests, and the people committed more and more offences, which were just like the abominations of the nations, and rendered unclean the house of Yahweh which he had consecrated at Jerusalem. ¹⁵ Yahweh God of their fathers continuously sent [word] to them through his messengers because he had compassion on his people and on his dwelling place. ¹⁶ But they ridiculed the messengers of God, despised his words, and mocked his prophets until the wrath of Yahweh became so violent against his people that there could be no redress. ¹⁷ So he brought up against them the king of the Chaldeans, slew their young men with the sword in the house of their sanctuary, without compassion for young man, or virgin, or old man, or the infirm; he gave them all into his hand. ¹⁸ All the articles of the house of God, both large and small, the treasures of the house of Yahweh, the treasures of the king and his officials, all of them he brought to Babylon. ¹⁹ He burned down the house of God and broke down the wall of Jerusalem; he burned with fire its palaces and destroyed all its precious articles. ²⁰ Those who es-

† II Chron xxxvi 11–21 ‖ II Kings xxiv 18–xxv 12.

ᵃ⁻ᵃ Add with LXX.

caped the sword he exiled to Babylon and they became slaves to him and his sons until the rise of the kingdom of Persia— 21 to fulfill the word of Yahweh through Jeremiah. Until the land had compensated for the neglect of its sabbaths, all the days of its desolation, it rested until the seventy years were complete.

NOTES

xxxvi 20. Cf. Jer xxvii 7 and vss. 22, 23 below (Sec. 43).

COMMENT

Only the barest outline of the history of Zedekiah is given. He was a full younger brother of Jehoahaz (II Kings xxiv 18; Jer lii 1) and hence the uncle of Jehoiachin. In a way, the important item about Zedekiah is that he too was a son of the revered Josiah, and doubtless picked in part for that reason. His eleven-year reign marked a period of vacillation and indecision due to the circumstances surrounding the status of Jehoiachin; the pro-Egyptian elements also may have had something to do with it since they may have been inspired by Psammeticus II and Hophra, both of whom had designs on Syria.

As always, the Chronicler is interested chiefly in the theological aspects of the story. This is the sermon of the writer informing his hearers of the reason for exile and at the same time pointing out the plan of Yahweh in which they are the participants. Chief blame for the debacle falls upon the king because he consistently refused to follow the directions of the prophets, notably Jeremiah (cf. Jer xxxvii 2). Although there is some indication in the Book of Jeremiah that Zedekiah was the captive of his own officials and vacillated considerably, the Chronicler rightly interprets the over-all picture, the king having lacked the strength to make any unequivocal declaration for Yahweh. The sum (and substance) of the matter was simply that the persistent preachments of the prophets met with equally persistent ridicule. Associated with the king were the officials (vs. 14)—really the powers behind the throne. They had relapsed into the same errors (cf. Jer xxxii 30–35) prevalent before Josiah's reform (cf. Ezek viii for an excellent illustration of idolatrous practices). In addition there was Zedekiah's rebellion against Nebuchadnezzar, who was declared by the prophets to be the instrument of Yahweh to chastise his people (cf. Ezek xvii 11–21; Jer xxv 19, xxvii 6–9). Thus Jerusalem was destroyed, the temple leveled, and the people taken into exile because of the wrath of Yahweh kindled by the refusal of king and officials to listen to his word. That was precisely what Jeremiah had predicted again and again (vs. 21). Whatever may be the precise significance of vs. 21b, the general import appears to be that the future was not without hope. The Exile was a purifying process carried out in line with the law (Lev xxvi 34 f., 43 f.) and the prophets (Jer xxv 11 ff., xxix 10). After the seventy years' rest, God moved again on behalf of his people. See R. Borger, JNES 18 (1959), 74; O. Plöger, "Siebzig Jahre," in Festschrift Friedrich Baumgärtel, 1959, pp. 124–30; W. F. Albright, FSAC, 1957, p. 18.

43. THE DECREE OF CYRUS (ca. 538 B.C.)
(xxxvi 22–23)†

XXXVI ²² In the first year of Cyrus, the king of Persia—to
fulfill the word of Yahweh through Jeremiah—Yahweh aroused
the spirit of Cyrus, the king of Persia, to make a proclamation
throughout all his kingdom which he also put in writing as follows: ²³ "Thus has Cyrus the king of Persia said: Yahweh God
of the heavens has given me all the kingdoms of the earth and
he has appointed me to build for him a house in Jerusalem which
is in Judah. Whoever among you belongs to all his people, may
Yahweh his God be with him and let him go up."

† II Chron xxxvi 22–23 ‖ Ezra i 1–4.

NOTES

xxxvi 22. *Persia*. This is the first mention of Persia in any of the
historical and prophetical books, apart from Ezekiel (xxvii 10, xxxviii 5)
where the references are clearly to the Persia before the conquests of
Cyrus and before its emergence as a world power. Cf. the similar
references to Persia in the Assyrian inscriptions of the ninth–seventh
centuries B.C.

COMMENT

This is the connecting link between Chronicles and Ezra, where
these verses are repeated. Cyrus acts in harmony with the predictions of Jeremiah (xxv 11 ff., xxix 10), only this time for salvation,
that is, the return and rehabilitation of the people. Verse 23 may
allude vaguely to Isa xliv 28.

APPENDIXES

APPENDIX I: PARALLELS

I Chronicles

i 1–4	Gen v
i 5–7	Gen x 2–4
i 8–16	Gen x 6–8, 13–18
i 17–28	Gen x 22–29, xi 14–26
i 29–31	Gen xxv 13–16
i 32–33	Gen xxv 2–4
i 34–37	Gen xxv 19, 24–26, xxxvi 10–19
i 38–42	Gen xxxvi 20–28
i 43–54	Gen xxxvi 31–43
ii 1–2	Gen xxxv 23–26
ii 3–9	Gen xxxviii 2–5, 7, 29, 30, xlvi 12; I Kings iv 31 (v 11H); Josh vii
ii 10–17	Num i 7; Ruth iv 19–22
ii 18–24	I Chron ii 42–49, 50–55
ii 25–41	cf. I Sam xxvii 10, xxx 29
ii 42–45	———————
iii 1–9	II Sam iii 2–5; I Chron xiv 3–7
iii 10–24	———————
iv 1–10	———————
iv 11–20	Num xiii 6; Judg i 13
iv 21–23	———————
iv 24–43	Gen xlvi 10; Num xxvi 12; Josh xix 1–8
v 1–3	Gen xxxv 22, xlvi 9; Exod vi 14; Num xxvi 5–6
v 4–22	———————
v 23–26	cf. Num xxxii 39; II Kings xv 19 f., xvii 6, xviii 11
vi 1–15	Gen xlvi 11; Exod vi 18; Num xxvi 59, 60
vi 16–30	Num iii 17–20; I Sam i 1
vi 31–53	———————
vi 54–81	Josh xxi
vii 1–5	Gen xlvi 13; Num xxvi 23–24
vii 6–12	Gen xlvi 21; Num xxvi 38–40

vii 13	Gen xlvi 24; Num xxvi 48–49
vii 14–19	cf. Num xxvi 29–33
vii 20–29	Num xxvi 35–36
vii 30–40	Gen xlvi 17; Num xxvi 44–46
viii 1–5	Gen xlvi 21; Num xxvi 38–40
viii 6–32	—————
viii 33–40	I Sam xiv 49–51
ix 1	—————
ix 2–3	cf. Neh xi 4a
ix 4–6	cf. Neh xi 4b–6
ix 7–9	cf. Neh xi 7–9
ix 10–13	cf. Neh xi 10–14
ix 14–16	cf. Neh xi 15–18
ix 17–18	cf. Neh xi 19
ix 35–44	I Chron viii 29–38
x 1–14	I Sam xxxi
xi 1–3	II Sam v 1–3
xi 4–9	II Sam v 4–10
xi 10–47	II Sam xxiii 8–35
xii 1–40	—————
xiii 1–14	II Sam vi 2–11
xiv 1–7	II Sam v 11–16
xiv 8–17	II Sam v 17–25
xv 1–24	—————
xv 25–29	II Sam vi 12–19
xvi 1–3	II Sam vi 17–19
xvi 4–43	Pss cv 1–15, xcvi, cvi 1, 47, 48; II Sam vi 19–20
xvii 1–15	II Sam vii 1–17
xvii 16–27	II Sam vii 18–29
xviii 1–13	II Sam viii 1–14
xviii 14–17	II Sam viii 15–18
xix 1–19	II Sam x 1–19
xx 1–8	II Sam xi 1, xii 26, 30, 31, xxi 18–22
xxi 1–30	II Sam xxiv 1–25
xxii 1–19	—————
xxiii 1–32	—————
xxiv 1–31	—————
xxv 1–31	—————
xxvi 1–28	cf. I Chron ix 17–27, xvi 37–43; Ezra ii 42; Neh vii 45, xi 19
xxvi 29–32	—————
xxvii 1–34	—————

xxviii 1–21   ————————
xxix 1–25   ————————
xxix 26–30   I Kings ii 10–12

II CHRONICLES

i 1–13   I Kings iii 1–15
i 14–17   I Kings x 26–29
i 18–ii 15   cf. I Kings v 1–12 (v 15–26H), vii 13–14
ii 16–17   I Kings v 13–18 (v 27–32H)
iii 1–17   I Kings vi 1–38; cf. vii 15–22
iv 1–22   I Kings vii 23–50
v 1–14   I Kings vii 51–viii 11
vi 1–42   I Kings viii 12–53
vii 1–10   I Kings viii 54, 62–66
vii 11–22   I Kings ix 1–9
viii 1–18   I Kings ix 10–28
ix 1–12   I Kings x 1–13
ix 13–28   I Kings x 14–29, v 6, 1a
ix 29–31   I Kings xi 41–43
x 1–19   I Kings xii 1–20
xi 1–4   I Kings xii 21–24
xi 5–17   I Kings xii 25–33
xi 18–23   ————————
xii 1–9   cf. I Kings xiv 25–26
xii 10–14   cf. I Kings xiv 27–28, 21–22
xii 15–16   I Kings xiv 29–31, xv 6
xiii 1–3   I Kings xv 1, 2, 6
xiii 4–21   ————————
xiii 22–23   I Kings xv 7–8
xiv 1–7   I Kings xv 11–12
xiv 8–14   ————————
xv 1–7   ————————
xv 8–15   cf. I Kings xv 12
xv 16–19   I Kings xv 13–15
xvi 1–6   I Kings xv 17–22
xvi 7–10   ————————
xvi 11–14   I Kings xv 23–24
xvii 1–19   cf. I Kings xv 24c
xviii 1–34   I Kings xxii 1–36
xix 1–11   ————————

xx 1–30	———————
xx 31–34	I Kings xxii 41–47
xx 35–37	I Kings xxii 48–50
xxi 1	I Kings xxii 51
xxi 2–4	———————
xxi 5–11	II Kings viii 17–22
xxi 12–15	———————
xxi 16–20	II Kings viii 23–24
xxii 1–9	II Kings viii 24b–29, ix 21, 27–28
xxii 10–12	II Kings xi 1–3
xxiii 1–11	II Kings xi 4–12
xxiii 12–21	II Kings xi 13–20
xxiv 1–3	II Kings xii 1–4
xxiv 4–14	II Kings xii 5–16
xxiv 15–22	———————
xxiv 23–27	II Kings xii 18–22
xxv 1–4	II Kings xiv 2–6
xxv 5–16	II Kings xiv 7
xxv 17–28	II Kings xiv 8–20
xxvi 1–5	II Kings xiv 21–xv 4
xxvi 6–15	———————
xxvi 16–23	II Kings xv 5–7
xxvii 1–9	II Kings xv 32–38
xxviii 1–4	II Kings xvi 1–4
xxviii 5–8	II Kings xvi 5
xxviii 9–15	———————
xxviii 16–21	II Kings xvi 7–9
xxviii 22–27	II Kings xvi 19, 20
xxix 1–2	cf. II Kings xviii 1–3
xxix 3–36	———————
xxx 1–27	———————
xxxi 1–21	cf. II Kings xviii 4
xxxii 1–23	II Kings xviii 13–37, xix 14–19, 35–37; Isa xxxvi 1–22, xxxvii 14–19, 36–38
xxxii 24	II Kings xx 1–3; Isa xxxviii 1–3
xxxii 25–26	II Kings xx 12–19; Isa xxxix 1–8
xxxii 27–31	———————
xxxii 32–33	II Kings xx 20–21
xxxiii 1–10	II Kings xxi 1–10
xxxiii 11–17	———————
xxxiii 18–20	II Kings xxi 17–18
xxxiii 21–25	II Kings xxi 19–24

xxxiv 1–2	II Kings xxii 1–2
xxxiv 3–7	————————
xxxiv 8–13	II Kings xxii 3–7
xxxiv 14–21	II Kings xxii 8–13
xxxiv 22–28	II Kings xxii 14–20
xxxiv 29–33	II Kings xxiii 1–3
xxxv 1–19	II Kings xxiii 21–23
xxxv 20–27	II Kings xxiii 28–30
xxxvi 1–3	II Kings xxiii 30b–33
xxxvi 4–8	II Kings xxiii 34–xxiv 7
xxxvi 9–10	II Kings xxiv 8–17
xxxvi 11–21	II Kings xxiv 18–xxv 12
xxxvi 22–23	Ezra i 1–4

APPENDIX II. GENEALOGICAL CHARTS

A. NOAH (I Chron i 5-23)

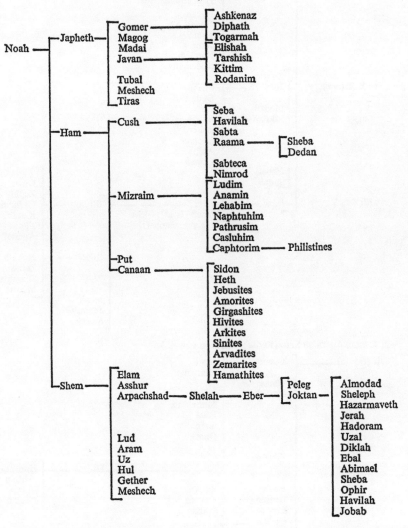

B. ABRAHAM'S DESCENDANTS

(Females designated by *italics*)

1. DESCENDANTS OF ABRAHAM (I Chron i 29–37)

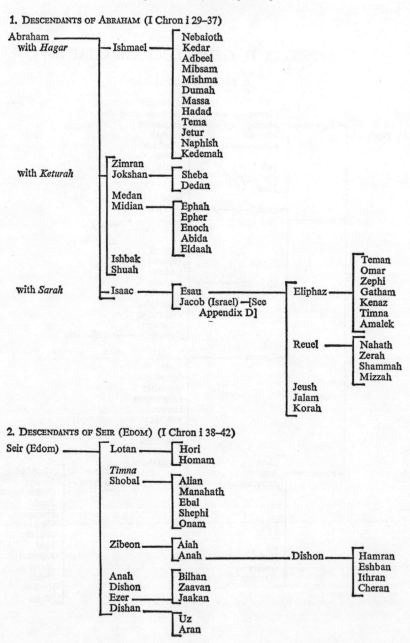

2. DESCENDANTS OF SEIR (EDOM) (I Chron i 38–42)

C. EDOM: KINGS AND CHIEFS

1. KINGS OF EDOM (I Chron i 43–50)

King	Father	City
Bela	Beor	Dinhabah
Jobab	Zerah	Bozrah
Husham		Teman
Hadad	Bedad	Avith
Samlah		Masrekah
Saul		Rehoboth
Baal-hanan	Achbor	
Hadad		Pai

2. CHIEFS OF EDOM (I Chron i 51–54)

Timna
Aliah
Jetheth
Oholibamah
Elah
Pinon
Kenaz
Teman
Mibzar
Magdiel
Iram

D. JACOB*

1. JACOB AND LEAH

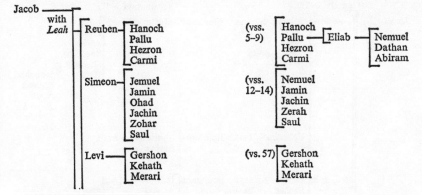

(Gen xlvi 8–25)   (Num xxvi 5–57)

Jacob
with Leah

Reuben — Hanoch / Pallu / Hezron / Carmi

(vss. 5–9) Hanoch / Pallu — Eliab — Nemuel / Dathan / Abiram / Hezron / Carmi

Simeon — Jemuel / Jamin / Ohad / Jachin / Zohar / Saul

(vss. 12–14) Nemuel / Jamin / Jachin / Zerah / Saul

Levi — Gershon / Kehath / Merari

(vs. 57) Gershon / Kehath / Merari

*The Chronicler gives the genealogy of each of Jacob's sons separately, as may be seen from the subsequent charts. This chart gives an over-all picture of the twelve tribes and how their lines of descent are handled in the Chronicler's sources: Gen xlvi 8–25 and Num xxvi 5–57. The order in which Jacob's sons appear in Genesis is listed at the left; the descendants of his sons, as they appear in Numbers, are listed at the right, with the verses in Num xxvi in which they occur. The order of their appearance in Numbers is as follows: Reuben, Simeon, Gad, Judah, Issachar, Zebulun, Manasseh, Ephraim, Benjamin, Dan, Asher, Naphtali, and Levi.

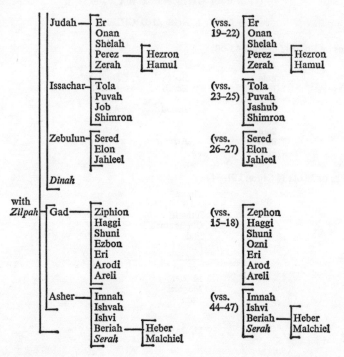

2. JACOB AND RACHEL

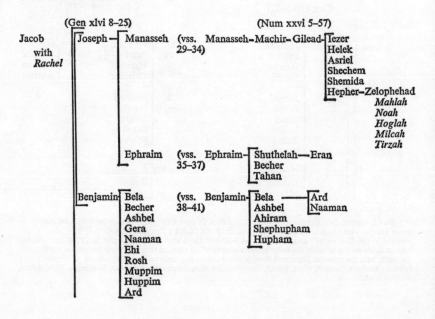

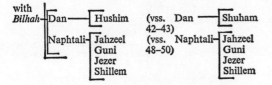

```
with
Bilhah┤Dan────┤ Hushim      (vss.  Dan ───┤ Shuham
                            42-43)
        Naphtali┤ Jahzeel    (vss.  Naphtali┤ Jahzeel
                 Guni        48-50)         Guni
                 Jezer                      Jezer
                 Shillem                    Shillem
```

E. THE LINE OF JUDAH

1. JUDAH (I Chron ii 3-8)

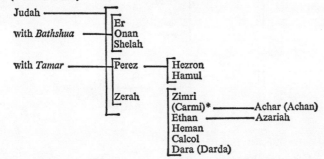

```
Judah ────────────┐
                  ┌Er
with Bathshua ────┤Onan
                  └Shelah

with Tamar ───────┤Perez ──────┐Hezron
                               └Hamul

                  └Zerah       ┌Zimri
                               │(Carmi)* ────────Achar (Achan)
                               │Ethan ──────────Azariah
                               │Heman
                               │Calcol
                               └Dara (Darda)
```

2. ANCESTORS OF DAVID (ii 9-17)

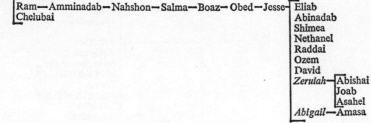

```
Hezron─┤Jerahmeel
        Ram─Amminadab─Nahshon─Salma─Boaz─Obed─Jesse┤Eliab
        Chelubai                                    Abinadab
                                                    Shimea
                                                    Nethanel
                                                    Raddai
                                                    Ozem
                                                    David
                                                    Zeruiah─┤Abishai
                                                             Joab
                                                             Asahel
                                                    Abigail─Amasa
```

F. CALEBITES

1. CALEBITES I (I Chron ii 18-24)

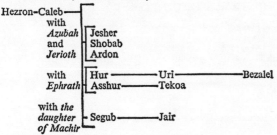

```
Hezron-Caleb──────┐
    with           ┌Jesher
    Azubah         │Shobab
    and            └Ardon
    Jerioth

    with           ┌Hur ──────Uri──────────Bezalel
    Ephrath        └Asshur────Tekoa

    with the
    daughter      ┤Segub───────Jair
    of Machir
```

*Carmi not mentioned among the five sons of Zerah listed in vs. 6.

2. CALEBITES II (ii 42–49)

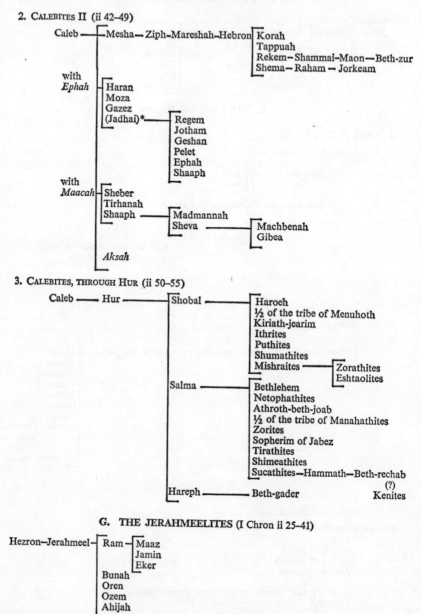

Caleb —[Mesha — Ziph — Mareshah — Hebron [Korah
                                                 Tappuah
                                                 Rekem — Shammai — Maon — Beth-zur
                                                 Shema — Raham — Jorkeam

with *Ephah* —[Haran
              Moza
              Gazez
              (Jadhai)* —[Regem
                                  Jotham
                                  Geshan
                                  Pelet
                                  Ephah
                                  Shaaph

with *Maacah* —[Sheber
                Tirhanah
                Shaaph —[Madmannah
                             Sheva —[Machbenah
                                         Gibea

Aksah

3. CALEBITES, THROUGH HUR (ii 50–55)

Caleb — Hur —[Shobal —[Haroeh
                                  ½ of the tribe of Menuhoth
                                  Kiriath-jearim
                                  Ithrites
                                  Puthites
                                  Shumathites
                                  Mishraites —[Zorathites
                                                   Eshtaolites
                Salma —[Bethlehem
                                Netophathites
                                Athroth-beth-joab
                                ½ of the tribe of Manahathites
                                Zorites
                                Sopherim of Jabez
                                Tirathites
                                Shimeathites
                                Sucathites — Hammath — Beth-rechab
                Hareph — Beth-gader
                                                   (?)
                                                   Kenites

G. THE JERAHMEELITES (I Chron ii 25–41)

Hezron — Jerahmeel —[Ram —[Maaz
                                  Jamin
                                  Eker
                       Bunah
                       Oren
                       Ozem
                       Ahijah

*Jadhai not mentioned among the sons of Caleb by *Ephah* listed in vs. 46.

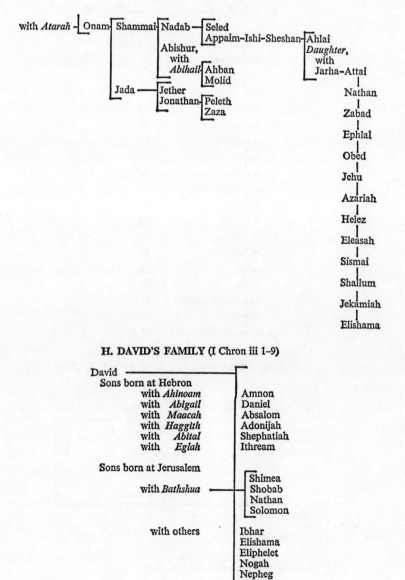

```
with Atarah ─┤ Onam┤ Shammai┤ Nadab ──┤ Seled
             │                        │ Appaim─Ishi─Sheshan┤ Ahlai
             │       Abishur,         │                    │ Daughter,
             │       with             │                    │ with
             │         Abihail┤ Ahban │                    │ Jarha─Attai
             │               └ Molid  │
             └ Jada ──┤ Jether        │                           Nathan
                        Jonathan┤ Peleth                             │
                               └ Zaza                               Zabad
                                                                     │
                                                                   Ephlal
                                                                     │
                                                                   Obed
                                                                     │
                                                                   Jehu
                                                                     │
                                                                   Azariah
                                                                     │
                                                                   Helez
                                                                     │
                                                                   Eleasah
                                                                     │
                                                                   Sismai
                                                                     │
                                                                   Shallum
                                                                     │
                                                                   Jekamiah
                                                                     │
                                                                   Elishama
```

H. DAVID'S FAMILY (I Chron iii 1–9)

David ────────────────────┐

Sons born at Hebron
- with *Ahinoam* — Amnon
- with *Abigail* — Daniel
- with *Maacah* — Absalom
- with *Haggith* — Adonijah
- with *Abital* — Shephatiah
- with *Eglah* — Ithream

Sons born at Jerusalem

- with *Bathshua* — Shimea, Shobab, Nathan, Solomon

- with others — Ibhar, Elishama, Eliphelet, Nogah, Nepheg, Japhia, Elishama, Eliada, Eliphelet

I. KINGS OF JUDAH (I Chron iii 10–16)

Name	Age at Death
Solomon	?
Rehoboam	58
Abijah	?
Asa	?
Jehoshaphat	60
Joram	40
Ahaziah	23
Joash	47
Amaziah	54
Azariah (Uzziah)	68
Jotham	41
Ahaz	36
Hezekiah	54
Manasseh	67
Amon	24
Josiah	39
Jehoahaz (Jonathan)	23+
Jehoiakim	36
Jehoiachin (Jeconiah)	18+
Zedekiah	32

J. EXILIC AND POSTEXILIC LINE (I Chron iii 17–24)

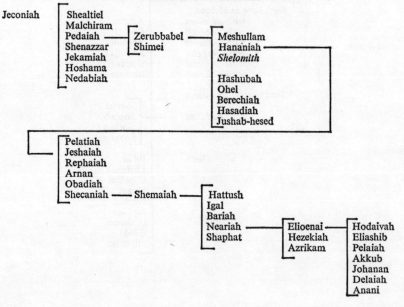

Jeconiah

Shealtiel
Malchiram
Pedaiah ——— Zerubbabel ——— Meshullam
Shenazzar   Shimei   Hananiah
Jekamiah   Shelomith
Hoshama
Nedabiah   Hashubah
                                    Ohel
                                    Berechiah
                                    Hasadiah
                                    Jushab-hesed

Pelatiah
Jeshaiah
Rephaiah
Arnan
Obadiah
Shecaniah ——— Shemaiah ——— Hattush
                                Igal
                                Bariah
                                Neariah ——— Elioenai ——— Hodaivah
                                Shaphat   Hezekiah   Eliashib
                                               Azrikam   Pelaiah
                                                               Akkub
                                                               Johanan
                                                               Delaiah
                                                               Anani

K. SOUTHERN FAMILIES

1. Southern Family at Zorah (I Chron iv 1–2)

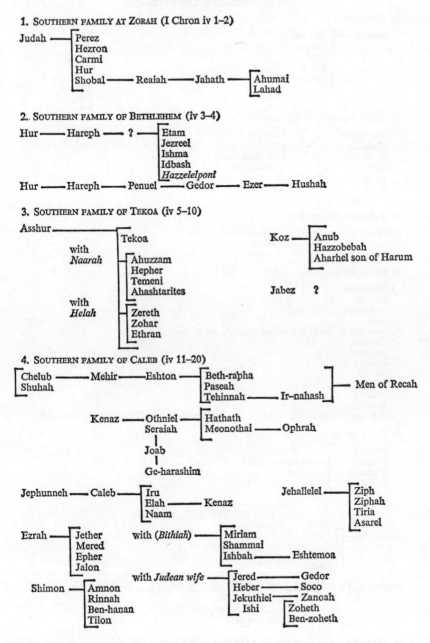

2. Southern Family of Bethlehem (iv 3–4)

3. Southern Family of Tekoa (iv 5–10)

4. Southern Family of Caleb (iv 11–20)

L. SIMEON (I Chron iv 24–43)

1. GENEALOGY

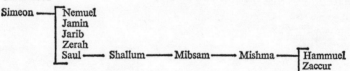

Simeon —
- Nemuel
- Jamin
- Jarib
- Zerah
- Saul —— Shallum —— Mibsam —— Mishma —— Hammuel / Zaccur / Shimei

2. CITIES OCCUPIED BY SIMEON

Beer-sheba	Hormah
Moladah	Ziklag
Hazar-shual	Beth-marcaboth
Bilhah	Hazar-susim
Ezem	Beth-biri
Tolad	Shaaraim
Bethuel	

3. THEIR SETTLEMENTS

Etam	Tochen
Ain	Ashan
Rimmon	

4. THEIR OFFICIAL GENEALOGY

Meshobab
Jamlech
Joshah son of Amaziah
Joel
Jehu son of Joshibiah, son of Seraiah, son of Asiel
Elioenai
Jaakobah
Jeshohaiah
Asaiah
Adiel
Jesimiel
Benaiah
Ziza son of Shiphi, son of Allon, son of Jedaiah, son of Shimri, son of Shemaiah

5. THE LEADERS

Pelatiah
Neariah
Rephaiah
Uzziel
} sons of Ishi

M. REUBEN (I Chron v 1–10)

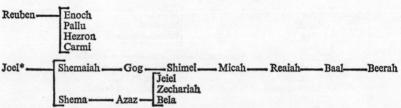

Reuben —
- Enoch
- Pallu
- Hezron
- Carmi

Joel* —— Shemaiah —— Gog —— Shimei —— Micah —— Reaiah —— Baal —— Beerah
                    Jeiel / Zechariah
        Shema —— Azaz —— Bela

Territory occupied: Aroer; as far as Nebo and Baal-meon; Gilead.

*Syr. makes Joel the son of Carmi, but we cannot be sure.

N. GAD AND ½ MANASSEH

1. GAD (I Chron v 11–22)

a. Genealogy:

Gad— ? —Buz—Jahdo—Jeshishai—Michael—Gilead—Jaroah—Huri—Abihail—

Joel
Shapham
Janai
Shaphat
Michael
Meshullam
Sheba
Jorai
Jacan
Zia
Eber

b. Chief: Ahi, son of Abdiel, son of Guni.
c. Territory occupied: Gilead, Bashan, Sharon.

2. ½ MANASSEH (TRANSJORDAN) (v 23–26)

Chiefs: Epher, Ishi, Eliel, Azriel, Jeremiah, Hodaviah, Jahdiel.

O. CHIEF PRIESTS (I Chron vi 1–15)

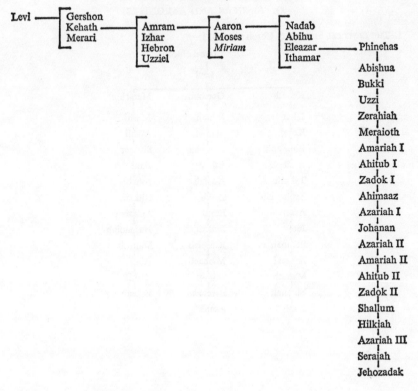

Levi — Gershon, Kehath, Merari — Amram, Izhar, Hebron, Uzziel — Aaron, Moses, *Miriam* — Nadab, Abihu, Eleazar, Ithamar — Phinehas

Abishua
Bukki
Uzzi
Zerahiah
Meraioth
Amariah I
Ahitub I
Zadok I
Ahimaaz
Azariah I
Johanan
Azariah II
Amariah II
Ahitub II
Zadok II
Shallum
Hilkiah
Azariah III
Seraiah
Jehozadak

P. OTHER DESCENDANTS OF LEVI (I Chron vi 16–30)

Levi

Gershom		Kehath				Merari	
Libni	Shimei	Amram	Izhar	Hebron	Uzziel	Mahli	Mushi
Jahath			(Amminadab)			Libni	
Zimmah			Korah			Shimei	
Joah			Assir			Uzzah	
Iddo			Elkanah — Amasai			Shimea	
Zerah			Ebiasaph	Ahimoth		Haggiah	
Jeatheri			Assir	Elkanah		Asaiah	
			Tahath	Zophai			
			Uriel	Nahath			
			Uzziah	Eliab			
			Saul	Jeroham			
				Elkanah			
				Samuel — Joel / Abijah			

Q. SINGERS AND AARONITES

1. THE LEVITICAL SINGERS (I Chron vi 31–47)

Israel (Jacob)

Levi

Kehath	Gershom	Merari
Izhar	Jahath	Mushi
Korah	Shimei	Mahli
Ebiasaph	Zimmah	Shemer
Assir	Ethan	Bani
Tahath	Adaiah	Amzi
Zephaniah	Zerah	Hilkiah
Azariah	Ethni	Amaziah
Joel	Malchijah	Hashabiah
Elkanah	Baaseiah	Malluch
Amasai	Michael	Abdi
Mahath	Shimea	Kishi
Elkanah	Berechiah	Ethan*
Zuph	Asaph*	

Toah
|
Eliel
|
Jeroham
|
Elkanah
|
Samuel
|
Joel
|
Heman*

2. THE AARONITES (vi 50–53)

Aaron —— Eleazar —— Phinehas —— Abishua —— Bukki —— Uzzi —— Zerahiah
|
Meraioth
|
Amariah
|
Ahitub
|
Zadok
|
Ahimaaz

*Singers appointed by David.

R. ISSACHAR, BENJAMIN, DAN, NAPHTALI

1. ISSACHAR (I Chron vii 1–3)

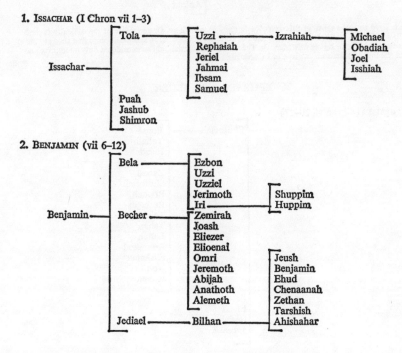

Issachar —— Tola —— Uzzi —— Izrahiah —— Michael
Rephaiah   Obadiah
Jeriel   Joel
Jahmai   Isshiah
Ibsam
Samuel

Puah
Jashub
Shimron

2. BENJAMIN (vii 6–12)

Benjamin —— Bela —— Ezbon
Uzzi
Uzziel
Jerimoth
Iri —— Shuppim
Huppim

Becher —— Zemirah
Joash
Eliezer
Elioenai
Omri —— Jeush
Jeremoth   Benjamin
Abijah   Ehud
Anathoth   Chenaanah
Alemeth   Zethan
                Tarshish
Jediael —— Bilhan —— Ahishahar

3. DAN (vii 12b)?

Dan? ———Hushim

4. Naphtali (vii 13)

Jacob ——————— Naphtali ——— Jahaziel
with *Bilhah*   Guni
                                        Jezer
                                        Shallum

S. MANASSEH (I Chron vii 14–19)*

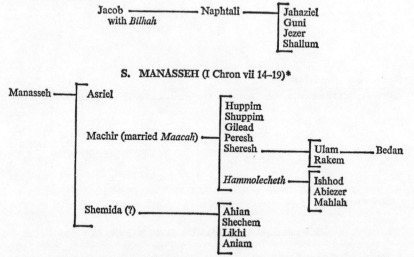

*It is hard to make sense of this exceedingly garbled genealogy. One example of the difficulty is that vs. 17b has the sons of Sheresh as descendants of Gilead, although vs. 16 specifically says that they are the descendants of Machir by his wife Maacah. Therefore, this chart should be considered only an approximation of the line of Manasseh as given in I Chronicles.

T. EPHRAIM AND ASHER

1. EPHRAIM (I Chron vii 20–27)

Ephraim ——— Shuthelah——— Bered
                                         Tahath
                                         Eleadah
                                         Tahath
                                         Zabad
                                         Shuthelah
                                         Rephah
                                         Resheph
                                         Telah
                                         Tahan
                                         Ladan
                                         Ammihud
                                         Elishama
                                         Non
                                         Joshua

                             Ezer
                             Elead
                             Beriah
                             Sheerah

2. ASHER (I Chron vii 30–39)

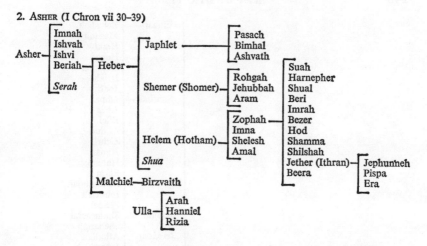

U. BENJAMIN (I Chron viii 1–32)

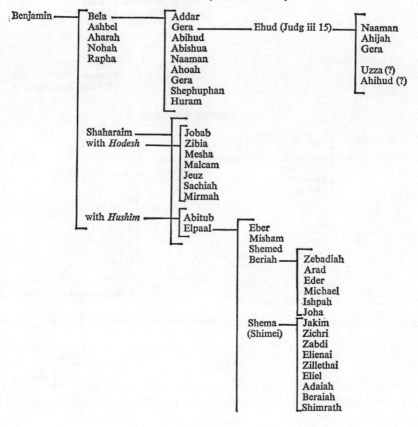

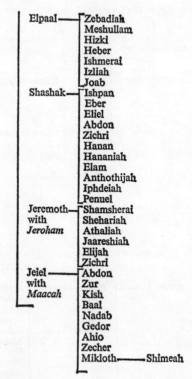

Elpaal———┌Zebadiah
          │ Meshullam
          │ Hizki
          │ Heber
          │ Ishmerai
          │ Izliah
          └Joab
Shashak——┌Ishpan
          │ Eber
          │ Eliel
          │ Abdon
          │ Zichri
          │ Hanan
          │ Hananiah
          │ Elam
          │ Anthothijah
          │ Iphdeiah
          └Penuel
Jeremoth——┌Shamsherai
with   │ Shehariah
Jeroham │ Athaliah
          │ Jaareshiah
          │ Elijah
          └Zichri
Jeiel————┌Abdon
with   │ Zur
Maacah │ Kish
          │ Baal
          │ Nadab
          │ Gedor
          │ Ahio
          │ Zecher
          └Mikloth———Shimeah

V. THE FAMILY OF SAUL

1. THE FAMILY OF SAUL (I Chron viii 33–40)

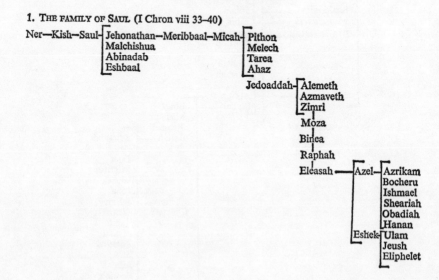

Ner—Kish—Saul—┌Jehonathan—Meribbaal—Micah—┌Pithon
              │ Malchishua   │ Melech
              │ Abinadab   │ Tarea
              └Eshbaal   └Ahaz
                                  Jedoaddah—┌Alemeth
                                            │ Azmaveth
                                            └Zimri
                                             Moza
                                             Binea
                                             Raphah
                                             Eleasah———Azel—┌Azrikam
                                                            │ Bocheru
                                                            │ Ishmael
                                                            │ Sheariah
                                                            │ Obadiah
                                                            └Hanan
                                                       Eshek—┌Ulam
                                                             │ Jeush
                                                             └Eliphelet

2. The Abiel Family (I Sam xiv 49–51)

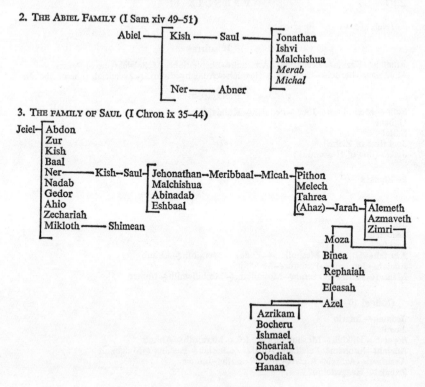

3. The family of Saul (I Chron ix 35–44)

W. RETURNEES

1. Laymen

(I Chron ix 1–9)

JUDAHITES

Uthai Ammihud Omri Imri Bani (of the line of Perez)
Asaiah (of the line of Shelah)
Jeuel (of the line of Zerah)

BENJAMINITES

Sallu Meshullam Hodaviah Hassenuah
Ibneiah Jeroham
Elah Uzzi Michri
Meshullam Shephatiah Reuel Ibnijah

(Neh xi 3–9)

JUDAHITES

Athaiah←Uzziah←Zechariah←Amariah←Shephatiah←Mahalalel (line of Perez)
Maaseiah←Baruch←Colhozeh←Hazaiah←Adaiah←Joiarib←Zechariah (line of Shelah)

BENJAMINITES

Sallu←Meshullam←Joed←Pedaiah←Kolaiah←Maaseiah←Ithiel←Jeshaiah
Gabbai
Sallai
Joel (line of Zichri)
Judah (line of Hassenuah)

2. PRIESTS

(I Chron ix 10–13)

Jedaiah
Jehoiarib
Jachin
Azariah←Hilkiah←Meshullam←Zadok←Meraioth←Ahitub
Adaiah←Jeroham←Pashhur←Malchijah
Maasai←Adiel←Jahzerah←Meshullam←Meshillemith←Immer

(Neh xi 10–14)

Jedaiah←Joiarib
Jachin
Seraiah←Hilkiah←Meshullam←Zadok←Meraioth←Ahitub
Adaiah←Jeroham←Pelaliah←Amzi←Zechariah←Pashhur←Malchijah
Amashsai←Azarel←Ahzai←Meshillemoth←Immer
Zabdiel←Haggedolim?

3. LEVITES

(I Chron ix 14–16)

Shemaiah←Hasshub←Azrikam←Hashabiah (line of Merari)
Bakbakkar←Heresh←Galal←Mattaniah←Mica←Zichri (line of Asaph)
Obadiah←Shemaiah←Galal (line of Jeduthun)
Berechiah←Asa←Elkanah

(Neh xi 15–18)

Shemaiah←Hasshub←Azrikam←Hashabiah←Bunni
Shabbethai
Jozabad
Mattaniah←Micah←Zabdi (line of Asaph)
Bakbukiah
Abda←Shammua←Galal (line of Jeduthun)

INDEX OF PLACE AND PERSONAL NAMES

NOTES

1. The transcriptional spelling is generally that appearing in the first reference. Important variations are, however, noted where they do occur.

2. It is often difficult, perhaps impossible, to distinguish between personal and place names, especially those of the twelve tribes of Israel. The latter are all listed as personal names.

3. The general practice has been followed in transcriptions—

' = *aleph*	s = *samek*
' = *ayin*	ṣ = *tsade*
ḥ = *heth*	ś = *sin*
h = *he*	š = *shin*
ṭ = *teth*	y = *yod*
t = *taw*	

No attempt has been made to distinguish between consonants with or without *dagesh*.

PLACE NAMES

Abel-maim (*'bl-mym*)   II Chron xvi 4

Adoraim (*'dwrym*)   II Chron xi 9

Adullam (*'dlm*)   I Chron xi 15; II Chron xi 7; Neh xi 30

Aijalon (*'ylwn*)   I Chron vi 69, viii 13; II Chron xi 10, xxviii 18

Arabia (*'rb*)   II Chron ix 14

Aram (*'rm*)   II Chron i 17, xvi 2,7, xviii 10,30,34, xxii 5,6, xxvi 5,23

Ashdod (*'šdwd*)   II Chron xxvi 6(*bis*)

Assyria (*'šwr*) I Chron v 6,26(*bis*); II Chron xxviii 16,20,21,
xxx 6, xxxii 1,4,7,10,11,21,22, xxxiii 11; Ezra vi 22; Neh ix 32
Azekah (*'zqh*) II Chron xi 9; Neh xi 30

Baalath (*b'lt*) I Chron iv 33, xiii 6; II Chron viii 6
Babylon (*bbl*) II Chron xxxii 31, xxxiii 11, xxxvi 6(*bis*), 7(*bis*),
10,18,20; Ezra i 11, ii 1(*bis*), v 12(*bis*), 13,14(*bis*), 17, vi 1,
5, vii 6,9,16, viii 1; Neh vii 6, xiii 6
Beer-sheba (*b'r-šb'*) I Chron iv 28, xxi 2; II Chron xix 4, xxiv
1, xxx 5; Neh xi 27,30
Ben-hinnom (*bn-hnm*) II Chron xxviii 3, xxxiii 6
Beracah (*brkh*) II Chron xx 26(*bis*)
Bethel (*byt-'l*) I Chron vii 28; II Chron xiii 19; Ezra ii 28; Neh
vii 32, xi 31
Beth-horon (*byt-ḥwrwn*) I Chron vi 68, vii 24; II Chron viii
5(*bis*), xxv 13
Bethlehem (*byt lḥm*) I Chron iv 22, xi 16,17,18,26; II Chron xi
6; Ezra ii 21; Neh vii 26
Beth-shemesh (*byt šmš*) I Chron vi 59; II Chron xxv 21,23,
xxviii 18
Beth-zur (*byt ṣwr*) II Chron xi 7; Neh iii 16

Carchemish (*krkmyš*) II Chron xxxv 20

Damascus (*drmśq*) I Chron xviii 5,6; II Chron xvi 2, xxiv 23,
xxviii 5,23

Edom (*'dwm*) I Chron i 43,51,54, xviii 11,12,13(*bis*); II Chron
viii 17, xx 2 (MT=*rm*), xxi 8, xxv 19,20
Egypt (*mṣrym*) I Chron xiii 5, xvii 21; II Chron i 17, v 10, vi 5,
vii 8,22, ix 26,28, x 2(*bis*), xii 2,9, xx 10, xxvi 8, xxxv 20,
xxxvi 3,4(*bis*); Neh ix 9,17 (with Greek), 18
Eloth (*'ylwt*) II Chron viii 17, xxvi 2
En-gedi (*'yn gdy*) II Chron xx 2
Ephron (*'prwn*) II Chron xiii 19
Etam (*'yṭm*) I Chron iv 32; II Chron xi 6
Euphrates (*prt*) I Chron v 9, xviii 3; II Chron xxxv 20
Ezion-geber (*'ṣywn gbr*) II Chron viii 17, xx 36

Gath (*gt*) I Chron vii 21, viii 13, xviii 1, xx 6,8; II Chron xi 8, xxvi 6

Geba (*gbʿ*) I Chron vi 60, viii 6; II Chron xvi 6; Ezra ii 26; Neh vii 30, xi 31, xii 29

Gederoth (*gdrwt*) II Chron xxviii 18

Gerar (*grr*) II Chron xiv 12,13

Gibeah (*gbʿh*) I Chron xi 31; II Chron xiii 2

Gibeon (*gbʿwn*) I Chron viii 29, ix 35, xiv 16, xvi 39, xxi 29; II Chron i 3,13; Neh iii 7, vii 25

Gihon (*gyḥwn*) II Chron xxxii 30, xxxiii 14

Gimzo (*gmzw*) II Chron xxviii 18

Gur-baal (*gwr bʿl*) II Chron xxvi 7

Hamath (*ḥmt*) I Chron xiii 5, xviii 3,9; II Chron vii 8, viii 4

Hamath-zobah (*ḥmt ṣwbh*) II Chron viii 3

Hassis (*ḥṣyṣ*) II Chron xx 16

Hazazon-tamar (*ḥṣṣwn tmr*) II Chron xx 2

Hebron (*ḥbrwn*) I Chron iii 1,4, vi 55,57, xi 1,3(*bis*), xii 24,39, xxix 27; II Chron xi 10

Horeb (*ḥrb*) II Chron v 10

Ijon (*ʿywn*) II Chron xvi 4

Jabneh (*ybnh*) II Chron xxvi 6

Jericho (*yrḥw*) I Chron vi 78, xix 5; II Chron xxviii 15; Ezra ii 34; Neh iii 2, vii 36

Jeruel (*yrwʾl*) II Chron xx 16

Jerusalem (*yrwšlm*) I Chron iii 4,5, vi 10,15,32, viii 28,32, ix 3, 34,38, xi 4, xiv 3,4, xv 3, xviii 7, xix 15, xx 1,3, xxi 4,15,16, xxiii 25, xxviii 1, xxix 27; II Chron i 4,13,14,15, ii 6,15, iii 1, v 2, vi 6, viii 6, ix 1,25,27,30, x 18, xi 1,5,14,16, xii 2,3,4,5,7,9, 13(*bis*), xiii 2, xiv 14, xv 10, xvii 13, xix 1,4,8(*bis*), xx 5,15, 17,18,20,27(*bis*), 28,31, xxi 5,11,13,20, xxii 1,2, xxiii 2, xxiv 1,6,9,18,23, xxv 1(*bis*), 23(*bis*), 27, xxvi 3(*bis*), 9,15, xxvii 1, 8, xxviii 1,10,24,27, xxix 1,8, xxx 1,2,3,5,11,13,14,21,26(*bis*), xxxi 4, xxxii 2,9(*bis*), 10,12,18,19,22,23,25,26,33, xxxiii 1,4,7,9, 13,15,21, xxxiv 1,3,5,7,9,22,29,30,32(*bis*), xxxv 1,18,24(*bis*), xxxvi 1,2,3,4,5,9,10,11,14,19,23; Ezra i 2,3(*bis*), 4,5,7,11, ii 1,68,

70, iii 1,8(*bis*), iv 6,7,8,12,20,23,24, v 1,2,14,15,16,17, vi 3, 5(*bis*), 9,12,18, vii 7,8,9,13,14,15,16,17,19,27, viii 29,30,31,32, ix 9, x 7(*bis*), 9; Neh i 2,3, ii 11,12,13,17(*bis*), 20, iii 8,9,12, iv 1,2,16, vi 7, vii 2,3(*bis*), 6, viii 15, xi 1(*bis*), 2,3,4,6,22, xii 27(*bis*), 28,29,43, xiii 6,7,15,16,19,20
Jeshanah (*yšnh*) II Chron xiii 19
Jezreel (*yzr⁽l*) I Chron iii 1; II Chron xxii 6(*bis*)
Joppa (*ypw'*) II Chron ii 15; Ezra iii 7
Jordan (*yrdn*) I Chron vi 78, xii 16,38, xix 17, xxvi 30; II Chron iv 17

Kidron (*qdrwn*) II Chron xv 16, xxix 16, xxx 14
Kiriath-jearim (*qryt y'rym*) I Chron xiii 5,6; II Chron i 4; Neh vii 29

Lachish (*lkyš*) II Chron xi 9, xxv 27(*bis*), xxxii 9; Neh xi 30
Lebanon (*hlbnwn*) II Chron ii 7(*bis*), 15, viii 6, ix 16,20, xxv 18(*tris*); Ezra iii 7
Libnah (*lbnh*) I Chron vi 57; II Chron xxi 10

Mareshah (*mršh*) II Chron xi 8, xiv 8,9, xx 37
Megiddo (*mgdw*) I Chron vii 29; II Chron xxxv 22
Millo (*mlw'*) I Chron xi 8; II Chron xxxii 5
Mizpah (*mṣph*) II Chron xvi 6; Neh iii 7,15,19
Mount Ephraim (*hr 'prym*) I Chron vi 67; II Chron xiii 4, xv 8, xix 4
Mount Moriah (*hr hmwryh*) II Chron iii 1
Mount Seir (*hr ś'yr*) I Chron iv 42; II Chron xx 10,22,23
Mount Zemaraim (*hr ṣmrym*) II Chron xiii 4

Negeb (*ngb*) II Chron xxviii 18

Ophel ('*pl*) II Chron xxvii 3, xxxiii 14; Neh iii 26,27, xi 21
Ophir ('*wpyr*) I Chron xxix 4; II Chron viii 18, ix 10

Parvaim (*prwym*) II Chron iii 6
Persia (*prs*) II Chron xxxvi 20,22(*bis*); Ezra i 1(*bis*), 2,8, iii 7, iv 3,5(*bis*), 7,24, vi 14, vii 1, ix 9

Ramah (*hrmh*) II Chron xvi 1,5,6, xxii 6; Ezra ii 26; Neh vii 30, xi 33

Ramoth-gilead (*rmwt glʻd*) II Chron xviii 2,3,5,11,14,19,28, xxii 5

Rock (*slʻ*) II Chron xxv 12(*bis*)

Samaria (*šmrwn*) II Chron xviii 2,9, xxii 9, xxv 13,24, xxviii 8, 9,15; Ezra iv 10,17; Neh iii 34

Sheba (*šbʼ*) II Chron ix 1,3,9,12

Shechem (*škm*) I Chron vi 67, vii 28; II Chron x 1(*bis*)

Shephelah (*šplh*) I Chron xxvii 28; II Chron i 15, ix 27, xxvi 10, xxviii 18

Soco (*škw*) II Chron xi 7, xxviii 18

Succoth (*skwt*) II Chron iv 17

Tadmor (*tdmr*) II Chron viii 4

Tarshish (*tršyš*) II Chron ix 21(*bis*), xx 36,37

Tekoa (*tqwʻ*) II Chron xi 6, xx 20

Timnah (*tmnh*) II Chron xxviii 18

Tyre (*ṣr*) I Chron xiv 1; II Chron ii 10

Valley of Salt (*gyʼ hmlḥ*) I Chron xviii 12; II Chron xxv 11

Zarethan (*ṣrdh*) II Chron iv 17

Zephathah (*ṣpth*) II Chron xiv 9

Zion (*ṣywn*) I Chron xi 5; II Chron v 2

Ziph (*zyp*) II Chron xi 8

Zorah (*ṣrʻh*) II Chron xi 10; Neh xi 29

PERSONAL AND OTHER NAMES

Aaron (*ʼhrn*) I Chron vi 3(*bis*), 49,50,54,57, xii 28, xv 4, xxiii 13(*bis*), 28,32, xxiv 1(*bis*), 19,31, xxvii 17; II Chron xiii 9,10, xxvi 8, xxix 21, xxxi 19, xxxv 14(*bis*); Ezra vii 5; Neh x 39, xii 47

Abdi (*ʻbdy*) I Chron vi 44; II Chron xxix 12; Ezra x 26

Abdon (*ʻbdwn*) I Chron viii 23,30, ix 36; II Chron xxxiv 20

Abihail (*'byhyl*)   I Chron ii 29, v 14; II Chron xi 18

Abijah (*'byh*)   I Chron iii 10, vi 28, vii 8, xxiv 10; II Chron xi 20, 22, xii 16, xiii 1,2,3,4,15,17,19,20,21,22,23, xxix 1; Neh x 8, xii 4,17

Abraham (*'brhm*)   I Chron i 27,28,32,34, xvi 16, xxix 18; II Chron xx 7, xxx 6; Neh ix 7

Absalom (*'bšlwm*)   I Chron iii 2; II Chron xi 20,21

Adaiah (*'dyh*)   I Chron vi 41, viii 21, ix 12; II Chron xxiii 1; Ezra x 29,39; Neh xi 5,12

Adnah (*'dnh*)   II Chron xvii 14

Adonijah (*'dnyh*)   I Chron iii 2; II Chron xvii 8; Neh x 17

Ahab (*'ḥ'b*)   II Chron xviii 1,2(*bis*), 3,19, xxi 6(*bis*), 13, xxii 3,4,5,6,7,8

Ahaz (*'ḥz*)   I Chron iii 13, viii 35,36, ix 42; II Chron xxvii 9, xxviii 1,16,19,21,22,24,27, xxix 19

Ahaziah (*'ḥzyhw*)   I Chron iii 11; II Chron xx 35,37, xxii 1(*bis*), 2,6,7,8(*bis*), 9(*bis*), 10,11(*bis*), xxv 23 (with Greek; MT reads *yhw'ḥz*)

Ahijah (*'ḥyh*)   I Chron ii 25, viii 7, xi 36; II Chron ix 29, x 15; Neh x 27

Ahikam (*'ḥyqm*)   II Chron xxxiv 20

Amariah (*'mryh*)   I Chron vi 7(*bis*), 11(*bis*), 52, xxiii 19, xxiv 23; II Chron xix 11, xxxi 15; Ezra vii 3, x 42; Neh x 4, xi 4, xii 2,13

Amasa (*'mś'*)   I Chron ii 17(*bis*); II Chron xxviii 12

Amasai (*'mśy*)   I Chron vi 25,35, xii 19, xv 24; II Chron xxix 12

Amasiah (*'msyh*)   II Chron xvii 16

Amaziah (*'mṣyhw*)   I Chron iii 12, iv 34, vi 45; II Chron xxiv 27, xxv 1,5,9,10,11,13,14,15,17,18,20,21,23,25,26,27, xxvi 1,4

Ammon (*'mwn*)   I Chron xviii 11, xix 2,3,6(*bis*), 7,9,11,15,19, xx 1,3; II Chron xx 1,10,22,23, xxvii 5(*tris*)

Ammonite (*'mwny*)   I Chron xi 39; II Chron xii 13 (fem.), xxiv 26 (fem.); Ezra ix 1; Neh ii 10,19, iii 15, iv 1, xiii 1,23 (fem.)

Amon (*'mwn*)   I Chron iii 14; II Chron xviii 25, xxxiii 20,21,22, 23,25; Neh vii 59

Amorite (*'mry*)   I Chron i 14; II Chron viii 7; Ezra ix 1; Neh ix 8

Amoz (*'mwṣ*)   II Chron xxvi 22, xxxii 20,32

Arabs (*'rby'ym; 'rbym; 'rbyym*)   II Chron xvii 11, xxi 16, xxii 1, xxvi 7; Neh iv 1

Aramaean (*'rmyh, 'rm*) I Chron vii 14, xviii 5,6(*bis*), xix 6,10, 12,14,15,16(*bis*), 17,18(*bis*), 19; II Chron xxii 5 (as in II Kings viii 28), xxiv 23,24

Asa (*'s'*) I Chron iii 10, ix 16; II Chron xiii 23, xiv 1,7,9,10,11,12, xv 2(*bis*), 8,10,16(*bis*), 17,19, xvi 1(*bis*), 2,4,6,7,10(*bis*), 11,12, 13, xvii 2, xx 32, xxi 12

Asahel (*'śh'l*) I Chron ii 16, xi 26, xxvii 7; II Chron xvii 8, xxxi 13; Ezra x 15

Asaiah (*'śyh*) I Chron iv 36, vi 30, ix 5, xv 6,11; II Chron xxxiv 20

Asaph (*'sp*) I Chron vi 39(*bis*), ix 15, xv 17,19, xvi 5(*bis*), 7, 37, xxv 1,2(*tris*), 6,9, xxvi 1; II Chron v 12, xx 14, xxix 13,30, xxxv 15(*bis*); Ezra ii 41, iii 10; Neh ii 8, vii 44, xi 17,22, xii 35,46

Asher (*'śr*) I Chron ii 2, vi 62,74, vii 30,40, xii 37; II Chron xxx 11

Asherah(s) (*'śrh, 'śrwt*) II Chron xv 16, xix 3, xxiv 18, xxxi 1, xxxiii 3,19, xxxiv 3,4,7

Asherim (*'śrym*) II Chron xiv 2, xvii 6

Athaliah (*'tlyh*) I Chron viii 26; II Chron xxii 2,10,11,12, xxiii 12,13,21, xxiv 7; Ezra viii 7

Attai (*'ty*) I Chron ii 35,36, xii 12; II Chron xi 20

Azaliah (*'ṣlyhw*) II Chron xxxiv 8

Azariah (*'zryh*) I Chron ii 8,38,39, iii 12, vi 9(*bis*), 10,11,13,14, 36, ix 11; II Chron xv 1, xxi 2(*bis*), xxiii 1(*bis*), xxvi 17,20, xxviii 12, xxix 12(*bis*), xxxi 10,13; Ezra vii 1,3; Neh iii 23,24, vii 7, viii 7, x 3, xii 33

Azaziah (*'zzyhw*) I Chron xv 21, xxvii 20; II Chron xxxi 13

Azrikam (*'zryqm*) I Chron iii 23, viii 38, ix 14,44; II Chron xxviii 7; Neh xi 15

Azubah (*'zwbh*) I Chron ii 18,19; II Chron xx 31

Baal (*b'l*) I Chron v 5, viii 30, ix 36; II Chron xvii 3, xxiii 17(*bis*), xxiv 7, xxviii 2, xxxiii 3, xxxiv 4

Baasha (*b'š'*) II Chron xvi 1,3,5,6

Benaiah (*bnyhw*) I Chron iv 36, xi 22,24,31, xv 18,20,24, xvi 5, 6, xviii 17, xxvii 5,6,14,34; II Chron xx 14, xxxi 13; Ezra x 25,30,35,43

Eden (*'dn*) II Chron xxix 12, xxxi 15

Edom, Edomite (*'dwm, 'dwmy*) II Chron xxi 9,10, xxv 14, xxviii 17

Eliab (*'ly'b*) I Chron ii 13, vi 27, xii 10, xv 18,20, xvi 5; II Chron xi 18

Eliada (*'lyd'*) I Chron iii 8; II Chron xvii 17

Eliakim (*'lyqym*) II Chron xxxvi 4; Neh xii 41

Eliel (*'ly'l*) I Chron v 24, vi 34, viii 20,22, xi 46,47, xii 12, xv 9, 11; II Chron xxxi 13

Eliezer (*'ly'zr*) I Chron vii 8, xv 24, xxiii 15,17(*bis*), xxvi 25, xxvii 16; II Chron xx 37; Ezra viii 16, x 18,23,31

Elijah (*'lyhw*) II Chron xxi 12; Ezra x 21,26

Elishama (*'lyšm'*) I Chron ii 41, iii 6,8, vii 26, xiv 7; II Chron xvii 8

Elishaphat (*'lyšpṭ*) II Chron xxiii 1

Elizaphan (*'lyṣpn*) I Chron xv 8; II Chron xxix 13

Elkanah (*'lqnh*) I Chron vi 23,25,26,27,34,35,36, ix 16, xii 7, xv 23; II Chron xxviii 7

Ephraim (*'prym*) I Chron vi 66, vii 20,22, ix 3, xii 31, xxvii 10, 14,20; II Chron xv 9, xvii 2, xxv 7,10,23, xxviii 7,12, xxx 1,10, 18, xxxi 1, xxxiv 6,9

Ethiopian(s) (*kwšy, kwšym*) II Chron xii 3, xiv 8,11(*bis*), 12, xvi 8, xxi 16

Gad (*gd, gdy*) I Chron ii 2, v 11,18,26, vi 63,80, xii 15, xxi 9,11, 13,18,19, xxix 29; II Chron xxix 25

Gershunnite (*gršny*) I Chron xxiii 7, xxvi 21, xxix 8; II Chron xxix 12

Hadlai (*ḥdly*) II Chron xxviii 12

Hadoram (*hdwrm*) I Chron i 21, xviii 10; II Chron x 18

Hanani (*ḥnny*) I Chron xxv 4,25; II Chron xvi 7, xix 2, xx 34; Ezra x 20; Neh i 2, vii 2, xii 36

Hananiah (*ḥnnyh*) I Chron iii 19,21, viii 24, xxv 4,23; II Chron xxvi 11; Ezra x 28; Neh iii 8,30, vii 2, x 24, xii 12,41

Hashabiah (*ḥšbyh*) I Chron vi 45, ix 14, xxv 3,19, xxvi 30, xxvii 17; II Chron xxxv 9; Ezra viii 19,24; Neh iii 17, x 12, xi 15,22, xii 21,24

Hasrah (*ḥsrh*) II Chron xxxiv 22

Hazael (*ḥz'l, ḥzh'l*)   II Chron xxii 5,6

Heman (*hymn*)   I Chron ii 6, vi 33, xv 17,19, xvi 41,42, xxv 1, 4(*bis*), 5(*bis*), 6; II Chron v 12, xxix 14, xxxv 15

Hezekiah (*ḥzqyhw*)   I Chron iii 13,23, iv 41; II Chron xxviii 27, xxix 1,18,20,27,30,31,36, xxx 1,18,20,22,24, xxxi 2,8,9,11,13,20, xxxii 2,8,9,11,12,15,16,17,20,22,23,24,25,26(*bis*),   27,30(*bis*), 32,33, xxxiii 3; Ezra ii 16; Neh vii 21, x 18

Hilkiah (*ḥlqyh*)   I Chron vi 13(*bis*), 45, ix 11, xxvi 11; II Chron xxxiv 9,14,15(*bis*), 18,20,22, xxxv 8; Ezra vii 1; Neh viii 4, xi 11, xii 7,21

Hiram (*ḥyrm*)   I Chron xiv 1; II Chron ix 10

Hittite (*ḥty*)   I Chron xi 41; II Chron i 17, viii 7; Ezra ix 1; Neh ix 8

Hivites (*ḥwy*)   I Chron i 15; II Chron viii 7

Huldah (*ḥldh*)   II Chron xxxiv 22

Hur (*ḥwr*)   I Chron ii 19,20,50, iv 1,4; II Chron i 5; Neh iii 9

Huram (*ḥwrm*)   I Chron viii 5; II Chron ii 2,10,11, iv 11(*bis*), viii 2,18, ix 21

Huramabi (*ḥwrm-'by*)   II Chron ii 12, iv 16

Iddo (*ydw, y'dy, 'dw, 'dw', 'dw*)   I Chron vi 21, xxvii 21; II Chron ix 29, xii 15, xiii 22; Ezra v 1, vi 14, viii 17(*bis*); Neh xii 4,16

Imlah (*yml'*)   II Chron xviii 7,8

Imnah (*ymnh*)   I Chron vii 30; II Chron xxxi 14

Isaac (*yṣḥq*)   I Chron i 28,34(*bis*), xvi 16, xxix 18; II Chron xxx 6

Isaiah (*yš'yhw*)   II Chron xxvi 22, xxxii 20,32

Ishmael (*yšm''l*)   I Chron i 28,29,31, viii 38, ix 44; II Chron xix 11, xxiii 1; Ezra x 22

Ismachiah (*ysmkyhw*)   II Chron xxxi 13

Israel (*yśr'l*)   I Chron i 34,43, ii 1,7, v 1(*bis*), 3,17,26, vi 38,49, 64, vii 29, ix 1(*bis*), 2, x 1(*bis*), 7, xi 1,2(*bis*), 3(*bis*), 4,10(*bis*), xii 33, 39(*bis*), 41, xiii 2(*bis*), 4,6,8, xiv 2(*bis*), 8, xv 3,12,14,25, 28, xvi 3,4,13,17,36,40, xvii 5,6,7,9,10,21,22,24(*bis*), xviii 14, xix 10,16,17,18,19, xx 7, xxi 1(*bis*), 2,3,4,5,7,12,14(*bis*), xxii 1, 2,6,9,10,12,13,17, xxiii 1,2,25(*bis*), xxiv 19, xxvi 29,30, xxvii 1, 16,22,23,24, xxviii 1,4(*tris*), 5,8, xxix 6,10,18,21,23,25(*bis*), 26, 27,30; II Chron i 2(*bis*), 13, ii 3,11,16, v 2(*bis*), 3,4,6,10, vi

3(*bis*), 4,5(*bis*), 6,7,10(*bis*), 11,12,13,14,16(*bis*), 17,21,24,25, 27,29,32,33, vii 3,6,8,10,18, viii 2,7,8,9,11, ix 8,30, x 1,3,16(*tris*), 17,18,19, xi 1,3,13,16(*bis*), xii 1,6,13, xiii 4,5(*bis*), 12,15,16, 17,18, xv 3,4,9,13,17, xvi 1,3,4,7,11, xvii 1,4, xviii 3,4,5,7,8,9, 16,17,19,25,28,29(*bis*), 30,31,32,33,34, xix 8, xx 7,10,19,29,34, 35, xxi 2,4,6,13(*bis*), xxii 5, xxiii 2, xxiv 5,6,9,16, xxv 6,7(*bis*), 9,17,18,21,22,23,25,26, xxvii 7, xxviii 2,3,5,8,13,19,23,26,27, xxix 7,10,24(*bis*), 27, xxx 1(*bis*), 5(*bis*), 6(*tris*), 21,25(*bis*), 26, xxxi 1(*bis*), 5,6,8, xxxii 17,32, xxxiii 2,7,8,9,16,18(*bis*), xxxiv 7, 9,21,23,26,33(*bis*), xxxv 3(*tris*), 4,17,18(*bis*), 25,27, xxxvi 8,13; Ezra i 3, ii 2,59,70, iii 1,2,10,11, iv 1,3(*bis*), v 1,11, vi 14,16, 17(*bis*), 21(*bis*), 22, vii 6,7,11,13,15,28, viii 18,25,29,35(*bis*), ix 1,4,15, x 1,2,5,10,25; Neh i 6(*bis*), ii 10, vii 7,61,72(*bis*), viii 1,14,17, ix 1,2, x 40, xi 3,20, xii 47, xiii 2,3,28,26(*bis*)

Issachar (*yśśkr*) I Chron ii 1, vi 62,72, vii 1,5, xii 33,41, xxvi 5, xxvii 18; II Chron xxx 18

Jachin (*ykyn*) I Chron ix 10, xxiv 17; II Chron iii 17; Neh xi 10

Jahath (*yḥt*) I Chron iv 2(*bis*), vi 20,43, xxiii 10,11, xxiv 22; II Chron xxxiv 12

Jahaziel (*yḥzy'l*) I Chron xii 4, xvi 6, xxiii 19, xxiv 23; II Chron xx 14; Ezra viii 5

Jebusite (*ybwsy*) I Chron i 14, xi 4,6, xxi 15,18,28; II Chron iii 1, viii 7; Ezra ix 1; Neh ix 8

Jecoliah (*ykylyh*, Kethib) II Chron xxvi 3

Jeduthun (*ydwtwn*) I Chron ix 16, xvi 41,42, xxv 1,3(*tris*), 6; II Chron v 12, xxix 14, xxxv 15; Neh xi 17 (Kethib has *ydytwn*)

Jehallelel (*yhll'l*) I Chron iv 16; II Chron xxix 12

Jehiel (*yḥy'l*) I Chron xv 18,20, xvi 5, xxiii 8, xxvi 21,22 (*yḥy'ly*), xxvii 32, xxix 8; II Chron xxi 2, xxix 14 (Kethib has *yḥw'l*), xxxi 13, xxxv 8; Ezra viii 9, x 2,21,26

Jehizkiah (*yḥzqyhw*) II Chron xxviii 12. See also Hezekiah

Jehoaddan (*yhw'dn*) II Chron xxv 1

Jehoahaz (*yhw'ḥz, yw'ḥz*) II Chron xxi 17, xxv 17,25, xxxiv 8, xxxvi 1,2,4

Jehohanan (*yhwḥnn*) I Chron xxvi 3; II Chron xvii 15, xxiii 1, xxviii 12; Ezra x 6,28; Neh vi 18, xii 13,18,42

Jehoiachin (*yhwykyn*) II Chron xxxvi 8,9

Joash (*yw'š, yw'š*) I Chron iii 11, iv 22, vii 8, xii 3, xxvii 28; II Chron xviii 25, xxii 11, xxiv 1,2,4,22,24, xxv 17,18,20,21, 23(*bis*), 25(*bis*)

Joel (*yw'l*) I Chron iv 35, v 4,8,12, vi 28,33,36, vii 3, xi 38, xv 7,11,17, xxiii 8, xxvi 22, xxvii 20; II Chron xxix 12; Ezra x 43; Neh xi 9

Joram (*ywrm*) I Chron iii 11, xxvi 25; II Chron xxii 5,7

Josiah (*y'šyhw*) I Chron iii 14,15; II Chron xxxiii 25, xxxiv 1, 33, xxxv 1,7,16,18,19,20(*bis*), 22,23,24,25(*bis*), 26, xxxvi 1

Jotham (*ywtm*) I Chron ii 47, iii 12, v 17; II Chron xxvi 21,23, xxvii 1,6,7,9

Jozabad (*ywzbd*) I Chron xii 5,21(*bis*); II Chron xxxi 13, xxxv 9; Ezra viii 33, x 22,23; Neh viii 7, xi 16

Judah (*yhwdh*) I Chron ii 1,3(*bis*), 10, iv 1,21,27,41, v 2,17, vi 15,55,65, ix 1,3,4, xii 17,25, xiii 6, xxi 5, xxvii 18, xxviii 4(*bis*); II Chron ii 6, ix 11, x 17, xi 1,3(*bis*), 5,10,12,14,17,23, xii 4,5,12, xiii 1,13,14,15(*tris*), 16,18, xiv 3,4,5,6,7,11, xv 2,8, 9,15, xvi 1(*bis*), 6,7,11, xvii 2(*bis*), 5,6,7,9(*bis*), 10,12,13,14, 19, xviii 3,9,28, xix 1,5,11, xx 3,4(*bis*), 5,13,15,17,18,20,22,24, 27,31,35, xxi 3(*bis*), 8,10,11(*bis*), 12,13,17, xxii 1,6,8,10, xxiii 2(*bis*), 8, xxiv 5,6,9,17,18,23, xxv 5(*bis*), 10,12,13,17,18,19, 21(*bis*), 22,23,25,26,28, xxvi 1,2, xxvii 4,7, xxviii 6,9,10,17,18, 19(*bis*), 25,26, xxix 8,21, xxx 1,6,12,24,25(*bis*), xxxi 1(*bis*), 6(*bis*), 20, xxxii 1,8,9,12,23,25,32,33, xxxiii 9,14,16, xxxiv 3,5,9, 11,21,24,26,29,30, xxxv 18,21,24,27, xxxvi 4,8,10,14,23; Ezra i 2,3,5,8, ii 1(*bis*), iii 9, iv 1,4,6, v 1,8, vii 14, ix 9, x 7,9,23; Neh ii 5,7, iv 4,10, v 14, vi 7,17,18, vii 6, xi 3,4(*bis*), 9,20,24, 25,36, xii 8,31,32,34,36,44, xiii 16

Kehathite (*qhty*) I Chron vi 33,54, ix 32; II Chron xx 19, xxix 12, xxxiv 12

Kish (*qyš*) I Chron viii 30,33(*bis*), ix 36,39(*bis*), xii 1, xxiii 21,22, xxiv 29(*bis*), xxvi 28; II Chron xxix 12

Korahites (*qrḥym*) I Chron ix 19,31, xii 7, xxvi 1; II Chron xx 19

Kore (*qwr'*) I Chron ix 19, xxvi 1; II Chron xxxi 14

Levite(s) (*lwy, lwym*) I Chron vi 19,48,64, ix 2,14,26,31,33,34, xii 27, xiii 2, xv 2,4,11,12,14,15,16,17,22,26,27, xvi 4, xxiii 2,3, 26,27, xxiv 6(*bis*), 20,30,31, xxvi 20, xxvii 17, xxviii 13,21;

II Chron v 4,5,12, vii 6, viii 14,15, xi 13,14, xiii 9,10, xvii
8(*bis*), xix 8,11, xx 14,19, xxiii 2,4,6,8,18, xxiv 5(*bis*), 6,11,
xxix 4,5,12,16,25,26,30,34(*bis*), xxx 15,16,17,21,22,25,27, xxxi
2(*bis*), 4,8,12,14,17,19, xxxiv 9,12(*bis*), 13,30, xxxv 3,5,8,
9(*bis*), 10,11,14,15,18; Ezra i 5,40, ii 70, iii 8(*bis*), 9,10,12, vi
16,18,20, vii 7,13,24, viii 15,20,29,30,33, ix 1, x 5,15,23; Neh iii
17, vii 1,43,72, viii 7,9,11,13, ix 4,5, x 1,10,29,35,38(*bis*),
39(*bis*), 40, xi 3,15,16,18,20,22,36, xii 1,8,22,23,24,27,28,30,
44(*bis*), 47(*bis*), xiii 5,10(*bis*), 13,22,29,30
Libyans (*lwbym*) II Chron xii 3, xvi 8

Maacah (*m'kh*) I Chron ii 48, iii 2, vii 15,16, viii 29, ix 35, xi 43,
xxvii 16; II Chron xi 20,21,22, xv 16
Maaseiah (*m'śyhw*) I Chron xv 18,20; II Chron xxiii 1, xxvi
11, xxviii 7, xxxiv 8; Ezra x 18,21,22,30; Neh iii 23, viii 4,7,
x 26, xi 5,7, xii 41,42
Mahalath (*mḥlt*) II Chron xi 18
Mahath (*mḥt*) I Chron vi 35; II Chron xxix 12, xxxi 13
Manasseh (*mnšh, mnšy*) I Chron iii 13, v 18,26, vi 61,62,70,71,
vii 14,17,29, ix 3, xii 20,21(*bis*), 32,38, xxvi 32, xxviii 20,21;
II Chron xv 9, xxx 1,10,11,18, xxxi 1, xxxii 33, xxxiii 1,9,10,
11,13,14,18,20,22(*bis*), 23, xxxiv 6,9; Ezra x 30,33
Masseboth (*mṣbwt*) II Chron xiv 2
Mattan (*mtn*) II Chron xxiii 17
Mattaniah (*mtnyh*) I Chron ix 15, xxv 4,16; II Chron xx 14,
xxix 13; Ezra x 26,27,30,37; Neh xi 17,22, xii 8,25,35, xiii 13
Merari (*mrry*) I Chron vi 1,16,19,29,44,47,63,77, ix 14, xv 6,
17, xxiii 6,21, xxiv 26,27, xxvi 10,19; II Chron xxix 12, xxxiv 12;
Ezra viii 19
Meshillemoth (*mšlmwt*) II Chron xxviii 12; Neh xi 13
Meshullam (*mšlm*) I Chron iii 19, v 13, viii 17, ix 7,8,11,12; II
Chron xxxiv 12; Ezra viii 16, x 15,29; Neh iii 4,6,30, vi 18, viii
4, x 8,21, xi 7,11, xii 13,16,25,33
Meunites (*m'ynym, m'wnym*) II Chron xx 1, xxvi 7,8; Ezra ii
50; Neh vii 52
Micah (*mykh*) I Chron v 5, viii 34,35, ix 40,41, xxiii 20, xxiv
24(*bis*), 25; II Chron xviii 14, xxxiv 20; Neh xi 17
Micaiah (*mykyh, mykhw*) II Chron xiii 2, xvii 7, xviii 7,8,12,13,
23,24,25,27; Neh xii 35,41

Michael (*myk'l*) I Chron v 13,14, vi 40, vii 3, viii 16, xii 21, xxvii
18; II Chron xxi 2; Ezra viii 8

Miniamin (*mnymn*) II Chron xxxi 15; Neh xii 17,41

Moab, Moabite (*mw'b, mw'by*) I Chron iv 22, xi 22,46, xviii 2;
II Chron xx 1,10,22,23, xxiv 26; Ezra ix 1; Neh xiii 1,23

Moses (*mšh*) I Chron vi 3,49, xv 15, xxi 29, xxii 13, xxiii 13,14,
15, xxvi 24; II Chron i 3, v 10, viii 13, xxiii 18, xxiv 6,9, xxv 4,
xxx 16, xxxiii 8, xxxiv 14, xxxv 6,12; Ezra iii 2, vi 18, vii 6; Neh
i 7,8, viii 1,14, ix 14, x 30, xiii 1

Naamah (*n'mh*) II Chron xii 13

Nahath (*nḥt*) I Chron i 37, vi 26; II Chron xxxi 13

Naphtali (*nptly*) I Chron ii 2, vi 62,76, vii 13, xii 35,41, xxvii 19;
II Chron xvi 4, xxxiv 6

Nathan (*ntn*) I Chron ii 36(*bis*), iii 5, xi 38, xiv 4, xvii 1,2,3,15,
xxix 29; II Chron ix 29, xxix 25; Ezra viii 16, x 39

Nebat (*nbṭ*) II Chron ix 29, x 2,15, xiii 6

Nebuchadnezzar (*nbkdn'ṣr, nbwkdn'ṣr*) I Chron vi 15; II Chron
xxxvi 6,7,10,13; Ezra i 7, ii 1, v 12,14, vi 5; Neh vii 6

Neco (*nkw*) II Chron xxxv 20,22, xxxvi 4

Nethanel (*ntn'l*) I Chron ii 14, xv 24, xxiv 6, xxvi 4; II Chron
xvii 7, xxxv 9; Ezra x 22; Neh xii 21,36

Nethaniah (*ntnyh*) I Chron xxv 2,12; II Chron xvii 8

Nimshi (*nmšy*) II Chron xxii 7

Obadiah (*'bdyh*) I Chron iii 21, vii 3, viii 38, ix 16,44, xii 10,
xxvi 19; II Chron xvii 7, xxxiv 12; Ezra viii 9; Neh x 6, xii 25

Obed (*'wbd*) I Chron ii 12(*bis*), 37,38, xi 47, xxvi 7; II Chron
xxiii 1

Obed-edom (*'bd-'dm*) I Chron xiii 13,14(*bis*), xv 18,21,24,25,
xvi 5,38(*bis*), xxvi 4,8(*bis*), 15; II Chron xxv 24

Oded (*'wdd*) II Chron xv 1,8, xxviii 9

Omri (*'mry*) I Chron vii 8, ix 4, xxvii 18; II Chron xxii 2

Ornan (*'rnn*) I Chron xxi 15,18,20(*bis*), 21(*bis*), 22,23,24,25,
28; II Chron iii 1

Pekah (*pqḥ*) II Chron xxviii 6

Perizzite (*przy*) II Chron viii 7; Ezra ix 1; Neh ix 8

Pharaoh (*pr'h*) I Chron iv 18; II Chron viii 11; Neh ix 10

Philistine (*plštym*) I Chron i 12, x 1(*bis*), 2,7,8,9,11, xi 13(*bis*),
    14,15,16,18, xii 20(*bis*), xiv 8(*bis*), 9,10,13,15,16, xviii 1(*bis*),
    11, xx 4,5; II Chron ix 26, xvii 11, xxi 16, xxvi 6(*bis*), 7, xxviii
    18

Rehoboam (*rḥb'm*) I Chron iii 10; II Chron ix 31, x 1,3,6,12,13,
    17,18(*bis*), xi 1(*bis*), 3,5,17,18,21,22, xii 1,2,5,10,13(*bis*),
    15(*bis*), 16, xiii 7(*bis*)
Remaliah (*rmlyhw*) II Chron xxviii 6

Samuel (*šmw'l*) I Chron vi 28,33, vii 2, ix 22, xi 3, xxvi 28, xxix
    29; II Chron xxxv 18
Seir (*ś'yr*) I Chron i 38; II Chron xx 23, xxv 11,14
Sennacherib (*snḥryb*) II Chron xxxii 1,2,9,10,22
Shallum (*šlwm*) I Chron ii 40,41, iii 15, iv 25, vi 12,13, vii 13,
    ix 17(*bis*), 19,31; II Chron xxviii 12, xxxiv 22; Ezra ii 42, vii
    2, x 24,42; Neh iii 12, vii 45
Shamiraimoth (*šmrymwt*) II Chron xvii 8
Shaphan (*špn*) II Chron xxxiv 8,15(*bis*), 16,18(*bis*), 20(*bis*)
Shecaniah (*šknyh*) I Chron iii 21,22, xxiv 11; II Chron xxxi 15;
    Ezra viii 3,5, x 2; Neh iii 29, vi 18, xii 3
Shelomith (*šlmyt*) I Chron iii 19, xxiii 9 (Qere, Kethib have
    šlmwt), 18; II Chron xi 20; Ezra viii 10
Shemaiah (*šm'yh*) I Chron iii 22(*bis*), iv 37, v 4, ix 14,16, xv
    8,11, xxiv 6, xxvi 4,6,7; II Chron xi 2, xii 5,7,15, xvii 8, xxix 14,
    xxxi 15, xxxv 9; Ezra viii 13,16, x 21,31; Neh iii 29, vi 10, x 9,
    xi 15, xii 6,18,34,35,36,42
Shemariah (*šmryhw*) I Chron xii 6; II Chron xi 19; Ezra x 32,41
Shephatiah (*špṭyh*) I Chron iii 3, ix 8, xii 6, xxvii 16; II Chron
    xxi 2; Ezra ii 4,57, viii 8; Neh vii 9,59, xi 4
Shilhi (*šlḥy*) II Chron xx 31
Shilonite (*šylwny*) I Chron ix 5; II Chron ix 29, x 15; Neh xi 5
Shimeath (*šm't*) II Chron xxiv 26
Shimei (*šm'y*) I Chron iii 19, iv 26,27, v 4, vi 17,29,42, viii 21,
    xxiii 7,9,10(*bis*), xxv 3,17, xxvii 27; II Chron xxix 14, xxxi 12,
    13; Ezra x 23,33,38
Shimri (*šmry*) I Chron iv 37, xi 45, xxvi 10; II Chron xxix 13
Shimrith (*šmryt*) II Chron xxiv 26
Shishak (*šyšq*) II Chron xii 2,5(*bis*), 7,9

Sibbecai (*sbky*) I Chron xi 29, xx 4, xxvii 11
Simeon (*šm'wn*) I Chron ii 1, iv 24,42, vi 65, xii 26, xxvii 16;
II Chron xv 9, xxxiv 6
Solomon (*šlmh*) I Chron iii 5,10, vi 10,32, xiv 4, xviii 8, xxii
5,6,7,9,17, xxiii 1, xxviii 5,6,9,11,20, xxix 1,19,22,23,24,25,28;
II Chron i 1,2,3,5,6,7,8,11,13,14,16,18, ii 1,2,10,16, iii 1,3, iv
11,16,18,19, v 1(*bis*), 2,6, vi 1,13, vii 1,5,7(*bis*), 8,10,11(*bis*),
12, viii 1,3,6,8,9,10,11,12,16,17,18(*bis*), ix 1(*tris*), 2(*bis*), 3,9,
10,12,13,14,15,20(*bis*), 22,23,25,28,29,30,31, x 2, xi 3,17(*bis*),
xii 9, xiii 6,7, xxx 26, xxxiii 7, xxxv 3,4; Ezra ii 55,58; Neh vii
57,60, xi 3, xii 45, xiii 26
Sukkiim (*skyym*) II Chron xii 3

Tilgath-pilneser (*tlgt-pln'sr, tlgt-plnsr*) I Chron v 6,26; II Chron
xxviii 20
Tobiah (*twbyhw, ṭbyh*) II Chron xvii 8; Ezra ii 60; Neh ii 10,19,
iii 35, iv 1, vi 1,12,14,17(*bis*), 19, vii 62, xiii 4,7,8
Tyrian (*ṣry*) I Chron xx 4; II Chron ii 13; Ezra iii 7; Neh xiii 16

Uri (*'wry*) I Chron ii 20(*bis*); II Chron i 5; Ezra x 24
Uriel (*'wry'l*) I Chron vi 24, xv 5,11; II Chron xiii 2
Uzziah (*'zyh*) I Chron vi 24, xxvii 25; II Chron xxvi 1,3,8,9,11,
14,18(*bis*), 19,21,22,23, xxvii 2; Ezra x 21; Neh xi 4
Uzziel (*'zy'l*) I Chron iv 42, vi 2,18, vii 7, xv 10, xxiii 12,20,
xxiv 24, xxv 4, xxvi 23; II Chron xxix 14; Neh iii 8

Zabad (*zbd*) I Chron ii 36,37, vii 21, xi 41; II Chron xxiv 26;
Ezra x 27,33,43
Zadok (*ṣdwq*) I Chron vi 8(*bis*), 12(*bis*), 53, ix 11, xii 29,
xv 11, xvi 39, xviii 16, xxiv 3,6,31, xxvii 17, xxix 22; II Chron
xxvii 1, xxxi 10; Ezra vii 2; Neh iii 4,29, x 22, xi 11, xiii 13
Zaham (*zhm*) II Chron xi 19
Zebadiah (*zbdyh*) I Chron viii 15,17, xii 8, xxvi 2, xxvii 7; II
Chron xvii 8, xix 11; Ezra viii 8, x 20
Zebulun (*zblwn*) I Chron ii 1, vi 63,77, xii 34,41, xxvii 19; II
Chron xxx 10,11,18
Zechariah (*zkryhw*) I Chron v 7, ix 21,37, xv 18,20,24, xvi 5, xxiv
25, xxvi 2,11,14, xxvii 21; II Chron xvii 7, xx 14, xxi 2, xxiv

KEY TO THE TEXT

Chapter	Verse	§	Chapter	Verse	§
i	1–17	1	xxi	1	22
	18	2		2–20	23
ii	1–17	2	xxii	1–9	24
iii	1–17	3		10–12	25
iv	1–22	4	xxiii	1–21	25
v	1	4	xxiv	1–27	26
	2–14	5	xxv	1–28	27
vi	1–42	6	xxvi	1–23	28
vii	1–10	7	xxvii	1–9	29
	11–22	8	xxviii	1–27	30
viii	1–18	9	xxix	1–36	31
ix	1–28	10	xxx	1–27	32
	29–31	11	xxxi	1–21	33
x	1–19	12	xxxii	1–23	34
xi	1–23	13		24–33	35
xii	1–16	14	xxxiii	1–20	36
xiii	1–23	15		21–25	37
xiv	1–14	16	xxxiv	1–33	38
xv	1–19	17	xxxv	1–19	39
xvi	1–14	18		20–27	40
xvii	1–19	19	xxxvi	1–10	41
xviii	1–34	20		11–21	42
xix	1–11	21		22–23	43
xx	1–37	22			

A Proper
Pursuit

LYNN AUSTIN

A Proper Pursuit

BethanyHouse

MINNEAPOLIS, MINNESOTA

Published by Bethany House Publishers
11400 Hampshire Avenue South
Bloomington, Minnesota 55438

Bethany House Publishers is a division of
Baker Publishing Group, Grand Rapids, Michigan.

Printed in the United States of America

Paperback:　ISBN-13: 978-0-7642-2891-9　ISBN-10: 0-7642-2891-9
Hardcover:　ISBN-13: 978-0-7642-0440-1　ISBN-10: 0-7642-0440-8

Library of Congress Cataloging-in-Publication Data

Austin, Lynn N.
　A proper pursuit / Lynn Austin.
　　p.　cm.
　ISBN 978-0-7642-0440-1 (alk. paper) — ISBN 978-0-7642-2891-9 (pbk.)
1. Young women—Fiction.　2. Chicago (Ill.)—Fiction.　3. United States—History—
1933–1945—Fiction.　I. Title.
　PS3551.U839P76　　2007
　813'.54—dc22

2007023563

To my family
Ken, Joshua, Benjamin, Maya, and Vanessa
I love you all.

Books by
Lynn Austin

FROM BETHANY HOUSE PUBLISHERS

All She Ever Wanted

Eve's Daughters

Hidden Places

Wings of Refuge

A Woman's Place

A Proper Pursuit

REFINER'S FIRE

Candle in the Darkness

Fire by Night

A Light to My Path

CHRONICLES OF THE KINGS

Gods and Kings

Song of Redemption

The Strength of His Hand

Faith of My Fathers

Among the Gods

LYNN AUSTIN is a three-time Christy Award winner for her historical novels *Hidden Places, Candle in the Darkness,* and *Fire by Night*. In addition to writing, Lynn is a popular speaker at conferences, retreats, and various church and school events. She and her husband have three children and make their home in Illinois.

Chapter

Saturday, May 20, 1893

I couldn't imagine more shocking news.

I sat at Widow Maude O'Neill's dining room table and stared at my father as the overcooked mutton on my plate grew cold. I would have cried out in protest and begged him to reconsider, but as a recent graduate of Madame Beauchamps' School for Young Ladies, I'd learned that a proper young lady never caused a scene at the supper table, especially if she was a guest.

Father looked immensely pleased with himself. He leaned back in his chair, his hand thrust inside his suit coat as he played with his watch chain. Maude, dressed in widow's black for the last time, wore the phony smile that she reserved for my father and did her best to blush like a maiden. She had won a valuable prize in my father, John Jacob Hayes, and she knew it.

I glanced at her unpleasant children, Horace and Harriet, and knew by their smug expressions that my father's marriage proposal wasn't news to them. Maude had scrubbed their piggy pink faces so thoroughly it looked as though she had boiled them. I wished she had.

My father's smile faded as my silence lengthened. "Well, say something, Violet. Have you forgotten your manners?"

I looked down at my hands, folded primly in my lap. "No, Father. I haven't forgotten." Good manners prevented me from telling my father that he was a fool. Or from smacking the smile off Maude's pinched face.

"Congratulations, Father," I said in my sweetest voice. "And best wishes to you, Widow O'Neill." I had learned the proper responses from Madame Beauchamps: *"Never congratulate the bride; offer her your best wishes."*

"Thank you, Violet," Maude replied. If her narrow rat face had whiskers, she would have preened them.

"We hope to be wed this coming fall," my father continued. "It will be a small, private affair at home with only a few relatives and guests in attendance."

"Excuse me, Father," I said politely, "but aren't you forgetting something?"

"What's that?"

"You already have a wife—my mother."

He cleared his throat. "Yes ... well, perhaps I neglected to explain it to you, but the fact is, I've been free to marry for some time." He sawed off another rubbery morsel of mutton and chewed it vigorously, as if unaware that this second piece of news had shocked me even more than the first.

"Free to marry?" I echoed, careful to keep my tone mild. Young ladies never burst into tears in public.

"Yes. You were away at school, and I didn't want to upset you with the news."

I quietly wadded Maude's damask napkin into a ball as I pondered his words. Why did people always tiptoe around me as if I reclined on a bed of violets that might be crushed beneath their feet?

"Poor, pitiful Violet. Her mother became ill, you know, when she was only nine. She's an only child, always daydreaming. . . ."

"When did Mother die?" I had to struggle against the lump in my throat.

"We'll talk about it later, Violet."

"Excuse me once again, Father, but I believe I should have been informed of her passing. You might have—"

He cleared his throat, interrupting me. "This is hardly the proper time to discuss the matter." He nodded discreetly toward Horace and Harriet, who had stopped gnawing their mutton to gaze at me with their round piggy eyes. "I realize, now, that I should have explained everything to you ahead of time, and I apologize for that. But let's not spoil Maude's wonderful supper or this momentous occasion with details that can wait until we're home, shall we?"

Evidently, my mother's demise was a detail. I would have excused myself from the table in order to allow my tears to fall, but I was a guest in Widow O'Neill's home. Leaving midmeal would be unspeakably rude. Weeping at the supper table would be rude as well. Besides, my tears were more for myself than for a mother I barely remembered. Even so, Father might have mentioned her death.

Maude lifted the platter of meat and offered it to my father. "Would you care for more, John?"

Maude had poisoned her first husband—I was certain of it. I had read about women like her in my favorite dime novels and pulp fiction magazines. My best friend, Ruth Schultz, smuggled copies of *True Crime Stories*, *The Illustrated Police News*, and *True Romance Stories* into our dormitory at Madame Beauchamps' School for Young Ladies along with dime novels in bright orange jackets. We hid them beneath our mattresses so we could read them after lights-out. Of course, proper young ladies never read such trash—but Ruth and I did.

What would become of me after Maude poisoned my father the same way she had poisoned her first husband? Would she drive me from my home to beg for alms in the gutter? I pictured myself on a street corner as snow swirled around me, a tattered shawl clutched around my shivering shoulders, my gaunt hand outstretched in supplication. Then the image faded as I realized that I was much too old to beg for alms. As a pretty young woman of twenty years, a much worse fate awaited me: I would have to become a woman of the night! A warm blush spread across my cheeks at the prospect.

While it may sound vain to call myself *pretty*, I had heard enough people use that adjective when describing me to convince myself that it must be true. My thick, curly hair was the color of strong coffee, my eyes just as dark. And even though Madame Beauchamps had referred to my complexion as a bit *swarthy* and had cautioned me to stay out of the sun lest I resemble *une paysanne*, she had also described me as *très jolie*. A careful examination of my face in a hand mirror confirmed to me that I was, indeed, quite pretty.

"Would you like some more meat, Violet?" Maude offered the platter to me next, her teeth bared in a grin. What if she planned to poison me along with my father, so that Horace and Harriet could inherit our entire estate? I declined politely, then pushed away my dinner plate, my appetite suddenly gone. For all I knew, Maude may have begun the slow, poisonous process this very evening.

"I believe our news has upset you, Violet," Maude said, her head tilted to one side in sympathy. "We were so hoping that you would be happy for your father and me. And that we would all become one big family." Horace and Harriet had laid down their forks as if waiting for me to graft them into the family tree with my butter knife. They would have a very long wait. I felt a greater kinship with the poor dead sheep on the serving platter than I did with them.

In the long silence that followed I heard a horse trotting up the street. If only it were a young, fair-haired lieutenant, newly arrived from the western Indian wars, riding to my rescue . . . *He had been gravely wounded by a native's savage arrow, his uniform in bloody tat-*

ters, but his undying love for me had kept him alive, and now we would be reunited at last, and . . .

The horse cantered past the house, followed by the unmistakable rumble of carriage wheels over the rutted street. Maybe it was a sign from Providence. Perhaps the passing carriage had been sent to tell me that I must run away from home at the first opportunity.

Did twenty-year-old women run away from home? And if so, how did they accomplish it? Did they tie their belongings in a shawl and sling the bundle over their shoulder? A steamer trunk would be much more convenient, considering how many belongings I possessed. The trunk I had taken to school with me would suffice, although I doubted if proper young ladies pushed their own steamer trunks through the streets. Madame Beauchamps had never specifically addressed the subject of proper etiquette when running away from home, but I was quite certain she would consider pushing one's own trunk through the streets of Lockport, Illinois, unacceptable.

"Violet . . . Violet. . . ?" I looked up when I heard Father addressing me. "Daydreaming again," he muttered. "Kindly pay attention, Violet. Mrs. O'Neill has asked you a question."

"Oh, pardon me. Would you be kind enough to repeat it, Mrs. O'Neill?"

Maude's smile may have appeared innocent to the untrained eye, but I thought I detected the proverbial "gleam of malice" as she said, "I understand that Herman Beckett has been courting you. He is such a fine young man, isn't he?"

"Yes, ma'am. Mr. Beckett is certainly above reproach. But I would hardly regard our two Sunday afternoon outings to Dellwood Park as a courtship."

I searched for a way to change the subject. It seemed obscene to discuss my own courtship so soon after hearing the shocking news about Maude and my father. Old people had no business courting, much less getting married. But Maude seemed determined to engage

13

me in a verbal tennis match. I knew the rules of polite conversation, but I lacked the will to play.

"I happen to know that young Mr. Beckett is quite serious about your courtship," Maude said, leaning closer. "I know his mother very well, and it seems that he is absolutely smitten by you."

She had lobbed the ball into my court, but I let it lay there. If Herman Beckett was truly smitten with me, he hid the evidence well. I longed for a suitor who would gaze deeply into my eyes the way the heroes in Ruth's romance stories always did. Someone who would kiss my ivory fingertips and whisper endearing words in my ear. The beau in one story had even nibbled on his beloved's earlobe. That didn't strike me as romantic at all, but perhaps my imagination had been tainted by an adventure story I had read the same week that had featured cannibals.

"Herman comes from such a fine family," Maude insisted.

"Yes, ma'am."

"You would be wise to encourage him before some other girl snatches him up."

"Yes, ma'am."

I had no idea what else to say. I wished Madame Beauchamps had spent less time teaching me the proper way to consume a dinner roll—*"Delicately tear off one small morsel at a time, girls, and apply butter to each individual piece with your butter knife"*—and more time teaching me how to rid my life of scheming widows with romantic designs on my father. I had no heart for meaningless conversation after Father's absurd news. I wished I were a child of nine or ten, like Horace and Harriet, who were expected to be seen and not heard.

After supper, good manners required me to play the piano for everyone's enjoyment. Maude's piano sounded as out of tune as a hurdy-gurdy, but I poured all of my sentiment into the music—and I had a great deal of sentiment that evening. If only a world-famous impresario would chance to walk down the street on his evening constitutional and hear my earnest performance and pound on Maude's door, declaring that my song had touched his very soul!

"Let her come with me," he would beg. "Let me nourish her budding talent until it blooms and flowers!" We would travel the world together, and I would perform before the crowned heads of Europe. Later we would be married, and—

"It's time to go home, Violet." My father stood beside the piano, holding my wrap.

"Thank you for a lovely evening," I said dutifully as I rose from the piano stool. I scurried through the door as Maude lunged to embrace me.

"I would like to know where Mother is buried," I said as soon as Father and I started walking up the hill toward our home. "I would like to visit her grave."

"Listen, Violet—"

"I know that everyone considers me fragile and frail, someone who must be protected from every unpleasantness in life. But I'm no longer a schoolgirl, Father. I'm a woman."

"Yes, I'm well aware of that." His voice sounded flat and emotionless. The village streets were too dark for me to see his face and discern if he was grieving for my lost childhood or if I had angered him with my demands. I plowed forward.

"And you had no right to hide the news about Mother from me. I have every right to grieve and mourn her death, even if I haven't seen her in years—"

"She isn't dead, Violet."

"I should have attended her funeral, at the very least, and ... w-what did you say?"

"Your mother isn't dead." He stopped, winded from the uphill climb.

I stared at him, stupefied. "Then how can you possibly marry Mrs. O'Neill?"

Father exhaled a long, slow sigh like a train releasing steam at the end of a weary journey. "Our marriage has been dissolved by the courts. Your mother and I are divorced."

"But that's so heartless! Marriage vows promise 'in sickness and in health until death do you part.' How could you even dream of abandoning Mother when she's ill? That's so cold and . . . and cruel . . . and—"

He gripped my shoulders and gave them a gentle shake. "Stop the theatrics, Violet, and listen to me. Your mother was never ill. She left home of her own free will."

"Never ill? Of course she was ill! She—"

He shook his head. "She hated her life with me, hated living in a small town like Lockport, hated being tied down. So I let her go."

"That means . . . That means you lied to me?"

"You were a child. I thought at the time that it would be kinder to lie than to tell you the truth. But the fact of the matter is, she abandoned us."

"I don't believe you," I said in a whisper. Then my voice grew louder and louder as my shock turned to anger. "If you admit that you lied eleven years ago, why should I believe anything you tell me now?"

"I'm sorry, Violet. I'll show you the divorce papers when we get home, if you'd like, but I'm telling you the truth."

I demanded to see them. We went straight into Father's study the moment we arrived home, still wearing our cloaks. Father removed a sheaf of papers from his desk drawer. The top one bore the official seal of the State of Illinois, and I saw several sentences that all began with *Whereas*. Then I saw my mother's name: Angeline Cepak Hayes. Beneath the printed type was her signature—bold, flamboyant.

Alive.

I remembered her then—the woman she had been long ago when I was very young, not the tired, sad woman who had gone away. Her dark, untamed hair, so like my own, had been a wild tangle of curls. I'd inherited my dark eyes from her as well. She had worn bright, silky clothing that had blazed with color, and I remembered how she had danced with me, lifting me into her arms and laughing as we whirled breathlessly around the parlor. She smelled like roses.

"I'm sorry, Violet," Father said again. "I should have told you the truth years ago."

I glimpsed a Chicago address beneath Mother's name before Father whisked away the papers and stuffed them into the drawer. I stared at my father as if at a stranger as I struggled to grasp the truth.

"Why didn't you tell me?" I murmured.

He took a moment to reply, silently fingering his watch chain. When he spoke, his voice sounded hushed. "I'm sorry. . . . I think . . . I think I always hoped she would come home to us again."

Chapter

2

I couldn't fall asleep that night. I had too much information to digest along with Maude's indigestible mutton. My stomach ached in protest.

Father's engagement to Widow O'Neill had shocked me badly. But to suddenly learn that my real mother hadn't been ill all these years but had abandoned us to live in Chicago—I couldn't comprehend it. My mother was a traitor, my father a traitor *and* a liar. Where did that leave me?

I had to stop Father's wedding, of course. I'd always thought of the two of us as happy, living a quiet, comfortable life in our home on the hill overlooking the canal in Lockport. We had Mrs. Hutchins to keep house for us and cook our meals—wasn't that enough for my father? How in the world could he expect me to share him with a stringy widow and her dreadful children, Homely and Horrid? I had decided I would secretly refer to Harriet and Horace by those more appropriate names. Yes, I must stop the wedding at all costs. But how?

I climbed out of bed and lit the gas lamp, then retrieved my journal from under my mattress and opened it to a clean page. I wrote *PREVENT FATHER'S MARRIAGE!!!* in bold letters across the top and underlined it three times, breaking the pencil point in the process. I found another pencil and numbered the page from one to ten.

What to do? What to do?

Perhaps with a little detective work I could prove that Maude had murdered her first husband and send her and her odious offspring to prison for the rest of their lives. Homely and Horrid had been accomplices—I was certain of it.

I wrote:

#1. Investigate Mr. O'Neill's death, then added: *(Re-read* The Adventures of Sherlock Holmes *and Allan Pinkerton's detective book for inspiration.)*

I spent the next ten minutes drumming the pencil against the page as I searched in vain for another idea.

When my head began to ache from thinking too hard, I turned off the lamp, climbed beneath the covers again with my journal and pencil, and pondered the second piece of shocking news I'd received: My mother had abandoned us.

For eleven years, I'd imagined Mother pining away in a stark sanitarium as she valiantly struggled to regain her health and come home to us. The scene always scintillated in dazzling light: *White hospital walls, white sheets, white-clad nurses, and Mother in the middle of it all, her skin as pale as alabaster, clothed in a frothy white nightgown. She kept a photograph of Father and me at her bedside, and she wept with longing whenever she gazed at it.*

Now, with three cold, blunt words, my father had shattered that ethereal image.

She abandoned us.

It couldn't be true. Why would Mother do such a thing? What

was wrong with me that had made her decide to leave? I couldn't recall being a demanding or difficult child, but perhaps my memory was faulty.

I closed my eyes, trying to remember what life had been like before my mother left us. Days and days would go by when she wouldn't get out of bed—which surely meant that she was ill, didn't it? Father hired a young Swedish girl who barely spoke English to take care of me during that time, and Mrs. Hutchins had cooked and cleaned for us for as far back as I could recall. But I remembered crying one day and throwing a temper tantrum because it was Mrs. Hutchins' day off and I was hungry. I escaped from my Viking jailer and tugged on Mother's limp arm as I tried to rouse her from her lethargy, demanding that she get out of bed and fix me some lunch. What I really wanted was for her to get dressed in one of her rainbow-hued gypsy dresses and whirl around the parlor with me, laughing the way she used to do. Had my tantrum driven her away that day? I wished I knew.

In the wee hours of the morning, after covering my diary page with dark, impassioned doodles, I realized that if I found my mother I could solve both of my dilemmas at the same time. She would see that I was a young woman now, a graduate of Madame Beauchamps' School for Young Ladies and no longer prone to temper fits. Once I convinced her to come home, Father would have no reason to marry Murderous Maude. And if Mother still wouldn't come home, I could escape from my father's impending marriage by moving to Chicago to live with her.

But how in the world would I find her?

Getting permission to travel alone to Chicago would be my first hurdle. I would figure out how to find Mother once I arrived.

I remained in bed until eleven o'clock the next morning. When I finally did rise, I refused to write Maude a proper thank-you note for last night's dinner. I also refused to speak to my father for an entire day.

I was sitting alone in the parlor after supper, reading a proper, boring novel, when Herman Beckett came to call. Herman was an earnest young man of twenty-three and my only suitor, so far. I hadn't decided if I would allow the courtship to continue or not. Herman worked as a clerk for a shipping company, and on our first outing I made the mistake of asking him which commodities his company shipped and where he shipped them. His answer proved so long and boring that I actually dozed off for a moment. Madame B. would have poked me with her parasol for committing such a social *faux pas*.

"Good evening, Miss Hayes," Mr. Beckett said upon arriving at our door. He bowed as if his dark, dreary suit was too tight and might split at the seams. "I was taking my evening constitutional and thought I would pay you a visit. We could get to know one another a little better—that is, if you're free to accept callers."

If he hadn't explained his purpose, I would have guessed by his somber expression and sober attire that he was on his way to a wake rather than paying a social visit. I weighed the merits of my boring book against an hour spent with Herman and decided to invite him to come inside. Father came out of his study to chat with Herman while I fetched glasses of cider for Herman and me. My traitorous father could fetch his own cider.

When I returned, Father retreated into his study across the hall from the parlor, leaving both doors wide open, of course. It took only a few minutes of idle chitchat to discover that I had made a poor choice; Herman was even more boring than my book had been. I had to do something—and quickly—in order to stay conscious.

"If you could choose," I asked him during a long, embarrassing pause in the conversation, "would you rather be a horse or a carriage?"

My friend Ruth and I used to entertain each other for hours debating questions such as this one, but Herman gripped his cider glass with both hands and bolted upright in his chair as if the fate of the world might depend on his reply.

"I-I don't understand."

"It's a simple question. If you could choose, which one would you rather be? There are advantages and disadvantages to each, you see. A horse is alive and can fall in love with another horse and have baby horses—"

"Oh my! Miss Hayes!" His face turned a remarkable shade of red.

"A carriage can't fall in love, but it has the advantage of traveling to exciting, faraway places and conveying interesting people—perhaps even royalty. So which would you choose?"

He gulped a mouthful of cider, as if stalling for time, then said, "I-I wouldn't care to be either one."

Herman didn't get it. I would have to make the game simpler. "Okay, then. Would you rather be unbelievably handsome but poor, or enormously rich but disfigured?"

This time his reply came quickly. "I'd rather be myself, thank you." He frowned in a way that made his bushy black eyebrows meet in the middle, forming one long caterpillar-like eyebrow. I wanted to point out that the frown was quite unbecoming, but the resemblance to a caterpillar reminded me of another one of Ruth's favorite questions.

"What's the most disgusting thing you've ever eaten, Mr. Beckett? I hear that in some countries people eat things like insects and dogs and cats. Would you sample one if given the opportunity?"

"No."

"What if you were *starving*? Or if you were a missionary to a pagan country and they offered caterpillars to you, and you had to accept them in order to be polite? What if your missionary endeavors would suffer if you didn't eat one?"

"I hardly think—"

"At Madame Beauchamps' school she once served snails because she wanted us to learn what the special fork was used for and how to handle it properly. Madame is from France, you see, and snails are a delicacy over there. As soon as Madame tugged one from its shell my friend Ruth gagged at the sight of the slimy thing and had to leave the table. None of the other girls wanted to eat one, but I removed my snail from the shell with great ease and gulped it right down. It wasn't so bad. The only thing I could taste was the garlic butter. The snail was so slippery that it slid right down—"

"Please, Miss Hayes."

"What's wrong?"

"I'm beginning to feel quite ill."

I refused to give up. "So what was the most . . . *adventuresome* . . . thing you've ever eaten?" His mouth hung open, but no sound came out. "How about buffalo, Mr. Beckett? Would you eat a buffalo steak? They serve them out west, you know."

Herman didn't reply. He obviously had no imagination at all. I could see that a lifetime with him would be uneventful and predictable. Surprises would fall into the same category as typhoid fever: something to be avoided at all costs. I felt grateful to have discovered this truth about Herman now rather than after I'd consented to marry him. I would sooner become a spinster than spend a lifetime with a boring, unimaginative man.

Had that been the reason my mother had left us? My father could be boring and pedantic too. *"She hated her life with me,"* my father had said, *"hated living in such a small town."* Had the monotony so wearied her that she simply had to leave? But then why not take me with her? *"She hated being tied down,"* Father had said. That must have included me. I must have tied her down.

"Miss Hayes?" Herman was staring at me as if I had devoured an entire bucketful of snails.

"I'd much rather eat buffalo," I told him, "than dine on—" I nearly slipped and mentioned Maude O'Neill's mutton, which had been as tough and tasteless as horsehide—not that I've ever tasted horsehide, mind you. But just in time, I recalled Maude's friendship with Herman's mother. I remembered the plans I had outlined in my journal last night to investigate her husband's death and decided to steer the conversation in a different direction.

"That reminds me, Herman. I understand that we have a mutual acquaintance, Maude O'Neill?"

"Why, yes. My family knows her very well."

"It's so tragic that she was widowed at such a young age, isn't it? I was away at school when her husband died, so I'm not sure I ever heard the cause of his demise."

"It was most unfortunate, I'm sorry to say. He tumbled down the cellar stairs and struck his head."

Ah ha! Just as I thought! Murderous Maude had pushed him! Homely and Horrid had probably strewn objects in his path to aggravate his fall, and greased the handrail for good measure. I masked my glee with what I hoped was a look of horror.

"How perfectly awful for Mrs. O'Neill! I hope she wasn't home at the time."

"I'm afraid she was. She sent poor little Harriet to fetch Dr. Bigelow, but he arrived too late."

Probably *hours* too late—and only after Maude had caved in his skull with a sledgehammer for good measure. I was deep in thought, pondering these highly suspicious circumstances, when Herman cleared his throat again.

"Did I mention that I'm going to Chicago to see the World's Columbian Exposition?"

"Really? When?" I handled the abrupt change in topics with finesse, taking care not to reveal the fact that I was investigating Mr. O'Neill's murder.

"I plan to go next month, when the weather warms up a bit."

Herman blathered on and on about the fair's architectural marvels and educational wonders until, once again, his monotone began to induce a hypnotic stupor. My eyes watered from stifling yawns.

"Are you and your father planning to visit the fair, Miss Hayes?"

His question gave me a brilliant idea: I could use the Exposition as an excuse to travel to Chicago and find my mother! I would begin badgering my father to go immediately.

As soon as Herman finished his cider—I didn't offer him a refill—and I'd closed the front door behind him, I turned to my father, who had ambled out to the foyer to bid Herman good-night.

"Herman is going to Chicago to visit the Exposition this summer. I would very much like to go as well."

"It so happens I've planned a trip to Chicago. I thought that we all could go."

"*All* of us? You don't mean Maude and her children?"

"Well, yes—"

"Father, please—no! I don't want to go with them. I'm a grown woman, not a child like Homely and Horrid." I didn't realize that I had used my secret names for them until I saw Father's shocked expression.

"Violet! I'm surprised at you."

"Sorry," I muttered.

"It's unlike you to be cruel, Violet. Are you . . . might you be . . . a bit jealous of them?"

"Certainly not! They're children and I'm a grown woman—and that's the point I'm trying to make, don't you see? Maude spoke last evening as if we will all settle down and become one happy family, but her expectations aren't realistic. I won't be linking hands with her little urchins as we skip through the Exposition with a picnic basket. I would much rather see the fair with companions who are my own age."

"I understand. But it's out of the question for you to accompany Mr. Beckett without a chaperone."

"What about Grandmother? Why couldn't I spend a few weeks in Chicago visiting with her?" The idea came to me in a flash of genius. My father could hardly argue that his own mother was an unfit chaperone. Grandmother kept quite busy working for several charitable causes, so I was certain that I could slip away from her for a few hours to search for my mother once I was in Chicago.

"I don't think that's wise, Violet. Your grandmother doesn't need the added responsibility of watching over you. She has enough to deal with as it is, with her sisters."

"But I wouldn't be any trouble at all. There's plenty of room for me in that huge old house. Please, Father? Grandmother is always inviting me to come and stay with her every time she writes. Why won't you ever let me go?"

Father paused as if carefully phrasing his reply. "You're a very . . . impressionable . . . young lady. I fear that the Howell sisters would have a disruptive influence on you."

His words intrigued me. Here was another mystery to solve. How could my devout grandmother and her three aging sisters possibly have a bad influence on me? I was more determined than ever to go—just to find out. I chose my next words with care.

"You began courting Widow O'Neill while I was away at school and never breathed a word of it to me. Instead, you've sprung the news of your engagement on me without any warning and without ever asking for my opinion on the matter. Next, I discover that you've been lying to me about Mother for more than ten years, telling me that she's ill when it seems she isn't ill at all. Taking all of this into consideration, one might say that you've been extremely unfair to me. And faced with such lies and betrayals, one might simply decide to leave home unannounced—*and* without a chaperone." I had delivered a threat without raising my voice. Madame Beauchamps would have approved.

"I never intended to hurt you, Violet, I thought that—"

"Then you might show your remorse by treating me as a grown woman instead of a child. I'm merely asking to take a brief trip away from home to see the World's Columbian Exposition. Perhaps the time away will help me accustom myself to the new state of affairs here at home. And I'll be in the company of your own mother during that time."

"That's what worries me," he mumbled.

"Why? What's wrong with Grandmother?"

He gazed into the distance, slowly shaking his head. His eyes wore the vacant gaze of a stuffed elk.

"Father, why is it that we so rarely see Grandmother when she lives a mere train ride away in Chicago?"

"It's complicated, Violet. . . ." Father groped for the comfort of his watch chain, as if reaching for a weapon to defend himself.

I refused to back down. "May I travel to Chicago to visit with her or not?" He opened the watchcase and stared at the dial before snapping it closed again. I was quite certain that he couldn't have said what time it was.

"Let me think about it, Violet."

"Very well." I turned and glided regally up the stairs. "I will write a letter to Grandmother while I await your reply."

Chapter

3

Monday, June 5, 1893

I settled onto the stiff, velvety train seat, adjusting my skirts before waving a curt good-bye to my father, who stood outside on the platform. Then I turned my back on him. Maude O'Neill and her ill-behaved brats had accompanied us to the train station, and I had no wish to gaze upon them for another moment. She was not my mother and never would be. Homely and Horrid, who had entertained themselves by making ugly faces and rude noises at the other passengers, would never be my siblings. All in all, my send-off had been nearly unendurable. Maude talked on and on about Herman Beckett until I wanted to scream—in spite of everything I'd learned in school about proper manners.

"Mr. Beckett will be *so* lonely without you," she'd insisted. "I understand Mr. Beckett is eager to accompany you to the fair . . ." *Mr. Beckett this . . . and Mr. Beckett that!* If she had mentioned how "smitten" he was with me one more time I would have lost control and smitten her.

I had managed to hold my tongue by imagining what my real

mother would be like, and how she would handle my courtship to a bore like Herman Beckett. I convinced myself that any gentleman Mother picked out for me would be infinitely more exciting than Herman.

The more Maude had hovered over me, the more determined I became to find my real mother—even if it was the last thing I ever did. Once I found her, I would convince her to come back to Lockport to live with Father and me. Wouldn't Maude O'Neill be surprised when she invited herself to my welcome home reception and met the *real* Mrs. John Jacob Hayes?

Of course, I hadn't told Father that I intended to find my mother or he never would have allowed me to go to Chicago. I didn't inform Grandmother of my true plans either.

I wiggled in place, trying to make myself comfortable on the hard train seat, willing the whistle to blow and the train to hurry up and steam out of the station. I sensed Father's worried gaze on me through the window, and I feared that at any moment he would change his mind and charge onto the train to yank me off. It had required prodigious efforts of persuasion on my part before he allowed this trip in the first place. And he had nearly postponed it when no one could be found to accompany me on the train.

"A woman needs a gentleman to watch over her," he'd fussed. "Her husband or father or brother . . ."

"What for?" I had asked him. "I can watch out for myself well enough."

"It just isn't right. Who will handle your trunk and so forth? And what if there's a problem? You wouldn't know what to do."

"I know everything I need to know. I'll board the train in Lockport, sit in my seat—watched over by a very competent conductor—and get off at Union Depot, where Grandmother will be waiting for me. What could go wrong? Besides, the world is on the brink of a brand-new era, Father. We're about to enter the twentieth century, and young ladies are being allowed a bit more freedom. After all, I am twenty years old."

I'm not sure if I truly convinced him or if I simply wore him out. Either way, I was pleased when he'd finally consented and purchased my train ticket. I was slightly less pleased when he agreed to Herman Beckett's request to meet me in Chicago later in the month so he could take me to see the Columbian Exposition, accompanied by his married sister. I doubted if I ever could convince a man as unimaginative as Herman to help me find my mother. Besides, Herman's mother was Maude's friend, and they were certain to gossip about my activities in Chicago.

At last the train lurched forward and began to move. I risked a final glance out of the window and saw Maude cheerily waving her handkerchief as if I were a soldier leaving for the battlefield. Father looked very worried and sorry he had ever agreed to let me go. Little Horrid stuck out his tongue at me. I resisted the temptation to return the gesture.

As soon as the beige limestone train station was out of sight, I heaved a sigh of relief. Madame Beauchamps would have been appalled.

I was leaving Lockport, Illinois, behind and speeding toward Chicago. I felt like pinching myself to see if I was dreaming. I was riding the train into the city—alone! For the first time in my life I felt like an adult. I closed my eyes and imagined that I was running away. I had already decided that if I couldn't prevent Father's wedding, I wouldn't return home. After all, Father had lied to me—all these years!

It didn't take long for the view of flat, monotonous prairie land to bore me. I wondered if God had run out of ideas after creating the mountain ranges and the mighty Mississippi River and had nodded off when He was supposed to be designing the middle portion of America. Was Illinois the result of an unfortunate catnap? Or perhaps, in a gesture of beneficence, the Almighty had delegated the task to a less imaginative underling. If so, I hoped the underling had been fired for his lack of creativity.

As I continued to gaze at the uninspiring terrain, I tried to think of it as a symbol of the larger journey on which I had embarked. Our literature teacher had labored to interest us in things like symbolism and similes, but I confess such imagery bored me when compared to the graphic, lurid details I read about in Ruth's *Illustrated Police News*. But maybe it would help to think of my journey as symbolic: I was leaving my boring life behind along with the terrain and embarking on an exciting new life in Chicago.

To be honest, my stomach churned quite unpleasantly whenever I thought about what might lie ahead. Many of those shocking *True Crime Stories* I used to read had taken place in cities like Chicago, and I was keenly aware of the dangers that might await a young woman such as myself.

Eventually I grew tired of trying to dredge up symbolism from a boring view and I pulled a book from my satchel, settling back to read. I had barely begun the first chapter when I felt the train's momentum begin to slow, and a few minutes later we made a brief stop at the train station in Lemont. The village held little interest for me, but I spotted an intriguing traveling salesman—more commonly referred to as a drummer—waiting to board the train with his suitcase full of wares. I guessed his age to be about the same as Herman Beckett's, but the similarities began and ended right there. Herman dressed like an undertaker's assistant, while this man's unbecoming suit was as garish as a circus clown's, sewn from cheesy plaid material that sagged at the knees and had been worn to a shine on the elbows and rump.

I would have described him as good-looking if his smile wasn't so phony or his hair so slicked-back with Macassar oil that it reflected light. I watched him climb aboard and search for his seat, and he seemed to have absorbed the greasy oil through his scalp until it lubricated him from within. His movements were so smooth that he glided when he walked, as if his bones were as pliable as cheese. A dime novel would have described him as "a slippery character."

I thought him wonderfully dangerous! Everyone warned innocent girls such as myself to stay far away from unsavory men like him. In fact, he was exactly the type of man that my father had worried about when I'd embarked on this trip. In short, the drummer fascinated me.

His restless eyes roved all around the passenger car as if searching for a hidden compartment or a clue to a mystery, and I saw his gaze slide over me a few times, lingering a trifle too long to be proper. I immediately looked away, pretending to read, but I confess that my heart raced with excitement.

He spoke in a very loud voice to the conductor and the other passengers—who seemed reluctant to converse with him. He laughed much too loudly. Once the train resumed its journey, he couldn't seem to settle down, stirring restlessly as if unable to sit still, crossing and uncrossing his legs. He opened his newspaper and began to read, making such a racket that the rustling pages sounded like a forest fire. He finally put the crumpled pages down again. He shifted the position of his sample case three times, opening it briefly to glance inside before stowing it beneath his seat again. At length, he removed a cigar from inside his jacket and left the coach.

I wondered if his unease was caused by a guilty conscience. What crime might he have committed to make him so unsettled? Murder? I must try to look for bloodstains beneath his fingernails when he returned. Theft? It seemed unlikely since he'd boarded the train with no luggage except his sample case. But diamonds were small—might he be a jewel thief?

Ten minutes later the drummer returned from the smoking car, bringing the aroma of cigars with him. I made the mistake of watching him glide down the aisle, and when he saw me he nodded in an overly familiar way. His manners were exceedingly improper and much too forward. His smile was what Madame Beauchamps had called a "candelabra grin."

"Never overdo your enthusiasm, girls, especially with members of the

opposite sex. A slender taper of light is all that one needs to send forth. Be mysterious and enigmatic." Ruth and I had practiced our *enigmatic* smiles in front of a mirror every night until we could no longer suppress our giggles.

I quickly looked away from the salesman's frank gaze, but once again, a thrill of excitement shivered through me. His crime must be adultery. He had what the romance novels referred to as "charisma." He probably knocked on weak-willed women's doors with his suitcase full of samples and sidled his way into their parlors . . . and their affections.

I didn't dare look up again. Instead, I rummaged through my satchel, pretending to search for something, and spotted my mother's address. I had tiptoed into Father's office while he was at work and found the divorce papers, then carefully copied down the address printed beneath Mother's signature. Tears filled my eyes at the memory of her flamboyant signature. It wasn't the handwriting of an invalid, but of a woman who was very much alive. And healthy enough to be a mother to me.

"She abandoned us," my father had said. The more I pondered the truth of her desertion, the smaller and more worthless I felt. No one discarded a treasure, did they? Only worthless things were left behind. Before I could stop them, my tears began to fall.

"Are you in distress, miss?"

I looked up to find the drummer hovering in the aisle beside my seat. My heart began to race, outpacing the train.

"I-I seem to have something in my eye," I lied, quickly applying my handkerchief. Lies must be a family trait.

"Want me to have a look and see if I can fish it out?"

"Um . . . no, thank you." The last thing I needed was a mysterious man gazing deeply into my eyes. I stole a quick glance at his face and saw that his eyes were as flashy as the rest of him, their color such a bright, clear shade of blue that they made me thirsty.

"My name's Silas—Silas McClure." He held out his hand for me to shake, evidently unaware that a gentleman always waited for a lady to offer her hand first—if at all. I couldn't be rude and leave it hanging in midair, so I briefly grasped his fingertips for a dainty shake.

"Violet Hayes." I hated my name the moment I spoke it. *Violet.* It sounded old-fashioned and as limp as velvet. I longed for a more dramatic name and decided that I would change it when I arrived in Chicago. I would introduce myself as Athena or Artemesia or maybe Anastasia. "How do you do, Mr. McClure?"

"I do just fine. . . . Say, don't tell me, let me guess—I'll wager you're going to Chicago to see the fair. Am I right?"

"Um . . . yes. Are you going as well?"

"I've already seen it—three times, in fact. But I'm going again, first chance I get." He propped one foot on the seat that faced mine and folded his arms on his raised knee. "The fair is really swell. I could give you some pointers—what to see and what's a waste of time—if you want me to."

Before I could reply, he dropped his leg and slid into the seat facing me, perching on the very edge so that our knees were practically touching. His manners were outrageous! I imagined Madame Beauchamps flapping her hands as if shooing away pigeons and saying, *"No, no, no, Miss Hayes! You must never, never accept advances from such a creature."* Anyone unsavory was a *creature* to Madame B.

But in the next moment, I found myself wondering whether to believe Madame or not. If my father had lied to me my entire life, why should I obey anything else I'd been taught? Anger swelled inside me, making it difficult to speak. I had felt it growing in strength since the night I'd first learned about Maude and about my mother, slowly rising and expanding like bread dough in a warming oven. The more I thought about the wedding, the deplorable stepchildren, and my father's lies, the more I wanted to punch something the way Mrs. Hutchins punched the rising bread dough so she could shape it into loaves.

The safe cocoon in which I'd been wrapped all my life suddenly felt

34

suffocating. Madame had taught me to be a proper young lady, demure and sedate, but beneath the surface I longed to fly as freely as a butterfly, to do something bold and daring. I scooped up my satchel and placed it on my lap to make room for Mr. McClure on the seat beside me. I even patted the cushion lightly, beckoning him to sit there.

"I would love to hear all about the fair. But please, tell me all about yourself first, Mr. McClure."

"Well, I'm a drummer, as you can probably guess," he said, dropping into the seat. "I sell Dr. Dean's Blood Builder—a nutritive tonic."

"Is it really made from *blood*?"

"No," he said, laughing. "Our specially patented formula is made from the highest-quality beef extract, fortified with iron and celery root. If you're suffering from extreme exhaustion, brain fatigue, debility of any kind, blood disorders, or anemia, our Blood Builder will enrich your blood and help your body throw off accumulated humors of all kinds. It's guaranteed to stimulate digestion and improve blood flow, or we'll give you your money back. Why, we have testimonials from thousands of satisfied customers, people who've suffered all sorts of maladies from nervous exhaustion and weakness to general debilitation. You can find inferior goods anywhere, these days—at twice the price of our tonic, I might add. But only Dr. Dean's Blood Builder offers a thirty-day money-back guarantee. You should try it, Miss Hayes. I'll wager you'll feel renewed, or I'll refund your money."

"Your presentation is quite convincing, Mr. McClure. Do you use the tonic yourself?"

"Of course."

He did appear unusually healthy and robust, and so filled with energy that he could scarcely stay in his seat. Hoards of army ants might have been crawling up his pant legs. I wasn't sure I wanted to have that much vigor. I imagined it would feel quite uncomfortable to be so energetic—and completely unladylike.

"Do you enjoy the life of a traveling salesman, Mr. McClure?"

"Oh, I love riding the rails. There's a new adventure around every corner. I could never stand being a clerk, cooped up in an office all day."

I thought of Herman Beckett.

"And you mentioned the fair—did you find it as exciting as you had hoped?"

"Oh, boy! And then some! Make sure you ride Mr. Ferris' wheel when you go. What a thrill! I happened to be there on the day they gave it the very first test run. They had only attached the first six cars, you see, and nobody had ever ridden it before. It wasn't even open to the public yet, and nobody knew if passengers would even live through the experience. But Mr. Ferris' wife volunteered to be the first one to try it, and she climbed into the first car like she was going for a Sunday afternoon carriage ride. Well, when we saw her going up in the air, the whole crowd of us pushed forward to get onboard the second car— even though the wheel's operators were hollering at us to get back."

"How did you know it was safe if it had never carried passengers before? Weren't you frightened?"

"I was having too much fun to be scared. Although I did have second thoughts for a moment when a bunch of loose nuts and bolts started showering down on us like hailstones. And the gears made a terrible racket at first, crunching and grinding like they were about to give out. But then the car started climbing, up and up, until I had the best view I wager I'll ever see." He gazed into the distance as if seeing it all over again.

"You can see the whole fair from up there, Miss Hayes, all laid out like a little toy village. Lake Michigan is in the distance, and the skyline of the city . . . Well, it takes your breath clean away. As soon as I reached the bottom and stepped off, I wanted to get right back on and ride it all over again. Everyone else had the same idea, and there was a huge rush to get on board—even though the wheel wasn't officially open. Like I said, they had only attached the first six cars at the time. But I managed to squeeze my way forward and go for a second ride—and I would have jumped on and gone around a third time, but the men operating it finally said that if any more people forced their way on board, they'd run us up to the top and leave us there for the night. That wheel is one of the Seven Wonders of the World—or are there eight wonders? I forget ... Anyhow, nothing like it has ever been attempted before."

"It sounds exhilarating!" I wondered if Herman Beckett would dare to go for a ride. I made up my mind that I would ride the wheel, with or without him. "You should have been an explorer, Mr. McClure!"

His daring proved so contagious that in the next moment I found myself asking, "If you could choose, would you rather perish in a terrible cataclysm such as a train wreck or a collapsing Ferris wheel and die amid twisted iron and splintered wood, hearing the screams of trapped and suffering humanity—or would you prefer to die a long, slow death at home in your bed, your body growing ever thinner, your breath leaving you in painful gasps?"

His eyes widened, slightly, and I saw him lean almost imperceptibly away from me. "You have quite an imagination, Miss Hayes."

I was too caught up in my own drama to notice that I had shocked him. "I think I would rather die quickly and spectacularly," I said. "If I were given the choice."

"Would you, now? Well ... let's hope today isn't the day. Anyhow, it looks like we're getting close to the city." He nodded his glossy head toward the window where the view of the prairie had changed to one of factories and warehouses and the backs of buildings. While we had been conversing, the brilliant sky had gradually dimmed to a dull gray, like tarnish on fine silver, and the air had taken on the unmistakable odor of the stockyards.

"May I ask, Miss Hayes—if I'm not being too pushy—would you consider going to the fair with me the next time I'm in Chicago? I'd love to show you around."

"I would enjoy that very much." Father would be scandalized, but I didn't care. I gave Silas McClure an encouraging smile, but he seemed to be waiting for something more. "Was there anything else you wanted to ask, Mr. McClure?"

"I'll need to know where you're staying, Miss Hayes."

"Oh, how silly of me." He gave me one of his calling cards, and I copied down Grandmother's address for him on the back of it. Then the conductor entered the car, toddling down the aisle, punching tickets. Mr. McClure returned to his seat and his suitcase full of tonic as the train slowed. My heart raced with anticipation as I glimpsed Chicago's towering buildings.

I gathered my belongings and crowded into the aisle with the other passengers once the train stopped. The conductor placed a small stool below the passenger car, and he offered me his hand to help me down. The air stank of rotting garbage and hot metal as I hurried down the long platform, following the others.

As soon as I entered the cavernous Union Depot, I began looking around for my grandmother. I heard joyful salutations and saw warm embraces and even tears as the other passengers met their loved ones, but there was no such greeting for me. Even Mr. McClure had been welcomed by two unsavory-looking men in dark coats and bowler hats.

Where could my grandmother be? I visited so infrequently that perhaps we'd failed to recognize each other. But eventually the lobby cleared as porters and baggage agents hefted suitcases and trunks, conveying them to waiting carriages and drays. My fellow passengers hurried away to their destinations. And there I stood, quite alone.

"Is this yours, miss?" I turned to find a baggage porter pointing to my steamer trunk, now loaded onto a cart. He was waiting for his tip, no doubt, but I had no idea how much money to offer him. I had only a few dollars to my name.

"Yes, that's my trunk. My family should be along any minute to fetch me." He rolled his eyes before drifting away.

My earlier euphoria vanished as I realized my helplessness. I had been abandoned. I was lost and alone in an unfamiliar city with little money. I didn't know what to do. Madame Beauchamps may have taught me proper social etiquette, but I was thoroughly unprepared for real life.

I wandered as far as I dared without losing sight of my trunk and saw people rushing to catch their trains, newsboys selling papers, and ragged urchins who probably were waiting to pick pockets or snatch purses. Where could Grandmother be?

Time passed, and still she didn't come. I stood alone, guarding my trunk, for what felt like hours. What if night fell and I was left here with no one to protect me from the ravages of beastly men? What if a stranger abducted me at knifepoint or even gunpoint! I recalled one of Ruth's true crime stories where a man assaulted an innocent maiden in the most dreadful way and—

"Miss Hayes?" When the male voice spoke close behind me I nearly leaped from my skin. "Hey, sorry. I didn't mean to scare you." It was the drummer, Silas McClure. If he hadn't gripped my arm I would have run straight out the door and into the path of an oncoming train. "You need a lift somewhere?" he asked.

"My family is supposed to be here to fetch me." I looked around again as I battled my tears and tried to slow my galloping heart. "I can't imagine why they're so late."

"I'll wager they're stuck in traffic. I've seen snarls so bad it takes ten policemen to unravel them. You get a bunch of wagons and carriages and streetcars all trying to go one way, see. And they crowd right up against each other like freight cars. But the cross traffic is trying to go forward at the same time and so they meet in the middle." He gestured with his hands to show the resulting collision. "There's no room for anybody to go around because you got wagons and carriages parked along both sides of the street. Then you toss in a bunch of pedestrians trying to get across the road, and pushcarts and newsboys, and—well, you can see that you got a real mess in no time at all. Once they all get jammed up in the middle of the intersection like that, nobody can move."

"That sounds awful."

"Yeah, I'll wager that's what happened. But I'd be happy to help you hail a cab, if you'd like."

"What happened to your two friends?"

"Huh? Oh . . . don't worry about them. They had business elsewhere."

My fear battled with my anger. I had been cruelly abandoned once again. First my mother had deserted me, then Father had decided to shove me aside for Maude and her impertinent imps, now my grandmother was taking her turn. My fury made me courageous. I would leave the whole lot of them behind and go straight to my mother's house. I pulled her address from my satchel and showed it to Mr. McClure.

"Are you familiar with the city—do you have any idea where this address might be?"

He studied it for a moment, scratching his glossy head. I hoped his fingers didn't leave grease marks on the paper and cause the ink to run. "It's not too far from here, Miss Hayes. I believe it's in the downtown area."

"Would it cost much? To take a cab there, I mean. I don't have very much money, and I have no idea what a cab would cost." Once again, I wished Madame B. had taught us practical information.

"It can't be more than two bits or a half-dollar. But you can always take a streetcar if you're worried about money."

"What about my trunk?"

He turned to look at it and made a face. "I'll wager you won't get that thing on a streetcar. You'll need a cab for sure. Listen, do you want me to tag along?"

"Would you? Don't you have your own business to attend to?"

"Nothing that can't wait. I'm always happy to help a lovely damsel in distress."

He grinned his wide candelabra grin as he offered me his arm, reminding me of a picture from one of my childhood storybooks: a wolf, dressed in a nightgown and floppy cap, smiling at Little Red Riding Hood. *"Grandmother! What big teeth you have!"*

But what other choice did I have?

"Thank you, Mr. McClure. I'll accept your kind offer."

Chapter

4

———✦———

I tossed all of my common sense to the wind and took Silas
McClure's arm. I was about to hail a cab with a traveling tonic
salesman and drive to an unknown address. But before we could get
the baggage porter's attention, someone called my name.

"Violet! Violet Rose!"

My grandmother hurried toward me out of breath, towing my
great-aunt Bertha by the hand. Relief settled over me like warm bath
water the moment I saw them. Grandmother drew me into her
embrace, obviously as relieved to see me as I was to see her.

"I'm so sorry, dear. We made a terrible mistake and went to the
wrong train station. And the traffic gets so tangled up this time of
day. Thank goodness you're all right."

She finally released me and waved to the baggage agent. He raced
over to fetch my trunk and his long-awaited tip. Mr. McClure
watched the drama in bemused silence as if viewing a theatrical pro-

duction. Then I saw my grandmother looking him over and I remembered my manners.

"Grandmother, I'd like you to meet a friend of mine, Mr. Silas McClure. . . . This is my grandmother, Mrs. Florence Hayes, and her sister, Mrs. Bertha Casey."

Grandmother nodded politely. "How do you do, Mr. McClure."

"I do just fine."

Aunt Bertha gave me a fervent hug. Then, much to Silas' surprise, she proceeded to hug him too. She was opening her arms to embrace the baggage agent when Grandmother said, "No, no, Birdie, dear. That gentleman isn't an acquaintance of ours."

My aunt Bertha's sisters had nicknamed her Bertie, but when I was a child I thought they were saying *Birdie*. The name seemed to fit her, and she had been known as Birdie ever since. She always wore a dreamy smile on her face and a faraway look in her eyes, her brows raised in gentle surprise, as if she were listening to a pleasant conversation that only she could hear. Her expression was so unchanging that I often wondered if the faint smile and uplifted brows were there while she slept. She had seemed childlike to me when I was younger, more of a playmate than an adult. Now that I was older, she just seemed odd.

"Are you heading off to the war?" she asked the baggage clerk, "or returning home from it?"

"That's a railroad uniform he's wearing," Grandmother told her, "not an army uniform."

"Oh, how nice. My husband, Gilbert, is fighting with General McClellan in the Peninsula Campaign, you know. He wants to help Mr. Lincoln free the slaves."

I waited for my grandmother to correct her. I knew that Aunt Birdie's husband had been killed in the War Between the States. But Grandmother linked arms with her sister and said, "Come, Birdie, we need to take Violet home. She must be exhausted from her trip."

How could she deceive poor, naïve Aunt Birdie? Father had lied to me the same way, and it infuriated me. But before I had a chance to speak up, my grandmother turned to Mr. McClure and said, "Thank you so much for accompanying my granddaughter. It was kind of you to wait here with her when I'm sure you must be anxious to see your own family. I trust we'll be seeing you again soon?"

Grandmother had mistaken Mr. McClure for Herman Beckett! My father must have told her that a suitor would be escorting me to the Exposition and she thought Silas was the one. I decided to let my grandmother assume whatever she wished. Fortunately, Mr. McClure's mouth had dropped open in surprise and he hadn't responded.

"Yes, Mr. McClure will be calling on us in the very near future. Isn't that right?" I asked him, gently nudging his arm.

He smiled his ornate grin and said, "I wouldn't miss it for the world."

We arrived home an hour later to find my great-aunt Matilda pacing in the front foyer like a circus lion. "I was beginning to think something terrible had happened. Was the train late? If women ran the world, the trains would all run on time, you know."

"The train was on time," Grandmother told her. "Birdie and I were the ones who were late. We went to Dearborn Station instead of Union Depot."

Aunt Matilda glared at Grandmother as if she deserved a rap on the knuckles with a hickory stick. To tell you the truth, I had always been a little afraid of my great-aunt Matilda—Aunt Matt for short. She was the oldest of the four Howell sisters and still a spinster. She always wore a look of displeasure, as if spoiling for a fight, her eyebrows knit together, her mouth downturned. She seemed perpetually disgusted with life in general and with men in particular. To Aunt Matt, men were the chief perpetrators of everything unfair.

"*If women ran the world . . .*" she would insist, "*tea wouldn't be so expensive . . . the politicians would be honest . . . the sun would set at a more convenient hour . . .*" She held her hands curled tightly into fists, her knuckles white, as if she needed to be prepared at all times to punch someone.

"Well, dinner's ready," she said with a sniff. "We'd better eat it before it's thoroughly ruined."

"Dinner can wait five more minutes," Grandmother told her. "I believe Violet Rose would like to freshen up after her journey."

"Well, don't blame me if the food is stone-cold."

"We won't, Mattie, dear. It's my fault entirely. I had no idea there were two train stations in Chicago."

"If women ran the world, there would be only one station so people wouldn't get confused." Aunt Matt marched into the dining room like a general charging into battle, shoulders set, head thrust forward.

"Come, Violet," Grandmother said, steering me away. "I asked the driver to carry your steamer trunk up to your room." As she led me down the front hall, Aunt Birdie stopped us.

"Would you like to stay for dinner?" she asked me in her fluttery voice. "I'm sure we have plenty of food."

"I am staying for dinner, Aunt Birdie. I'm staying for a month, in fact."

"Oh, how nice."

The tall case clock in the foyer chimed six o'clock as I followed Grandmother upstairs to the guest room. I loved this grand old house. My great-grandfather, the Honorable Judge Porter C. Howell, had built the graceful Greek Revival-style home in 1830 and raised my grandmother and her three sisters here. Grandmother, Aunt Birdie, and Aunt Matt still lived here, while the fourth sister, Aunt Agnes, lived across town with her husband.

According to my father, this house had narrowly escaped the Great Fire that destroyed much of Chicago more than twenty years ago, the flames halting a mere city block away. Great-grandfather Howell had deeded the house to Aunt Matilda, who had never married. Aunt Birdie had moved in after her husband died in the war, and my grandmother joined them when her husband died. It remained a mystery to me why my grandmother hadn't moved in with Father and me, since my mother had already left us by then.

I was very hungry, so I washed quickly using the pitcher and bowl on my washstand, then tidied my hair. On my way down to the dinner table, I paused to peek into the other bedrooms, glimpsing how very different the Howell sisters were from one another. My grandmother's room resembled a monk's cell, with bare wood floors, a simple dresser and mirror, and a plain white spread on the narrow bed. A spare wooden cross was the only wall decoration.

Aunt Birdie's room across the hall was packed to the ceiling with color and pattern and ornately carved furniture. A scarlet Turkish rug stretched across the floor; pink floral wallpaper clashed with framed botanical prints and lush landscapes; a red floral bedspread and dozens of tapestry pillows covered the bed; and gold brocade curtains hung on the windows. Jammed into the room beside the four-poster bed were two dressers, a wardrobe, a mirrored dressing table, two end tables, two slipper chairs, and a washstand, barely leaving room to walk.

Aunt Matt's bedroom on the first floor had once been my great-grandfather's study—and it still resembled one except for the quilt-covered daybed shoved against one wall. A massive desk, buried beneath piles and piles of papers, took up most of the room. Glass-fronted barrister's shelves filled with my great-grandfather's books lined two walls. I had no idea where Aunt Matt kept her clothing; the room had neither dresser nor wardrobe. I suppose it didn't matter because she always looked the same to me and might well have owned only one dress: high collared, ankle length, prim, and black.

The three women had filled the remaining rooms of the house with the accumulated possessions of all their lives, and I had fun trying to guess which items belonged to whom.

I slipped into my place at the mahogany dining table, where the Howell sisters sat waiting for me. We bowed our heads as Grandmother said grace.

"Did Father tell you he's planning to remarry?" I blurted moments after Grandmother said "Amen."

"Oh, how nice," Aunt Birdie said. "I love weddings."

Aunt Matt huffed in disgust. "I'll never understand why any woman in this modern era would feel the need to subject herself to a man's control."

"Yes, your father told me he'd met someone," Grandmother said with a sigh. She rested her hand on my arm in a gesture of comfort. My grandmother used her hands more than any person I knew—touching, caressing, or gently laying them on someone's shoulder or arm. When her hands weren't soothing they were working: scrubbing, baking, cleaning, cooking. Then when her other work was finished, she would sit in the parlor to do her darning, mending, crocheting, or knitting. *Idle hands are the devil's playthings,* she often insisted.

I took another bite of mashed potatoes and returned to the subject of my father, hoping to win my devout grandmother as an ally. "Have you given his marriage your blessing?" I asked. "I would think that divorce and remarriage are against your religious principles."

"Your father didn't ask for my opinion, dear—or my blessing."

"Well, did you know that he's been lying to me all these years, telling me that my mother was ill? I learned only this month that she hasn't been sick at all. And now he has divorced her!"

"I gather you don't think much of his decision to remarry. Do you know this Mrs. O'Neill very well?"

"I hate Maude O'Neill!" I said, banging my fist on the table and rattling the silverware. There. I'd spoken the truth. Grandmother laid her hand on my arm once again.

"The Bible says we mustn't hate anyone, Violet Rose."

"Hatred is what's causing this terrible War Between the States," Aunt Birdie added.

I might have known my grandmother would react this way. She was the walking embodiment of the fruit of the Spirit, carrying love, joy, peace, and all the rest around with her as if toting an invisible basket, passing them out freely to everyone she met.

"Please don't let hatred overtake you, Violet." Jesus' eyes must have looked just like my grandmother's: kind, loving, sorrowful, or sometimes filled with righteous indignation—over the very same things that moved my grandmother. She turned her woeful Jesus eyes on me now until I had to look away in shame.

"I'm sorry," I mumbled. "But I can't help disliking Maude. Father gave me no warning at all. I arrived home from boarding school one day, and he announced his engagement the very next evening."

"Marriage is bondage," Aunt Matt declared. "This widow ought to think twice before sacrificing her freedom. Did she inherit any property from her late husband?"

"She has a house . . . and two perfectly wretched children."

"My husband adores children," Aunt Birdie said dreamily. "We plan to have a large family once he returns from the war. He has to conquer Richmond and defeat Robert E. Lee first."

"Maybe I should have a word with this Widow O'Neill," Aunt Matt said. "Someone needs to tell her how much she stands to lose if she remarries."

"Oh, I wish you would speak to her, Aunt Matt." If anyone could frighten Maude into canceling the wedding, it was my militant Aunt Matt.

"Now, Mattie," Grandmother said, "you know John would never allow you to interfere with his life—"

"Did you know," Aunt Matt continued, "that when a woman marries, her property, her wages, and her inheritance all become the property of her husband?"

"No, I didn't," I said in surprise. "I think someone had better warn Maude right away before—"

"There are poor women in this city who labor for twelve hours a day in sweatshops and factories, yet by law, their drunken husbands can take their wages straight to the saloon and indulge themselves with what she's earned by the sweat of her brow, leaving her and her children to starve."

I had never heard Aunt Matt express her views so strongly. Perhaps it was because I'd never visited my grandmother's house alone before. My father always accompanied me. He was probably the reason my aunts never talked about my mother. I decided to steer the conversation back to her.

"I think I deserve to know something about my mother."

"She was ravishingly beautiful," Aunt Birdie said, gazing into the air above our heads. "She was Juliet to Johnny's Romeo." I waited to hear more, but Aunt Birdie seemed to have lost her train of thought. My grandmother and Aunt Matt fell silent, eating their food without looking up.

"Is that true?" I finally asked. "Were my parents like Romeo and Juliet, living in feuding households?"

"I never met your mother's parents," Grandmother said quietly. "There was no feud. . . . Listen, Violet. I know you're upset with all this secrecy, and I don't blame you. But asking about your mother will only lead to more grief in the end. Sometimes it's best to leave the past in the past—and this is one of those times. Besides, we're all tired tonight. Supper was later than usual, thanks to the station mix-up. And right now it's time for our evening devotions."

She rose to fetch her Bible from the buffet and rustled through the fading, onionskin pages until she found her place. I didn't comprehend a single word that she read as I battled tears of anger and frustration. I would learn nothing more about my mother tonight.

Ten minutes later Grandmother ended with a lengthy prayer, thanking the Almighty "for safely delivering our Violet Rose" and finishing with "Amen."

"Amen," Aunt Birdie echoed. Grandmother rose quickly again.

"I believe we've lingered here long enough for one evening. Mattie, it's our turn to do the dishes. Violet, why don't you go upstairs and unpack?"

She didn't wait for a reply but gathered up as many dishes as she could carry and headed to the kitchen, her steps brisk and purposeful as if unwilling to waste a single one of them. My grandmother believed that waste of any kind offended God, especially wasting time.

I lacked enthusiasm for the task of unpacking, but I dutifully went upstairs and removed my dresses from the trunk and hung them in the empty wardrobe, which smelled of mothballs. I arranged my comb and brush and other toiletries on the dresser top and tossed my stockings and undergarments into the empty drawers. I spent the longest amount of time searching for a place to hide my journal, finally deciding to stuff it underneath my mattress, as usual.

Grandmother and Aunt Matt were still in the kitchen when I went downstairs again. Aunt Birdie sat alone in the parlor, gazing into space with a contented smile, her hands folded loosely in her lap. She had soft, limp hands, like aging goose-down pillows with nearly all of the stuffing gone. I sat beside her on the horsehair sofa, hoping for a few minutes alone with her before the others joined us.

"Aunt Birdie, did you know my mother?"

"Of course. I knew her very well."

My hopes soared. "Would you tell me something about her, please?"

"I'd be happy to. Let's see now . . ." Her pause lasted a very long time. I waited, thinking that she was searching for a place to begin. But finally she looked up at me and asked, "Who are you again?"

"I'm Violet Rose Hayes. Your nephew, John Hayes, is my father." When Birdie still seemed puzzled, I added, "I'm Florence's grand-daughter."

"Why, what a coincidence! I'm Florence's sister."

"Yes, I know. Aunt Birdie, you said that my parents were like Romeo and Juliet. Do you remember when they got married?"

"Like it was yesterday. I even have a picture. Would you like to see it?"

"I would love to!"

50

She rose gracefully to her feet and removed a framed photograph from the curio cabinet in the corner, wiping a layer of dust from it with her sleeve, then blowing on it to remove the rest. I held my breath in anticipation as she handed the photo to me. My hopes plummeted quickly when I saw that the bride in the photograph was Aunt Birdie.

"I think this is you, Aunt Birdie. You and your husband."

"Gilbert is off fighting in the war, you know. He's with General McClellan in Virginia on the Peninsula Campaign. I miss him terribly." Tears filled her gray eyes.

I fumbled for something to say. "He's . . . he's a fine-looking man."

"Yes, isn't he, though? Is there someone special in your life, dear?"

"Not really. Herman Beckett from back home asked my father for permission to court me, but he's my only suitor so far." Unless I wanted to count Silas McClure, the traveling salesman—which I didn't.

"Do you love this Mr. Beckett?"

"Certainly not!"

"Well, then. That says it all, doesn't it? Make sure you marry for love, dear."

"I really don't know much about love, Aunt Birdie. My friend Ruth and I used to read *True Romance Stories* and they made falling in love sound like a bad case of influenza. Your stomach goes all aflutter and your palms sweat and your head starts spinning. I'm not sure I would like the sensation, to tell you the truth. Does love really feel that way?"

"My husband fell in love with me the moment he first laid eyes on me. He saw me across the room and he said to his brother, 'Look! Isn't she the most beautiful woman you've ever seen?' He couldn't take his eyes off of me. 'I'm going to marry her,' he vowed, 'if it's the last thing I ever do.' He begged my father for permission to court me, but it wasn't enough for Gilbert to win Father's permission or even my consent to marry him. He was determined to win my love. And so he did." She sighed and wiped away the tear that had rolled down her soft cheek. "Then this terrible war started, and we've been apart ever since."

"I'm sorry," I said, gently squeezing her hand. "I hope I meet a gentleman who loves me that much."

"Make certain you marry for love. My sister Agnes married for money, and Florence married so she could serve God, and poor Mattie never married at all. But I was the fortunate one. I married for love."

"Do you know why my father and mother got married? Their names are John and Angeline Hayes."

"Oh yes. That was true love. Deep and passionate. Like my husband's and mine."

"Won't you please tell me their story?"

"Their passion was ignited the night of the Great Fire, and the fervor of their love was as all-consuming as the flames."

Wow! Aunt Birdie could write True Romance *stories!* But was it the truth? I knew that the Great Fire had occurred in October of 1871. I was born in April of 1873. Allowing a few months for courtship and marriage, and nine months for pregnancy, the timing did seem to make sense.

"What happened then, Aunt Birdie?"

"It began to rain early on Tuesday morning and the fire finally stopped. If it hadn't been for the rain, this house would have burned up with all the others."

"I mean what happened with my parents? Do you have a photograph of their wedding?"

"Yes. Would you like to see it?" She lifted her wedding photo from her lap and showed it to me again. I was disappointed but not surprised.

"I think this is you, Aunt Birdie."

"Darling Gilbert. He's the love of my life. He's fighting in Virginia to help free the slaves, you know. Make sure you marry for love, dear."

I gave up. Trying to get information from Aunt Birdie was probably a lost cause. A few minutes later, Grandmother and Aunt Matt finished the dishes and joined us in the parlor.

"Unpacked already?" Grandmother asked. "That didn't take long."

"I'm letting my dresses hang in the wardrobe for a while before I press them."

"Well, if you'll excuse me," Aunt Matt said, "I have an article to write. Good night." She crossed the front hall to her room and closed the door.

"That reminds me," Aunt Birdie said. "I need to write a letter to Gilbert. It always cheers him to receive mail from home." She stood and floated to the tall secretary across the room, unfolding the drop leaf so it formed a desk. She sat down gracefully and took out her stationery and a pen. Meanwhile, my grandmother had retrieved a bag of yarn and knitting needles and settled into a rocking chair.

"What are you making?" I asked.

"Socks. They're for the children down at the settlement house. Some of those poor little dears run around in the snow all winter with bare feet in their raggedy shoes. Do you know how to knit, Violet?"

"I learned how to once, but I'm not very good at it. I can't say that I enjoy it."

"Well, if you ever feel like helping me, I have extra knitting needles and plenty of yarn. I could use all the help I can get."

I sat watching the women work. The only sounds were the steady ticking of the clock in the hallway, Grandmother's knitting needles clacking rhythmically, and Aunt Birdie's pen scratching across the page. I wondered if I'd made a terrible mistake in coming to Chicago to live with a spinster and two widows. Was every evening going to be as boring as this one? I missed my friend Ruth from school, and I especially missed her exotic reading material.

I would have to come up with a plan to find my mother soon— before I died of boredom.

Chapter

5

———— ❧ ————

Tuesday, June 6, 1893

I slept late the next day. By the time I came downstairs for breakfast, the others already had eaten. "Where's my grandmother?" I
asked Aunt Matt. She was trying to fasten a hat to her head with a
long hatpin, stabbing it into the straw so fiercely I feared she would
draw blood.

"Florence left the house hours ago to do her charity work," she
said. "She told me to let you sleep, so I did. She also told me to fix
you some breakfast when you finally woke up, so what do you want?"

Judging by Aunt Matt's expression and tone of voice, it was going
to be a terrible imposition for her to wait on me. She obviously had
more important things to do.

"Thank you, but I'm not hungry. I never eat much for breakfast."

"All right, then. I'm off to do the shopping." She strode through
the back door as if heading off to war, marching to the grocery store
to conquer the cabbages. Once again, I was alone with Aunt Birdie.

I found her in the parlor, daintily scattering dust as she skimmed a feather duster over the room's bric-a-brac. Neither she nor the feathers did much good, as far as I could see. Dust motes danced in the slanted sunbeams for a few seconds, then settled back into place on the cluttered furnishings. When Birdie saw me she hurried over to embrace me, as if I had just arrived home from a very long journey.

"Good morning, dear. Did you sleep well?"

"Yes, very well."

It wasn't exactly true. I hadn't slept well at all. But Madame Beauchamps had insisted that most people really didn't want to know the answer to polite questions such as "How are you?" or "Did you sleep well?" The inquirers were simply making small talk, and so the proper reply should always be something like, "Fine, thank you. And yourself?"

In truth, my grandmother's refusal to discuss my mother had upset me a great deal. I had spent a portion of the night tossing and turning on the lumpy guest-room bed, trying to devise a way to escape from the house so I could search for my mother. I then wasted a few more hours trying to figure out how I could get Aunt Matt to deliver her lecture on remaining free from domineering husbands to Maude O'Neill. When I finally did fall asleep, I dreamed that Chicago was on fire again and my father and I were racing through the flames to find my mother.

"I'm so glad you slept well, dear," Aunt Birdie said. "We have a big day ahead of us, you know. It's a good thing you got your rest."

"Pardon me . . . ? Um, what is it, exactly, that we're supposed to be doing today?"

Aunt Birdie leaned close to me and whispered, "It's a secret!" She winked.

I had no idea if she was making sense or not. My grandmother hadn't mentioned a "big day" or a secret. A moment later, Birdie returned to her dusting, and I spotted the wedding picture she had shown me last night still lying on the parlor sofa. I picked it up and studied this younger and surprisingly pretty Aunt Birdie.

"Do you have any more pictures, Aunt Birdie? Maybe a scrap-book of photographs that we could look at together?" I would rec-ognize my parents, even if Aunt Birdie didn't.

"Oh, yes. I have quite a collection of photographs. They're not in a scrapbook, though."

"That's okay. I would still like to see them."

"You would?" She smiled her dreamy smile. "Oh, how nice."

Birdie went to the secretary and removed an entire drawer brim-ming with photos and other mementos. She carried it over to the sofa and sat down beside me with a sigh. I wanted to root through the pictures quickly, searching for my parents, but Aunt Birdie seemed to have all the time in the world for this task. Shielding the drawer from my grasping fingers, she patiently pulled out each picture, one by one, and described it to me in excruciating detail.

"This first one is my sister Agnes and her husband, Henry. She married Henry in 1847 . . . or was it 1848? His last name is Paine—Henry Paine. His people are very well-to-do, you know. Those are their two boys, Henry Junior and Michael. They're grown now, of course, with children of their own. But aren't they darling in this picture? I think little Michael must have been about twelve . . . or was he older? Let me think . . ."

At the rate she was going, I would be grown and have children myself by the time we reached the bottom of the drawer. I decided to hurry things along.

"It doesn't matter how old he was, Aunt Birdie. Who is that in the next picture? Is that my grandmother?"

"Yes, this is Florence and her husband, Isaac. Too bad he isn't smiling—he looked much nicer when he smiled. But, then, Isaac never did smile very much. He was a minister, you see. One of those fire-and-brimstone preachers you hear so much about, and he never seemed to think there was much in this life worth smiling about. Now in heaven, on the other hand . . . He would preach about heaven too, once in a while. . . ."

I gritted my teeth, struggling to be patient. We had reached only the third photo—one of Aunt Birdie's father, taken shortly before he died—when I heard a horse and carriage drawing to a halt out front. I was afraid that it was my grandmother and that she would take away the photos or hide all the ones of my mother before Aunt Birdie could show them to me. I jumped up and parted the front curtain to peer out.

An enclosed carriage, complete with a driver and a matched team of horses, had parked by our front walk. I couldn't see the occupants, but the elegant vehicle was a far cry from the run-down hansom cab and old nag that my grandmother had hired to fetch me from the train station yesterday.

"Does my grandmother—Florence—ever hire a carriage and driver?" I asked, ready to yank the drawer full of photos from Aunt Birdie and stuff it back into the secretary.

"Florence rides the streetcar, dear."

"Well, someone is here to pay us a visit in a very expensive-looking rig."

"Oh, how nice."

The driver dismounted from his seat and hurried to open the carriage door. My suspense ended as I watched my great-aunt Agnes climb down. She was a stout woman, the most full-figured of the four sisters—and also the wealthiest. Prosperity, respectability, and the aura of riches hung from her like diamonds. She swept regally up the walkway, as if balancing a crown on her head. I could easily picture an invisible entourage of velvet-clothed pages rolling a red carpet before her and lifting a long, elegant train in her wake.

"*Bonjour*, my dears," she sang as she flowed through the front doorway. An engraved calling card dangled from Aunt Agnes' gloved fingertips. Madame Beauchamps would have praised the way she held her pinkie finger daintily outstretched. Aunt Birdie hurried out to the foyer to give Agnes one of her bone-crushing embraces.

"Where is the tray, Bertha?" Agnes said, smoothing the wrinkles from her gown again. "I know you own a perfectly fine silver tray for receiving calling cards. I'm the one who bought it for you."

Madame Beauchamps had drilled into us at some length the importance of the calling-card ritual. I felt compelled to search for the lost tray immediately and correct this horrendous oversight. Since I had no idea what it looked like or where to find it, I turned in useless circles, peering beneath the hall table and into the coat closet while Aunt Agnes waited and Aunt Birdie stared dreamily into space.

"Never mind," Agnes finally decided. The card fluttered from her fingertips and landed on the hall table. "Come here and let me look at you, Violet."

She held me at arm's length, studying me with a keen, critical eye. I feared she would find fault with my dark eyebrows and dusky complexion, but my great-aunt's round, regal face broke into a genial smile.

"Why, you're quite lovely. You should do very well—very well indeed. I'll introduce you straightaway."

"Oh, how nice," Aunt Birdie said.

"Introduce me to whom, Aunt Agnes?"

"Why, to Chicago society, of course. You do have calling cards, don't you? Properly engraved?"

"Yes, ma'am." Madame B. had made certain of that.

"And suitable apparel, I presume? A proper hat? Gloves? Well, I can remedy that easily enough, if you don't. I hope you speak French. I understand that you attended that boarding school in Rockford? What was it called?"

"Madame Beauchamps' School for Young Ladies."

"That's the one. You may not be aware, but I was the one who recommended it to your father. I assume they taught you French there?"

"*Oui, Tante Agnes. Je parle très bien français.* Madame wouldn't have allowed me to graduate unless I'd mastered French along with the rules of etiquette and other social necessities."

"Wonderful."

"Madame also insisted that we learn a smattering of Italian in case the need ever arose to converse with a Venetian count; that we played the piano and sang; that we knew how to find her French homeland and other important countries on a map; and that we had a passing knowledge of poetry and literature."

"*Très bon*, Violet," Aunt Agnes said. "You seem very well prepared. It's about time that your father decided to do right by you and send you to Chicago to find a proper husband."

I stopped breathing.

"A-a husband?"

"Yes, certainly. Why do you think you were sent to Chicago? To see the fair?" She laughed at her own joke. "Mind you, I told your father it was almost too late, that you were almost too old. But I shall endeavor to make up for lost time."

Was this really the reason my father had agreed to let me come? I was so astounded by Aunt Agnes' news that I had no idea what I was supposed to say. Fortunately, Madame Beauchamps had taught us that expressions of profuse gratitude were suitable for nearly every occasion.

"Thank you, Aunt Agnes. *Merci*. I'm so very grateful." But in truth, the idea of shopping for a husband made my heart pound—though whether from fear or excitement I couldn't have said. Perhaps a bit of each.

"I'll call for you tomorrow at two o'clock," Agnes said. "Make sure you tell your grandmother that I'm coming. Bertha won't even remember that I've called, the poor dear. And wear a hat. And gloves."

She turned toward the door in a swirl of swishing taffeta, calling "*Au revoir*, Bertha," as if poor Aunt Birdie were deaf as well as simple. To me she said *sotto voce*, "Don't forget your calling cards. *Au revoir*."

I must have looked like Aunt Birdie as I stood staring dumbly into space, completely flabbergasted by Aunt Agnes' visit. The scent of her perfume lingered long after she left, along with her tantalizing words.

A *husband*! I could well imagine what Aunt Matt would have to say about that.

I was still standing in the hallway in shock when I heard someone coming through the kitchen door. I quickly raced into the parlor and stuffed the drawer full of photos back into the desk. Now that I knew where Aunt Birdie kept them, I could browse through them on my own another day. I picked up the feather duster and pretended to dust—just as my grandmother walked in from the kitchen to hang her hat on the hall tree.

"Did you mail my letter to Gilbert?" Aunt Birdie asked after greeting her with an embrace.

"I took care of it."

It surprised me that my grandmother, a good Christian woman, would be deceitful. Evidently I came from a long line of accomplished liars. I knew firsthand the pain and disillusionment of being lied to for years and years, so I gave the feather duster to Birdie and followed my grandmother into the kitchen.

"Why don't you tell Aunt Birdie the truth about her husband and the war?" I asked in a hushed voice.

"We have told her, dear. Countless times. And every time, when she finally grasps it, she grieves inconsolably for days and days. Then, by God's mercy, she wakes up one morning and has forgotten what year it is and she's happy again—writing letters to Gilbert, awaiting his arrival. We don't intentionally deceive her, and whenever she asks me for the truth I don't lie to her. But it's so much kinder for her this way, don't you think?"

"I'm not sure. My father might have thought he was being kind by sparing me the truth about my mother, but my shock upon learning the truth has been truly upsetting. It's one of the reasons I needed to get away from home for a while."

"I'm so sorry." She rested a soothing hand on my shoulder. "I told John how displeased I was when he first invented his lie. That's probably why he never allowed me to see much of you over the years. He knew I wouldn't lie if you asked about your mother. But he made me promise not to talk about her. I may be John's mother, but he made it clear that his marriage was none of my business."

"Well, I would like to know the truth now."

"What good can that possibly serve, Violet?" She slid her hand down my arm and took my hand in hers.

"I already know that Mother was never really sick, was she."

"Not unless you count being sick at heart."

"But what was she like? I barely remember her."

Grandmother paused as she released my hand and picked up her apron, tying the strings behind her back. "In the beginning . . . ? Your mother was full of life. Vibrant. Vivacious. And very beautiful. You resemble her, you know."

I shook my head. "I hardly remember what she looked like. Why aren't there any pictures?"

But just as I was learning some useful information, Aunt Birdie interrupted us. She walked into the kitchen carrying Agnes' calling card in the palm of her hand as if it were made of glass.

"We had a social call, Florence—and I couldn't find the silver tray!"

"Was it Agnes? Let me see that." She lifted the card from Birdie's hand.

"Aunt Agnes is coming for me tomorrow at two o'clock," I said.

"Oh, dear." Grandmother's shoulders sagged. "I was hoping she'd be too busy to subject you to her social rounds—unless you want to be subjected, that is. You're a grown woman, so I suppose it's your choice."

"What's wrong with making social calls with Aunt Agnes?"

"Nothing. It's just that she hobnobs with people like the Palmers and the Pullmans and the Fieldses, drinking gallons of tea, and I see no point in all of that social folderol. There are so many more important things to do in this brief life."

"Aunt Agnes said my father sent me here to find a husband." Unfortunately, Aunt Matt picked that moment to march through the back door. She nearly dropped all of her parcels when she overheard me.

"Agnes said *what*? Over my dead body she will!"

I felt like I was standing in the middle of one of those traffic snarls Mr. McClure had described, with vehicles colliding all around me.

"But where is the silver tray, Florence?" Aunt Birdie asked. "I can't find it anywhere."

"I put the tray away in the buffet, dear. It was badly tarnished and I didn't have the time or the patience to polish it—especially when Agnes is the only person who ever comes calling these days."

"Now, Florence," Aunt Matt said sternly. "Promise me that you won't allow Agnes to sell your innocent granddaughter into servitude!"

"Don't be melodramatic, Matt. You make it sound as if Agnes wants Violet to be an indentured servant instead of a wife."

"There is very little difference," Matt said with a sniff.

"Are we all out of silver polish?" Aunt Birdie asked from inside the pantry. "I can't find it."

"Look on the shelf behind the ammonia," Grandmother called to her. She turned back to Aunt Matt. "Besides, it's up to Violet and her father to decide whether or not she marries, not us."

"Well! We shall see about that." Aunt Matt dropped her parcels on the kitchen table and stomped off.

I worried that I had made her angry, and I couldn't afford to do that. I needed Aunt Matt to talk Maude out of marrying my father. But at the same time, I wanted to go visiting with Aunt Agnes. How could I turn down the opportunity to hobnob with Chicago's high society—not to mention, find a husband?

"I think I'd like to go calling with Aunt Agnes tomorrow," I told my grandmother. "Would you mind?"

"That's entirely up to you. Just watch out or she'll quickly take over your life with her nonsense."

"Here it is!" Aunt Birdie announced. She emerged from the pantry looking disheveled but triumphant, waving a very tarnished silver tray and the container of silver polish. "Now we'll be prepared when callers arrive at our door!"

And if Aunt Agnes had her way, one of those callers just might be my future husband.

Chapter

6

Wednesday, June 7, 1893

I tried on three dresses before deciding which one I would wear to make social calls with Aunt Agnes. I finally chose one that accentuated my small waist, even though I couldn't cinch myself very tightly without my friend Ruth's help. She had been able to make me quite svelte—and quite breathless.

Ruth Schultz had been an expert on what a girl could do to improve her figure, and everyone at school had come to her for help. When it came to nipping, tucking, and reshaping, Ruth's knowledge of corsets was second to none. She also recommended daily doses of an Egyptian elixir that promised to provide "a graceful plumpness" to poorly endowed girls if taken regularly. It tasted like bile. Fortunately, my endowments didn't need plumping.

"Small-waisted girls who are too top-heavy always look as though they're in danger of falling over," Ruth had counseled me. *"Especially if they have tiny feet."*

I took a long time pinning up my hair, unable to get it just right.

I felt absurdly nervous, as if I were about to take an examination at school and all of the skills and lessons Madame B. had taught me would be put to a final test. What if I tripped over a rug and fell flat on my face in front of everyone? What if I dropped my teacup and it turned out to be a priceless heirloom that had been rescued from the Great Fire, the only surviving item of a precious family inheritance, absolutely irreplaceable and—

I stopped, took a deep breath, and told myself to think of all the good things that might happen today instead of the bad. What if I met a man who was everything I've ever dreamed of: handsome, charming, rich . . . but most of all, daring, adventuresome, imaginative? What if he fell in love with me at first sight, the way Aunt Birdie's husband had fallen in love with her? My dream man would set out to win my heart, courting me in all of the most romantic ways, just like the heroes in Ruth's *True Romance Stories*. Our story would be so touchingly beautiful that it would become a classic, read by millions of envious girls for decades to come. In fact, we would—

"Violet?" Aunt Birdie interrupted my flight of fancy, calling to me from the front foyer. "Agnes is here. Her carriage just arrived."

"Coming." I quickly pinned on my hat, gathered my gloves and calling cards, and hurried downstairs.

I couldn't recall ever riding in a carriage as fine as my aunt's, but a lesser vehicle would have looked completely out of place stopping at the elegant townhouse we visited first. A uniformed servant met us at the door and received our calling cards on a Chinese enameled tray. I wanted to gaze all around at the lavishly appointed rooms as he ushered us inside, but good manners forbade me to gawk. The small glimpses I did steal convinced me that this was the finest home I ever had visited. The servant led Aunt Agnes and me to the drawing room, where a handful of well-dressed women gathered around the tea cart.

I walked into the room with practiced grace and faultless posture: back erect, shoulders straight, and head held high. I had spent hours at Madame Beauchamps' school walking with a book balanced on top of my head before being allowed to graduate to the next level of difficulty. I then was expected to gracefully sit down while holding a cup of hot tea and still balancing the book on my head.

"Ladies," Aunt Agnes said in her cultured voice, "I would like to introduce my great-niece, Violet Rose Hayes. She's visiting my sister Florence Hayes and our fair city of Chicago this summer."

The ladies greeted me with pleasant smiles and a chorus of lilting voices: "Hello . . . How nice to meet you . . . Welcome, Violet. . . ."

"Thank you so much."

I paid very close attention as our hostess introduced each of the women to me, recalling Madame B.'s stern warning: *"I cannot emphasize strongly enough the importance of remembering the name of each person to whom you are introduced."* She would place strangers' photographs on a row of chairs and make fake introductions so we could practice recalling names.

I had perfected my own secret system of memorization, fabricating scandalous stories about each person based on her name or physical attributes. For instance today, when our hostess introduced a Mrs. Smith, I imagined that the dear woman was having a secret romance with a large, muscular blacksmith.

Our hostess served tea to everyone from an engraved silver teapot, and we all sat down to drink it. A thrill of anticipation coursed through me. So many of the things one learns in school are quickly forgotten and never used, but now, in this very room, all of my hard work and diligent study would finally be put to use. I had always feared that my impeccable training would languish from lack of use back home in Lockport and eventually go to waste. But thanks to Aunt Agnes, I had finally found my place in life.

I spread the miniscule napkin on my lap, balanced the delicate teacup just so, and took the tiniest of sips. The afternoon sun dappled across the beautifully polished furnishings and exquisite carpet. I could get used to this life. I sat among some of Chicago's most prominent women, the cream of society from one of America's premier cities. Excitement filled me as I anticipated a discussion that would be both edifying and stimulating.

"Beautiful weather we're having, isn't it?" our hostess began.

"My, yes. I cannot recall another June in recent years that has begun as lovely as this one has."

"Let's hope the summer continues to be as nice."

"Mmm . . ." the ladies murmured in chorus, plumed hats bobbing. "Let's hope so."

"I so dislike the hot, muggy summers we sometimes have in Chicago."

"I believe everyone does."

"Fortunately, we have a home on one of the Finger Lakes in New York State, so we can always escape."

"Yes, you are fortunate."

The conversation seemed to be rolling along nicely when suddenly, a brief lull occurred. I stopped breathing as the silence lengthened into several tense seconds. *"One must never allow the conversation to lag,"* Madame B. had instructed. *"A lengthy silence spells the death of every social event."*

But just as a bead of sweat began to trickle down beneath my hat, our hostess asked the other women, "What did you think of the thunderstorm we had the other evening?" My admiration for her abilities soared.

"I found it rather frightening," someone replied.

"Did you? I quite enjoy thunder."

"As do I—providing it isn't too loud."

"I don't mind *loud* thunder as long as it isn't accompanied by *wind.*"

"Oh, yes. Wind!"

"Too much wind can be quite vexing."

The ladies went on and on this way for some time, delicately sipping tea and discussing the merits of thunder and wind and several other weather-related phenomena, until I feared I might nod off. I hadn't slept well the previous night as I'd nervously anticipated meeting my future husband. My eyes actually may have fallen closed in a prolonged blink when the hostess suddenly decided that the proper time had come to include me in the conversation.

"Do you enjoy the summer months, Miss Hayes?"

I felt the way I had in school whenever I'd been caught daydreaming—which was often. I gripped the teacup in my shaking fingers so it wouldn't rattle. My heart raced as I formulated my reply.

"Yes. I've always enjoyed summer. But then, I enjoy all of the seasons equally well. It's so nice to live in a climate that offers a variety of seasons, so one doesn't become bored with any of them. Don't you agree?"

I could tell by their smiles and nods of approval that I had answered well. I had spent hours practicing the art of conversation at school, and I knew that simply answering the question was insufficient. One must always add a question of one's own to keep the conversation alive. Madame had compared a proper conversation to an elegant tennis match: *"One must not only keep the ball in the air, but also return the serve with grace and finesse."*

I knew I had passed my first test. But by the time Aunt Agnes and I finished our tea and took our leave—and I had bidden farewell to each woman by name, of course—I confess that I felt a bit disappointed. I hadn't encountered my future husband.

"That was for practice, Violet," Aunt Agnes said as we settled into the carriage once again. "You did very well, by the way. But this next call is much more important."

"Oh? Why is that?"

"Our next hostess, Mrs. Kent, has better social connections, for one thing. But more important, she has a very eligible grandson, as do some of the other ladies who will be calling on her. Mind you, there also may be young ladies your age present, so stay focused and make sure you don't underestimate the competition."

"You mean we'll be competing for the same suitors?"

"Why, of course."

I couldn't help smiling at the challenge. I realize that it was extremely unfeminine of me, but I enjoyed competition of any kind. I once tried to organize a betting pool at school where each girl would contribute two bits and the "pot" would be awarded to whoever scored the most points on an upcoming exam. But only one other girl besides Ruth and me had been willing to risk expulsion by taking part in a gambling ring—and none of us would risk it for only seventy-five cents. It was probably my competitive streak that contributed to my lack of interest in Herman Beckett; no other girl in Lockport seemed to want him.

Aunt Agnes and I called at a stately mansion on Prairie Avenue next, and this time the conversation took a much more interesting turn, even if it did revolve around my appearance for a while.

"Your niece is lovely, Agnes," our hostess, Mrs. Kent, announced. "Where have you been hiding her all this time?"

"Violet has been studying at one of the finest boarding schools in Illinois. She speaks French as if she'd grown up in Paris. And wait until you hear her skills on the piano. She'll take your breath away!"

Since my aunt had never heard me play the piano, her boast struck me as an astonishing leap of faith. I decided it would be prudent to begin practicing on my grandmother's piano in my spare time.

I was the center of attention as the ladies gathered around, sizing me up as if I were merchandise on display at Mr. Marshall Field's famous store. Their comments were all complimentary until Mrs. Grant joined the discussion.

"Don't you think her complexion is a little dark? Violet has a bit of a gypsy look to her."

Mrs. Grant had come calling with two daughters of her own, Hattie and Nettie, who were close to my age. Her unkind remarks had the same effect on me as a shot from a starting pistol at the beginning of a race. I remained composed as I sized up my competition. Neither of the Grant sisters was as pretty as I was, even with my dusky skin. And their assets could have used a little plumping from Ruth's Egyptian elixir. But we were in a race to the altar, and I wasn't about to offer any advice to my rivals.

"Violet is well aware that she needs to stay out of the sun," Aunt Agnes said. "Aren't you, dear?"

"A parasol is an essential summer accessory for every woman," I replied.

"I find that her unusual coloring adds to her mystique," my aunt said.

"What about suitors?" my hostess asked. "Do you have any gentlemen callers, Violet?"

I didn't dare tell them about stodgy Herman Beckett, the shipping clerk from Lockport. Then, to my horror, I recalled giving the traveling salesman, Silas McClure, permission to call on me at Grandmother's house. What on earth would I do if he showed up at my door with his garish plaid suit, flashy grin, and oiled hair? I couldn't invite him in! His head would leave grease stains on our upholstery! Why, oh why, had I given him Grandmother's address?

"I've arrived in the city only recently," I replied, dodging the question. "I've been away at Madame Beauchamps' School for Young Ladies in Rockford."

"That's a fine institution."

"Yes, wonderful reputation."

"Agnes, dear, why don't you bring Violet to the fund-raiser for the Art Institute? I would like my grandson, George, to meet her."

My heart sped up.

"And I would love for her to attend my *soirée*. My grandnephew Edward will be in attendance."

One of the Grant sisters gave me a malevolent glare at the mention of Edward. But soon the women lost interest in me, and the conversation shifted—or dare I say degenerated—into gossip. No one's private life seemed off limits as they talked about who was courting whom, how the courtship was progressing, which gentlemen had proposed, which ones were never likely to, and so on. I stayed alert, cataloging the information, aware that my future success might depend on it.

Later, as Aunt Agnes and I were taking our leave along with the other women, our hostess caught my arm and whispered, "Stay for a moment, Violet. There's someone I'd like you to meet." She beckoned to a serving girl, who hurried over. "Katya, please ask Nelson to come downstairs for a moment."

The serving girl hesitated as if she hadn't understood the command. But her questioning eyes met mine, not Mrs. Kent's. I had the distinct feeling that she was sizing me up the same way that I had sized up the Grant sisters. Katya was young—no more than seventeen or eighteen—and very pretty, with slanted blue eyes and wheat-colored hair and sharp, Slavic cheekbones. She dropped her gaze and curtsied.

"Yes, ma'am. Right away, ma'am." I could have sworn I saw tears in her eyes.

Of course! She was in love with her employer's grandson, this Nelson whom she had been sent to fetch. Maybe he was in love with her too, but their love had to be kept secret because she was an immigrant serving girl and totally unsuitable for a man of his social standing.

They met on back stairways and in the darkened garden after midnight, exchanging tearful embraces and passionate kisses. Katya had begged Nelson to run away with her, but he was torn between his love for her and his love of money. Then, one stormy night—

"Katya emigrated from Poland," Mrs. Kent explained while we waited. "She didn't speak a word of English when we first hired her, but she is improving every day."

A few minutes later, Nelson arrived—without Katya. I imagined her weeping in the linen closet, using the spare blankets and bed sheets to muffle her jealous tears.

Nelson Kent ambled out to the foyer dressed for the tennis courts, and I had to bite my bottom lip to keep my mouth from dropping open. He was the living embodiment of every romance story's hero: tall, slender, fair-haired, and handsome. And if this home was any indication, he was also extraordinarily rich.

"Nelson, dear, I'd like you to meet Miss Violet Hayes. She is my dear friend Agnes Paine's great-niece and has just arrived in Chicago. She needs to meet some other young people her age. Violet, this is my grandson, Nelson Kent."

"How do you do?" I breathed. I was grateful that I'd practiced my mysterious smile so I wouldn't appear too eager. It wouldn't do for me to greet him with a grin like the Cheshire cat from *Alice in Wonderland*. Too bad Madame B. had never taught us how to speak when we've just had the wind knocked out of us by a handsome, wealthy man.

"I'm pleased to meet you," Nelson replied. He seemed cordial but cool. Unlike Aunt Birdie's husband, it wasn't love at first sight for young Mr. Kent.

"Be a dear, Nelson, and take Violet for a stroll around the garden, would you? There's something I need to discuss with Agnes."

"I would be delighted." He offered me his arm and escorted me down the hallway toward the rear of the house.

If I had to describe my first suitor, Herman Beckett, in one word, it would be *stodgy*. Silas McClure's word would be *slippery*. But the only word that could possibly sum up Nelson Kent was *smooth*. He seemed so at ease with proper etiquette, so casual with the trappings of wealth and his elevated social standing, that it was as if he had never been required to learn such things but had emerged from the womb with them.

I imagined him socially at ease the very first time guests arrived to view him, mere days after his birth. I could picture him smiling casually and confidently from his cradle and passing out his own cigars: *"Mr. Mayor, how are you? Mr. McCormick, so nice of you to visit. Would you care for a drink? I'll have one of the servants fix you one."*

"How long have you been in Chicago, Miss Hayes?" he asked as we walked through a set of French doors onto a veranda.

"Only a few days—and you?"

"I've lived here all my life, except for the years I was away at university. How do you like the city so far?"

"It seems like a very nice place."

My heart skipped a beat when I realized I had just halted the conversation. It was hard to concentrate when strolling on the arm of a man like Nelson Kent.

"What lovely gardens," I said, since that had been the pretense for the stroll.

"You are by far the loveliest flower in them, Violet." Something about his words sounded phony. I quickly glanced at his face to gauge his sincerity. His pleasant smile hadn't changed, but his eyes seemed very sad.

"Thank you for the compliment, Mr. Kent."

"Please. It's Nelson."

As we made our tour around the garden, I waited for the influenza-like symptoms of true love to strike me: the dizziness, the heart palpitations, the fluttering stomach and fevered brow. If Nelson Kent was destined to become my true love, I should feel something immediately, shouldn't I? Instead, I felt disappointingly healthy.

"Have you been to the Columbian Exposition?" I asked him.

"Yes, several times. Have you?"

"Not yet, but I would like very much to go."

"Perhaps you would allow me to escort you there one day." This was my third offer. I wondered how Chicago's young lovers ever undertook a decent courtship before the fair was built. I gazed up at Nelson again and gave him my well-rehearsed, enigmatic smile.

"Perhaps I will."

I had been taught to act mysterious with suitors, to be shy yet flirtatious, to play hard to get. *"Men enjoy the pursuit,"* I'd been coached. *"Chase him until he catches you."* But I had the distinct feeling that Nelson Kent was playing the same game with me, acting charming enough to gain my interest while remaining coolly aloof. And he was a much better player than I was.

"Might I be seeing you at the fund-raiser for the Art Institute?" he asked.

"Yes, you might."

"Then I hope you will save one dance for me."

My only reply was another enigmatic smile. I longed to ask him one of my favorite questions just to get a sense of who he truly was: *"If you had to choose between being struck blind and never being able to see the face of your beloved again, or becoming permanently deaf, and being denied the sound of music and of a child's laughter, which would you choose?"* But I didn't dare ask Nelson Kent such a question. Madame B. had warned against the indiscriminate use of our imaginations.

"If you could visit only one pavilion at the fair," I asked instead, "which one would you choose?"

"The Electricity Building," he answered immediately. "It's a showcase of modern progress and innovation. I predict that electric lighting will make gaslights obsolete one day. Just wait until you see the White City all lit up at night. It's astounding. I'm trying to convince my father to invest in some of the modern inventions that are being introduced at the fair."

"Did you ride Mr. Ferris' wheel?" I asked, recalling Silas McClure's description of it.

"Not yet. I went to Paris for the previous World's Fair and saw Mr. Eiffel's Tower. There has been quite a controversy over which is the more impressive achievement."

"What is your opinion?"

He gave me his gentle, charming smile. "I'll let you know after I ride on the wheel."

We made a circuit of the garden—it wasn't very large—and arrived back at the French doors.

"Thank you so much for the garden tour," I said as we joined the others in the foyer.

"The pleasure was all mine, Miss Hayes. I hope to see you again soon." He gave a slight bow and strolled away, his hands slipping casually into his pockets.

"You carried yourself very well this afternoon," Aunt Agnes told me on the way home. "All the ladies seemed quite taken with you."

"Thank you, Aunt Agnes. I confess that I was a bit nervous. Did it show?"

"Not at all. In fact, did you notice how they all competed for you? You can expect several invitations to arrive in the coming weeks. The women are always excited when someone introduces new blood."

"New *blood*?" I shivered involuntarily, wishing I had never read Ruth's cannibal story.

"Yes. After a while, everyone ends up related to everyone else and it becomes a bit . . . unseemly, if you know what I mean. One could lose track of who is a first cousin and who is a second—and that would never do. But if we can manage to marry you well, then our families—the Howells and the Hayeses and the Paines—will all move up a notch or two in the social ladder."

I suddenly felt like the prize money in a betting pool—winner takes all. It was not a pleasant feeling.

"Young Nelson Kent seemed quite enamored with you."

"Did he? He was very pleasant and well-mannered."

"Be careful not to let him monopolize your time too quickly. I hope he didn't rush to fill your calendar already."

"He mentioned escorting me to the fair. And he asked me to save a dance for him at the fund-raiser."

"Oh, dear. He does move quickly. Mind you, he is an excellent catch as far as husbands are concerned, but take your time making your selection. One never knows when an even bigger fish might come along."

"Do society men and women ever marry for love?"

"Love!" She laughed. "My dear, you've been spending too much time with my sister Birdie. Do I dare ask how you answered Mr. Kent's invitations?"

"I gave him a very vague reply."

"Good. Good. Never appear too eager. Keep him in suspense awhile longer."

"But I would like to see him again," I said, thinking that perhaps a fire wasn't always kindled with one match. "Do you think he'll ask?"

"Don't worry—you'll see him quite soon. His grandmother told me that she plans to hold a party at her home and invite you and Nelson and all the young men and ladies your age, including some of your second cousins. I've always thought it such a pity that you don't know your extended family very well."

"Speaking of family, may I ask you a question, Aunt Agnes? Everyone commented on my skin tone, which is quite unlike my father's. Did I inherit my dark coloring from my mother, by any chance?"

"We will not discuss your mother, Violet Rose, under any circumstances. Do not mention her ever again." With that, Aunt Agnes' lips drew closed in disapproval, as if they were attached to an invisible drawstring.

Once again I had encountered a wall of silence from my relatives. I was beginning to wonder if there was more to my mother's story than I had imagined.

Chapter

7

Friday, June 9, 1893

Violet . . . Violet!"

I opened my eyes to find Aunt Matt standing alongside my bed, whispering my name in an urgent voice. I sat up in alarm.

"What's wrong?"

"You need to get up and get dressed, quickly. We don't have much time."

I swung my legs out of bed and sniffed the air. I had been dreaming about the Great Fire again, and I expected to smell smoke. Instead, I smelled bacon.

"Not much time? To do what, Aunt Matt?"

"There's going to be a march today, and I think you should see it. Your father is dead set against my work, and he told Florence and Agnes to keep you well away from it, but Florence left for the settlement house and won't be home until this afternoon."

I stared at her sleepily, trying to digest her words.

"Well, come on. Why are you wasting time? Don't you want to

come with me and help shape the future for all women?"

"Yes, of course. I'd love to go with you." Especially if my father had forbidden it. I was still angry with him for lying to me and for bringing Maude O'Neill into our lives. Besides, if I armed myself with Aunt Matt's ammunition, perhaps I could scare Maude away by myself.

I climbed out of bed and opened the doors to my wardrobe. What did one wear to a march for women's rights? I couldn't recall ever studying that in school. I decided to take my cue from Aunt Matt's prim attire and chose a long, dark gray skirt and a high-collared white shirtwaist. I pinned up my long hair in a tight bun. But when I came downstairs, Aunt Matt was so focused on the upcoming battle that I don't think she would have noticed if I were wearing only my muslin undergarment.

"Do you want breakfast?" she asked. "There isn't time for it, but I suppose if you're really hungry I can find you a hard-boiled egg."

After feasting on sugary tea cakes and watercress sandwiches the past two days with Aunt Agnes, I could see that the battle for women's rights was going to involve great personal sacrifice.

"No, thank you, Aunt Matt. I'm not hungry."

"Good. Let's go, then."

I barely had time to pin on a straw boater hat before we marched out the front door. I had a hard time keeping up with my aunt as she charged down the block to the nearest streetcar stop. I should have worn sturdier shoes. Thank goodness I hadn't laced my corset very tightly.

"Now the first thing I want you to do," Aunt Matt said when we reached the streetcar stop, "is to forget everything you were taught in that ridiculous finishing school you attended. Women aren't silly, delicate creatures, incapable of grasping intelligent ideas. They are not the weaker sex. The act of childbearing alone should tell you how strong we are. Women are perfectly capable of going to the same universities as men and getting an identical education. There is already a school for women physicians, and someday women will be scientists and judges and company presidents too."

My facial expression must have revealed my shock and disbelief because she quickly added, "I doubt if I'll see it my lifetime, but why not, Violet? It isn't a question of ability—it's a question of opportunity. Women aren't going to tolerate being tied down much longer."

Her words reminded me of my mother. Father said she had hated her life, hated being tied down. Could this be what he'd meant?

A streetcar approached, the horses' hooves clopping noisily and raising a cloud of brown dust. We climbed aboard and Aunt Matt paid our fares. I waited until we were seated and the streetcar had lurched forward before asking, "Is that why my mother left us? My father said that she felt tied down."

"I really couldn't say. But I doubt if she left in search of educational opportunities." I detected scorn in Aunt Matt's tone.

"Then why did she leave?"

My aunt gave an impatient wave. "Listen, you aren't paying attention to the bigger picture, Violet. That's what I'm trying to show you. Our individual lives as women aren't nearly as important as the overall movement."

"Will this march take long? I'm afraid that if Aunt Agnes comes—"

"Too bad for her. She had you all week, and now it's my turn. I want you to see that there are alternatives to the life my sister has planned for you. You don't need a husband in order to be fulfilled as a woman."

"Are you against marriage?"

"Certainly not. There are some very good men in the world who treat their wives as equals. Elizabeth Cady Stanton's husband is one of them. But marriage is not for me. I see no reason to surrender my independence for a life of servitude."

"Aunt Birdie says I should marry for love."

"I suppose it's possible. She and Gilbert did seem to love each other. But who knows what sort of a husband he would have turned out to be over the years if he had lived."

I suddenly realized that I should be paying attention to where we were going and watching the street signs we passed. I needed to learn my way around the city if I ever hoped to find my mother's address on my own. It had been impossible to see any signposts at all when riding inside Aunt Agnes' carriage.

"Every married woman is an actress," Aunt Matt continued. "Each time she's with her husband it's as if she is onstage, playing the part that he expects her to play. The only time she can stop acting is when he leaves the stage."

I thought of the act I had been taught to play, the delicate art of flirtation I had rehearsed with Nelson Kent the other day. Would I have to continue acting, continue smiling enigmatically even after I was married? What if I could never be myself again, reading detective novels and letting my imagination run wild? The thought made me shudder.

"But I want you to understand, Violet, that if you do marry, it should be to someone who allows you to be your own person, not his ornament or prize. Let me ask you this: do you enjoy all that social-izing and calling-card folderol that you do with Agnes? Do you really want to get married and be like those women, serving tea and gossip-ing for the rest of your life?" My grandmother had asked a similar question.

"I confess that I did find it a little boring when we discussed the weather for twenty minutes. But Aunt Agnes says we're going to attend cultural events too. And book discussions."

"Book discussions," Matt said derisively. "Those women should read something with substance, like Mary Wollstonecraft's master-piece, *A Vindication of the Rights of Women*."

I didn't say so, but I couldn't picture Aunt Agnes' crowd delving into a book with such a formidable title. "What is it about?" I asked.

"Mary Wollstonecraft was years ahead of her time. She wrote that book one hundred years ago, in 1792. She said it was time for women to rise up and revolt against the status quo—the way our ancestors rebelled during the revolution. The patriots protested against taxation without representation. But do you realize that, as a woman, I'm forced to pay taxes on my home, yet I cannot vote for the man who imposed those taxes?"

"That doesn't seem fair."

"Of course it isn't fair. As one woman in the suffrage movement has said, 'I don't know what women's rights are, but I have suffered under a sense of women's wrongs.'"

People were getting on and off the streetcar as Aunt Matt lectured, and at times the car became quite crowded. She paid no attention to the other passengers, nor did she seem to care if anyone overheard the controversial things she was saying. Her booming voice was filled with righteous indignation as she lectured me.

I was listening so intently to my aunt's speech that I almost missed the signpost as the streetcar rumbled past LaSalle Street. That was it! LaSalle was the name of the street where my mother lived. It would be easy for me to retrace my steps and find it again. All I had to do was board the same streetcar, ride it straight to LaSalle, and get off. I could figure out which direction to turn on LaSalle once I got there, but hopefully it wouldn't be a long walk to my mother's house from the intersection.

"Are you paying attention, Violet?" Aunt Matt asked. I had swiveled around in my seat to get a good look at the street, but I quickly turned back again.

"Yes, Aunt Matt. Please go on. It's very interesting."

"Thousands of women became involved in the abolition movement before the War Between the States, and we worked very hard to bring an end to slavery. It was easy for us to sympathize with the slaves, you see. We understand what it's like to be considered inferior and to be denied all of the privileges that white men take for granted.

"Then the Fifteenth Amendment was passed, allowing Negro

men to vote—but the women who had fought so hard to help them win that right were left out! The new amendment stated that no one could be denied the right to vote on the basis of race, color, or the fact that he was previously a slave. It said absolutely nothing about gender. Now tell me, Violet: If it was wrong for a Negro man to be held in bondage, to be considered the property of a white man, then why is it all right for a woman to be enslaved to her husband? To be considered his property? For her wages to go to him?"

"It doesn't make sense," I admitted. The more I listened to Aunt Matt, the easier it was to understand why she always looked so furious. I was starting to clench my fists too.

"Another of our leaders, Susan B. Anthony, made up her mind to register to vote in Rochester, New York, along with her sister and several friends. Of course the men tried to intimidate them, but on election day, Miss Anthony and sixteen other registered women cast their votes. The U.S. Chief Marshal served her with a warrant, charging her with voting illegally. The court fined her one hundred dollars. She refused to pay it. That was twenty-one years ago, and she still hasn't paid. Miss Anthony is the current president of the National American Women's Suffrage Association, by the way—at the age of seventy-three."

"What's the point of women voting?" I asked.

"What's the point!"

I knew by her look of horror that I'd asked the wrong question. "Madame Beauchamps told us that it isn't feminine for women to take an interest in politics," I quickly explained.

"What?"

I lowered my voice to a near whisper after my aunt's shout drew stares. "Madame said that ladies needed to know only enough about politics and things like that to attract a man's interest. She said men didn't like women who were too intelligent."

"Lies! Male propaganda!" she sputtered. "What a horrible thing to teach impressionable young girls! How could your father send you to such a ridiculous institution? He's just like all the other men, trying to keep women in subjection! I don't suppose they taught you anything about modern science or mathematics or . . ."

My aunt was raving. I knew she didn't expect me to reply, so I didn't. Besides, I was busy trying to sink down in my seat to avoid being noticed.

"I can see that you'll require an entirely revised education," she continued. "The question is where to begin? You've obviously been wrongfully indoctrinated already. But you seem very bright, Violet. Have you ever thought of furthering your education?"

"I have a high-school diploma," I replied. I remembered all the hard work it had required to balance books on my head and to memorize names, and I added, "I graduated from Madame Beauchamps' School for—"

"Not that moronic place! I mean a real college, where women are allowed to learn alongside men, studying the sciences and so forth, not how to bat your eyelashes and flutter your fan."

I felt hurt that she would insult my school. But in truth, I had been terribly bored there. My friend Ruth and I hated all of the restrictions we faced as "proper young ladies." And so we had rebelled by covertly reading detective stories and dime novels. *If I were a man,* I often told Ruth, *and I could be anything I wanted to be, I think I would become a detective.*

"I must show you the Woman's Pavilion at the World's Columbian Exposition," Aunt Matt said. "All of the planning, as well as the daily operation, has been under the guidance of the Board of Lady Managers. Even the building was designed by a female architect, Sophia Hayden." Aunt Matt pulled herself to her feet as the streetcar slowed to a halt. "Come, Violet. This is where we get off."

We stepped off the streetcar and walked two blocks to where a crowd of women had gathered outside a brick building. A sign above the storefront read: *Women's Suffrage Headquarters.* A second sign in the window read: *Come in and learn why women ought to vote.*

"Hurry," Aunt Matt said, tugging me by the arm. "The speeches are about to start."

I watched in surprise as a woman stepped up on a raised platform in front of the building to enthusiastic applause. The idea of a woman delivering a speech in a public place was outrageous. I glanced around, wondering if the police would rush forward to arrest her.

"Men want to deny women the right to speak in public," Aunt Matt said, as if reading my mind. "But we won't be denied."

"As many of you know," the speaker began, "this July marks the forty-fifth anniversary of the first Women's Rights Convention in America. In July of 1848, our tireless colleagues Elizabeth Cady Stanton and Lucretia Mott gathered with a group of like-minded women to discuss their rights and protest their condition. They drew up our Declaration of Sentiments and Resolutions, stating that the Creator has endowed *women* with certain unalienable rights too. Our declaration calls for an end to the absolute tyranny of men over women; for equality in higher education and in economic opportunity; for the right to equal child custody provisions; the right to speak in public and to testify in court. Most of all, the declaration calls for a woman's right to vote. Ladies and gentlemen, that's why we're here today."

She paused, waiting for the cheers and applause to die away. "Fifteen years ago, in 1878, our leader, Miss Susan B. Anthony, persuaded one courageous United States senator to propose a Constitutional Amendment guaranteeing women the right to vote. It was defeated. And it has been repeatedly defeated every year for the past fifteen years. But we will not let those defeats stop us!"

This time I got swept away too and found myself applauding with Aunt Matt and the other women.

"Thousands of women have signed our petition once again," the speaker continued, "asking our United States senators to support a constitutional amendment granting women the right to vote. I urge you to join our demonstration as we march to our senator's office today and present him with our request. We *will* be heard!"

Before I knew what was happening, someone handed signs to Aunt Matt and me and we were swept along as the crowd marched down the street. One group of women carried a banner that read *National American Women's Suffrage Association*. I hadn't felt such a thrill of excitement since the night Ruth Schultz and I crept into the school's basement at the stroke of midnight, carrying a candle, in an attempt to divine who our future husbands would be.

Cross traffic came to a halt as Aunt Matt and I surged down the middle of the street with hundreds of other women. Heads turned and pedestrians stopped to watch as we marched past. Cab drivers and teamsters shook their fists at us in rage for blocking traffic. We were definitely attracting attention.

Then I spotted an expensive carriage similar to Aunt Agnes', and I stopped in my tracks. Neither she nor her wealthy friends would be caught dead at this rally. What if one of them saw me? Would it ruin my chances for a wealthy husband?

The woman behind me bumped into me, forcing me forward again. But I had lost my enthusiasm for the cause, knowing that I had a great deal more to lose. What did it matter if I won the right to vote if I never found true love?

I instinctively lowered my sign. I was afraid to look at the crowds of people lining the sidewalks as we marched past. I heard angry catcalls and wished I were shorter, or that I could hide in the center of the procession. If only I had worn a larger hat—or one with a veil.

Yet the rebel in me realized that Aunt Matt had made some excellent points. In spite of Madame B.'s indoctrination, I did balk at the idea that I was somehow inferior. Besides, on the train ride into the city I had decided to leave my suffocating cocoon and fly freely, and this certainly felt like flying. I lifted my sign again, proud to be supporting a good cause. And maybe, if I held my sign just right, I could fight for women's suffrage and shield my face from view at the same time.

I marched for several more blocks in this proud yet timorous state—until I spotted a squad of uniformed policemen armed with billy clubs moving into the middle of the street to stop us.

"Aunt Matt? Are . . . are the police going to arrest us?"

"It wouldn't be the first time. Honestly! The city officials should be ashamed of themselves for sending the police. This is a peaceful march. The constitution grants men the rights to freedom of speech and freedom of assembly; shouldn't women be accorded the same rights?"

"I-I guess so."

The parade halted. As I watched the policemen move in, I imagined what it would be like to be taken into custody by a handsome young Irish policeman with curly dark hair and Irish-green eyes. I made up my mind to struggle so that he would have to take me into his brawny arms to subdue me and carry me away, but of course he would fall hopelessly in love with me the moment he lifted me off my feet. He would try to find a way to spring me from jail, but I would refuse to accept his offer, preferring to suffer with my fellow suffragettes. What fun it would be—and so dramatic—to be arrested and locked inside a cell and forced to spend the night in jail! I might even have to share a cell with so-called "women of the night" and listen to their scandalous stories as we ate our meal of bread and water. I would have a prison record and—

I would have a prison record?

I saw all of my chances for a society husband going up in smoke. I tugged on my aunt's arm to get her attention.

"Um . . . Aunt Matt?"

"Yes?"

"While I clearly see the merit in what you're trying to accomplish, and I agree wholeheartedly with everything you've said . . .

um . . . I don't think Grandmother or my father would be very pleased if we got arrested."

She frowned as she considered my words. "I suppose you're right," she said in disgust. "Maybe another day. This is only your first march, after all." She grabbed my sign and gave it to one of the other women, along with her own. Then we stepped out of the street and onto the sidewalk to walk back the way we had just come. I could see that Aunt Matt was furious, but whether it was with me or with all the injustice she had endured in life, I didn't know. I decided to remain quiet.

We returned to the streetcar stop and climbed aboard the first car that arrived. Aunt Matt released an enormous sigh as she sank onto the seat.

"How did you get involved in the suffrage movement?" I asked her—just to let her know I was still on her side.

"One of my earliest memories is of my father's reaction when my sister Florence was born. 'If only she had been a boy,' he said over and over again. 'Why couldn't she have been a boy?' It seemed as though a great tragedy had occurred in our home, like a death in the family. He had the same reaction when Agnes and Bertha were born—deep, deep disappointment.

"As I grew older, I tried very hard to make him proud of me, to show him that I was just as good as any son. I began reading his newspapers, following his court cases, and discussing current events with him. I even learned how to research law cases for him. I wanted to be everything to him that a son would have been.

"But even as he lay dying, he told me, 'Too bad you weren't a boy. . . . It's my lifelong regret that I never had a son to carry on my work.' He was disappointed in me and there wasn't a thing I could do about it. It didn't matter how sharp my mind was or how well I could converse with him. He never forgave me for being trapped in a woman's body."

"That doesn't seem fair," I said.

"Nearly all men are the same. They want sons. And they blame their wives for failing if they produce only daughters. My mother had a very difficult time delivering Bertha and nearly died. She never should have had another child. But Father insisted that she produce a son for him. My mother died in childbirth along with her fifth child—her fifth daughter."

By the time Aunt Matt finished her story we were home. I didn't know what to say to her, but fortunately she went straight into her room and closed the door. Her story left me feeling very sad. I wondered if my father had decided to marry Maude so that he could have a son.

I went into the parlor and collapsed onto the sofa, exhausted and invigorated at the same time. Compared to sipping tea and discussing the merits of thunder, it had been an exhilarating day.

Could Aunt Matt and her friends be right? Were women just as smart and strong and deserving of a good education as men? And should women be allowed to vote? I had a lot to think about.

I hadn't seen my grandmother's hat on the hall tree, so I knew she was still out. I would have a few minutes alone with Aunt Birdie's photographs. I crept over to the secretary, opened the drawer, and had just picked up the first photo when Aunt Birdie came in.

"That's a picture of Matt," she said, peering over my shoulder. I had to look very closely before I could see that she was right. Aunt Matt was smiling. And slender. And pretty. She wore a light-colored dress. And jewelry.

"She looks so different," I said.

"It's her engagement picture. She had it taken for her beau."

"I didn't know Aunt Matt was engaged."

"We didn't think she would ever get married. She was thirty-one when she met Robert. He was one of my father's acquaintances, and he came to visit when Father was dying. The rest of us were all married and had left home by then. Matt lived here alone, taking care of him. His illness was very hard on her. But then Robert Tucker came to call, and Matt fell in love. Oh my, she was *so* in love!"

"What happened?"

"It turned out he was a thief," Aunt Birdie whispered.

"What do you mean, a *thief*?"

"Well, a thief is someone who robs people of their money and all their valuables and—"

"Yes, yes, I know what a thief *does*, but what kinds of things did this man steal? And how did Aunt Matt find out about it?"

"Why, she found out when he stole her heart, of course."

"But—"

"Oh, good. There's the postman," Aunt Birdie said as the daily mail suddenly fell through the slot in our front door with a plop. "I do hope I get a letter from Gilbert today. He hasn't written in ever so long."

I studied Aunt Matt's picture, unable to get over the enormous change in her. Aunt Birdie was right: Robert Tucker was a thief. He'd stolen Aunt Matt's smile and all of her joy . . . along with her heart.

Chapter

8

Saturday, June 10, 1893

Madame Beauchamps had prepared us for a variety of occasions and circumstances, including how to eat snails and nibble caviar, but she had never warned us that being sociable could be so exhausting. I found out just how tiring it was on the evening of the fund-raiser for the Art Institute of Chicago. Aunt Agnes and Uncle Henry took me to the gala event, and from the moment we strode through the door, the evening felt like a test of physical endurance combined with one of Madame's grueling final examinations.

I also discovered the extreme pain involved in the life of a socialite. I acquired rows of welts around my middle from lacing my corset too tightly and bubbly blisters on my feet from dancing in delicate silk slippers all evening. My head throbbed from staying constantly alert, remembering dozens of names, and keeping the conversational tennis ball in play. But the part of me that ached the most was my face. Holding a mysterious smile in place for four or five hours was very hard work.

My evening did not get off to a very good start either. Aunt Matt happened to be standing in the foyer when I descended the stairs in my finery, and I knew from the frown on her face that I had disappointed her.

"So. I see you're still running around with Agnes."

"I'm sorry, Aunt Matt." I felt the need to apologize, but I didn't know why. "She and Uncle Henry are taking me to a fund-raiser for the Art Institute. Aunt Agnes says they've opened a new building on Michigan Avenue recently, and now they're raising money to expand their art collection."

Aunt Matt clucked her tongue in disapproval. "It's just a veiled excuse for Agnes to find you a rich husband. Listen to me, Violet. Agnes married Henry Paine for his money. So before you blindly follow the path she took, I suggest that you ask her how happy her marriage has been."

"That's a rather personal question, isn't it? I-I really wouldn't feel right asking her such a thing."

"Then I'll tell you. Henry keeps a mistress." If Aunt Matt intended to shock me, she had succeeded. She had also given me more information than I cared to know.

"Oh . . . I see."

"Wealthy society men all have them, you know. They marry a suitable woman—whom they don't love—for propriety's sake and keep a mistress on the side. Nobody ever talks about this dirty little secret, though, do they?"

"No," I said quietly. I could feel my cheeks burning.

"If you're going to run with Agnes' crowd, then you need to know the truth about them."

I wanted desperately to change the subject. "But the Art Institute is a good cause, isn't it? Art and culture aren't frivolous."

"No, they aren't frivolous. But I would be willing to bet that very few of the funds they raise will be used to support female artists. It's all right for a woman to be the *object* of art, but that's all she's allowed to be—an object. It's too bad, because there are some very fine female artists, you know. The American painter Mary Cassatt helped design the interior of the Woman's Pavilion at the Columbian Exposition."

"I'll be very eager to see it when you take me there, Aunt Matt. But I need to leave now. I think Aunt Agnes' carriage is here."

"Be very careful, Violet," she said ominously.

"I will." I hurried out the door.

I felt quite differently toward Uncle Henry after learning that he was an adulterer. Fortunately, it was dark inside the carriage, so I didn't have to face him. Aunt Agnes started dispensing advice the moment the horses began to move.

"Now, don't be nervous, Violet. I'm sure you'll do just fine. You've handled yourself splendidly so far. The other ladies have been very favorably impressed with you. But tonight will be an important evening for you. Everyone who is anyone will be there—and that includes several potential suitors, of course."

She went on and on this way for the entire carriage ride, so I didn't have to do much more than nod my head and murmur in agreement. Uncle Henry said nothing at all.

From the moment we arrived at the fund-raiser, the gaiety and glitter swept me away. The event was held in a private residence overlooking the lake, a mansion by anyone's standards. The party was already in full swing, and the magnificent ballroom, which occupied the entire third floor, echoed with music and the laughter of hundreds of vivacious guests. I soon discovered that Aunt Matt had been right; the event had very little to do with art but was all about gowns and jewels and hobnobbing with the elite. For Aunt Agnes, it was an opportunity to find me a wealthy husband.

The Grant sisters greeted me like a long-lost friend. Their real names were Hattie and Nettie, but I secretly called them Haughty and Naughty. They pretended to be nice to me, and they made a huge fuss over my gown, but I could tell that their comments were insincere. I'd spent hours learning how to make idle, insincere chitchat at Madame Beauchamps' school, so it was easy for me to recognize it. Haughty made such a show of fluttering her fan to command attention that I wanted to yank it out of her hand and toss it into the fireplace.

Eventually a group of eligible bachelors joined us, and since mine was a new face among these pitifully bored creatures, the men accorded me a great deal of attention. Several of the women I'd met during my afternoon teas eagerly introduced me to their nephews and sons and grandsons. Naughty's fixed smile slipped into a narrow-eyed glower of jealousy when one of the women introduced me to her great-nephew Edward. It didn't take Sherlock Holmes to deduce that Naughty had designs on him.

The orchestra kept the event merry, playing an endless variety of waltzes, and I danced with dozens of young men. After a while, my would-be suitors seemed as alike as peas and as phony as wooden nickels. We might have been at a masquerade ball, where all of the men wore the same mask to hide their true identities. I was disappointed that none of them fell in love with me at first sight the way Aunt Birdie's husband had fallen for her. Nor did I feel the fever of true love toward any of them.

After countless dances, several glasses of punch, and a few trips to the buffet table with my pea-pod partners, I wanted to collapse in exhaustion. I extricated myself from a conversation with one of the peas and was trying to slip away for a few moments alone—mostly to give my tired face a rest—when Nelson Kent came up beside me.

"This is quite a feat of endurance, isn't it, Miss Hayes? How are you holding up?" His was the first sincere expression I had seen all night. I took a chance and wiped the enigmatic smile off my face and answered truthfully.

"To be honest, I'm exhausted. I was just sneaking away from it all to rest for a few minutes."

"Good idea. Come on. I know where there's a balcony. We can get a breath of fresh air. Well, as fresh as the air ever gets here in

Chicago." He linked arms with me and led the way outside to a spacious, third-floor balcony. A dozen other people already milled around out there, so I knew we would be well chaperoned.

"How do you like the view?" he asked, pointing to the night sky above Lake Michigan. "Whenever I get tired of all this rigmarole, I like to go outside and look at the stars. They remind me of what's real and true."

Handsome, elegant Nelson Kent intrigued me. He was so casual and comfortable with the socially elite and with all of this wealth, yet he didn't keep his mask in place like the others had. Of all the young gentlemen with whom I'd danced and sipped punch, he alone seemed genuine—and I felt at ease with him for some reason, as if we were old friends.

We talked for several minutes about real things, and I didn't feel the need to pretend. The only time Nelson's mask went up was when someone approached us. He would offer his charming smile as he greeted them, shaking hands, saying a personal word or two, and asking a question to show he was interested in them—obviously as well trained as I had been—but I could tell that his heart wasn't in it.

"Tell me who you really are, Nelson," I said between interruptions.

"What do you mean?"

"Well . . . for starters, do you work here in Chicago?"

"I just graduated from university last month. I'm taking some time off before I begin working with my father's firm."

"What does your father do?"

"Several different things—he's a property manager, a real-estate developer, an investor. He wants me to learn his business from the ground up, but he promised me an executive position alongside him once I've settled down."

"And do you want to settle down?"

"I don't know," he said with a shrug. "I'm his only son, so it's expected of me."

He looked so unhappy that I felt compelled to ask, "If you could choose to be anything you wanted to be, what would you choose?"

"That's a good question. I would have to think about it. . . ." His worried frown deepened, and he gazed out over the lake for a moment before saying, "I know I'd choose something challenging—that's for certain. I like the business world, but I doubt if working for my father will be very demanding. His business is well established. Safe. Secure. . . . But if I could choose for myself, I'd like to take more risks, branch out into something new and modern—maybe I'd invest in one of the new horseless carriages or a flying machine or some other novel invention."

"Why don't you do it, then?"

"I have no capital of my own," he replied, showing me his empty hands. "And my father is a very conservative investor. He would never take a chance on something unless it's tried and true. . . . But what about you, Violet? What would you like to do if you had a choice?"

"The proper answer to that question is to get married and have a family," I told him. "Women aren't supposed to dream of anything else."

He must have picked up a note of discontent in my tone or expression because he said, "I get the feeling that you're different. That you find this life rather boring. . . . Oh, don't worry—it's boring to me too. So tell me the truth, Violet. What would you really like to do?"

I took a chance and let my own mask slip a little further. "This is very scandalous, so please don't tell my Aunt Agnes, but I took part in a march for women's rights with my Aunt Matilda the other day."

"No kidding? Good for you. So what did you think? Are you going to join them and be a suffragette too?"

"I wouldn't dare," I laughed. "My father would tie me up and carry me back to Lockport in a gunnysack if he ever found out. But my aunt and all the others in the movement are dreaming of a future when women will be accepted as equals with men. She thinks women will be able to get an education and hold professional positions some-day. Do you believe that?"

"I don't see why not." He looked me right in the eye when he said it, and I knew he was one of the few good men that Aunt Matilda had mentioned. "So if things were different, Violet, and men accepted women as equals, what would you become?"

"A detective."

"Really." He smiled. A genuine one. He wasn't laughing at me or my idea. And he seemed very pleased that I had told him the truth.

"I would love to solve mysteries and help catch notorious criminals," I told him, though I realized that my career as a detective hadn't gotten off to a very good start. I had lived in Chicago for nearly a week and still hadn't found my mother.

"How is it that you became interested in detective work?" he asked. But I never had a chance to reply. We were interrupted again by one of the peas I had danced with earlier.

"There you are, Nelson. Hiding out here, are you? And with the prettiest woman at the party too. The Grant sisters are looking for you," he told Nelson. "They said that you promised both of them a waltz, and time is running out."

"I'll be there in a minute." He turned back to me with a sigh. When the pea moved on and we were alone again, he asked, "Have you met the Grant sisters?"

"Oh, yes—Haughty and Naughty."

Nelson broke into a wide grin. "What did you call them?"

I clapped my hand over my mouth. How had I allowed my secret names for them to slip out?

"Come on," he said, laughing. "Tell me what you just called them. . . . Please?"

"Promise you won't tell anyone?"

"Of course not. It'll be our little secret."

"Well, I invented a system for recalling names, you see. I make up a fake one that's similar to the real one, based on the person's attributes. I know the Grant sisters' real names are Hattie and Nettie—but I've nicknamed them Haughty and Naughty."

Nelson laughed so loudly that people turned to stare in our direction. "You are one of a kind, Violet Hayes." He took my hand in his and squeezed it. "And by the way, you look lovely when you blush."

Someone else interrupted us, looking for me, this time. "Your Aunt Agnes wants you right away."

"She probably found another bachelor to introduce me to," I mumbled, loud enough for only Nelson to hear. "I'd better go." He tightened his grip on my hand to prevent me from leaving.

"Wait. I want to ask you something first." He turned to the messenger and said, "Tell Mrs. Paine that Miss Hayes will be there in a moment." Nelson was still holding my hand when he asked, "Will you let me escort you to that silly party my grandmother insists on giving next week? I like you, Violet. You're different from all the others. You don't playact with me. I think we could become good friends. Besides, I don't think I have the energy to go through these phony dating rituals all over again next Saturday. Do you?"

I didn't care about playing the coquette. And I was no longer sure that I wanted a rich husband if he was going to turn out to be unfaithful like Uncle Henry. I was tired of flirting and very tired of smiling enigmatically. It was true that my heart didn't flutter uncontrollably when I was with Nelson, but he already seemed like a good friend, even though I barely knew him.

"I agree with you," I told him. "This is very tiring. I would be happy to let you escort me on Saturday."

"Good. I'll pick you up around seven o'clock. And I'll want to know what other names you've dreamed up for people . . . and what you call me."

"Now that you mention it, I've never made up one for you." I smiled—a genuine one—and hurried off to find Aunt Agnes. She would be disappointed with me for accepting Nelson's offer and not playing the game a little longer, but I think Aunt Matt would be pleased with my decision. Of course Aunt Birdie would remind me to make sure I married for love, and my grandmother . . . I had no idea what she would say. I had been ignoring her terribly while running around the city with her two sisters.

When I found Aunt Agnes, she had a smile of satisfaction on her face and another eligible bachelor in her clutches. I managed to hold up and keep smiling for the remainder of the evening, but I felt enormously relieved when it was time to go home.

Uncle Henry climbed into the carriage with us, leaned back against the seat, and promptly fell asleep. I sighed with relief. I had dreaded conversing with him, especially after watching him flirt with every attractive matron at the party. I wished that Aunt Matt had never told me about his mistress. I would have been content to ride home in silence, but Aunt Agnes wanted to review the entire evening in great detail.

"You certainly attracted a great deal of attention among the eligible bachelors tonight. I daresay you danced with every one of them. Did you enjoy yourself this evening?"

"Yes, very much. Thank you for inviting me." I tried not to sound as weary as I felt. "I met a lot of nice people. And the food was delicious too."

"Anyone in particular who struck your fancy?"

"No—not really."

"Well, I noticed that you spent a considerable amount of time in the company of young Nelson Kent out on the balcony." And if Aunt Agnes had noticed, so had everyone else at the ball.

"He's different from the others."

"I think I know why he is so eager to move quickly with you. His grandmother told me that Nelson's father promised him a place in his firm once he settles down."

"Yes, Nelson told me the same thing."

"You know what that means, don't you? He won't get ahead until he is suitably married. The sooner he finds a wife, the sooner he'll get his hands on his father's money."

Was that why he'd been so friendly to me? Had I misread him

completely? If what Aunt Agnes said was true, then Nelson wasn't being genuine with me at all; he was looking for someone he could court and marry quickly. I was new, with no suitors competing for my hand, and he probably considered me an easy catch. After all, I'd admitted that I didn't enjoy playing the flirtatious game of cat and mouse.

"I like Nelson, Aunt Agnes, but I'm not in a hurry to rush to the altar with him."

"Well, you should be in a *bit* of a hurry at your age. A woman's beauty fades very quickly after her twentieth birthday, you know. And her choice of suitors thins considerably too."

I didn't care if my beauty was fading—I wasn't ready to settle down yet. If only I could enjoy a little freedom before I went from being under my father's protection and supervision to being under my husband's rule. According to Aunt Matt, I would become my husband's property once I married, and I'd have to act the part he expected me to play for the rest of my life. Was I being naïve to want love? Was it only the stuff of romance stories or the musings of my addled aunt Birdie?

The carriage hit a bump in the road and Uncle Henry shifted positions, snorting loudly in his sleep. We happened to be passing beneath a gaslight and I saw the look Aunt Agnes gave him before she turned away; it was not a loving one. Except for the carriage ride to and from the ball, I hadn't seen my aunt and uncle together all evening. Aunt Matt had piqued my curiosity, but I would never dare ask someone about her marriage.

"I'm going to send over my seamstress on Monday morning, Violet. You're going to need a new gown for the party at the Kent home next Saturday."

"Thank you. That's very generous of you." But I knew that my aunt's offer wasn't entirely altruistic. She would move up the social ladder along with me if I married well.

The lights were still glowing in our parlor when I arrived home, and I was surprised to find my grandmother waiting up for me, knitting a pair of socks. She looked tired. According to the hall clock, it was nearly one in the morning.

"I'm sorry I'm so late."

"That's okay, dear. How was the party? Did you have a good time?"

"I guess so."

"You don't sound very enthused."

I watched her put away her knitting and slowly rise to her feet, leaning on the arms of her chair. I wondered if she was as disappointed in me as Aunt Matt was for getting so caught up in the social scene. Grandmother worked very hard for several charitable causes, yet I'd shown no interest at all in what she did. She had asked me to help her knit socks, but I hadn't taken time to do that either.

"To tell you the truth, Grandmother, a lot of what goes on at these high-society functions seems a bit . . . phony. I want to find a good husband but . . ." I shrugged and left the sentence dangling. She rested her hand on my arm.

"What is your definition of *good*? A wealthy one?"

"I don't know anymore. According to Aunt Agnes, Father sent me to Chicago to find a proper husband. So does that mean he wants me to marry into high society?"

Grandmother removed her hand and turned away. "I really don't know, dear. Your father doesn't tell me what he's thinking." Her voice sounded sad.

"But you're his mother. Why doesn't he—?"

"It's very late," she said, stifling a yawn. "We'd better go to bed. Will you be coming to church with me tomorrow?"

Attending weekly church services was a chore to me, and I longed to sleep until noon on Sunday. But I didn't want to hurt Grandmother's feelings—especially after she'd waited up for me tonight.

"Yes," I replied. "I would be happy to go to church with you."

Chapter

9

Sunday, June 11, 1893

Sunday morning dawned much too soon. I regretted my promise to attend church services with my grandmother the moment she tapped on my bedroom door to awaken me.

"Violet Rose? If you still want to come to church with me you'll need to get up soon."

"Okay," I mumbled. "I'm up." But I waited until the last possible moment to climb out of bed, just as I had in boarding school. I could get dressed faster than any of the other girls could. It helped that I always skipped breakfast—as I planned to do this morning.

Grandmother was waiting for me in the front hall when I finally descended the stairs. I still wore my hair pinned up from last night— a trick I'd learned that helped me get ready faster—but it looked very disheveled. I had also learned that I could avoid fussing with it by wearing a very large hat.

"Ready?" Grandmother asked.

I managed to nod in reply. I could barely keep up with her as she set off briskly down the street. Maybe I could squeeze in a short nap during the sermon.

"How far away is your church?" I asked, hoping it belonged to the steeple I saw on the next block.

"We'll have to take a streetcar. It's too far to walk. The church is downtown, on the corner of Chicago and LaSalle Streets." I perked up at the name LaSalle, the street where my mother lived. If only I had thought to bring her address.

We took the same streetcar that Aunt Matt and I had taken and got off at the LaSalle Street stop. Then we boarded another car that drove straight up LaSalle. I studied all of the buildings we passed, wondering if my mother was inside one of them at this very moment, a stone's throw away from me. Most of the buildings looked more like offices than residential dwellings.

My grandmother took me by the arm the moment we stepped off the streetcar and towed me behind her like a tugboat hauling an overloaded barge. She seemed flushed and excited and in a great hurry to get to church.

"What's the rush?" I asked as I stumbled along behind her. "Are we late?"

"Not yet. But there's someone I want you to meet before the service starts." She led me to an enormous brick building, several stories tall, with an even taller, castlelike tower.

"I can't believe this is a church," I said, gazing up at the imposing building.

"The first church that Dwight Moody founded was over on Illinois Street, but it burned down during the Great Fire. He dedicated this building five years later."

I was wide-awake now. My mother and father had met during the Great Fire. Maybe I could find another clue to the mystery.

"Did my grandfather preach at that other church?" I asked. "Did you live in Chicago at the time of the fire?"

"No, your grandfather's church was in Lockport—you know that."

I feared that my arm would come out of the socket as she pulled me up the stairs and into the building. She stopped once we reached the dim foyer and craned her neck to look around at the milling crowd, searching for someone.

"Ah, there he is!" she said with a smile of relief. "Yoo-hoo! Louis! Here we are!" She towed me by the arm toward a young man in his midtwenties who was kneading his hat in his hands.

"Louis, this is my granddaughter, Violet Rose." She beamed as if presenting him with the grand prize in a prestigious contest. "And, Violet, I'd like you to meet a dear young friend of mine, Louis Decker."

"How do you do, Miss Hayes? Your grandmother has told me so much about you. I've been looking forward to meeting you."

"Um . . . a pleasure, Mr. Decker."

I confess that I was much too surprised to say anything else. Was he the reason why my grandmother had been so eager for me to accompany her? Was she trying to find a husband for me too? I suppose it was only fair, since Aunt Agnes was doing the same thing, but I had never expected matchmaking from my grandmother.

Louis Decker was a compact, vigorous-looking young man with dark, discerning eyes behind his smudged, wire-rimmed spectacles. He was the first man I'd met in Chicago who seemed able to look at me rather than at my pretty facade. Nevertheless, I wished I had taken more time with my appearance.

"Louis is a student at the Chicago Evangelistic Society," Grandmother explained. "We've both been helping with Mr. Moody's campaign to win souls for the Lord while the Columbian Exposition is in town."

"Are you interested in Mr. Moody's work too, Miss Hayes?" he asked.

"I'm sorry, but I've never heard of him."

He blinked and his eyes widened in surprise.

"I've been away at boarding school for the past three years," I quickly explained, "and I've only been in Chicago for a week."

"I see. Well, Dwight L. Moody is a very famous evangelist who has traveled all over the United States and England, leading people to the Savior. And now that the whole world is coming to Chicago for the Exposition, he has organized a special campaign to preach the Gospel all over the city."

"Louis is very dedicated to Mr. Moody's work," my grandmother added, patting his shoulder. "And he also helps me with my work with the poor."

Louis held up his hands in protest. "It's all for the Lord's glory. After all, He has done so much for me." They might have been speaking a foreign language.

The best word to describe Louis Decker would be *intense*. He had a sense of urgency about him, as if a celestial clock was ticking away the seconds and soon he would have to give a thorough accounting of himself to the Almighty. Louis had longish hair and he wore a rumpled suit, but unlike my own tousled appearance, which was the result of my own laziness, Mr. Decker's dishevelment seemed the result of his having more important matters to attend to than his appearance.

"Why don't you take Violet Rose to see the Sunday school?" Grandmother asked. "There's time before the service starts. I'll meet you back here in a few minutes."

Louis nodded and led the way, plowing a path through the crowd for me. He was either too shy or too focused on his mission to offer me his arm, so I followed him as best I could. Nothing could have prepared me for what I saw.

The Sunday school children—and there were hundreds of them—were the poorest, most bedraggled souls I'd ever seen. Not one of them wore a decent set of clothing. I saw outfits that were many sizes too big or too small, ragged, worn out, falling apart at the seams. Most of the children were without shoes, and the shoes I did see obviously didn't fit—or were about to disintegrate. I thought of the cold winters in Illinois and knew that if Grandmother and I both knit from now until Christmas, we would never be able to make enough warm socks for all those dirty, callused little feet.

"Oh my!" My hands fluttered helplessly. "Oh, the poor little dears!" I looked at their matted hair and scabby faces, and I couldn't help comparing them to pudgy, well-scrubbed Horace and Harriet, who had probably never known a day of want in their lives. Louis Decker must have noticed the tears that had sprung to my eyes.

"We can always use an extra pair of hands around here," he said gently.

"Yes . . . I-I can see that you might."

"The Gospel gives them hope, Miss Hayes. Jesus was born into poverty, just as they were. And He loved these little ones. He said, 'Suffer the little children to come unto me, and forbid them not: for of such is the kingdom of God.' That's what our work is all about—building the kingdom."

"They seem very happy here." It was true. I saw smiles on nearly every little face in spite of their destitution.

"Mr. Moody started out as a shoe salesman," Louis told me. "He saw kids like these roaming Chicago's streets, and he made up his mind to start a Sunday school for them. His father had died when he was a child, and he understood what it was like to grow up desperately poor. But he also knew that God promises to be a Father to the fatherless."

"What about the motherless?" I murmured.

Louis bent his head toward mine and cupped his ear. "I'm sorry, I couldn't hear you above the noise."

"Nothing. Please continue."

"Mr. Moody's first Sunday school classes met in a converted saloon, but when that space became too small, he raised money to build his first church over on Illinois Street. He eventually had fifteen hundred children in his classes. President Lincoln heard about it and paid the Sunday school a visit. Mr. Moody is still a salesman—and I mean that in the best sense of the word. Only now he's using his talent to pitch the Gospel instead of shoes."

I could only nod, too moved by all of the ragged, exuberant

children to speak. I recalled the fervor of Mr. McClure's presentation aboard the train for Dr. Dean's Blood Builder, and I tried to imagine that same fervor applied in selling religion. Louis Decker reminded me of Silas McClure and of Herman Beckett all rolled together into one man; he had the same restless energy I'd seen in the elixir salesman, combined with Herman's somber earnestness. If he had Nelson Kent's fortune, he could have transformed the world.

"We'd better find your grandmother," Louis finally said. He gently led me away from the pitiful children, walking back the way we had come. I confess that I couldn't have turned aside on my own.

"Have you enjoyed your visit to Chicago so far, Miss Hayes? How have you been occupying your time?"

His question caused the tears in my eyes to overflow. I couldn't reply. My own superficiality horrified me. I'd spent my time sipping tea and preening to win a wealthy husband. I shuddered at the thought of all the wasted food I'd seen at Aunt Agnes' parties, at all of the money her society friends spent on gowns and jewels, and at the shallowness of my pea-pod dancing partners. Louis Decker lived a life that was meaningful, and mine felt banal and superficial in comparison. What good were all of the fine manners I'd learned at Madame Beauchamps' School for Young Ladies when children were shivering and hungry?

"I would like to help you with your work," I said, wiping a tear.

He smiled for the first time. "I'd be honored, Miss Hayes. Do you play the piano, by any chance?"

"Yes, a little. I haven't practiced in weeks though. Why do you ask?"

"We're desperate for a pianist for some of our evangelistic services. Mr. Moody rents theaters in various parts of the city and puts up tents in order to preach to the crowds wherever he finds them. You could be a tremendous help if you would be willing to accompany us on the piano for our song services."

"Oh, but I'm not a professional by any means."

"That doesn't matter. The music is quite simple—four-part

hymns, usually. I could give you a copy of Mr. Sankey's songbook so you could practice in advance."

"I-I guess I could give it a try." I was glad that at least one other thing I'd learned at Madame B.'s besides my enigmatic smile would be put to good use.

"I understand that your grandfather was an outstanding preacher—and that your father worked for Mr. Moody around the time of the Great Fire."

"What? Not *my* father. You must be mistaken. He owns a bunch of grain elevators in Lockport."

"I'm sorry. Perhaps I'm mistaken. I must have misunderstood what your grandmother told me."

What had she told Louis? And what other secrets was my family keeping from me? Anger boiled up inside me the way it had the night I'd learned the truth about my mother. I was trying not to let it spew out when Louis spoke again.

"I would love to hear your testimony, Miss Hayes."

"My what?"

"Your testimony—the story of your faith."

I drew a deep breath, not sure of what he meant. "There isn't much to tell. My father and I usually attend a small church in Lockport, but religion doesn't seem to interest him very much— which is why I'm certain you're mistaken about his working for Mr. Moody. When I went away to boarding school, the headmistress required all of us to attend church services on Sunday. It was our duty, Madame B. said. She called it our 'weekly obligation.' My grandmother is much more religious than Father and I are. She pours all of her energy into her causes, as I'm sure you know. My grand-father was a minister, as you also know, but my father seems rather indifferent when it comes to religion."

"What about you, Violet? I'm not asking about your father's faith or your grandmother's. I want to know about yours."

I had no idea what to say. Going to church was simply something everyone did on Sunday. The religious traditions were especially nice during the holidays. But Louis Decker seemed to imply that there should be more to it than that.

"I didn't mean to put you on the spot," he said when I didn't reply. "I'd just like to get to know you a little better." He removed his smudged spectacles and pulled a handkerchief from his pocket to clean them. I saw no difference at all when he'd finished rubbing them and had put them on again.

"I would like to know you better too," I said.

I longed to ask him one of my "If you could choose" questions, but I didn't dare. I didn't want him to know how frivolous and shallow I really was. My wild flights of imagination seemed immature compared to the serious work he did every day. For some reason I wanted Louis to like me, to approve of me—and I sensed that he would be shocked to learn that I enjoyed reading detective stories and dime novels. I had just met Louis Decker a few minutes ago, yet I cared very much about what he thought of me. Was it for my grandmother's sake or for my own?

We found my grandmother again, and she looked so hopeful as she studied our faces that I was certain she was indeed playing matchmaker. I never would have expected it of her.

"I look forward to seeing you again, Miss Hayes," Louis said as we parted.

"Yes. So do I." I meant it too.

The Sunday worship service in my grandmother's church was very different from the one back home in Lockport. The music was livelier, the preaching more passionate, and for once I had no trouble at all staying awake during the sermon.

"Is this where you come to do your charity work every day?" I asked her later as we rode the streetcar home.

"This is just one of the places where I'm needed. Why do you ask?"

"Mr. Decker asked me to come back with you some time and play the piano for the song services."

"And are you going to?"

"I told him I would try. I'm not a very accomplished player. And I'm horribly out of practice."

"Louis is a very fine young man. He works tirelessly for the Lord."

"He asked if he could see me again. He wants to get to know me better."

"I'm so glad." Grandmother and I sat side by side on the wooden streetcar seat and she rested her hand on top of mine. "I realize that Louis Decker can't compete with all of the wealthy suitors Agnes has lined up for you. But I think that in the long run you would find life with a man like Louis much more meaningful than a life of endless parties and teas."

I suspected that she was right. And I was quite certain that a man like Louis Decker wouldn't commit adultery.

"Can I ask you something?" I said after a moment. "Louis said that my father used to work with Mr. Moody. Is that true?" The streetcar rumbled down an entire city block before she replied.

"Your father was a volunteer with Mr. Moody's Yokefellows."

"What are Yokefellows?"

"It's a group of layman he started. They go around to saloons and bars searching for converts."

Now it was my turn to pause as I summoned the courage to ask my next question.

"Was that how he met my mother?"

"No," she said quietly. "I don't know all the details of the night they met, but I know that it wasn't in a saloon."

"Aunt Birdie said that my parents met during the Great Fire. Is that true?"

Again Grandmother hesitated for a long time, as if deciding whether or not to talk about my mother. I knew that she might not answer, but I also knew that she wouldn't lie.

"Yes, it's true," she said quietly. "Your father rescued her."

"Rescued her? How?"

"Your father had gone to the evening service at Mr. Moody's Illinois Street church. It was a beautiful building with Sunday school classrooms, an office, a library ... He told me that Mr. Moody preached a sermon on the life of Jesus. The service was still in progress, in fact, when they heard all the fire engines rushing past. Then the great courthouse bell began to toll in warning, and the congregation started to grow restless, concerned about all the noise and confusion in the streets outside. Mr. Moody ended the service so everyone could leave. The fire swept through the city that night, burning Mr. Moody's church and his home to the ground."

"Did my father—?"

She shook her head. "I'm sorry, Violet Rose, but you need to ask him these questions, not me. . . . Now, you wanted to know what some of my other work projects are. I'm also involved with the Temperance Union. Our goal is to have all alcoholic beverages banned and all of the saloons closed for good. We want to put an end to drunkenness and to the lawlessness that goes hand in hand with it. We're trying to have the alcohol removed from patent medicines as well—or else have them banned outright. Most people don't even know that these so-called 'medicines' contain alcohol, but many of them do. They have caused untold sorrow when people unknowingly become addicted to them."

I wondered if Dr. Dean's Blood Builder contained alcohol. If so, Silas McClure better not try to peddle any of it to my grandmother.

"But I spend most of my time working at Jane Addams' settlement house," Grandmother continued. "Louis Decker works there too. He's wonderful with the children and very handy at repairing things."

"What's a settlement house?"

"It's not something I can explain easily—you should come down and see it for yourself. In fact, you're welcome to come with me tomorrow, if you'd like. We can always use an extra pair of hands. And Louis will be there too," she added with a smile.

I could hardly say no. I'd gone to the suffrage rally with Aunt Matt and to parties and social events with Aunt Agnes. How could I refuse my grandmother? And when I remembered the pitiful children I'd seen today, I knew I couldn't turn my back on them.

"I would like that," I replied.

I lay in bed that night, trying to imagine my father going into saloons and talking to drunken patrons about God. I couldn't do it. I found it impossible to imagine that he'd ever been as intensely passionate about religion as Louis Decker was. In fact, it was hard to imagine my staid, unemotional father being passionate about anything. Had all of his feelings died when my mother left us?

My father rescued my mother from the fire.

I imagined him running down the street, flames licking at his heels as he carried a load of Bibles in his arms. *Suddenly he heard desperate cries. He looked up, and the most beautiful woman he had ever seen stood before an open second-story window, trapped inside the burning building, choking on thick clouds of smoke. He dropped the Bibles, knowing that God would surely understand, and urged—no, begged—the beautiful maiden to leap from the window, promising to catch her . . .*

Or maybe my mother had been running in terror through the flaming, smoke-filled streets—barefooted, fear-crazed, as burning buildings fell into piles of rubble all around her. *Suddenly she twisted her ankle and fell to the ground. No one would help her. People trampled over her. And as the flames raced toward her along with billows of hot, choking smoke, my father suddenly heard her desperate cries for help. He dropped the Bibles he had been trying to save—certain that God valued life more than mere paper, regardless of how holy it was. Giving no thought to his own safety, he ran back through the flaming debris to rescue her, heedless of the heat and smoke. He swooped her up into his arms and carried her to safety, falling in love with her the moment he looked into her fear-filled eyes. In fact, they both fell passionately in love. . . .*

What would it feel like to fall passionately in love?

I fell asleep thinking about Louis Decker and Herman Beckett and Nelson Kent and wondering if I would ever know true love.

Chapter

10

Monday, June 12, 1893

I hadn't risen early enough to eat breakfast since coming to Chicago a week ago, but I crawled out of bed on Monday morning determined to work at the settlement house with my grandmother and Louis Decker. I staggered downstairs and found her and my two aunts seated at the table, feasting on bacon and eggs.

"Good morning, Violet," Grandmother said. She was one of those perennially cheerful people who managed to rise from her bed with a smile on her face. I, on the other hand, was not one to rise early—and certainly not cheerfully. At school, I considered myself fortunate if I made it to my first class on time, let alone to the breakfast table.

"Morning," I rasped. Grandmother sprang from her seat, bouncing around the kitchen like an overfilled tennis ball.

"Come in and sit down, Violet dear. I'll fix you a plate."

"I'm really not hungry. I don't usually eat breakfast...." She ignored my words and heaped a plate with scrambled eggs, several rashers of bacon, and two thick slices of toast.

My eyes weren't quite open yet, and everything looked blurry, but I saw that my Aunt Matt was engrossed in reading a newspaper, her face hidden behind it. Madame Beauchamps would not have approved. In the first place, it was very rude to ignore the rest of us who were seated at the table with her, and in the second place, proper ladies weren't supposed to take an interest in such a masculine thing as a newspaper.

"What's the latest news on the war, Matilda?" Aunt Birdie asked her. "Has General McClellan conquered Richmond, yet?"

In the short time that I'd lived here, I'd changed my mind about telling poor Aunt Birdie the truth. She had such a gentle, loving heart that I could see how discovering the truth about her beloved Gilbert might cause her deep anguish. But I had also learned that Aunt Matt was very forthright and direct. I couldn't imagine her lying to Birdie about the war, anymore than I could imagine my grandmother lying. I held my breath, wondering what Aunt Matt would say. She lowered the paper and faced her sister.

"I didn't see any articles about General McClellan or Richmond, Bertha. But you're welcome to read the paper for yourself when I'm finished with it."

"The print is too small," Birdie said. "It hurts my eyes to read it."

"There is one article, however, that I think we all should pay attention to." The pages rattled as Aunt Matt folded the paper into a smaller square. She cleared her throat as if about to make an important announcement. "From now on we need to be very cautious about opening the door to strangers. It says here in the paper that ever since the Exposition came to Chicago, thieves have been roaming around posing as traveling salesmen. The phony drummer comes to the door, selling all manner of things from household brushes to patent medicines. He is friendly and amusing as he charms his way into the house, but whether or not he makes a sale is immaterial. . . . Are you listening to this, Bertha?" She tapped her finger against the page for emphasis.

Aunt Birdie focused on Aunt Matt once again instead of gazing into the air above her head. She nodded solemnly. But in truth, not only would Birdie let a thief inside, she probably would give him a hug.

"If the drummer does make a sale," Aunt Matt continued, "he uses the opportunity to make note of where the lady of the house keeps her cash. But the salesman's real objective is to observe the home's layout and the whereabouts of any valuables. He later relays the information to his partners, and they break into the house when no one is home and steal all of the family's silver and other valuables."

"Oh, I do hope they don't take our silver tray," Aunt Birdie said. "I worked so hard to polish it."

"I doubt if robbers would bother with our house," Grandmother said, patting Birdie's hand. "We really don't have much worth stealing."

I couldn't help wondering about the drummer I'd met on the train. Could Silas McClure be one of the thieves the newspaper warned against? He had seemed very friendly and charming—exactly the type of person the paper had described. I recalled how restlessly he'd behaved, and how I'd suspected him of being a criminal. Then I recalled giving him my grandmother's address! I would feel terrible if he came to call on me, then robbed us while we were all away. But more than a week had passed since I'd met Mr. McClure, and I hadn't heard one word from him. I hoped he had lost our address or forgotten all about me by now.

"I know that the Columbian Exposition has attracted a lot of unsavory people," my grandmother said. "But it also has provided an ideal climate for Mr. Moody to spread the Gospel. So you see? Every cloud has a silver lining."

"Well, I'm warning all of you to be careful," Aunt Matt said. "That fair has more than its share of sneak thieves, pickpockets, and purse snatchers. One of the women I know from the suffrage association had all of the money stolen from her purse. She thinks it happened while she was visiting the Woman's Pavilion, of all places. And she wasn't the first one to be robbed there either. At least two other women had the same thing happen to them."

"Can't they do something to make it safer?" Grandmother asked.

"We are doing something. The lady managers have hired Pinkerton's Detective Agency to help capture the thieves."

"The Pinkertons will catch those criminals—you can be sure of that," I said. I was wide-awake now. "I read all about it in Allan Pinkerton's book, which was based on his crime-fighting adventures. They're famous all over America for solving robberies. During the war, they helped arrest a bunch of spies, and they even foiled an assassination attempt on President Lincoln's life. Too bad they couldn't have prevented the second one, though."

Aunt Birdie suddenly looked alert. "What did you say about President Lincoln? Is someone trying to kill that nice man?"

"Not to worry," Grandmother assured her. "Have some more eggs. And, Violet dear, where in the world did you run across a book about detectives?"

"Um . . . at Madame Beauchamps' school."

"I'm surprised they would allow impressionable young ladies to read about robberies and murders and things of that nature."

"The book wasn't mine. It belonged to a friend." I hoped Grandmother wouldn't probe further. "By the way, Aunt Matt—how did your friends go about hiring the Pinkertons?"

"They have a branch office here in Chicago."

"They do? Does it cost much for their services?"

"I have no idea. Why do you ask?"

The directness of her question left me at a loss. I wanted to hire them to find my mother and to prove that Maude O'Neill had murdered her husband, but of course I couldn't tell Aunt Matt the truth.

And I didn't want to lie either. I should have kept my mouth shut altogether.

"I'm just curious," I said with a shrug. "It doesn't matter."

The clock in the front hallway struck eight and Grandmother sprang from her seat. "Come, Violet. We really must be on our way."

I hurried to the hall tree to fetch my hat, grateful for the timely escape. I was pinning it to my hair when someone knocked on the front door. I opened it cautiously, remembering Aunt Matt's warning. I half expected to see Silas McClure or some other thieving salesman on our doorstep. Instead, I saw a skinny birdlike woman carrying two bulging carpetbags the size of prize-winning hogs.

"Good morning. I'm Ethel Riggs." She dropped one of the bags and extended her hand. "Mrs. Paine sent me here to make a gown for Miss Violet Hayes."

"Oh no." I struck my forehead in dismay. I had forgotten all about Aunt Agnes' promise to send a seamstress. "I'm Violet Hayes—but I was just about to leave. Will this take very long?"

"Oh my, yes. At least two or three hours. And if I don't get started on your dress today, I'm afraid it will never be finished by Saturday night."

I saw no way out. I already had accepted Nelson Kent's invitation to escort me on Saturday night, and I had nothing new to wear.

"Never mind, Violet dear," my grandmother said. She had come out to the foyer to fetch her own hat and had overheard us. "We'll miss you at the settlement house, but you can come to work with Louis and me another day. I really have to run along now. Bye-bye."

Aunt Birdie smiled and waved good-bye to her, then greeted skinny little Ethel Riggs with a warm hug as she invited her inside.

Aunt Matt left the house a few minutes later, growling about the important suffrage meeting that I should be attending with her and how degrading it was for women to adorn themselves for the purpose of enticing a man.

"And remember, now, don't open the door to any traveling salesmen," she warned Aunt Birdie. The door closed behind her with a bang.

I spent all morning with the seamstress. One of Mrs. Riggs' carpetbags contained a pile of the latest fashion books from Paris. We paged through them for nearly an hour, searching for a style for my new gown.

"I've never seen so many beautiful dresses in my life. How in the world will I ever choose one?"

Mrs. Riggs gave me a long, appraising look, twirling one end of the measuring tape that was draped around her neck. Then she wet her forefinger and quickly paged through one of the pattern books.

"I think this is the dress we should make for you." She pointed to one with a low-cut neckline. "You have a wonderful bosom. Why not show it off?" Her mind was made up even if mine wasn't. She closed all of the other fashion books and stuffed them back into her satchel.

"It's a beautiful gown," I told her, "but I'm worried that my grandmother will find it immodest."

"Nonsense. I'll make sure it covers all of your essentials. These large, puffy sleeves are all the rage this year. And see these silk flowers on the shoulder and waist? I'll make an extra spray of them for your hair. You'll look lovely."

"I've never owned such a beautiful dress before."

"Mrs. Paine told me that you needed an outstanding one in order to attract a wealthy husband."

"She said that?" I knew my aunt's goal was to find me a rich husband, but Mrs. Riggs made us sound like cheap hucksters looking for a hapless victim to defraud.

"If this dress does the job, you can use it for your wedding gown," she added with a smile. "See these ruffled inserts in the sides of the skirt? They're called *godets*. We'll use a contrasting fabric for them— maybe a spotted voile." She opened her second bag, which fairly exploded with fabric samples in a variety of colors.

"I don't know how I will ever decide."

"May I make a suggestion? I think the dress would look lovely made from silk brocade. And the color should be . . . let's see . . . how about this gorgeous ivory, with pale blue for the accent color? It would be a magnificent contrast to your dark hair."

Mrs. Riggs measured every last inch of me—twice, it seemed. "I'll return tomorrow morning, bright and early," she promised.

My grandmother would have to go to work without me once again. Meanwhile, I hoped she wouldn't tell Louis Decker the reason I had stayed home.

I stood for hours the following morning while Mrs. Riggs pinned and basted the muslin pattern. Then I raced upstairs to change my clothes in order to make social calls with Aunt Agnes in the afternoon.

While I waited for my aunt to arrive I decided to spend a few minutes practicing the piano in case she asked for a command performance at one of our teas—and in case I ever made it downtown to play hymns for Louis Decker. I was practicing my scales so energetically, running my fingers up and down the keys, that I never heard the knock on our front door. I didn't realize that Aunt Birdie had gone to answer it until I played the final note—just in time to hear her say, "Why, yes, Violet is here. Won't you come in?" I leaped up from the piano stool and hurried into the foyer.

I almost didn't recognize the man who stood there until he smiled at me: Silas McClure, the traveling salesman. The very person I had worried about only yesterday.

"Good afternoon, Miss Hayes." A candelabrum was much too dim to describe his grin. His entire face seemed to glow as if lit by a spotlight. He had on a conservative brown suit this time instead of his garish plaid one, and he must have run out of Macassar oil since the last time we'd met, because his wavy brown hair looked clean and nicely combed. Except for his blinding smile, he might have been a different man altogether.

My heart began to gallop like a team of horses at breakneck

speed. "Mr. McClure!" I couldn't seem to draw a deep enough breath to say more.

"I was in town for a few days and thought I'd stop by like I promised."

"Oh, how nice," Aunt Birdie said. "I'm Violet's aunt, Mrs. Casey."

"Yeah, we met before. Great to see you again. Silas McClure's the name."

Aunt Birdie retrieved the silver tray from the hall table and held it out to receive his calling card.

"Here you are, young man . . ."

Mr. McClure took the tray right out of her hand and gave it the once-over, as if estimating how much cash he could get for it from a pawnbroker.

"Looks like good sterling silver," he said, tapping his forefinger against it with a resounding ring.

"Oh yes. It is sterling silver," Aunt Birdie assured him.

I couldn't breathe. What if he and his partners came back this afternoon while Grandmother was downtown and Aunt Matt was at her suffrage meeting, and I was making social calls with Aunt Agnes? Poor Aunt Birdie would be here all alone! Mr. McClure and his chums could tie her up and stuff her inside the pantry with a gag in her mouth and steal every stick of furniture in the house—and it would be entirely my fault.

"You rarely see one this shiny," he added, admiring his reflection.

"Why, thank you," Aunt Birdie replied. "I polished it myself. It's for calling cards. Do you have one?"

"Oh!" he said, as if finally catching on. "Yeah, just a minute." He handed the tray to Birdie and groped in the breast pocket of his jacket for one. His business card had the words *Dr. Dean's Blood Builder* on it in blood-red letters.

"Does your tonic contain alcohol?" I asked, groping for something to say. He found my question amusing, for some reason. His smile widened—something I wouldn't have thought possible—until he resembled a display of fireworks.

"Absolutely not. There's not even a trace of alcohol in it. Dr. Dean believes in strengthening the blood, not diluting it with alcohol."

"Let's not keep the nice man standing in the hallway, Violet. Won't you come in, Mr. McClure?"

I didn't want him to come in, but what could I do? Aunt Birdie hung his hat on the hall tree and led him into our parlor.

"Nice place you have here, Miss Hayes," he said, looking all around.

"It isn't my house," I said quickly—and emphatically. "I'm just visiting. My widowed grandmother and her two sisters live here." I wanted him to know whom he was robbing, so he at least would be conscience-stricken afterward. "They really don't have much that's worth stealing."

"Stealing?" he repeated. He seemed very amused. "It's a nice place. Reminds me of home."

"My husband is fighting with General McClellan in Virginia," Aunt Birdie told him. "Why aren't you in uniform, young man? Are you home on furlough from the war?"

For a horrible moment I feared that Silas would laugh at her or else try to convince Aunt Birdie that the year was 1893, not 1864. But my esteem for Mr. McClure rose immeasurably when he took Aunt Birdie's hand in his and replied, "I haven't received a draft notice, Mrs. Casey."

"Oh, how nice. . . . Well, I'll go fix us some lemonade—unless you'd prefer tea?"

"Lemonade's fine," I said quickly. Tea would take too long. Aunt Agnes was due to arrive any minute, and I needed to get rid of Silas McClure before she did. But as soon as Aunt Birdie left the room, he moved a step closer to me.

"You're even more beautiful than I remembered, Miss Hayes."

"Um . . . thank you . . ." I backed away, unaware that I was about to collide with the parlor sofa. I lost my balance and fell backward onto it with an undignified plop. My skirts flew up to reveal my ankles and ruffled petticoats. What on earth was wrong with me today? Madame Beauchamps would be horrified by my gracelessness.

"I-I'm sorry but our visit will have to be a short one," I explained as I rearranged my dress. I decided it was best to remain seated. I didn't think my legs could hold me. "I have an engagement with my aunt Agnes this afternoon, you see. She will be arriving momentarily and—"

As soon as the words left my mouth I realized my mistake. I had informed a potential thief that I was leaving soon. If Silas McClure was a thief—and I was almost certain that he was—then by the time I returned from my social calls, the house would be ransacked.

"May I call you Violet?"

"I-if you'd like." I didn't know what else to say. Everything I'd learned about making polite conversation seemed to have flown from my head. If the art of conversation was like a graceful tennis match, then I had lost track of the ball, the racket, and the score. Worse, I felt as though I'd become entangled in the net.

"Won't you have a seat, Mr. McClure?"

"Okay. Thanks. But please drop the 'mister' stuff and call me Silas."

He sank down on the sofa right beside me. I would have chided him for being too forward, but I remembered how I had invited him to sit beside me on the train. It was my own fault that he was taking liberties. I couldn't inch away from him because I was already sitting right up against the armrest. Besides, he was gazing deeply into my eyes with his bright spring-water blue ones and his charm began to have a mesmerizing effect on me, just as it had on the train. I couldn't have moved away from him any more than the poles of two magnets could be pulled apart. This must be how he charmed all of the other unsuspecting women he robbed.

"Was that you playing the piano a minute ago? You sounded really good."

"Yes . . . Thank you."

"I haven't stopped thinking about you since we met on the train, Violet."

For the first time in my life I was utterly speechless. I could tell by the soft look in his eyes that he was telling the truth. I seemed to have a hypnotic effect on him as well. We might have sat gazing at each other for an eternity if Aunt Birdie hadn't returned to the parlor just then.

"Here's the lemonade," she sang sweetly. "I do hope it's to your liking." She handed Silas a glass, and he took a sip.

"Perfect!" he said, smacking his lips. "Not too sweet and not too sour."

"Oh, how nice." From the way Aunt Birdie beamed, he might have come to call on her instead of me.

Silas set his lemonade on the parlor table and focused all his attention on me again. "I've also been thinking about the question you asked me when we were on the train. I couldn't get it out of my mind, in fact."

"Which question was that?" My voice sounded strange to me, as if I had climbed up a very steep hill.

"You asked how I would prefer to die if given a choice: in a terrible cataclysm or from a long, slow death at home in my bed. I've decided that I would prefer to leave this world quickly, in a flaming accident."

"Oh, how nice," Aunt Birdie said. Silas glanced at her with a nervous smile.

"Why an accident?" I asked him.

"Well, we all have to die someday, right? And I would hate to reach the end of my life feeling as though I'd never really lived. Life is for living and for taking risks, regardless of the danger. I guess I'd prefer to live each day as if it were my last and go out with a bang."

"Me too," I said. "That's exactly the way I feel about it."

"Speaking of flames," Aunt Birdie said. "Were you here in Chicago the night of the Great Fire, young man?"

"No, ma'am," Silas said. "Were you?"

"Oh yes. And for a while we all believed that the end of the world had come. I feared I might truly lose my life. It was a dreadful experience."

"You really lived through it?" Silas asked. "I would love to hear about it, Mrs. Casey."

"Me too," I added. "Didn't you say that my parents met on the night of the fire?" But she didn't seem to hear me.

"The fire started on a Sunday night," Aunt Birdie began, as if reading the words from an invisible script above our heads. "I went to bed early, but I woke up in the middle of the night to the sound of someone pounding on our front door. It turned out to be friends of ours. The entire family was running from the fire with a wagon full of their household goods. Oh my, you should have seen the sky! It was all lit up to the south of us, glowing like a furnace—orange and yellow and red. The wind was blowing very hard that night, which is why the flames spread so quickly.

"Well, of course we let our friends come inside—they had several small children, you see, and an aging grandmother. And their house stood right in the flames' path. They lost everything that night but their lives and whatever they had managed to fit into their wagon. No one ever imagined that the fire would jump across the Chicago River, but it did.

"By dawn the streets were filled with refugees, and we started handing out sandwiches and glasses of water to the poor souls. Many of them were acquaintances of ours but we hardly recognized them with their faces blackened from smoke and soot. They told terrible tales of the damage and destruction—the entire city was burning! And thieves had come out as well, looting homes and businesses. One man told me he had loaded everything he could fit into his wagon and then he simply left his doors open so scavengers could take whatever they wanted—it was all going to burn up anyway.

"The fire raged all day Monday, and by Monday night it was so close to our house that we began to pack our own belongings, imagining the worst. But how does one decide what to pack and what to leave behind? We could hear the roar of the flames a few blocks away and feel the heat. Flaming cinders flew everywhere, blowing toward us on the wind, and we soaked blankets with water to protect ourselves in case we had to flee. Oh, it was a terrible, terrible time!"

"Did my mother and father come here for refuge that night?" I asked. "Grandmother said that Father rescued my mother from the fire."

Aunt Birdie gazed at me for a long moment, and I immediately regretted interrupting her. I could see that she had lost the thread of her story. She gazed at Silas and me as if we were soot-covered refugees whom she didn't recognize.

"Were you living in this house at the time of the fire?" Silas prompted.

"I-I don't recall. . . . My husband, Gilbert, was . . . Where was Gilbert again? I don't remember. I was here, I think . . . But why would I be here with Matilda and not in my own home?"

Oh no. The fire had occurred six years after Uncle Gilbert had died and the War Between the States had ended. Aunt Birdie was about to remember that her husband was dead. I needed to change the subject—fast!

"It must be hard on you to relive such a terrible night, Aunt Birdie. Let's not talk about it any more. Isn't it nice of Mr. McClure to pay us a visit? Tell us what brings you to the city today, Silas."

"I came back to see you, and to ask if I could take you to the fair. Have you seen it yet?"

"No, I haven't."

"I would love to show it to you."

Silas McClure—thief or elixir salesman—was not a suitable

escort to the fair or anywhere else. Yet of the three men who had offered to take me, Silas was the most unconventional one—and the one I longed to see it with the most.

"I would love to go with you, Mr. McClure, but we would need to be suitably chaperoned. My grandmother would never allow me to go otherwise."

"I see. But . . . how does that work, exactly?"

"Well, couples are usually accompanied by another woman, often a family member. Chaperones protect a young lady's reputation, you see. I'm afraid I would be unable to step out with you unless someone accompanied us."

He looked crestfallen. "Could your aunt come with us?" he asked, gesturing to Birdie.

"I don't think she could endure the excitement of the fair," I said, then added softly, "She's rather fragile."

"It's just that today is my day off, and I was hoping you would be free to go to the fair with me right now."

"I'm sorry, Mister . . . I mean Silas." And I truly was. "But as I said, I have another engagement this afternoon."

"Gee, that's too bad."

I suddenly remembered that Mr. McClure knew how to find my mother's address on LaSalle Street. He had offered to escort me there the day I came to Chicago before my grandmother arrived. If we went to the fair together, maybe I could ask him to take me to my mother's place afterward.

"I don't suppose you have a female relative or other acquaintance here in town who could accompany us to the fair on another day?"

"Hmm . . . I'll have to think about that." He was gazing into my eyes again. If I didn't look away soon, he would hypnotize me into following him anywhere. I picked up my lemonade and took a long drink. I wanted to hold the glass to my burning cheeks to cool them. Silas emptied his glass in a few gulps and set it on the table again.

"Suppose I came back for you the next time I'm in town—with a chaperone. Would that work? Would you come with me?"

"Yes, that would be acceptable."

"Good. Well, I guess I'd better be going, then." He rose to his feet and offered me his hand to help me up. I took it without a thought for propriety. His palm was hot, his grip strong—and his touch so shocking it was like shaking hands with the wrong side of a flat iron.

"Thanks for the lemonade, Mrs. Casey," he said on his way to the door.

Aunt Birdie hugged him good-bye. "Please, come again."

"I will. I'm looking forward to it, Mrs. Casey."

Silas wouldn't need to pick the lock in order to break in with his cohorts—Birdie would throw open the door and embrace the entire gang of thieves.

Aunt Agnes' lavish carriage pulled to a halt in front of our house just as Silas was leaving. He let out an appreciative whistle when he saw it.

"Wow! That's quite a rig. With a matched team of horses, no less. Someone's got plenty of dough."

"That's my aunt's carriage. But she doesn't live here with us. She lives . . . Oh, never mind. Good day, Mr. McClure."

I quickly closed the door behind him, leaning against it for support. I needed to collect my hat and gloves and calling cards—not to mention my scattered wits. Why had he had rattled me so?

"What a nice young man," Aunt Birdie said with a sigh. "He's very sweet on you, you know."

"What makes you say that?"

"Why, he could hardly take his eyes off you the entire time he was here."

That was when I realized how quickly my pulse was racing—and that it had been racing for the entire time that Silas McClure had visited us. My heart might not survive an afternoon at the fair with him.

"I think you must be sweet on him too, Violet."

"No, I can't be sweet on him, Aunt Birdie. He's . . . he's dangerous!"

"Well, come here and look." She took my arm and pulled me over to the mirror that hung in the front hall. "Just look how pink your cheeks are."

"But . . . I-I think he might be a thief."

"Oh, how nice. Has he stolen your heart?"

"No, not that kind of thief, a *real* thief—a criminal."

Aunt Birdie gasped. "He didn't take our silver tray, did he?" Her eyes grew wide as she clutched her heart.

"No. It's still here." I held it up to show her, and she sagged with relief.

"Well, then," she said, smiling once again. "That says it all, doesn't it."

Chapter

11

Friday, June 16, 1893

I didn't have a chance to accompany my grandmother to the settlement house until Friday. Mrs. Riggs arrived for the final fitting of my dress on Thursday, and we arranged to have it delivered in time for the party on Saturday night. I couldn't imagine how much the dress had cost, but as Aunt Agnes had said, if we wanted to catch a big fish, we needed to use extravagant bait.

I wore old clothes to the settlement house. Judging by the simple way that my grandmother lived and dressed, fashion didn't matter where we were going. We rode on streetcars, switching lines twice until we finally disembarked in a section of Chicago that seemed worlds away from the gracious mansions and elegant townhouses that Aunt Agnes and I had visited.

The smell of the neighborhood assaulted me first, hitting me hard enough to make me gag the moment I stepped off the streetcar. The stench smelled like a combination of rotting garbage, urine, and the decaying remains of scores of rats. Everywhere I looked I saw a dead one—and I saw a few living ones as well, scurrying away into the shadows as we approached.

The warm, humid June morning intensified the odors. We passed the open door of a butcher shop, and the stink of blood and raw meat made me gag again. Then I saw a cow tongue hanging in the smeared window by a giant hook and I nearly left my breakfast in one of the overflowing gutters.

"Careful! Watch your step, Violet," Grandmother warned as I stumbled from nausea. She seemed indifferent to the stench.

"This place smells terrible! How can you stand it?" My words came out muffled. I had covered my mouth and nose with my hand.

"I suppose I'm used to it."

I walked the entire length of the busy, overcrowded street with my nose and mouth covered, trying not to retch. Hundreds of people, the poorest I'd ever seen, went about the business of buying and selling, visiting and arguing as if the neighborhood smelled of perfume and roses. Children swarmed everywhere. Every immigrant mother had at least four or five dirty-faced urchins buzzing around her skirts like flies on a horse's rump. The men we passed stank so strongly of sweat that I doubted if they ever had taken a bath in their lives.

"Try not to step in any puddles if you can help it," my grandmother said. "This neighborhood had a cholera outbreak not too long ago." I was beginning to understand why she always walked so briskly. I also knew that I had lived a very sheltered life.

The noise of the neighborhood overpowered me nearly as much as the smell. Most of the talking and bartering and shouting were in languages I couldn't understand. Pedestrians haggled with pushcart owners and shopkeepers for their goods—everything from cabbages and soup bones to squares of brown soap and bolts of cheaply made cloth.

I glanced down a side lane as we crossed at an intersection and saw dozens of drooping clotheslines strung across the alley from one rickety tenement to the other. Flapping diapers, undergarments, bed sheets, and work clothes, all in the same dingy shade of gray, dripped down on a gang of youths playing stickball in the dirt below.

I wanted to turn around and run home. I had uncovered my mouth to say so when my grandmother reached for my hand.

"We're nearly there, dear. That's Miss Addams' house on the next block."

She pointed to a large two-story brick home, the only decent house in this overcrowded immigrant neighborhood. It was a little run-down, but it stood out like a swan in a flock of circling buzzards.

"Why in the world would anyone choose to live here?"

"Jane Addams is a pioneer, of sorts," Grandmother explained. "Everyone thought it was outrageous for a single woman to live in the slums, especially an educated woman from a wealthy family. But she made up her mind to rent this house—named Hull House after the original owner—and live among the people she wanted to help. I would live here, too, if . . . well, if things were different."

I picked up my pace, running toward the house for refuge. If Jane Addams was rich and educated, then surely her house would be clean and fresh smelling inside, wouldn't it?

"How does she help these people? I mean, look at this neighborhood! I wouldn't even know where to begin."

"Miss Addams envisions her settlement house as a community center where everyone will be treated equally whether they are rich or poor." Grandmother paused on the broad front porch as she explained. "By living in the neighborhood, Jane was able to see what the greatest needs were and try to meet them. Feeding the hungry came first, and then her Jane Club, which is a safe, affordable boardinghouse for working women. Now she's adding English lessons and a kindergarten, and she hopes to start a day-care center and construct a safe playground for the children too."

My lungs felt as if they might burst from holding my breath. I reached behind Grandmother and opened the door to flee inside. I stood in the foyer breathing deeply. It smelled like heaven. I could see that it had once been a lovely, gracious mansion with elaborately carved fireplaces and a broad, sweeping staircase. The unusual woodwork that decorated all of the windows and doorframes resembled thick, coiled ropes.

"I've never heard of such a thing as a settlement house," I said after inhaling and exhaling a few times.

"Twelve years ago, Miss Addams visited a settlement house in London, England, called Toynbee Hall. The idea is that if educated people live and work among the poor, both classes of people will benefit by learning from each other. Jane decided to do the same thing after she returned to America. By getting to know these people—experiencing how they live—she can learn what the causes of poverty are and try to eliminate them."

"I'd like to meet Miss Addams. She sounds very dedicated." *But not quite sane,* I added to myself.

"Unfortunately she is going to be out of town all this week. Perhaps the next time you come."

The next time?

I started to remove my hat, but Grandmother took my hand again and said, "We won't be working here today. I just wanted you to see Miss Addams' house. We're needed in the public kitchen down the street."

I drew a deep breath before venturing back outside, as if I was about to plunge into deep water. Thankfully, the café was just a short walk around the corner on Polk Street.

"We've opened a small restaurant," Grandmother explained, "where we serve simple meals such as soups and stews along with home-baked bread. The neighbors can buy a nutritious meal for ten or fifteen cents."

We walked through a small dining room filled with mismatched tables and chairs and into the kitchen in the rear. Grandmother introduced me to the two immigrant women who were washing and drying a sink full of dishes, but they didn't seem to understand much English.

"You'll need this," Grandmother said, handing me a well-worn apron. She tied another one around her own waist.

"Um ... what do I have to do, exactly?" I had never washed a dirty dish in my life, and I had no desire to disturb my record.

"Well, today we're serving a noon meal of soup and bread, so we'll need to get started on those right away. Do you want to help make the bread or cut up the vegetables for the soup?" I stared at my grandmother. "What's wrong, dear?" she asked, caressing my hair.

"I don't know a thing about cooking. Mrs. Hutchins did everything for us back home, and the cooks provided all of our meals at school."

"You mean they didn't teach you any practical homemaking skills at that school?" I shook my head. "How do they expect you to manage a household of your own when you get married and have a family?"

"Madame Beauchamps expected us to marry well and have servants," I said with a shrug. "In fact, she spent quite a lot of time teaching us how to manage a household staff."

"I see." Grandmother tried not to show how disappointed she was, but I detected it just the same. "Why don't you have a seat, then," she said with a sigh, "and you can just observe today."

Guilt draped over me like a very heavy coat. I recalled Aunt Matt's condemnation of the spoiled women in Aunt Agnes' crowd, and I rebelled at the notion that I was just like them.

"I-I'd be happy to help," I said with a gulp, "but you'll have to teach me how."

The back door opened and two more immigrant women joined us, chattering away in a very guttural language and toting large baskets filled with vegetables. My grandmother introduced the women to me, but their names sounded like gibberish. It shamed me to realize that I already had forgotten the names of the first two women.

Were my memory skills reserved for the rich? Had I not considered these women worthy of the effort? My shoulders sagged a few inches lower beneath my guilt overcoat.

The two newcomers washed their hands, then put on aprons and went to work as if they knew exactly what to do. One of them removed what appeared to be an elephant bone from a huge pot on the stove and began cutting off the cooked meat. The process looked so disgusting to me that I had to turn away. I would never be able to eat food that required so much handling on my part.

The other woman set the vegetable baskets on the table. I recognized carrots, onions, and potatoes, but there were several other lumpy things that looked as though they belonged in a witch's cauldron. I was quite certain that I had never eaten any of those things, nor did I want to sample them now.

"You would like to cut up?" one of the women asked. She offered me a knife.

"I guess so." I selected an onion since the skin was flaking off and it looked as though it would be the easiest thing to peel.

"I'm going to start the bread," my grandmother said. "If you need help with anything, just ask Magda." The vegetable woman smiled at me when she heard her name.

The onion's first layer came off fairly easily. Unfortunately, there were several more layers beneath it—and each layer proved more and more difficult to remove and more and more malodorous. The closer I got to the inside of the onion, the stronger the acid-like fumes became, until my eyes began to sting and stream with tears. I reached up to wipe them so I that could see what I was doing, but the onion juice was all over my fingers, and the moment I touched my eyes, the stinging turned to fire. They burned so badly that I dropped the onion and dug in my pocket for a handkerchief.

"Oh my! Oh dear!" Tears poured down my face as if my one true love had just jilted me.

I blew my nose and blotted my eyes—in time to see Magda turn away to hide a smile. I was not pleased at all to be the object of her amusement, so I picked up the onion again, determined to conquer it. The watering and stinging began in earnest the moment I did. If only my arms were longer so I could hold it farther away from me.

The last piece of skin finally slipped free and I set the brutish onion on the table with a victorious thump.

"Now you must chop," Magda said. "Like this . . ." She set one of the potatoes she had skillfully peeled on the chopping board and deftly hacked it into soup-sized pieces. I watched—and silently bid good-bye to my fingers.

But I refused to give up. I pinned the slippery thing to the board, drew a deep breath, and sliced into it. Fumes exploded from the cut onion like fireworks.

"Oh! Ow! Ow!" I gasped. I was quite certain that I'd been permanently blinded. I dug my fingers into my eyes, rubbing them—forgetting the important lesson I already had learned—and immediately made matters worse.

"Splash some water on your eyes, dear," my grandmother coached, leading me like a blind woman toward the sink.

I threw water on my face as if it were on fire, soaking my hair and the front of my shirtwaist in the process. When the burning and stinging finally stopped, I lifted my face from the sink—and there stood Louis Decker, offering me a towel, his brow furrowed in concern.

"Are you all right, Miss Hayes?"

"Where did you come from?" I asked in horror.

"I help out here sometimes. And these are two of my friends from school. I'd like you to meet Curtis and Jack. This is Mrs. Hayes' granddaughter, Violet."

Wonderful! More witnesses to my humiliation. Any pride I'd had in my appearance was thoroughly humbled as I greeted Louis and his two friends—soaked, red-eyed, and tear-streaked. I accepted the towel he offered and dried my face with it, wishing I could cover my head and run.

"It's wonderful to see you again, Miss Hayes," Louis said graciously.

"Yes . . . Nice to see you too." I sniffed. My nose wouldn't stop running. He gestured to the onion that sat waiting for me on the chopping board.

"I always leave onions to the experts."

It was a bit too late for that piece of advice.

"We need these many more," Magda said, setting two more of the unpeeled monsters on the board beside mine. "You like for me to chop?"

"Yes, please." I hung my head in defeat.

"Maybe you try this, yes?" She handed me an ugly brown lump with hairy tentacles sticking out of it. We could have played Animal, Vegetable, or Mineral? with the thing, but I wasn't in the mood.

"Is no smell in that one," Magda assured me.

"Good. Thank you."

Louis and his two friends donned aprons and began to work too. The sight of men doing women's chores astonished me. One of them added more wood to the fire in the huge kitchen stove. The other one began scrubbing out the pot that had held the elephant bone. Louis picked up another knife and began peeling potatoes for Magda now that she had taken over the onions. The fumes didn't seem to bother her in the least.

"I'm amazed that you would come here and help out this way," I said. "It's . . . it's so kind of you."

Louis dismissed my praise with a shake of his head. "It's not enough to call myself a Christian if my faith doesn't lead to action. In fact, that's exactly how Miss Addams herself describes this place: an experiment in translating Christian values into social action."

I looked down at the misshapen lump in my hand and was ashamed to admit that I lacked Louis' zeal.

"Miss Addams comes from a wealthy family," he continued. "She inherited quite a lot of money when her father died. She could be living in luxury, but she wanted to do something useful with her life. So she chose to live here and help make the world a better place. I want to do the same with my life."

I didn't want to interrupt Louis to ask what I was supposed to do with the mysterious mass, so I listened intently, nodding in all the appropriate places. I was willing to pitch in and help like the others—but I had no idea what the thing in my hand was, let alone what to do with it. When he finally set down the potato and took off his spectacles to clean them, I took advantage of the pause.

"Um . . . Louis? Do you know what I'm supposed to do with this?"

"You peel it—like a potato."

"Thanks."

I had watched him and Magda peeling things, and it didn't appear all that difficult. But as soon as I dug my knife into the tough outer skin, the wretched animal began to bleed all over me! The more I peeled, the harder it gushed.

"Miss Addams was raised a Quaker," Louis said, oblivious to the carnage I was wreaking. "They taught her to study society's problems and to work hard to correct injustice."

A beet! The cursed thing was a beet! And I knew enough about beet juice to know that it was as unforgiving as India ink.

"It's what Jesus would want us to do. 'What doth the Lord require of thee,'" Louis quoted, "'but to do justly, and to love mercy, and to walk humbly with thy God.' And the Apostle James wrote, 'For as the body without the spirit is dead, so faith without works is dead also.' Our Lord said that if we give even a cup of cold water in His name, we do it unto Him."

I had tears in my eyes again, but not from the sermon or the fumes. My hands would be indelibly stained from the beet juice by the time I finished, and I was supposed to attend a party with Nelson

Kent tomorrow night. But how could I lay the thing down and quit when Louis' soul-stirring speech was meant to inspire me to sacrificial service? I would be worse than a heathen.

"Jesus said, 'Blessed are the poor.' And if we turn aside and allow the poor among us to suffer, then the quality of all our lives suffers."

He went on and on, barely pausing for breath until he'd finished peeling and chopping the last of the potatoes. He tossed them into the soup pot with the meat from the elephant bone. By this time, Magda not only had dealt with all of the onions, but had scraped and chopped a basketful of carrots as well, and added them to the soup. My grandmother was covering a mound of yeasty bread dough with a towel and putting it into the warming oven to rise—and all I had to show for my morning's efforts were discolored hands and a few poorly peeled beets.

"Do you want help with those?" Louis asked, gesturing to the mound in front of me waiting to be peeled.

"Are they supposed to go into that pot of soup too?"

"No, I think one of the Russian ladies is going to make *borscht* out of them."

I nodded as if I understood, but I had no idea what he was talking about. "Yes, I could use some help," I admitted meekly. Louis picked up a beet and happily resumed his sermon.

"The settlement house helps people from a variety of races and backgrounds—Germans, Irish, Swedes, Italians, Poles, Russians, Greeks. Jesus looks past our ethnic and class differences and makes us into one new family—His kingdom, here on earth."

He continued in a similar vein as we attacked and conquered the beets together, but my mind drifted away from his lofty orations as I tried to think of a remedy for my stained hands. Lye soap, perhaps? It might remove the beet juice, but it would be at the expense of my skin. Which fate would be worse: red-stained hands or coarse, rough ones?

It sounded like one of the questions Ruth Schultz and I used to ponder: *"If your one true love took your hands in his, and you had to choose between having dry, scrub-maid hands or skin the color of beets, which would you choose?"* I tried to decide which fate Madame Beauchamps would tell me to choose, but she would be horrified that I'd found myself in this predicament in the first place. I would have to keep my gloves on tomorrow evening, which was not a socially acceptable thing to do when dining, but I saw no other way out of my dilemma.

We finally finished peeling the last beet. It seemed as though I had been in this kitchen for days. Louis removed his wire-rimmed spectacles again and polished them on his shirttail, which never seemed to stay tucked into his trousers. Once again, in spite of his vigorous efforts, the glasses looked just as smudged when he wrapped them around his ears again as when he'd started.

"It's almost lunchtime," he said. "We'll start serving the noon meal soon."

Indeed, the aroma of bread and soup had begun to fill the kitchen while we'd worked. My stomach rumbled with hunger. But when I recalled the nauseating smells that awaited me outside, I questioned the wisdom of eating anything at all. Hadn't I suffered enough humiliation for one day without losing my lunch in the street on the way home?

I helped carry stacks of bowls and spoons to the serving table while Louis and his friends lifted the soup pot from the stove.

"This is the part I love," he said. "Serving the needy, seeing their faces, offering that 'cup of cold water' in Christ's name. It makes all the hard work worthwhile, doesn't it?"

I glanced at my ruined hands and knew I couldn't answer his question truthfully. My stained nails looked as though I had murdered someone with my bare hands.

"I admire you, Mr. Decker. I don't believe I've ever met anyone quite like you."

"Please, Miss Hayes. God deserves all the glory, not me. I'm just His servant."

"You're a very good one, then."

As it turned out, my help wasn't required. When the doors opened and scores of hungry people came inside for a bowl of soup and a piece of bread, there were plenty of servers for the job. I watched my Grandmother and Louis and the others feeding the hungry and offering kind words of encouragement, and I doubted that I could ever dedicate my life to this work the way they were doing. What was wrong with me that given the choice I would rather be served than serve?

When the crowds left, we sat around the table in the kitchen where I had worked all morning and ate a bowl of soup for lunch. It was surprisingly delicious. I would have to write a letter to Ruth Schultz and tell her that my most adventurous meal might now be elephant soup. But when we'd all eaten our fill, I eyed the towering stacks of dirty soup bowls with dismay.

"We can help wash up another day," my grandmother said, resting her hand on my shoulder. "We have another job to do now. Let's go fetch our hats."

"Are we leaving?"

Grandmother nodded. I recalled my earlier experiences with onions and beets and didn't know whether to be happy that I'd escaped dishwashing or if an even worse fate awaited me.

"Where are we going?"

"A woman I know named Irina is ill. I've offered to bring some soup to her and her family. Louis is going to come with us. Here, you can carry this."

She handed me a loaf of bread wrapped in a kitchen towel. Louis already had the lunch bucket of soup in one hand, and he offered my grandmother his other arm. I drew a deep breath, inhaling the delicious aromas for the last time, then braced myself to walk outside.

The stench of the neighborhood had worsened in the afternoon sun. I usually reserved my prayers for bedtimes and Sunday church services, but I began to pray silently that this task wouldn't take too long or be very far away. Otherwise, my lunch was going to make a quick encore appearance.

I noticed the children as we walked. So many of them were ragged and barefooted, and so many of them were working rather than playing. Older girls aged eight or nine rocked babies and chased toddlers. Young boys, still in knee britches, hauled stacks of firewood on homemade carts.

"Where do they find wood in the city?" I asked Louis.

"They scavenge for it behind warehouses or along railroad tracks. Then they have to sell it all. They don't make much money, but every spare penny helps their families. A lot of our Sunday school boys work downtown all day selling newspapers or shining shoes."

Grandmother linked arms with me. "This is what hurts me, Violet—seeing all these children who have to work so hard when they should be in school getting a good education. Thank the Lord that you had a safe, happy childhood—these children certainly don't have one."

I thought I finally understood why my grandmother had moved to Chicago after my grandfather died instead of staying in Lockport and taking care of Father and me.

"Older children who should be in school are forced to find work in factories," she continued. "And much of the work that's given to women and children is either piecework or done in sweatshops."

"What's a sweatshop?"

"Any place besides a regular factory where work is done," Louis explained. "It's usually in a basement or a garage or a vacant tenement. Employers cram in a bunch of workers and treat them like slaves. Of course those places have very unsafe working conditions, and the workers have to put in long hours for very little pay."

"See that little boy?" Grandmother nodded toward a lad who couldn't have been more than eight years old staggering beneath an enormous bundle of fabric. "He's delivering piecework, probably to his mother and sisters. Those look like men's trousers. The family will finish all of the hand sewing at home, often after working all day at some other job. They'll get paid by the piece. Can you imagine little girls only seven or eight years old, sewing men's trousers day and night for seven cents a dozen?"

"That's all? Why so little?"

"Because there are hundreds of other destitute immigrants who are willing to work for those wages if they don't."

We turned down a crowded alleyway, and I had to pinch my nose closed again to block out the smell. I hadn't wanted to reveal my squeamishness in front of Louis Decker, but the entire lane reeked like an overflowing outhouse. I'd never seen so many flies in my life.

"Here, this is clean," Louis said, handing me his handkerchief. "The heavy rain we had the other night made all of the outhouses overflow. Is it any wonder that these neighborhoods have cholera and typhoid epidemics?"

"We're trying to educate people about the need for cleanliness," Grandmother added, "but there are just so *many* people. And, of course, language is a problem. That's why Miss Addams has added English lessons. . . . Well, here we are. This is where Irina and her family live."

The door to the tenement stood open, and I braced myself as we went inside, dreading how this dilapidated building might smell. It took a moment for my eyes to adjust to the dark, narrow foyer after the bright afternoon sunshine. I heard water running and identified the first odor as mildew.

A young boy stood at the base of the steps, filling an enamel basin with water from a sputtering faucet. He had spread a collection of cans, pots, and bowls on the floor, and he was slowly filling them, one by one.

"That's the only running water in the building," Grandmother said. "All of the people in these apartments have to share the same faucet—and they have to haul the water upstairs, of course."

"The tenants are probably thankful to have any water at all," Louis said. "Careful! Watch your step, Violet. . . ."

He took my arm to guide me across the slippery floorboards and around the boy's scattered containers. As I followed my grandmother up the rickety wooden stairs to the third floor, the odors changed from damp and moldy to the fragrant aroma of cooking food. I began to breathe more freely. I identified onions and boiled potatoes, but also the mysterious, spicy aromas of foreign foods. The air in the stairwell smelled delicious.

We climbed to the third floor and my grandmother knocked on one of the apartment doors. It opened a crack and a tousled boy with a dirt-smudged face peered out.

"It's me, Yuri—Mrs. Hayes," my grandmother told him. "I've brought your mother some soup."

"Yes, yes, let her come in, Yuri," Irina called from inside. He opened the door for us.

Irina was the thinnest woman I had ever met and also the palest. She sat propped up on one of the beds, her right leg immobilized by a bandage and wooden splint. She might have been a pretty woman, but the accident that had broken her leg had marred her face with purplish bruises. One eye was blackened and swollen shut, and her lips looked puffy and split. I wondered how she had been injured but knew enough about proper manners not to ask. She was top-stitching a man's suit coat; a pile of unfinished coats lay heaped on the bed beside her.

I counted three small children in the dismal room along with Yuri, and a fifth one asleep in a cradle that seemed much too short for her. I tried not to gape at the bare wooden floors, the lumpy beds, the chipped plates on the tilting table, knowing that it was just as rude to stare at the furnishings here as it had been in the mansions I'd visited.

"Irina, this is my granddaughter, Violet Rose. We brought you some soup."

"Thank you, thank you," she said, pronouncing it *tank you*. She set aside her sewing as one of the smaller children climbed onto the bed beside her. "How can I ever tank you? You would like to stay and visit? Yuri can make tea."

"No, we can't stay. Maybe next time, Irina."

"We're praying for you down at the church," Louis added. "I hope you'll soon be well again." He took the bread from me and set it on the table.

"Yes. Tank you."

"We miss you down at the kitchen," Grandmother said. "No one makes *borscht* as good as you do."

"Tank you." I saw Irina wipe away a tear as Grandmother closed the apartment door behind us.

"What happened to her?" I asked when we reached the stairwell. "How did she break her leg?"

"Her husband did that to her," Grandmother said.

I couldn't utter another word until we reached the foyer. The young boy was still standing at the water faucet, slowly filling a blackened teakettle.

"But—why would he do such a terrible thing?"

"He becomes violent whenever he has too much to drink. Irina would rather take the abuse herself than let him harm one of the children. I didn't want to stay and visit today for fear he would come home."

"Why in the world doesn't she leave him?"

"She has no way to support her children or pay the rent."

"Everyone at church is praying for her," Louis said. "And for her husband."

"Yes, Irina is such a dear woman."

Louis walked with us to our streetcar stop on a main thoroughfare. Finally, I dared to breathe deeply again. The smell of horse manure, factory fumes, and the ever-present stockyards seemed tame after visiting the slums.

"It was wonderful to see you again, Violet," Louis said as he waited with us for our car. "I enjoyed working with you."

"Yes. I hope we meet again."

"Well, now that you mention it . . ." He paused, removing his spectacles to polish them. "I don't want you to feel pressured, Violet. I mean, your participation should be absolutely voluntary . . . but if you are able to play the piano for us next Thursday, we really could use your help." He wrapped the wires around his ears and gazed at me with his dark, intense eyes.

"All right. I'll come." I needed to shrug off more of the guilt that was blanketing me. Playing the piano sounded much easier than cutting up vegetables. And it wasn't likely to ruin my hands either.

"Wonderful," he said. "We'll meet in front of the school at one o'clock. I'll see you then." Our streetcar arrived, and Grandmother and I climbed aboard, waving good-bye. She sank onto the seat with a sigh.

"So. What did you think of the settlement house?"

"I never realized what a hard life those immigrant women have."

"My sister Matt has her way of helping women, and I have mine. But our work overlaps in places too. We're both working to change the laws so that women can earn higher wages and work shorter hours. We'd both like to improve working conditions so factories are cleaner and safer. And we're both trying to get new child labor laws passed—and enforced—so that children can get out of the factories and sweatshops and into schools."

"Their living conditions are terrible."

"Yes. And you can see why so many of the ramshackle wooden tenements like the one we visited today burned up like matchsticks in the Great Fire. Afterward, the poor people who'd lived in them had no place to go. They didn't have much to begin with, and then they lost it all. Many, many of the people who died in the fire were poor."

"Did my mother live in a tenement before the fire?"

Once again, my grandmother hesitated—as she always did when I asked a question about my mother.

"I honestly don't know where she lived, Violet Rose. I only know that wherever it was, her home burned to the ground. She lost everything—clothing, personal items, heirlooms—everything."

"Did she—"

"That's really all I can say about her, Violet."

I huffed in frustration. "Why won't you ever talk about her?"

Grandmother took my hand in both of hers and squeezed it gently. She had beautiful hands—strong and work worn and scented with flour and yeast. A week ago I would have described them as chapped and reddened from too much work. Today they looked beautiful to me.

"I can't talk about your mother because I promised your father that I wouldn't." She quickly changed the subject. "Since most immigrants work very hard for very little pay, it's an even greater tragedy when some of them waste it all on alcohol. That's why my work with the Temperance Union is so important. It goes hand-in-hand with the work we did today. I'll take you with me to the Union another day."

"I still don't understand why women like Irina don't leave their husbands if they beat them and spend all their money in saloons."

"Because they have no place to go. And if they did leave their husbands, who would care for their children while they worked? One of the needs that Miss Addams hopes to address is low-cost housing and day care for the children of working mothers."

It occurred to me that perhaps my mother had wanted to take me with her when she left home, but she'd had no place to live and no one to take care of me. I wished I could find her and ask her about it, but how could I find her if no one would talk about her?

Chapter

12

~~~~~~~~

Grandmother and I returned home from our day at the settlement house to find Aunt Agnes sitting at our dining room table, drinking tea with Matt and Birdie.

"Sit down and join us, Florence," Aunt Matt commanded. "You never have time to visit with your own family anymore. You sit too, Violet."

"I believe I will," Grandmother said with a sigh. I could tell how weary she was by the way she lowered herself onto her chair. I sat down beside her as Aunt Birdie fetched each of us a clean teacup. It was the first time all four sisters and I had been together since I had arrived in Chicago nearly two weeks ago.

"I do hope you didn't wear Violet out this morning," Aunt Agnes said. "She has an important party to attend tomorrow night."

"There's no such thing as an *important* party, Agnes," Grandmother said.

"There certainly is! Isn't her future important to you? Marriage occupies the biggest portion of every woman's future."

"Who says?" Matt asked. No one answered her.

"Violet should have been making social calls with me this afternoon instead of running all around those appalling neighborhoods you visit." Aunt Agnes gestured broadly when she spoke, as if conscious of her many rings. She had elegant hands, in spite of the wrinkles, and her jewels glittered in the afternoon sunlight.

"Violet helped me work today. Didn't you, dear?" Grandmother said, patting my shoulder. I nodded lamely, feeling like a hypocrite. I knew how little I actually had accomplished. My tea was turning cold but I was afraid to reach for the cup, afraid that Aunt Agnes would notice my stained fingers.

"I could have used an extra pair of hands down at the Suffrage Association," Aunt Matt said. "The forty-fifth anniversary of the first Women's Rights Convention is coming up next month, and we need to get the information mailed out to our members. That convention has the potential to *greatly* improve Violet's future—and the future of *all* women."

"Nonsense!" Aunt Agnes said with a wave. "I happen to know that several very important young men are interested in our Violet. Marriage to one of them will make her future secure."

"Humph!" Aunt Matt grunted. "Her marriage is going to do more for *you* than it ever will for her—poor thing."

I wondered if Aunt Matt was right. Did I really want to be used as a prize to help increase my aunt's social standing? Meanwhile, I was supposed to be searching for my mother. That was the reason I had come to Chicago in the first place, yet I was no closer to my goal than the day I'd left Lockport.

"Poor thing indeed," Agnes sniffed. "She looks very peaked, Florence. I do hope she isn't getting ill. Heaven knows what sorts of diseases she might catch in that wretched neighborhood."

"She isn't ill," Grandmother said calmly. "She got up early this morning to go with me—that's all."

"And see how tired she looks? I do hope those bags beneath her eyes go away by tomorrow night."

"Oh, I do too," Aunt Matt added. "Get some rest, Violet. Otherwise you might fall asleep from boredom while discussing Mrs. Pullman's new spring hat."

"Don't be mean-spirited, Matilda. But speaking of fashion, Violet, I brought your new gown with me. Mrs. Riggs finished it. Be a dear and go try it on, will you? So I can see it? The Kents only invited young people to the party tomorrow night, so I won't be there to see you."

"Yes, I'd be happy to. Where is the dress, Aunt Agnes?"

"I believe Birdie hung it in your wardrobe."

I hurried upstairs, grateful to flee their discussion. But I wondered how the gown would look on top of the guilt overcoat I still wore. Irina's family probably could eat for a month on the money Agnes had spent. And while Mrs. Riggs had been sewing my new ivory brocade gown, frail eight-year-old girls had been forced to stitch men's trousers in dreary sweatshops for seven cents a dozen. How could I possibly enjoy myself in that dress, knowing the true cost?

Nevertheless, I slipped the gown over my head. The brocade felt like cool water against my skin. It swished magnificently when I walked. I never wanted to take it off.

"Lovely!" Agnes applauded when I descended the stairs. "You look beautiful, darling!"

"Oh, how nice," Aunt Birdie said.

"It's quite . . . revealing, isn't it?" Grandmother asked. She spread her hands across her own chest, forgetting that her dress buttoned clear to her neck. "What in the world will her father say?"

"Why don't you just put the poor girl on the auction block and sell her to the highest bidder?" Matt asked before huffing out to the kitchen with the empty teapot.

"Thank you for modeling it for me, dear," Agnes said, "but I'm

148

afraid I have to run along now. What time shall I have my driver pick you up tomorrow night?"

"Um . . . that won't be necessary, Aunt Agnes. Nelson Kent has offered to escort me."

"Oh, Violet! You didn't accept his offer? The point of the party was to give you another opportunity to play the field."

"Yes, Violet. Why settle for *rich* when there might be someone even *richer*?" Aunt Matt asked as she returned for the remaining teacups.

"There's no call for sarcasm, Mattie," Grandmother said. "Violet knows there is more to life than material riches. Don't you, dear?"

"There's love," Birdie said in her dreamy voice.

"I'm disappointed that you accepted Nelson Kent's offer so soon," Agnes said. Her ability to ignore all of her sisters and stick to the subject impressed me.

"I'm sorry, Aunt Agnes. Nelson caught me off guard, and I agreed to let him escort me before I had a chance to think it through."

"Apology accepted. Besides, he would be an excellent match. You could do much worse. And you are getting up in years . . ."

"Fiddlesticks," Grandmother said. "Violet is only twenty."

"That means she'll soon be twenty-one, and you know what *that* means." Agnes' voice dropped to a whisper. "You wouldn't want her to become an *old maid*, would you?"

"I really don't think Nelson intends to propose on Saturday night," I told my aunt. "But if he does, I'll tell him I have to think about it."

"Good girl." She grabbed my hands and squeezed them. Then her mouth dropped open in horror. "My stars, Violet! What in the world have you done to your hands?"

"It's beet juice. I helped peel some of them today at the settlement house." I was afraid she would be furious with me, but she directed all of her wrath at my grandmother.

"Florence Howell Hayes! Don't you care at all if your grand-daughter marries well? How could you make her slave all morning like a common servant? She should be commanding a household full of servants!"

"I didn't make her do anything, Agnes. She volunteered." Grand-mother caressed Agnes' arm as if smoothing her ruffled feathers. "You should be praising her for doing something useful to help others. Besides, it gave Violet a chance to meet some wonderful young people her age who volunteer there. They're students at the Chicago Evangelistic Society."

Aunt Matt stopped stacking teacups and planted her hands on her hips. "Don't tell me, Florence! Are you trying to match Violet with one of those radical young ministers?"

"Those students are fine young men."

"Shame on both of you! After all of the things the pair of you have suffered, why would you want Violet to follow either of your examples? Agnes, do you really want that girl to have a life like yours? And you, Florence—you, of all people, should have the blinders off when it comes to marrying a minister!"

Her words made my skin tingle. I knew what she was referring to in Aunt Agnes' marriage, but what about my grandmother's? I held my breath, waiting for more information, but for a long moment no one spoke.

"It's true, I've had my share of sorrows," Grandmother finally said. "But my blessings have far outweighed them. I would be proud to have Violet follow my example when it comes to helping others."

"Not by peeling vegetables!" Agnes said. "My stars! The women to whom I've introduced Violet are very active in charity work. Potter Palmer and his wife are two of Mr. Moody's biggest supporters. So are Marshall Field and Gustavus Swift and the banker Lyman Gage . . . They've all given money to Mr. Moody's campaigns."

"Is that true?" I asked.

Grandmother nodded. "Yes, all of those men have been very generous."

"Their wives and my other society friends spend a good deal of time raising money for charity too," Agnes added.

"I know they do," Grandmother said. "And I appreciate your generosity, Agnes. But I enjoy working with people, getting involved with them and not simply tossing money their way. It's just the way I am. Lord knows your work and mine are both necessary."

"If Violet marries well she can influence her husband to support your work. So you see? We are working for the same cause."

"Why does Violet's happiness depend solely on whether or not she gets married?" Aunt Matt asked. "Or does misery love company? You want her to be as miserable as you are?"

"Don't be spiteful, Matt."

Aunt Birdie cleared her throat. "I have just one thing to say about all of this," she announced in her wispy voice. She paused dramatically, as if delivering the final word on the matter. "Make sure you marry for love, Violet."

I wondered about her advice. If I fell in love as deeply as Aunt Birdie had, I also would risk having my heart broken.

"I need to be going," Agnes said. "Violet, make sure you wear gloves tomorrow night so no one sees those wretched hands."

"I will. And thank you again, Aunt Agnes, for the beautiful dress."

"You are quite welcome, dear. *Au revoir*, everyone."

Chapter

13

On Saturday night, Nelson Kent arrived in a splendid carriage, complete with a footman, to take me to his grandmother's party. I felt like Cinderella in my magnificent new gown, especially after laboring like a scullery maid the day before. If only I had a fairy godmother to wave her magic wand and fix my stained hands so I wouldn't need to wear gloves.

"You look beautiful, Violet," Nelson told me when we arrived at the party. "You are by far the loveliest woman here. I'm congratulating myself for having the foresight to claim you before anyone else had a chance." His eyes widened as he slipped my wrap from my shoulders. "Your dress is stunning!"

It was stunning, all right. Every man who gazed at the generous view of my assets looked as though he'd been stunned by a blow to the head. Men flocked to me like crows to a cornfield, but I noticed that very few of them looked me in the eye. Instead, their gaze seemed to stray twelve inches below my face. Nelson acted as the scarecrow, shooing them off as fast as they flew to me.

"Sorry, gentlemen," he said, linking my arm through his. "She's mine for the evening." He seemed to revel in his role as King of the Hill.

"Give us a chance, Nelson."

"Not tonight."

"We'd like to get to know Miss Hayes too."

"Then ask her out yourselves—some other time."

If Mrs. Riggs ever sewed another gown for me, I promised myself that I would choose my own pattern next time.

It wasn't only the men who noticed my apparel. "Your gown is exquisite," Haughty told me. Her dark brown eyes shone green with envy.

"Thank you, Hau—um . . . Hattie." I cleared my throat to make it seem like I had something caught there, but in truth I had nearly slipped and called her "Haughty" to her face. Nelson noticed and covered his mouth to hide his amusement.

"May I inquire where you had your dress made?" Naughty asked.

Competition for good dressmakers was always fierce—their names a closely-guarded secret. I couldn't allow the two Grant sisters to monopolize Mrs. Riggs' precious time.

"You'll need to ask my aunt for the woman's name," I said, avoiding an outright lie. "Aunt Agnes is the one who made all of the arrangements."

For the first hour or so, Nelson and I walked around, arms linked, conversing with his guests as we nibbled appetizers. I often felt excluded as they discussed people and past events that I knew nothing about.

"Everyone seems to know each other," I told Nelson as we moved from one group to the next.

"Yes, most of our families are longtime friends."

"Aunt Agnes told me that I was 'new blood.'"

"And very lovely blood, I might add. That's why they're swarming around you like mosquitoes. It's all I can do to swat them away."

Long before our hostess served dinner I'd grown bored. The girls spent all of their time flirting. And as I watched Haughty and Naughty working hard to be mysterious and coquettish, I felt relieved that I didn't have to play the field.

None of the men interested me, rich or not. They were the same phonies I'd danced with at the fund-raiser. They might have been nice underneath their facades, but no one gave me the opportunity to find out.

My trip to the settlement house had tainted this party for me. Everything we talked about now seemed unimportant and frivolous, the evening a shameless folly compared to the way that Louis Decker and his friends lived their lives. Nelson noticed that I had grown quiet.

"Will you excuse us?" he asked the group with whom we had been chatting. He pulled me aside and steered me out of the noisy parlor and into the hall.

"You look as tired of all this as I am, Violet. And we haven't even had dinner yet."

"Being nice is exhausting," I said.

"I've never heard it put quite that way, but you're right—this is hard work. Come on."

We crept out to the garden where Nelson and I had visited on the day we met, and stood side by side on the veranda, basking in the warm, starlit evening. We easily resumed the comfortable conversation we'd enjoyed at the fund-raiser a week ago.

"How have you been keeping busy since I saw you last?" he asked.

Did I dare tell him about the settlement house or my visit to Irina's tenement? "My grandmother and my aunts have kept me occupied, and I've seen a little more of the city since then."

"Have you been to the fair?"

"No, not yet."

"Good. I would like the honor of taking you for the first time. I'd love to see what you think of it. By the way, your hands must be sweating in those gloves. You can take them off, you know."

"No, I really can't. I'm afraid I've ruined my hands."

"Ruined them? Now I'm intrigued. Let me see." We laughed as Nelson began tugging playfully on one of my gloves.

"No, really . . . Aunt Agnes would have a fit!" But he managed to pull off one of them, and I finally relented. "Okay, but I'll only show you. And you can't tell anyone."

"It'll be our secret." He lifted my bare hand to the light that streamed from the mansion's windows. "What's all over them? Don't tell me you've murdered someone."

"It's beet juice. I volunteered to help my grandmother with her charity work, and she had me peeling beets. I peeled an onion too. I hope you aren't too shocked."

"I think it's sweet." He lifted my hand to his lips and kissed my fingers.

Nelson was the first man who had ever kissed me, and I was surprised by how warm and soft his lips felt against my skin. I wondered how his lips would feel against my own. But it was curiosity that I felt, not desire. Even so, it took me a moment to regain my balance.

"The . . . um . . . the place where my grandmother works seems like a different world compared to this one. I confess that I feel a little guilty for enjoying this life of luxury so much more."

Nelson's blasé smile vanished. "I know. There's a terrible gap between the rich and the poor. And there's an even larger gap socially. My father inherited our wealth from his father, and to be honest, he isn't as generous to the poor as some of the self-made men who've worked their way up from the bottom. Turlington Harvey, for instance."

"Who is he?"

"Chicago's lumber baron. The story goes that Mr. Harvey arrived in town with only a toolbox and a lucky penny. But he worked hard and eventually got rich rebuilding Chicago after the fire. Now he gives a great deal of money to charity."

"Do you ever feel guilty that we have so much and the immigrants in the tenements have so little?"

"I do." He was gazing back at the house, not at me. Light spilled from the windows, and we could see his servants preparing dinner in the kitchen. "I should probably get back," he said. "Do you mind?"

"Not at all. And by the way, I'm glad that I came to the party with you. This is a lot less work than coming unescorted and fighting off suitors."

He laughed and reached for the doorknob.

"Nelson, wait. I need to put my glove back on."

He still held it in his hand. He looked at me, and for a moment I thought he might kiss me. Then he smiled and held my glove open for me. I slid my hand into it and he offered me his arm.

I liked Nelson, but I still didn't observe the feverish symptoms of love in either of us. I longed for love and romance. Perhaps I had read too many of Ruth's novels, or maybe Aunt Birdie's unchanging refrain had influenced me, but I wanted to fall madly, crazily, head-over-heels in love. I couldn't stop thinking about her description of my parents: *"Their passion was ignited the night of the Great Fire, and the fervor of their love was as all-consuming as the flames. . . ."* Was I naïve to want the same thing?

Once again, I strolled around the party on Nelson's arm while he played the part of host. I was struck by how comfortable and natural he was with his role as the wealthy young heir to the Kent family fortune. He was very skilled at making polite conversation, pretending he was interested in everyone's stories, laughing at their jokes. One would never know that he considered it a chore.

And I was very comfortable with him. If he had proposed to me that evening I might have said yes, in spite of my promise to Aunt Agnes and in spite of the fact that I wasn't in love with him. Nelson Kent was a handsome, charming man. He had a wealthy family, a magnificent home, scores of servants—all of the things I had dreamed of having while studying in Madame Beauchamps' School for Young Ladies. Except for love, that is. But love had been the midnight musings of schoolgirls. Love had never been part of Madame Beauchamps' curriculum.

We finally moved into the enormous dining room and sat down at the dinner table, all twenty-four of us. Nelson cleverly swapped my place card with another so that I would be seated alongside him. The other women wore lovely gowns and had arranged their hair in elaborate styles, but I thought that the prettiest girl in the room was the young parlormaid, Katya, whom I'd met during my last visit.

She wore a long gray gabardine maid's uniform with a ruffled white apron and had tucked her wheat-colored hair beneath her white cap. Even without adornment, Katya resembled a Slavic princess, her natural beauty simple and unpretentious. I watched her remove our soup bowls when we finished the first course and saw that she had an inborn grace that hadn't come from walking around with a book on her head. Then I noticed that Nelson was watching her too.

"Your grandmother's servant is lovely."

"Yes . . . yes, she is." His voice sounded sad.

I recalled the suspicion I'd had the last time I'd visited, that Nelson and Katya were secretly in love, and for the first time all evening something intrigued me. I decided to pay close attention to them—as any good detective would do—and find out if my suspicions were correct or merely a figment of my imagination.

Each time Katya emerged through the servants' door, Nelson looked up at her—if only for a moment. He enjoyed the rear view just as much when she returned to the kitchen. For her part, Katya kept her eyes properly lowered as she served each guest—except for when she served someone directly across the table from Nelson. Each time, she couldn't seem to stop herself from briefly glancing up at him.

They clearly were watching one another, and their furtive game continued throughout the lengthy dinner. Then, for a single shocking moment, their eyes met. It happened as Katya reached to remove Nelson's plate. He turned and looked up at her, directly into her eyes. Their faces were inches apart, and the warmth of their mutual gaze could have melted the silverware.

"Thank you, Katya," he murmured.

That was unheard of! Servants were supposed to be ignored during dinner parties, treated as part of the furniture. Madame Beauchamps had lectured extensively on how to handle servants: *"One must treat them kindly but firmly. Never be overly friendly. You may call them by their first name, but they must refer to you as Miss or Madam. Eye contact is necessary only when being firm with them or when reprimanding them. Servants must always avert their eyes. Each of you must always, always, remember your place."*

Nelson and Katya both knew the rules. Clearly, I was not imagining a relationship.

After dinner we moved from the dining room to a small ballroom, where an orchestra had begun to play. With the lovely Katya out of sight, Nelson became my charming suitor once again.

"Would you like to dance, Violet?"

"Yes, thank you."

Nelson was a wonderful dancer. We were comfortable in each other's arms. As we waltzed around the dance floor for the next hour or so, I talked to him as easily as I had talked to Ruth Schultz.

"If you could choose," I asked, "which would you rather be: the captain of a pirate ship or the captain of a warship?" My question made him laugh out loud.

I happened to look up as Nelson laughed and spied Katya watching us. She had come into the ballroom presumably to collect the used punch glasses. But as Ruth's romance novels had phrased it: *Her love and her longing for him were written in her eyes.* Clearly, it broke her heart to see us together. She loved Nelson. I was certain of it. The question was, did he love her?

"That's a great question!" Nelson said when he stopped laughing. "I would have to say the captain of a warship." He swung me around, and Katya disappeared from view.

"A warship?" I repeated. "Now you have to tell me why."

"Well, let's see. . . . I love working in the business world, and it's very much like commanding a warship. It's all about taking charge, conquering new territory, building an empire. And also about accumulating wealth if you're the one who wins the war. And I like to win. Besides, some of the colonies I subjugate might be interesting places to visit."

"Have you traveled a lot?"

"Of course. It's expected. I've made the obligatory tour of the continent." He spoke casually, as if it was nothing special, yet I couldn't fault him. His sense of entitlement was part of him. He hadn't chosen to be born into wealth any more than Katya had chosen to be born an immigrant.

"I would love to hear about your travels. Tell me about the loveliest place you've ever visited."

"Let's see . . . There were so many, but I would have to say Italy. Especially Lake Como. It's a long, narrow lake surrounded by mountains and dotted with charming villages. You would love it."

"How do you know?"

"Well, for one thing, you would fit right in. You're as lovely as an Italian princess. The Mediterranean men would all flirt with you. I would love to take you there. You would be a fun traveling companion because you see things differently from other women.

"You view everything through fresh eyes. And you're very imaginative. That's obvious from the charming questions you ask. You aren't vain either. Most women I know are very self-focused. They want the whole world to look at them, and in the process they miss seeing the world."

The song ended and we sat down on a small loveseat to rest. I had enjoyed staying by Nelson's side all evening, but I didn't realize that people were getting the wrong impression of us until one of the young men I'd met last week came over to ask me to dance.

"Give someone else a chance, Nelson. We want to get to know Miss Hayes too."

Nelson turned him down. "Sorry. She's all mine."

"Oh, I see how it is. When's the wedding?" He stalked away.

"Does it worry you that people are talking about us?" I asked.

"Not in the least. I like you, Violet. In a few short hours, I've gotten to know you better than the girls I've known all my life. You're different from them. Don't you agree that we work well together?"

"Yes, I suppose."

I had to admit that I was content with him. Fair-haired Nelson was a prize by anyone's standards. But I suddenly had a disturbing thought. Was I merely a distraction? What if he had chosen me as a suitable woman who would keep his family from noticing his love for Katya?

"We enjoy each other's company," Nelson continued. "And we seem to enjoy the same things. You told me that you like this life of luxury, didn't you? I think we could be happy together."

Again, I had to admit he was right. Forgive me, but I loved this life—the fine food, the gracious home, the beautiful clothes. I never could live with the smells and distresses of the slums. But the weight of guilt that this confession caused me was as enormous as the gap between Irina's home and the one I stood in. I couldn't understand how people like my grandmother and Louis Decker could be so self-less. I never wanted to peel another onion as long as I lived. And if I did marry Nelson Kent, I could be as generous with my money as the other Chicago socialites were, couldn't I?

"What about love?" I asked Nelson.

"What about it? People in our social circle don't marry for love. There is usually an attraction, perhaps even fondness. But in most cases, marriages are all about family alliances and power and finding a wife who will be a social asset."

"Does that fondness ever turn into love?"

"Yes, it often does . . . Violet, it seems as though you become sad whenever you mention love. Tell me, did you have your heart broken?"

"No. I've never been in love. I was thinking of my parents. According to my aunt, my parents married for love. But something happened and now they're divorced. I wish I knew why."

"Come on, let's dance."

The music lifted both of our spirits until, once again, I saw Katya watching us. This time, I pointed her out to him.

"We're being watched." He followed my gaze and saw her. Their eyes met, and even from across the room I could sense the passion they shared. Then she quickly turned and hurried away. The song ended a moment later.

Nelson smiled at me and said, "Will you excuse me, Violet? I'll be right back."

I couldn't resist the impulse to follow him. He caught up with Katya in the front hall, and I ducked behind a door to listen. Eaves-dropping was an unforgivable offense. It would destroy my friendship with Nelson if he caught me. But I needed to know the truth.

For a long moment neither of them spoke. I risked another peek around the doorframe and saw that they were kissing. But this was no mere kiss—this was two starving people encountering food for the first time in days! I ducked behind the door again as the heat rose to my cheeks.

"Katya, wait!" I heard Nelson call a moment later. "Don't go! I want to explain."

"No, Nelson. You do not need to explain. She is very beautiful, and you must go back to her."

"Violet is just a friend—"

"Please stop. This is too hard. For both of us."

"Listen, I'm doing this for us. We—"

"But I don't want you to. It isn't right. . . . Good-bye, Nelson."

I peeked around the corner in time to see Katya run through the swinging door and disappear into the servants' quarters. Nelson didn't follow her. Instead, he stood for a long moment, staring at the door that separated them. Then his head drooped, his shoulders sagged.

If this had been a scene from a novel, our literature teacher would have pointed out the symbolism of that door, how it represented the division between them: master and servant, rich and poor, gentleman and immigrant. They lived separate lives in separate spheres, with barriers between them that could never be crossed.

Then I slipped from the doorway and hurried back to the party to avoid being caught. I quickly grabbed a glass of punch and sat down in an empty chair to think.

I had been right. Katya and Nelson were in love. How else could I interpret what I had just seen and heard? But it was forbidden love, the most difficult kind. Poor Nelson.

A cynic might have insisted that he was a spoiled rich boy who probably was taking advantage of an innocent girl whom he had no intention of marrying. But I'd seen his reaction when Katya turned away from him, and I didn't think so. Might he even go so far as to marry me—and keep Katya as his mistress on the side? I was pondering the situation when I felt Nelson's warm hand on my shoulder.

"I'm sorry for running off, Violet. I needed to speak to one of the servants. Ah, I see you helped yourself to more punch. Can I get you anything else?"

"No, thank you."

"Would you dance with me, then?"

I let him take me into his arms. We danced as smoothly as before, but now I was very conscious of his hand resting on the small of my back and of his other hand holding mine. I no longer felt comfortable in his arms, knowing the pain I was causing Katya—and perhaps

Nelson as well. I needed to complete my detective work, so I decided to ask him one more question.

"If you had to choose between living in poverty with your true love, or living alone with wealth and success, which would you choose?" This time he didn't laugh.

"I don't think I could choose," he said quietly. "I wouldn't know how to live without money. But I couldn't live alone either." Then he surprised me by asking, "Which would you choose, Violet?"

I thought for a moment and realized that I couldn't choose either. "I would like to think that I'd choose true love," I said. "But I've seen horrendous poverty, and I couldn't bear to live that way, even with a man I loved. I think that the struggle to survive would quickly choke out our love." I knew for the first time that it was true. Yet I couldn't live the way Aunt Agnes did either, having money without love.

"I would be very unhappy living without love," I added, "no matter how much money I had. My Aunt Birdie keeps telling me to make sure I marry for love, but I don't know what to think anymore. . . . Don't people ever find both—love and money?"

"As I said, that's not the way it's usually done in our social circle. It's a sad indictment . . . but it's true."

"Do you think poor people marry for love?"

"Ah, I see we've come full circle. We're back to the differences between rich and poor, aren't we? I'm afraid I don't know the answer to that. I've never been poor—nor do I ever intend to be."

Nelson Kent had a soft heart. He wasn't just a handsome shell. I wasn't in love with him, but I liked him. I considered him a good friend. I wished I could help him solve his dilemma with Katya.

By the time the evening drew to a close, he looked tired and strained. His grandmother announced that dessert and coffee were being served, but I noticed that Katya wasn't among the servants who waited on everyone. I watched Nelson make the effort to put his mask back into place as he conversed with his guests, but I could tell that he wished the party would end. I think we were both relieved when it did.

Chapter

14

V iolet! Come quick! You've received a letter!" Aunt Birdie's voice was breathless with excitement.

It was Aunt Birdie's job to fetch the mail every day, and it broke my heart to see how hopeful she became each time she heard letters slide through the mail slot. She never stopped believing that she would hear from Gilbert. I was tempted to hunt down some of his old letters and mail them to her, one by one, to cheer her. But today, the fact that I had received a letter seemed to cheer her as much as if it were her own.

"It's from your beau, Silas McClure." She said his name with the same glee that a child said "Santa Claus."

"He's not my beau, Aunt Birdie."

"Well, I think he would like to be." She handed me the envelope. I stared at Silas' name on the return address.

"Well, open it up! See what he says!"

I broke the seal and pulled out his letter. Silas had used stationery

164

from a hotel in Cleveland, Ohio. His chunky, schoolboy penmanship made me smile as I quickly skimmed the note.

"Well. . . ?" Aunt Birdie prompted.

"Mr. McClure is going to be in town this week."

"Oh, how nice."

"He would like to take me to the World's Fair on Tuesday."

"Tuesday? Why, that's tomorrow!"

"Yes. I know." He had also mentioned that he'd found a chaperone.

"Florence," Aunt Birdie sang, "Silas McClure is taking our Violet to the fair!"

"Do I know this gentleman?" Grandmother asked, hurrying out to the front hallway where we stood. "I'm responsible for her, you know."

"You met Mr. McClure at the train station," I said. "Remember? The day I arrived?"

"Oh yes. The gentleman who accompanied you from Lockport."

I didn't confirm or deny her assumption. She could think whatever she wanted to about him. Besides, if she was going to withhold information about my mother, why should I tell her about Silas?

"Did you notice what a nice smile Mr. McClure has?" Aunt Birdie asked.

"It's pretty hard not to notice it," I mumbled.

"And he has the most beautiful blue eyes too. They're the color of the sky on an autumn afternoon."

I looked at her in surprise. "An autumn afternoon? Why autumn? Aren't all blue skies the same?"

"Oh no, dear. Of course they aren't. Mr. McClure's eyes aren't summer blue—a summer sky is bleached from the heat. And they're not wintry blue either, when the cold air frosts the sky with silver. No, his eyes are the color of an autumn sky, warmed by the glorious leaves that have turned all those exciting colors."

I stared at her. She was exactly right. Silas McClure was warm and exciting at the same time. And he did have wonderful eyes.

"My Gilbert has blue eyes. Oh, I do hope the weather isn't too stormy in Virginia where he's fighting. I would hate to think of him tramping through the mud or shivering in the rain. Maybe I'll write him a letter to lift his spirits. See how much Mr. McClure's letter has lifted our Violet's spirits?"

I glanced in the mirror and caught myself smiling. And my cheeks were pink. "Excuse me," I mumbled as I raced up the stairs. At school we hadn't been allowed to race up the stairs—or to race anywhere for that matter. *"Slowly, girls. Slowly and gracefully. You must float when you walk."* Lately I seemed to be ignoring a lot of the things I'd learned.

I stuffed Silas' letter into my journal and shoved the journal beneath my mattress. Something about the unseemly Mr. McClure reminded me of the romance novels and true crime stories that Ruth and I had read, and we had kept those illicit books under the mattress too.

I didn't know why, but I had a hard time falling asleep that night. Was I excited about finally visiting the fair or nervous about going out with a man that none of my family members knew? A proper young lady sought her father's approval before courting someone. The young man's background would be thoroughly investigated to make certain that he wasn't a scoundrel. My grandmother could vouch for Louis Decker. Aunt Agnes knew Nelson Kent's family. Maude O'Neill had given Herman Beckett her support. But the only endorsement Silas McClure had was that Aunt Birdie liked his blue eyes. Was I behaving foolishly to trust him?

In truth, the lure of adventure far outweighed any fear I might have felt. I was tired of being a proper young lady, tired of all the social constraints that held me back and tied me down. I wanted the freedom that Aunt Matt's suffragettes had promised me, but I wanted it now. I finally fell asleep, anticipating a taste of that freedom in the morning.

My first thought upon awakening was of Silas McClure. What if he arrived in his baggy plaid salesman's suit and had his hair slicked with oil again? And what if someone from Nelson's social circle saw me with him at the fair? I never would be invited to another party. Aunt Agnes would disown me.

While it was true that Silas had looked presentable the last time he had called on me, I made up my mind to plead illness and stay home if his clothes and his hair were too embarrassing. My only reason for allowing him to escort me in the first place was so that he could take me to my mother's address.

When I opened the door he was grinning from ear-to-ear, as if he'd just won a thousand dollars—or maybe stolen it.

I breathed a sigh of relief. He obviously hadn't replenished his supply of Macassar oil yet, and his wavy brown hair looked clean and neat. So did his plain dark suit. He smelled faintly of shaving cream, and I noticed that he'd shaved so closely he had nicked himself in two spots. Was he nervous about seeing me—or too cheap to pay for a barber?

But he had come to the door alone.

"Good morning, Silas dear," Aunt Birdie said, hugging him like a long-lost friend. "It's wonderful to see you again."

"Great to see you too, Mrs. Casey."

"Where is our chaperone?" I asked in surprise.

"They wanted to wait outside."

"They. . . ?"

He gestured behind him, and I saw a woman in a long black dress standing by the curb with a short, bearded man in a straw hat. The woman was very tall and evidently very modest. In spite of the warm day, she wore a long-sleeved dress and a large black hat with a veil that covered her face. Her outfit was very much out of fashion unless she was in mourning. And if there had been a death in the family, why was she going to the fair?

"I figured if one chaperone was a good thing then two might be even better," Silas explained.

"Would they like to come in so you can introduce them properly?"

"No, they'd rather wait outside. I'll introduce everybody on the way there."

"Are they relatives of yours?" I asked. I turned to the hall mirror and fussed with my hatpin, stalling for time. From the moment I'd opened the door to him, my heart had begun beating like an African drum, and I was no longer sure I wanted to accompany him if he was going to have this effect on me.

"Nope. They're just friends of mine."

"Has she had a death in the family?" I whispered.

"I have no idea," he whispered back. "Are you ready?"

"I-I guess so . . . Maybe I should take my parasol . . . for the sun." It might also come in handy as a weapon if I needed to defend myself.

"Good-bye, you two," Aunt Birdie cheered. "Have fun!"

"I wager we will," Silas said. He offered me his arm and we walked down the front steps to where the chaperones waited. "These are my friends Josephine and Robert. And this is Violet Hayes, the lady I've been talking your ear off about."

"I'm pleased to meet you," I said, wondering if they had last names.

"Yeah."

"Likewise."

It was apparent that Josephine had never been to charm school.

"Did I exaggerate when I told you how pretty Violet is?" Silas asked, nudging Josephine in the ribs.

"She's lovely," Josephine said. "Let's get going." Her voice sounded hoarse, as if she had a cold. Perhaps she needed a dose of Dr. Dean's Blood Builder.

I couldn't get a very good look at Robert—he wore his hat down so low it nearly covered his eyes, and the rest of his face was hidden behind a bushy brown beard and exuberant mustache. But Josephine was very homely, and apparently quite hirsute—poor thing. I saw a fringe of dark hair poking out between her long sleeves and her gloves. She seemed very self-conscious about her appearance—and I would be too if I were as unpleasant looking as she was. Both chaperones kept their faces averted and their eyes lowered.

"Do you mind taking a streetcar?" Silas asked. "I can hail a cab if you want, but it might take a while to find one."

"I don't mind the streetcar if the others don't."

"They're fine with it."

I glanced over my shoulder. The two stayed several paces behind us as we walked to the streetcar stop. I wanted to be polite and include them in our conversation, but it was almost as if they were avoiding me. Maybe they had never played the role of chaperones before.

"It seems rude not to include them in our conversation, Mr. McClure. Should we slow down for them?"

"They're fine," Silas said. "They're as excited about going to the fair as I am."

I would have to take his word on faith because their grim expressions revealed little excitement. When they turned their backs on me and began whispering to each other as we waited for the streetcar, I saw no sense in worrying about being polite.

"By the way, will we be passing anywhere near LaSalle Street?" I asked Silas. This time I had remembered to bring my mother's address with me.

"LaSalle Street? Not really. Why?"

"There's someone I've been hoping to visit while I'm here in Chicago. Her address is on LaSalle Street."

"Oh, yeah, that's right. You showed it to me the day we arrived in town."

"Might it be possible to stop there on our way home?"

"Yeah, sure. We can arrange that." My heart leaped with excitement at the prospect. At last!

We rode the streetcar for several blocks—Silas and I sharing a seat, our chaperones sitting in the rear of the car—until we reached the south side elevated train station. The tracks were the oddest things I'd ever seen, suspended in the air above our heads on trestle-like bridges. We would have to climb a set of stairs in order to board them. I instinctively ducked as a train rumbled into the station and screeched to a halt overhead, blocking out the sun.

"What do you think?" Silas shouted, pointing up.

"Quite impressive," I shouted back. "I had heard that the city was building a set of train tracks up in the air, but I couldn't imagine such a thing."

"These are specially built to carry the crowds to the fair."

Another locomotive roared into the station as we climbed the stairs, and I had to grip my hat to keep it from blowing away in the wind. I felt the metal scaffolding shake beneath my feet.

"I hear they're planning to extend these elevated trains until they make a loop all around the city," Silas said. "Aren't they something?"

I didn't want to hurt his feelings, but I thought the steel framework was quite ugly. The trains did little to beautify the city and might better have been buried underground, as they were in other cities.

"It seems a little scary, doesn't it?" I shouted above the noise. "I mean, it's not every day that you see trains up in the air, above our heads."

"I think they're great! I get all pepped up, don't you? All that power and energy—it's contagious!"

"Yes." It must have been the excitement of the trains because my heart was banging like a factory in full swing. Our train arrived, and once again Josephine and Robert took seats well away from us when we boarded. "Have they ever chaperoned anyone before?" I asked.

"I don't know. Why?"

"Well, I suppose it's nice of them to give us privacy, but I feel rude for not including them in our conversation."

"They aren't very talkative."

I looked down at the streets below as the train propelled us through the air at breakneck speed, squealing into stations to pick up more passengers, then racing out again. In no time at all I caught my first glimpse of the fair up ahead. The day was magnificent without a cloud in the sky, and the white buildings and silvery water seemed to glow in the sunlight.

"Oh, it's wonderful!" I breathed.

"It's like a little piece of heaven just floated down to earth," Silas said when he saw my reaction. "You can see why they call it the White City."

"Beautiful doesn't seem descriptive enough."

"You should see it at night, all lit up with electric lights." I recalled Nelson Kent saying the same thing.

Silas paid my admission fee of fifty cents, but I thought it odd that our chaperones paid their own fare. As soon as we entered the gates, Josephine and Robert took the lead, walking briskly ahead of us as if they had an appointment to keep. Silas and I hurried to stay apace.

"That's the Transportation Building," he said, pointing to our left. "And that enormous one across the water is Manufactures and Liberal Arts. It has a walkway up on top, if you want to go up for a good view later on. And look—we can ride around the lagoon in a gondola."

"Oh, I would love to go for a gondola ride!" It was like a scene from a travel book with the gondolier in his brightly colored costume, propelling his passengers across the tranquil waters. The pristine white buildings in the background had arches and pillars and graceful statues. "This is amazing, Silas! It's like another world. I've always wanted to travel to faraway places."

"You name any country or state you want and they have a pavilion

171

or a display here. You can see the world for only two bits—Japan, Egypt, Africa . . . They even have an Eskimo village with reindeer."

Silas' childlike excitement was contagious. I didn't know which way to look or where I wanted to go first. I wanted to see it all, but Josephine and Robert had raced so far ahead of us that Silas and I had to hurry down the path or risk losing them.

"Why are they in such a hurry?" I panted.

"Josephine wants to see the Woman's Pavilion."

"I do too. My Aunt Matilda has been singing its praises."

Silas and I finally paused to rest once we arrived in front of the stately pavilion. "That's the Wooded Isle in the middle of the lagoon," he told me. "And that's the Swedish Pavilion on the other side with the thatched towers. That castlelike one is the Fisheries Building. They have the most amazing aquariums inside, with the strangest and most beautiful underwater creatures you could ever imagine."

"Where did our chaperones go?" I asked, glancing around.

"I think they went inside already."

"Without us? Shouldn't we go in with them?"

"You don't really want to see the Woman's Pavilion, do you? It's boring, Violet. The Midway is a lot more fun."

"I don't know . . . um . . . I guess—"

"We can meet up with them later. Come on."

"Where are we going?"

"To the big wheel, of course! You said you wanted to ride Mr. Ferris' wonderful wheel, remember? I thought we'd go there first."

"Alone?"

"Look—there it is." He took my shoulders and swung me around, pointing into the distance.

"Wow!" The moment I saw the huge mechanical wheel poking into the sky I no longer cared about Josephine and Robert. We hurried toward the broad Midway Plaisance and plunged into the buzzing crowd of people.

"I guess we really don't need chaperones in a crowd this big," I said.

"I don't understand why you need them at all. It's almost the twentieth century, you know? All this fuss over manners and things—that's from the olden days, isn't it?"

I couldn't seem to compose a reply. "I ... um ... I guess the assumption is that women should be protected."

"From what? People say women are helpless, but I don't buy it. You strike me as a sensible, intelligent woman. I'll wager you're quite capable of taking care of yourself. In fact, you've been gripping that parasol like it's a weapon ever since we left home. I'd sure hate to come between you and that thing." I had to laugh at his words. I also eased my grip on the umbrella handle.

The wild, chaotic Midway seemed like an entirely different world from the symmetry and beauty of the White City. Even the crowds seemed different. These were boisterous, commonplace folk, unlike the more genteel crowd I'd seen strolling past the lagoons.

Here was another example of the many contrasts I'd encountered since coming to Chicago: Nelson Kent's luxurious life compared to Irina's desolate one. Louis Decker's passion for God versus the religious indifference I'd grown up with. The narrow roles I had assumed all women must play contrasted with the opportunities that Aunt Matt and her friends foresaw for women. And the strict manners and rules I'd learned from Madame Beauchamps, which couldn't compare with the delicious freedom I felt walking down the Midway with Silas McClure—without a chaperone.

Silas stood a head taller than me, and it was hard to hold on to his arm in the crowded streets. I lost my grip momentarily when someone jostled us, and Silas reached for my hand as naturally as if we were children. Once again, the moment his strong, warm palm touched mine, the sensation was like gripping the wrong end of a flat iron.

"I would hate to lose you in this mob," he said when he saw my reaction. He lifted our entwined hands slightly and said, "This is so we don't get separated."

It was highly improper—wasn't it? But hadn't I held Nelson Kent's hand when we'd danced together? What was the difference?

I quickly forgot about propriety as we passed all sorts of fascinating displays—the Libby Glass Works, a Colorado gold mine, a rustic log cabin, the Hagenbeck Animal Show, an Irish village, a Japanese bazaar. The accompanying smells of woodsmoke and animals and exotic spices entranced me.

"What are those drums?" I asked. I hoped it wasn't the sound of my heart pounding for all to hear.

"There's a Javanese village on the right. We can go there later, if you want." The comfortable way he said "we" both frightened and thrilled me.

"I wish I had the freedom to go places on my own and make my own decisions," I said. "I've had my father hovering over me all my life when I wasn't in school. And my school was very strict. They told us that rules and chaperones were there to protect women. But you're right—who says I need to be protected?"

"I'll wager those rules will be out-of-date in a few years."

"Do you think so? That's what my Aunt Matt thinks too. She's a suffragette. What do you think of women voting?"

"I don't know. Why do they want to vote?"

I tried to recall what Aunt Matt had told me. "They want to be able to elect people who will represent their interests—women's interests."

"That makes sense to me." Silas McClure seemed to have very modern views as far as women were concerned. I decided to probe further as we walked past a genuine Bedouin Arab with his camel.

"What if you were ill and the only physician available was a woman. Would you let her care for you?"

"Sure, why not? But I can't say as I've ever met a woman doctor. I'll wager there aren't too many of them, are there?"

"My aunt spoke as if there were at least a few."

We arrived at the base of the wheel, and it was even more amazing up close than from a distance. The intricate spokes were enormous and graceful—but they looked quite insufficient to bear the weight of dozens of passenger carriages the size of streetcars. I had to look up and up to see the very top of the wheel—as high as the clouds, or so it seemed to me. My knees trembled as Silas paid our fares and we joined the line of waiting passengers.

"That's the Algerian Village over there," he said. "Maybe we can come back and get something to eat there later. They have amazing food with flavors like you've never tasted before."

"I hear that people in foreign countries eat all manner of interesting things."

"Yeah, like monkey meat and alligator and water buffalo," he said excitedly.

"What's the most adventurous thing you've ever eaten?"

"Rattlesnake."

"You didn't! Where? Were you stranded in the desert for days and days with nothing to eat after bandits attacked your train, and you had to kill the snake with your bare hands and eat it raw?"

"No," Silas laughed, "but I think I'll tell your version of the story from now on. It was in a saloon in Texas cattle country. They served pretty decent food for a saloon, so when I saw rattlesnake on the menu I figured I had to try it."

"You're very adventurous, Silas. What did it taste like?"

"A little bit like chicken. Only chewier." The line moved forward as the group in front of us boarded the wheel. We would board next. I wondered if Silas could feel my hand trembling as he held it in his.

"I read somewhere that the wheel is 265 feet high and can carry a total of 2,160 passengers at a time," he said.

"How can you remember all that?"

"I'm pretty good with numbers and things."

Finally it was our turn to step into the enormous car. Silas quickly pulled me over to the front window. "So we'll have the best view," he said.

The wheel operator closed the door and bolted it shut.

"Hang on!" Silas said.

His warning came too late. The car lurched as it began to ascend, and I fell forward against him. His arms encircled me, and he held me against his chest for a moment until I adjusted to the motion and regained my balance. He smelled good, like the barbershop in Lockport that I used to visit with my father on Saturday mornings. Silas had strong arms and a rock-hard chest.

"You okay?" he asked.

"Yes. Thank you." I pulled away reluctantly. "I lost my footing for a moment."

I had danced with Nelson and other gentlemen, but never before had I been held so closely by any of them. Hugging a man felt wonderfully different from hugging a woman's pillow-soft body. The only man I could recall embracing was my father, who had an ample belly-cushion in front. I envied Aunt Birdie's simple freedom of embracing everyone. Madame B. would wag her finger at me, but I began to hope that the car would lurch again so I could fall back into Silas' arms.

He gently took my hand in his again on the long, slow ride to the top. "Isn't this something?" he breathed.

"It sure is!" I gripped his hand tightly in return. In fact, our hands might have been glued together.

I risked looking down as we climbed and had the peculiar sensation that my stomach was sinking toward my toes. I had never been up this high before—and certainly had never dangled from such a spindly structure before. The sensation was dizzying. We were hanging over empty air, suspended from the slowly turning wheel. I tried to take it all in at once, watching the intricate steel supports drifting past, then gazing down at the ground, then at the distant view of the fairgrounds and the lake and the smoky city on the horizon.

"Wow! This is frightening—but fun!"

"I knew you would like it."

"I wish I could fly!"

"I know what you mean. I want to go for a ride in a balloon someday. They have a tethered one here at the fair that you can go up in, but I doubt it's as exciting as a real balloon ride."

"Tell me about your family, Silas. Where did you grow up? Is your family as adventurous as you are?"

"I was raised on a farm in Ohio outside a town you probably never heard of. I'm the fourth of seven kids. I left home after high school for the excitement of the city and never looked back. I'd see the whole world if I could afford it."

I hadn't thought of Silas as a thief all morning, but I suddenly had an idea how I could find out if he was one.

"If you could choose, would you rather be the captain of a pirate ship or the captain of a warship?"

"A pirate ship. No question about it." Somehow I knew that would be his choice.

"You have to tell me why."

"Wars are so long and drawn out and pointless. Nobody really wins them, do they? I don't hate anyone badly enough to fight them in a war. Besides, the captain of a warship has to follow orders. But the captain of a pirate ship, now he's his own boss. That's the life for me. Sailing the seas, seeking adventure. Finding buried treasure . . ."

"But pirates are outlaws."

"I know," he said with a grin. "And they get to hijack sailing vessels and carry off gold doubloons and beautiful maidens."

"You must have read the same adventure stories that I did."

"Which ship would you choose, Violet?"

He was gazing into my eyes, and it was so romantic to be climbing above the fairgrounds with an exciting, adventurous man that I lost my train of thought altogether. It took me a moment to remember the question.

"Well . . . I don't think women get to be ship captains."

"But what if you could be one?"

"If I could? . . . I guess I would want to be the captain a pirate ship too."

"Why?"

"I've been taught to follow the rules all my life. It might be fun to see what it was like to break a few."

"You're the most interesting woman I've ever met."

My heart was booming like a bass drum. I turned away to look at the view and to remind myself why I had agreed to come with him. Silas was going to help me find my mother on the way home. Winning his affections had not been part of my plan.

"I love your questions, Violet. Ask me another one."

"All right . . ." It took me a moment to think of one. "If you had to choose between going blind and never seeing the face of your beloved again, or becoming permanently deaf, so that you could never hear music or a child's voice, which would you choose?"

"I'd choose to be deaf. I think I would miss seeing beautiful things more than hearing them. Besides, people don't really need to talk, do they? They can say so much more with their eyes . . . don't you think?"

I made the mistake of looking up into his eyes, which were as blue as the distant lake. I felt breathless, as if I were treading water, trying not to drown. I quickly turned away and looked back out at the lake.

"Is that a boat out there?" I asked, pointing.

"It looks like one. . . . But tell me how you would answer that question, Violet. Would you rather be blind or deaf?"

"The same as you, I think. The world is much too beautiful to miss. Just look at that view."

We had been stopping to let passengers on and off as we'd slowly ascended, but now the wheel paused at the very top, swaying slightly in the breeze. The sounds from the Midway had grown faint, and a hush seemed to fall over the other passengers in our car as we gazed down from the dizzying height. But the view was wasted on Silas McClure. He never took his eyes off me.

"We've stopped," I murmured.

"To tell you the truth," Silas said softly, "I hope we get stuck up here for a few days."

"Me too." I didn't want the ride to end either. But a moment later I felt the sinking sensation in my stomach as our car started down again.

"Ask me one more question, Violet."

I decided to ask the same one I'd asked Nelson Kent—the one neither of us had been able to answer.

"If you had to choose between being desperately poor but in love, or being enormously wealthy but alone, which would you choose?"

"I'd choose love. A thousand times over. Life wouldn't be worth living without it."

"But you would be poor, remember?"

"I don't care. People get along fine without money all the time. But money can't buy the happiness that love brings."

I thought of how sad Nelson had seemed after Katya had disappeared through the servants' door, and I wondered if Silas was right.

"You believe in love, then?" I asked.

"Absolutely! Don't you?"

"I don't know. I was told that my parents married for love, yet somehow it died. I don't know why. Now they're divorced."

"Gosh, I'm sorry to hear that."

"My Aunt Birdie was madly in love with her husband, but as you've probably guessed, he died in the war. Now she's so lost and lonely without him."

"I know it seems very sad. But I'll wager that if you asked her, she would gladly trade her house and all of her money to have him back."

"You're probably right."

"But you haven't answered the question, Violet. You and your grandmother and your aunts seem pretty well off. Would you give it all up for love?"

"I'm not sure. My grandmother does charity work among the immigrants, and she took me with her the other day. I saw the terrible living conditions in those tenements, and I'm afraid my love might wear thin if I had to live in a place like that and struggle every day just to get enough to eat."

"But you said that the other choice was to be rich but alone, right?"

"I know. And I wouldn't like that either."

"Have you ever been in love, Violet?"

"No."

"Then maybe it's not fair to try to answer that question until you've experienced it."

Something about the way he was smiling made me wonder. "Have you been in love, Mr. McClure?"

"Yes, Miss Hayes. I have felt myself falling in love—just once. That's why I know I'd give up everything else for it."

He was gazing at me as if I was the one! I couldn't breathe. He was like a magician, dangling a shining object in front of me—back and forth—until I was hypnotized by him.

Suddenly the car lurched as it came to a halt at the bottom. This time I stumbled backward, away from him instead of into his arms, and my good sense returned. Silas McClure was a snake charmer, a salesman, and he'd been performing his trade on me. That's what thieves and con artists like him did, feeding their phony lines to weak-willed women and spinning their charms. He was obviously a master at this trade and I had nearly fallen for it. Fortunately the ride ended so I could come to reality.

"Wasn't that wonderful?" Silas asked. "I could ride all day."

"Yes, me too." I needed to let go of his hand and break the spell completely, so I slowly slid my hand from his and took his elbow again. I kept a safe distance between us as we walked.

"What shall we see now?" Silas asked. "You want to see the Street in Cairo, or the African dancers, or—"

"I think we had better find Josephine and Robert first."

"They're okay."

"I'm sure they are, Silas, but if someone were to see us walking together without a chaperone, it might ruin my reputation." I felt scared, not of him but of the way I had reacted to him. I was being drawn to him—and he was thoroughly unsuitable!

"Okay. Sure. We can go look for them." At least he was cheerful about it.

As we neared the main steps to the Woman's Pavilion, Josephine suddenly materialized out of the shadows. One moment no one had been there, and the next—there she stood, as if she had been hiding in the bushes, watching for us. She glanced all around nervously as we approached, then hurried forward and took Silas' other arm, steering us away from the building.

"We gotta go," she said.

"Wait, wait. What's the hurry?" Silas asked.

"I can't say in front of . . ." Josephine nodded toward me.

"Will you excuse us for a moment, Violet?" He pulled Josephine aside to talk. Their voices were so soft I could hear only snatches of their conversation.

"What happened?"

I heard Josephine say the words *caught* and *money*. My stomach began to sink as it had when riding the wheel.

"Can't you take care of things?" Silas asked. His voice rose in anger and so did Josephine's.

"Don't be stupid. I gotta leave right now and you gotta come with me."

Silas exhaled, then turned back toward me and linked my arm through his. "I'm sorry to end our day in a rush, Violet, but I'm afraid we have to go."

All three of us started walking briskly back toward the elevated train station. It was the first time I'd ever seen Silas without a smile on his face.

"But we just got here. And what about Robert? We're not going to leave him here, are we?"

They answered simultaneously: "He got tied up," from Silas. "He has business to take care of," from Josephine. They couldn't leave the fair quickly enough. Could what I suspected really be true? Were Silas and his friends truly thieves?

When we reached the station, Josephine scanned the platform as if searching for someone while Silas purchased our tickets. He offered me a seat on the bench while we waited for the next train to arrive, but he didn't sit. He paced in front of me, and Josephine paced a short distance away. Their eyes roved the station like searchlights.

Silas barely spoke on the ride home except to say, "I'm sorry, Violet." He had forgotten all about taking me to the address on LaSalle Street, and when I saw his worried expression, I didn't dare bring it up. Once again, I'd been thwarted in my search for my mother.

"This wasn't at all how I wanted our day to end," he said when we finally reached my front door. "Can you ever forgive me?"

"Of course. I enjoyed riding the wheel. . . ."

"Yeah. Me too."

"But I don't understand why—"

"I'm so sorry, Violet. I have to run."

He left me standing at the door and jogged down the block to the streetcar stop where we'd left Josephine. He didn't look back. I felt as though I'd been tossed from a train like a sack of mail. I was fighting tears of disappointment and frustration when Aunt Birdie greeted me in the front hallway with a hug.

"Back so soon? Did you have a nice time, dear? Why didn't you invite him in?"

I couldn't reply. How could I explain something that I didn't understand myself?

"You're crying, Violet. What happened?"

"Nothing. Our chaperones were . . . were called away. So we had to come home."

"Oh, what a shame. I would be disappointed too if I couldn't spend the day with my beau."

I started to protest that Silas wasn't my beau, then stopped. The real reason I was upset, I told myself, was because I still hadn't found my mother.

Wasn't it?

Chapter

15

Wednesday, June 21, 1893

Would you like to come with me to the settlement house?" my grandmother asked the following morning. "I think Louis Decker will be there. And we won't be cooking this time."

"Maybe another day. I'm supposed to play the piano for Louis tomorrow, and I really need to practice." I also needed a break from all of my would-be suitors after my unsettling day with Silas McClure.

I sat down at the keyboard and was warming up with a few scales when I remembered Aunt Agnes. If she found me at home today, she would want me to go calling with her. Maybe I should feign illness. Aunt Agnes was determined to find me a husband, and she was firing her Cupid's arrows at Nelson Kent.

I couldn't erase the image of him and Katya kissing. It had been like a scene from a romance novel. What would it be like to be kissed with such passion? Nelson had told her, *"Violet is just a friend . . . I'm doing this for us. . . ."* Doing what? Was Nelson using me?

I pounded out another set of scales on the piano. When I looked up, Aunt Matt stood in the parlor doorway with her hat, gloves, and parasol.

"I'm leaving now to work at the Suffrage Association."

I swiveled around on the piano stool and stood. Aunt Matt was the one person who wouldn't pressure me to find a husband.

"May I come with you?" I asked.

She looked surprised. "Certainly."

"Um . . . you're not marching today, are you?"

"No, not today. Why?"

"I-I need to know which shoes to wear." In truth, I had no desire to get arrested and end up in a jail cell alongside Silas and his thieving pals, Robert and Josephine—or whatever their real names were.

"We're not marching today; we're stuffing envelopes," Aunt Matt explained while I fetched my hat and gloves. "Next month is our anniversary rally. We need to spread the word so we'll get a good turnout."

"Yes, of course." I nodded as if I was as concerned with the turnout as she was, but as we headed toward the streetcar stop, I began formulating a scheme of my own.

"Aunt Matt? I noticed that we passed LaSalle Street the last time I went to the association with you, and I was wondering . . . Do you think we could make a stop on our way there? There's someone I've been meaning to visit who lives on LaSalle Street." I held my breath, hoping she wouldn't ask for a name.

"It will have to be on our way home, after our work is finished. They're expecting me at headquarters at ten-thirty sharp."

"Yes, I understand. That will be fine. On the way home, then."

My heart raced with excitement. Finally, I would see my mother. I bit my lip to keep from grinning foolishly and told myself to calm down. I had all morning to plan what I would say to her. In the meantime, I didn't want Aunt Matt to learn my true intentions.

"What will the rally be about?" I asked her.

"This July marks the forty-fifth anniversary of the first Women's Rights Convention in America. That was when Elizabeth Cady Stanton, Lucretia Mott, and the other women drew up our Declaration of Sentiments and Resolutions."

"Is that when the Suffrage Association got started?" A streetcar rounded our corner as I asked the question, the horses' hooves clomping noisily on the cobblestone street. Aunt Matt waited until the vehicle stopped and we'd taken our seats before answering.

"One of our organization's founders, Lucretia Mott, was a Quaker minister. They allow women to preach, you know. The Quakers also believe in equal education for men and women. Lucretia met another one of our leaders, Elizabeth Cady Stanton, at the World Anti-Slavery Convention in London, England. Elizabeth and her husband had traveled to England on their honeymoon just to attend the convention."

I nodded and began sliding down in my seat, already sorry that I had asked. I had forgotten how loudly Aunt Matt lectured—and how openly the other passengers stared at us.

"Several of the delegates arriving from America were women," she continued. "But they—along with Elizabeth and Lucretia—were forbidden to take part in the meetings with the men. Can you imagine traveling all that way and then not being allowed to participate? Simply because they were women? Instead, all of the women, even the duly elected delegates, were forced to sit in a separate gallery."

"That's terrible." My voice sounded like a whisper compared to hers.

"Of course they were outraged. Mr. Stanton was entirely sympathetic and supportive, but most husbands aren't, you know. That's when the two women decided to work together for women's rights here in America. They held the first convention in 1848."

"That seems like a long time ago."

"You're right, Violet. Progress has been much too slow."

My mind drifted back to my conversation with Silas yesterday.

He'd seemed sure that in the new century many of the restrictions on women, such as chaperones, would be considered outmoded. "How long until women have the same rights as men?" I asked.

"Well, even though victories have been few, we are making progress nonetheless. Three years ago, Wyoming became the first state to grant women the right to vote. Colorado will follow suit this year. We're focusing on voting rights because then we'll be in a position to influence lawmakers to make other changes."

"Is that why men don't want women to vote? Because we'll change things?"

"Yes, that's part of the reason. It's also because they would have to acknowledge the fact that women are capable of thinking for themselves. They would have to do away with the belief that a woman needs her father or her husband to make decisions for her."

"I want that freedom now, Aunt Matt. I wish I didn't need a chaperone, and that I could go wherever I wanted and do whatever I wanted instead of what my father wants me to do. Aunt Agnes said he sent me here to find a husband."

"And he probably told Agnes to keep you well away from me. . . . Here, this is where we get off," she said, rising from her seat. She set off down the street, walking at an even brisker pace than usual. Evidently our conversation had her up in arms.

"I understand why you don't want me to marry a rich husband," I said, puffing to keep up, "but how can I support myself if I don't get married?"

"Someday it will be different. Someday women will be able to earn a decent living, and we won't be dependent on our husbands or fathers. I'm not against marriage, Violet. It's the idea of marrying someone just for his money that seems wrong. There should be qualities in the man that draw you to make the commitment to him besides his money."

"Do you believe in love, Aunt Matt?"

She paused before replying. Too late, I remembered Aunt Birdie telling me that Aunt Matt had once been in love.

"It's better to marry someone for love than for his money," she finally said.

We reached the association headquarters and went inside. Aunt Matt introduced me to the president.

"It's so nice to meet you, Violet. We are very grateful for your help."

"I'm glad that I could come."

She and the other ladies seemed like gentle, intelligent women, not militant radicals or men-haters. We sat around a huge worktable with stacks of letters and envelopes piled in front of us. It was mindless work, folding letters and stuffing them into envelopes and licking them shut. I enjoyed it more than peeling vegetables at the settlement house though. Better to have a dry tongue and a few paper cuts than hands stained with beet juice—not that the state of my hands mattered much. I didn't plan on holding hands with Nelson anytime soon, nor with the devout Louis Decker—and never again with Silas McClure.

The women chatted while they worked. I wasn't paying too much attention until one of them said, "By the way, ladies, did you hear that there was another robbery at the Woman's Pavilion yesterday?"

I stopped licking. My entire body began to tingle as if I were being slowly submerged in boiling water.

"I didn't see anything in this morning's paper about it," Aunt Matt said. "What happened?"

"You know how the lady managers have their cookbooks for sale? Well, a pair of thieves came into the building, and one of them grabbed the money box when no one was looking."

My cheeks must have bloomed like hothouse roses as the heat rose to my face. I hoped no one would notice.

"That's the third robbery we've had, isn't it?"

"No, it's the fifth! And the worst one yet. In all of the other incidents, the women had things stolen from their purses. This time they snatched an entire strongbox full of cash. There were two of them, working together."

I stopped breathing. The Great Fire couldn't have burned hotter than I did.

"That's dreadful!" all the ladies agreed. "How frightening."

"They figure that the thieves must have been watching the sales booth for some time, because they knew exactly what they were doing. One of them distracted the clerk while the other one grabbed the money box. But what they didn't know was that we've hired the Pinkertons. They were guarding the pavilion at the time of the robbery, and they came running to the rescue as soon as the theft occurred. They caught one of the thieves—the one with the cash box, fortunately—but the other thief slipped away."

The room began to spin. I had to grip the edge of the table to keep from sliding out of my chair. I was involved with a gang of thieves! Silas McClure and his friends truly were thieves—and I had helped them escape! Did that make me an accomplice?

"Have they had thefts in any of the other pavilions?" someone asked.

"A few, I think. But not nearly as many as ours. We're presumed to be an easy target because we're 'helpless' women."

"I guess we showed them! We were clever enough to hire our own guards, weren't we?"

"Yes, but it's very costly to have Pinkerton's men there all the time."

"Where were the police? Doesn't the fair have security people?"

"They have the Columbian guards, but have you seen them? They're all young pups in their twenties with no experience doing police work. They can barely help lost children find their parents, let alone deal with professional thieves."

"What's this country coming to when one must hire private investigators?"

"W-were the thieves men or women?" I asked when I finally could speak.

"I don't know. I've never heard of women thieves, have you? But I suppose it's possible. Why?"

"No reason. But since it's the Woman's Pavilion, I just wondered . . ."

I suddenly recalled how oddly Josephine had behaved and how strange she had looked with her homely face and hairy arms. I added all of the clues together: her tall frame and unfashionable clothes, her hoarse voice and lack of manners. Of course! She had been a man disguised as a woman! I had been stupid not to figure it out the moment I met her. Silas McClure had intentionally deceived me.

I heard my aunt talking with the other women, but their voices grew softer and softer, drowned out by the rushing sound in my ears. The worktable slid out of focus. I felt as dizzy as I had when riding the giant wheel. I closed my eyes to make the dizziness stop, and the next thing I knew, Aunt Matt was calling my name.

"Violet. . . ? Violet! Are you all right?" She gripped my shoulders and gave me a little shake. "What's wrong? You look as though you're about to faint."

"She's as white as those envelopes."

"Is her corset too tight? Maybe she should unlace it."

"I-I don't feel well," I murmured. But it had nothing to do with my corset.

"It's my fault," Aunt Matt said. "I should have waited for you to eat some breakfast."

"Take her into the privy, Matilda, so she can unlace her corset."

"Corsets should be outlawed. It's a crime that young girls have to torture themselves simply for the sake of attracting a man."

"I-it's not my corset," I said. I didn't think I could stand, let alone walk to the privy. Someone brought me a glass of water, and I took a long drink.

"There. Feeling better?"

"Yes. Thank you. I guess I got dry after licking all those envelopes and stamps."

"If women ran the world, envelopes wouldn't need to be licked," Aunt Matt declared. "Stamps either."

I felt like one of the main characters in a *True Crime* story or Ruth's *Illustrated Police News*. If Pinkerton's men had captured all four of us yesterday, my picture might have been on the cover of it!

"I should take you home."

"I think it might be better if I stayed seated, Aunt Matt. I'll be all right. I want to help finish the envelopes."

"You've been burning the candle at both ends, haven't you, young lady? Rising at dawn to run all over the slums with Florence and going to parties with Agnes until all hours of the night? And weren't you at the fair yesterday?"

"Y-yes. I was."

Should I tell the authorities what I knew? But I really didn't know anything at all about "Josephine" or how to find him. No wonder Silas hadn't told me his last name. I had Silas' business card with his post office box information. I could give that to the authorities.

"What did you think of the fair, Violet? Did you see the Woman's Pavilion?"

"Just from the outside. I-I didn't go in."

"Good. I'd like to show it to you," Aunt Matt said. "They sponsor wonderful lectures by prominent women on all manner of subjects. We'll go some afternoon when the mailing is finished."

I wasn't sure I wanted to return to the scene of the crime, so to speak, but I smiled and said, "I would like that."

The conversation switched to other topics, and the opportunity to report what I knew about the robbery passed. I felt relieved. I really didn't want the police to arrest Silas. After all, he was with me at the time of the robbery. He wasn't responsible for his friends' actions, was he? But I made up my mind to have nothing more to do with Mr. McClure.

"Let me give you and your niece a ride home, Matilda," someone offered when we'd finished our morning's work. "She still looks pale to me."

I started to protest, but Aunt Matt overruled me. "Yes, thank you, Emily. We accept. That's very kind of you." I clenched my fists in frustration and disappointment. I couldn't impose upon Aunt Matt's friend by asking her to stop at LaSalle Street to visit my mother.

By the time we arrived home, I'd recovered from my shock and no longer felt faint. My heart was beating normally again—until Aunt Birdie greeted me at the door with an envelope.

"Violet! You've received *another* letter."

"W-who is it from?"

"Someone named"—she read the return address—"Herman Beckett."

"Oh no." I closed my eyes in dismay. I had forgotten all about him.

"Who is he, dear?" Aunt Birdie asked.

"A gentleman I know from back home in Lockport. Mr. Beckett courted me a few times before I came here."

"Oh, how nice."

I ripped open the envelope without benefit of an opener, guessing what it might say. Herman's printing was so small and neat it might have been made on a typing machine. The somber black ink nearly bled through the page. I scanned it quickly, wincing at every sentence.

"You have such a long face, Violet. I do hope it isn't bad news," Aunt Birdie said. "Is your young man fighting the Rebels?"

"No, Mr. Beckett isn't fighting. He's coming to call on me this weekend. He wants me to go to the fair with him and his sister."

"Don't you care to go with him?"

I not only didn't care to go with Herman Beckett, I didn't care if I ever returned to the fair.

"No," I sighed, "but I already promised him that I would go. My father gave Herman permission to court me. He likes Herman."

And so did Maude O'Neill, which was reason enough for me to hate him. But Herman was also my best source of information on Maude and my best hope of proving that she had murdered her first husband. If I wanted to stop Father's wedding, I had better not eliminate Herman from my life just yet.

"I suppose I'll go with him," I said.

"Oh, how nice."

That night I tried to sort out my thoughts by writing in my diary. I felt so confused. Suitors seemed to be piling up like cordwood in the three short weeks I'd lived in Chicago. I doodled on the page as I contemplated my gentlemen callers.

Nelson Kent was first and foremost. I did love his splendid life—most of the time—the food and the dancing, if not the incessant pretending. But I suspected that he was really in love with Katya, and that he was using me to gain his father's fortune. His actions might be deceitful, but they were no worse than making me an accomplice in a theft ring.

Stop thinking about Silas McClure!

Louis Decker lived a world away from Nelson Kent. Louis was doing something worthwhile with his life, helping the poor and needy. But I had no desire to join him in that work if it involved slaving in a kitchen, regardless of how worthwhile it might be. I had promised to help Louis tomorrow, and I should have stayed home today and practiced the piano. Then I never would have discovered what a no-good dirty-rotten scoundrel Silas McClure really was. At least Louis Decker was honest and upright and law-abiding, unlike . . .

I pushed Silas from my thoughts a second time.

And now Herman Beckett would reenter my life, arriving this weekend to take me to the fair. Maybe he would behave differently while on a holiday in the city. Maybe he would be more relaxed, less somber. I would have to take care not to play my "choosing" game with him. Herman didn't have a playful, imaginative bone in his body. He had become quite upset when I'd asked him if he'd rather be a horse or a carriage. Silas, on the other hand, had loved my questions. *"Ask me another one, Violet . . ."*

"Stop it!" I said aloud.

Silas McClure was part of a gang of thieves. Yet I liked him the best—stupid me. He was the easiest one to talk to, with no pretending—if you didn't count pretending to be respectable when he was really a rogue. Or pretending that "Josephine" was a woman. But Silas was fun. He made my heart race and my cheeks turn pink. He had actually eaten rattlesnake. . . .

"Stop it!" I would have nothing more to do with Silas McClure, even if he did love my questions.

I quickly flipped to the next page in my diary. I didn't have to decide tonight who I would marry, did I? I refused to worry about Aunt Agnes' warning that my beauty was fading or that I would be an old maid by the age of twenty-one. I had mysteries to solve. After all, that was the reason I had come to Chicago in the first place.

I wrote *Mysteries to Solve* on the top of the page. I had arrived in town with two of them and had made no progress at all in solving either one.

1. Why did Mother leave us? Where is she?
2. Did Maude O'Neill murder her first husband? How can I stop the wedding?

Instead, I had accumulated even more mysteries:

3. Why did Father change from being one of Mr. Moody's Yoke-fellows to being indifferent about religion?
4. Why are Grandmother and Father estranged? What were the "sorrows" she mentioned in her life with my grandfather? Why won't Father let her talk about my mother?
5. Was Aunt Matt's fiancé, Robert Tucker, really a thief, or was

Aunt Birdie simply rambling? Did Mr. Tucker get caught? Is he in prison?

Once again, my mind drifted back to thoughts of the thieving rogue Silas McClure. I quickly dismissed them.

6. Does Nelson Kent really love Katya, or is he using her? Is he using me?
7. And speaking of being used—is Silas McClure using me, or does he truly have feelings for me? And if he does care for me, then why didn't he tell his thieving friends to get lost so that we could stay at the fair?

I drew a line through the last question, crossing it off my list as the answer occurred to me: Silas and I couldn't stay at the fair without a chaperone.

My mind felt like a tangle of briars. The more I struggled to unsnarl things, the more ensnared I became. And those briars had thorns.

I turned off the lamp and pulled the pillow over my head. I could hear a horse trotting down the street outside my window, and I wished it could be my imaginary fair-haired lieutenant coming to rescue me. When the sound of horse hooves faded and the silence returned, I heard Aunt Birdie's feathery voice whispering in my mind.

"Make certain you marry for love, dear."

Chapter

16

———❦———

Thursday, June 22, 1893

G randmother and I waited for Louis Decker outside the
Chicago Evangelistic Society's stern brick building on
Thursday afternoon. It was near her church, which was on the
corner of Chicago Avenue and LaSalle—that tantalizing street. I
checked the house numbers while we waited and saw that we were
many blocks north of my mother's address. Would I ever have a
chance to search for her?

The door to the Evangelistic Society opened, and a group of
young men surged through it, their voices loud with excitement. I
thought one of them might be Louis—they were so much like him
in their intensity and passion—but he wasn't among them. They
politely tipped their hats to Grandmother and me and continued on
their way, their conversation sprinkled with references to books of the
Bible like powdered sugar on a pancake: "In Corinthians it says . . .
Yes, but in Ephesians . . . What about Paul's letter to the Galatians?"

"I think it's wonderful that you're willing to help Mr. Moody's campaign this way, Violet."

I turned my attention back to my grandmother. "I hope Louis isn't disappointed in me. I'm not a very accomplished pianist."

"I'm sure you'll do fine." Why did everyone seem to have more confidence in my musical ability than I did?

"What does the Chicago Evangelization Society do?" I asked, gesturing to the building behind us. "Did they build this place just for the fair?"

"No, it's a school, dear, where they train people to do mission work. The students are just ordinary men and women from all walks of life who will eventually spread out to evangelize the city and the nation. It used to be called the May Institute because classes met only one month a year—in May. But the school became a year-round institution nearly four years ago."

"So Louis Decker is a student here?"

"Mmm-hmm. And now that the World's Exposition is here in town, it's the perfect opportunity for him and the others to reach people from all over the world."

The sun disappeared behind a cloud, and it seemed as if someone had snuffed out the gaslights. I glanced up and saw dark, heavy clouds erasing the blue sky like words from a chalkboard.

"Where did those clouds come from?" I asked. "The sun was shining when we left home." Grandmother looked up at the sky and winced.

"The weather is so changeable here in Chicago. I do hope this storm blows over."

"Do you think Louis will cancel his plans if it rains?" I hoped so. In my mind, this was certain to be more of an ordeal than an adventure.

"Oh, I doubt that he would do that. We probably should have brought our umbrellas."

Wagons and horsecars had been coming and going along the

street as we talked, but a large open carriage, pulled by two horses, suddenly drew to a halt in front of us. I was surprised to see Louis Decker driving it. The carriage had a canopy for shade and was designed for passengers. A flatbed freight wagon carrying a small wooden shipping crate drew to a halt behind it.

"Violet! You came!" Louis leaped down from the seat and fastened the reins to the hitching post. "Thanks for bringing her, Mrs. Hayes. Are you ladies ready to go?"

"Yes, I've been looking forward to it all week," Grandmother replied. I said nothing. My apprehension had far outweighed my enthusiasm this past week.

"My friends Curtis and Jack are coming too," Louis said. "They should be here any minute. Do you mind waiting?"

"I don't mind," I told him. "Maybe you can explain what you'd like me to do in the meantime."

"We're going to drive these Gospel Wagons around and advertise some of the services Mr. Moody will be holding this weekend. I've got a stack of free tickets to give away too. We always start with some music to draw people's attention. That'll be your job, Violet, making the music."

"What will I use for a piano?"

"It's right there." He pointed to the freight wagon. The crate was about three feet high and four feet wide, much too small to hold a piano. "It's a traveling organ," he explained.

"Inside that box?"

"No, the box *is* the organ. Watch this." He climbed onto the wagon and undid the latches, folding back the top to reveal a small five-octave keyboard.

"That's amazing!"

With the top of the crate folded back, the inside of the lid became the front of the box, facing the audience. It had a Bible verse painted on it:

God so LOVED the world that HE GAVE His
Only begotten
Son that WHOSOEVER BELIEVETH in Him shall not
Perish but HAVE
Everlasting
Life

"See? It spells GOSPEL," Louis said. "And that verse is the heart of the good news we're sharing. Gospel means 'good news.' It's what the angel at Bethlehem came to announce when Christ was born. 'Behold, I bring you good tidings of great joy, which shall be to all people. For unto you is born . . . a Savior, which is Christ the Lord.'"

My grandmother ran her fingers down the letters that spelled GOSPEL. "This is very clever," she said.

Louis introduced us to Richard, the wagon driver, who was also a student. While Louis was closing the packing crate, his friends Curtis and Jack bounded out of the building, their faces alive with excitement. All of these young men oozed so much passion and fervor that I couldn't help wondering where it all came from. I compared their lively faces to the bored, aloof expressions that Nelson and his friends always displayed, and decided that if Louis could have bottled up his enthusiasm and sold it as an elixir like Dr. Dean's Blood Builder, he could have made a fortune. Herman Beckett from back home in Lockport could have used a dose or two as well.

Jack and Curtis unhitched the reins and took over the driver's seat. Louis helped Grandmother and me into the back of the carriage, then sat down alongside me.

"Here's Ira Sankey's songbook," he said, handing me a hymnal. Several more were stacked beneath the seat. "I'm sorry I didn't get this music to you sooner, but I believe you'll find that the songs are very simple to play."

I leafed through the book as the carriage began to move and saw that he was right. Most of the key signatures were simple, without too many sharps and flats. I began to feel a bit more confident—

while remaining mindful of my disgraceful performance the last time I had worked with Louis.

"Where are we going?" I asked.

"Mr. Moody divided the city into districts with a church head-quarters in each one. We're going to our assigned district so we can let everyone know about this weekend's services."

"So we're like those barkers who come to town before the circus arrives and try to drum up business?" I had hoped to elicit a smile from Louis, but he nodded earnestly.

"Yes, that's exactly what we're like. Except there are several shows to choose from. Our evangelistic teams hold as many as 125 services on a single Sunday, all over the city."

I heard the first few plops of rain hitting the carriage roof as we plodded along. I stuck my hand out the open side and drew it back, sprinkled with raindrops.

"It's starting to rain," I said, hoping we could turn back. Neither Louis nor my grandmother seemed to hear me.

"Mr. Moody isn't afraid to venture into the more disreputable areas of Chicago," my grandmother told me. "He even held a service in the Haymarket Theater."

"Where is that?"

"It might as well be hell itself," Louis said. "The Haymarket is surrounded by saloons and . . . well, I'm sure you don't want to know what else." He blushed so deeply that I knew exactly what he meant. *Bawdy houses.*

"Is that where we're going?" Now I really wanted to turn back.

"I would never ask you to venture there, Miss Hayes. Even though the Lord has promised that His angels will surround us."

"I'm surprised that Mr. Moody—and the Lord—don't distance themselves from such places."

"No, no. It's just the opposite. Jesus said it's the sick people who need a physician, not the healthy ones. Mr. Moody certainly doesn't approve of such places, but that's exactly where the Gospel is needed.

People matter the most to God. This campaign is all about finding people, regardless of their situation in life, and letting them know that God loves them. And not just the poor and the downtrodden, but even pickpockets and thieves and other criminals."

I knew a few criminals who needed a dose of religion.

"My sister Matilda showed me one of Mr. Moody's newspaper advertisements this morning," Grandmother said. "His service was listed right alongside Buffalo Bill's Wild West Show."

"That's because the people who frequent those amusements are the very people we're trying to reach," Louis said.

The neighborhoods rapidly deteriorated as we clopped along at a steady rate. Even if I had been blindfolded, I would have recognized the slums by their smell. To make matters worse, our carriage seemed to lack a proper set of springs, and we bounced and jostled unmercifully in the rutted, unpaved streets. Then I smelled something truly horrific and saw a dead horse rotting in the street, covered with flies and maggots.

"Oh! That's awful!" I fumbled for a handkerchief to cover my nose and mouth. I wanted to jump off and run home.

"The city is supposed to collect the garbage regularly," Grandmother said, "but as you can see—and smell—they tend to skip the poorer neighborhoods. And I'm sure you can also tell that not all of these tenements have been connected to the city's sewer system yet."

"I can't do this. . . ." I mumbled into my handkerchief. No one seemed to hear me. Nor did they seem to hear the rain plopping on the carriage roof, faster and faster, like popping corn.

"The crowds are coming to Chicago in record numbers this summer," Louis said, "from all around the world."

"This fair is a God-given opportunity to win souls," Grandmother agreed.

"Mr. Moody has been traveling all over the world for the past twenty-five years, and now the world is traveling right to his doorstep. This will be one of his greatest evangelistic campaigns ever."

The carriage slowed to a halt when we came upon two boys, no more than ten or eleven years old, fist-fighting in the middle of the rubbish-strewn street. One boy's face was already bloodied. A dozen more youths surrounded them, cheering them on and blocking our path.

"Look at those poor little souls," my grandmother said. Louis and Curtis jumped from our carriage and waded into the melee.

"Boys, listen—" Louis began. Within seconds, the kids scattered and vanished. He returned to the carriage, shaking his head in despair as our ride resumed.

"God loves them so much, and He longs to gather them in His arms as His children, and they don't even know it. These kids live such hard lives with so many needs, but their greatest need is for a loving Savior. I get overwhelmed when I see them . . . and I feel such a sense of urgency that I can scarcely sit still."

I couldn't sit still either, but it was because I wanted to jump off this rump-sprung carriage seat and run toward fresh air. What was wrong with me? Why couldn't I get past my own discomfort and see these people the way Louis did?

At the end of the block, we turned onto a wider thoroughfare lined with market stalls and jammed with people. The rain was falling steadily now. A few of the pedestrians had umbrellas, but most of them seemed oblivious to the rain as they went about buying and selling. Perhaps this was the only way they could take a weekly bath.

Several saloons competed for business along the street, and I saw a billboard advertising a burlesque show. Customers didn't need to read English in order to understand exactly what sort of risqué entertainment the show promised. I knew better than to stare, but I couldn't help myself. We had been as sheltered as nuns at Madame Beauchamps' School, and here was the real world.

"This is a great place to stop," Louis told the driver. Our carriage drew to a halt and the three men scrambled out of the wagon. Within moments, Curtis and Jack had drawn a small crowd while

Louis unlatched the crate containing the keyboard. He beckoned to me to come and perform. It was last thing in the world I wanted to do.

I had performed recitals at school for my classmates, and I had occasionally entertained family friends in our parlor after dinner. But I had never dreamed of playing in front of a burlesque theater on a rainy, stench-filled street to an audience of immigrants, vagabonds, vagrants, and criminals. I turned to my grandmother for help. She handed me a hymnal.

"Go on, dear. You don't need to be nervous. You'll do just fine." I climbed down from the protection of the covered carriage and into the rain. Louis helped me get seated on the open wagon.

"You have to pump the organ with your feet," he informed me.

"What should I play?"

"It doesn't matter—anything." When I just stared dumbly at him, he took the songbook from me and propped it open on the music stand. "Here—how about this one."

Thankfully, the audience made too much noise to hear my first fumbling attempts to play. But once I got the hang of pumping and playing simultaneously, the mob eventually quieted down to listen. They seemed very appreciative—applauding and whistling and shouting for more. I didn't want to play more. Rain poured from the sky, and I was getting quite wet.

Louis, Jack, Curtis, and Richard worked their way through the crowd as I played, passing out tickets and, presumably, God's love. Eventually, they grabbed hymnals and stood on the running boards to sing along on a few of the hymns in the style of a barbershop quartet.

One of their songs told the story of a shepherd who left his flock of ninety-nine sheep to search for his one lost lamb. The shepherd braved the dangers of a stormy night and towering cliffs, refusing to abandon his search until he had found his lamb. By the time they sang the last line, "Rejoice, for the Lord brings back His own," I could barely read the notes through my tears. They blended with the rain that was now dripping from my drenched hat brim.

I knew they were singing about Jesus, the Good Shepherd, but they made Him sound like a hero from *True Romances*. My favorite stories had always been the ones where the hero risked his life to rescue the damsel in distress. He would overcome terrible dangers as he searched for her, and he always arrived in the nick of time when all hope seemed lost. I had come to Chicago to search for my mother, but I wondered if she or anyone else would ever love me enough to search for me the way that shepherd had.

"One last hymn, please, Violet," Louis said. "How about page 186?" His glasses were slick with rain, and he took them off to dry them on his vest. As usual, his efforts did little good; his vest was as wet as his spectacles were. He still hadn't seemed to notice that it was raining.

I was soaked and miserable, but this was the last song. Then I could go home. And that was what the song was about. "'Come home . . . come home,'" the lyrics said. "'Ye who are weary, come home.'"

"Come home, my friends," Louis told the crowd when the song ended. "Come home and let the love of Jesus Christ wash you clean. That's all for today. See you at the rally."

"That's all"—the very words I longed to hear. I jumped down from the wagon without waiting for anyone's help and hurried toward the covered carriage. But in my haste to get out of the rain I forgot to watch where I was going and stepped into a deep puddle, immersing my foot up to my ankle in muddy water. It was such a shock that I lost my footing altogether and went down on my *derriere* with a splash.

I yelped in outrage. The streets weren't paved, of course, and the rain had turned the dirt into mud. It was mixed with horse manure, and the overflow from outhouses, and who knew what else—and I had landed in it!

I scrambled to my feet, fighting tears. At least my humiliating tumble had been hidden from Louis and the others by the carriage. They were still looking the other way. If I could reach the carriage and sit down before they turned around, they might not notice my muddy backside.

I stood, took one hurried step—and slipped on the slimy muck again! This time I fell forward. I reached out to stop my fall and landed on my hands and knees in the mire. I heard giggles. Glancing up, I saw four small children laughing at my predicament. I pulled my hands out of the mud, but there was nothing to wipe them on except the sides of my skirt. Now the others were certain to notice my disarray.

I stood once again, took a tentative step—and fell for a third time. The giggles turned to outright laughter.

"Violet?" Louis called. I heard him splashing to my rescue and felt the splatter from his shoes peppering my face. "Are you okay?" It would have been wrong to lie to a man of God, so I didn't reply. I let him take my arm and help me into the carriage—at last.

"Violet—what happened?" my grandmother asked.

"I slipped," I said with as much dignity as I could muster. "Can we go home now?" *Quickly, before I burst into tears.*

I thought I remembered a verse in the Bible about pride coming before a fall. If so, I was guilty. I had taken great pride in my faultless posture, my ability to walk gracefully with a book on my head as I'd paraded into fancy drawing rooms with Aunt Agnes. I had reveled in everyone's admiring stares as I had promenaded on Nelson's arm with my new silk gown swishing, my feet clad in dainty slippers. Yes, I had indeed fallen far.

At last the carriage began to move. I would never take sweet-smelling air or paved streets for granted again.

"I love that last song," Grandmother said as we rolled toward home. "It's about the Prodigal Son coming home, isn't it?"

Louis nodded. "The Prodigal Son is Mr. Moody's favorite sermon theme for this campaign. The city is filled with people who've moved here from their small towns and farms. And like the prodigal, they often take up lives of sin, falling for all the worldly temptations that the city offers—saloons, theaters, lusts of all sorts, including the lust for money. That's why Jesus' message of the prodigal son is so important. People can come home to the God of their youth, the God many of them left behind in their hometown churches."

"I think many of the immigrants can relate to that story too," my grandmother added. "They're far from their families and homelands, struggling to make a living. They hoped for a better life in America and have found only disappointment. Jesus, who was born into poverty, understands their plight."

"I've heard Mr. Moody preach on the prodigal many times, and I believe it is his most stirring sermon subject. Every time he preaches, dozens of people come forward to be saved."

As I listened to their excited chatter, I couldn't help thinking of Silas McClure. He had left his home on the farm and taken up with thieves. Maybe if he heard Mr. Moody preach he would give up his thieving ways.

"Could I have one of those tickets?" I asked Louis. "I know someone who might be interested in coming."

"Sure!" He pulled a wad of them from his pocket and fanned them out in his hand. "How many do you want?"

"Could you spare three?" Maybe Silas would share them with "Josephine" and Robert. I would mail them to him, anonymously of course, to the post-office box listed on his card. I had no intention of speaking to Silas McClure ever again.

"You did a wonderful job today, Violet."

"Thank you." Louis didn't say a word about my soaked, muddy clothes and dripping hat. He was either very polite or very oblivious to how disheveled I looked. My guess was oblivious.

"I hope you'll work with me again."

I gave him my well-rehearsed enigmatic smile in reply. I was trying not to weep. I never wanted to visit one of these wretched neighborhoods again for as long as I lived. I knew squeamishness was a poor excuse for refusing to serve the Lord, but I couldn't help it. Given a choice, I would sooner marry a wealthy, adulterous husband and contribute financially to Mr. Moody's campaigns than do this again.

"We work well together, don't you think?" Louis asked. I recalled Nelson Kent asking the same thing. Eager, sincere Louis Decker was dripping wet and awaiting my reply. I had to say something.

"It's refreshing to find an area of work where men and women can labor side by side," I replied. Aunt Matt would have been proud of me.

"You're right," Louis said. "The Scriptures tell us that in Christ there is neither male nor female, slave nor free man. The Lord's work couldn't proceed without women like you and your grandmother and all of the others—especially at the settlement house. And that reminds me . . . would you two ladies allow me to escort you to Folk Night down at the settlement house next week?"

"Oh, that's very sweet of you, Louis," Grandmother said. "We would love to go. You'll have a wonderful time, Violet."

"What is Folk Night?" I practically grunted the words. At the moment, I didn't want to go anywhere except home.

"It's the night when Miss Addams invites her neighbors and their families to share some of their ethnic customs and culture with everyone," Louis explained. "There's usually good music and folk dancing and sometimes food. I believe her Bohemian neighbors will have their turn next week, right?"

My grandmother nodded. "Folk Night lets people take pride in their heritage," she said. "Sometimes the poor need a sense of dignity much more than they need charity. We've had German songfests, Irish dancing, and wonderful Italian cooking."

"I'll pick you up at your home," Louis said, "so you ladies won't have to venture out alone after dark."

"That's so kind of you, Louis. Violet and I would appreciate that." Grandmother gazed at him in admiration. I couldn't recall agreeing to go.

The rain stopped, of course, by the time we arrived back at the Evangelistic Society. Louis' friends all climbed out, and he took the carriage reins again to drive Grandmother and me home. The sun shone through the thinning clouds, mocking me as we halted in front of the house.

"Thanks again, Violet," he said as he helped me down from my seat. "I'll see you next week." He smiled at me as if he hadn't even noticed that I looked like a drowned rat.

I hurried into the house, avoiding my reflection in the hall mirror. I was wet and muddy and miserable.

"You take off those wet clothes, dear, so we can soak the mud out of them. Birdie and I will fill the bathtub for you and make you some hot tea."

I plodded upstairs and stripped off my muddy dress. The remains of my hat went straight into the trash. I pulled all the pins out of my dripping hair, then burst into tears when I finally saw my filth-smeared reflection in the mirror. I didn't recognize myself. This certainly wasn't the princess who had floated into the ballroom on Nelson Kent's arm. And if Madame Beauchamps saw me now, she would revoke my diploma.

By the time I finished crying and went downstairs in my robe, Grandmother had filled the copper tub with warm water. She had set it up in the kitchen behind a folding screen. I stepped into the bath, gratefully and took the hot cup of tea she offered me.

"You and Louis Decker work so beautifully together, don't you think?"

"Mmm." If I said anything else I might start crying again.

"He is such a fine young man, isn't he?"

"Yes. Very nice."

And that was the problem—he was nice and I wasn't. Any prolonged niceness on my part was nothing but an act. I always grew weary of being nice after a few hours. I was certainly not nice unless I had to be, and I could never be nice for an entire lifetime. Being nice was exhausting. It implied conformity, and conformity had been a lifelong trial for me. It went against my nature—which is why I'd grown so weary of pretending at Aunt Agnes' parties. I was beginning to understand Aunt Matt's claim that all women were actresses. But could I ever act nice enough to marry a minister?

"You of all people should have the blinders off when it comes to marrying a minister," Aunt Matt had told my grandmother. I wondered what she had meant. My grandmother had pulled out a kitchen chair to sip a cup of tea with me. I decided to probe.

"Did my grandfather go into the streets and preach like Louis and Mr. Moody are doing?"

She shook her head. "He preached to his own little flock in his church in Lockport. He often railed against the evils of city life and would never have ventured to Chicago to preach the way Dwight Moody does."

"I don't remember Grandfather very well. To tell you the truth, I was a little afraid of him. He always looked angry."

"In some ways he was angry. He didn't preach about the love and grace of God very often, choosing to emphasize our need for obedience to Christ's commands instead."

"Wasn't one of those commands to love our neighbor?"

"That one often slipped his notice." She smiled faintly. "All in all, I think he was very disappointed with his life. When he died, my life changed completely. I had to leave Lockport and move in with Matt and Birdie to make room in the parsonage for the new minister."

"Why didn't you take care of us?"

"Your father didn't want me to."

"Why not?"

"I can't answer that. You'll have to ask him."

"You *can't* answer it, or you *won't*?" I asked angrily.

My grandmother smiled sadly. "I made a promise to your father that I would let him answer all of your questions. I'm so sorry, dear."

I handed her my empty cup and grabbed a bar of soap to scrub the mud off my face. I waited for my temper to cool before asking, "Is my father like the Prodigal Son?"

"I'm not sure what you mean."

"You told me he worked as a Yokefellow, and that he went into saloons and tried to convert people. He certainly doesn't do things like that anymore. What happened?"

She seemed very reluctant to reply. I was surprised when she did.

"There was a time in your father's life when he nearly became a preacher. But he found out, just in time, that he was doing it for the wrong reasons. It's never right to serve God out of guilt or in order to please someone else. Your grandfather wanted a son who would follow in his footsteps. He didn't understand that being a minister wasn't your father's calling."

"What do you mean—it wasn't his 'calling'? Going calling is what I do with Aunt Agnes, with our calling cards."

Grandmother smiled. "Your calling comes from God. It's what He would like you to do with your life. He calls some people to be evangelists and ministers, but most of us are called to serve Him in other ways. I believe my calling is to serve the poor in His name. But regardless of what God's plans for us are, He always gives us a choice. We can go our own way and do something else with our life if we choose to. God won't force us."

"How do I know what my calling is? Will I really hear Him calling? Like a voice in the dark?"

"No, although it would be a good deal simpler if He did call us that way. He'll ask you to do something that uses your unique gifts and interests."

"Like playing the piano? Is it my calling to play piano for Louis? Because if it is, God is going to have to do something about the stench, and the mud, and the dead horses, and—" My tears started to fall again, and I couldn't finish. Grandmother handed me her handkerchief to wipe my eyes.

"I'm wet all over, Grandma," I said, smiling at the irony. "It's useless to dry a few tears."

"Yes, I suppose so. . . . But listen, Violet, ministering to the poor may not be your calling. God has a reason for creating each of us as individuals, with no two people alike. He has a unique place for you in His kingdom. Look how different my three sisters and I are—and we all have different callings. We would be wrong to judge each other or to expect each other to do the same work."

I swished my hands through the water as I pondered her words. "At school, we were all taught to be alike. Madame Beauchamps wanted us to act the same and talk the same—we were even supposed to smile the same and walk the same. She told us that society has standards of decorum and proper manners, and we were taught to conform to them. We weren't supposed to stand out. We were punished if we did."

"I think that's very wrong, Violet. I agree that manners help keep our society civilized, but we're still individuals. Even twins aren't exactly alike."

I thought of all the "pea-pod" partners I had danced with at Aunt Agnes' parties, and how boringly alike they were. I'd been drawn to Nelson because he was different. He could conform as readily as the rest of them when he had to, but he behaved differently with me.

"Madame Beauchamps taught me how to be a proper young lady, but sometimes I don't want to be so prim and . . . and *boring*. It isn't the real me. I used to rebel—quietly—against some of the rules at school. I stayed in bed late and read books after lights-out with my friend Ruth, books that Madame B. would never approve of. A lot of the time I lived in my imagination. So how do I know if I'm still rebelling or if this is the way God made me? How can I tell the difference?"

"You be exactly who God created you to be," she said fervently, "and don't let anyone tell you otherwise. And whatever you do, don't make choices in life just to please somebody else. The only One you ever need to please is God."

"But how will I know what my calling is?"

"Do you ever pray, Violet?"

"Yes, on Sunday mornings ... and before I go to sleep. . . ." I gave a guilty shrug.

"From now on when you pray, ask God to show you what He wants you to do."

As I sank down into the tub to scrub my hair, I pictured Louis standing in front of the crowd in the rain shouting, *"Come home and let the love of Jesus Christ wash you clean."*

I knew then that even though Silas McClure and his friends might need to be washed clean, I was in no position to point a finger at them. When I went upstairs to my bedroom to get dressed, I tore up the rally tickets and threw them away.

Chapter

17

Saturday, June 24, 1893

I was upstairs still getting ready when Herman Beckett arrived on Saturday morning to escort me to the World's Fair. Aunt Birdie answered the door.

"Oh, Florence! Come quick!" I heard her cry out. "Someone died! The undertaker is here!"

I reached the top of the stairs in time to hear Herman say, "I'm here for Violet."

"Oh no! Not Violet!" Aunt Birdie moaned. "She was perfectly fine at dinner last night. How could she pass away so quickly?"

"Wait! I'm not dead, Aunt Birdie!" I thundered down the stairs as gracelessly as a six-year-old.

"Oh, thank goodness." She pulled me into her arms and hugged me tightly. I could feel her heart pounding. When she released me, she turned to Herman. "It seems that your services will not be needed after all, young man. Violet is perfectly fine. Good day." She closed the door in his face.

"Aunt Birdie, wait! Mr. Beckett is here to take me to the fair."

"Why in the world would you want to go to the fair with an undertaker?"

"Herman isn't an undertaker," I said, opening the door to him again.

"Well, he certainly looks like one. It just goes to show that you can't judge a book by its cover, Violet. Remember how you thought that other gentleman caller of yours was a thief? But see? Our silver tray is still here." She held it up for me to see.

"Have there been other gentlemen callers?" Herman asked in a worried voice.

"Please come in, Mr. Beckett," I said, ignoring his question. "I'm sorry for all the confusion."

Herman stepped aside and gestured for our chaperone to enter first. "I'd like you to meet my sister, Mary Crane," he said. She was dressed entirely in black and wore such a gloomy expression on her face, I could see how Aunt Birdie might have mistaken her and Herman for undertakers. The small picnic basket that she carried on her arm offered the only hint that we were out for a day of fun.

"Mary lives in Riverside with her husband and two children," Herman explained.

"Oh, will your family be joining us as well?"

"No. They won't."

Herman offered no explanation for the missing family, so I didn't pry—although my imagination quickly supplied several reasons. Maybe she had chained them in the cellar for a few hours so she could have a day of fun without them. Or maybe they were horribly disfigured and she was ashamed to have them be seen in public. Maybe they were feral children who ate raw meat and howled at the moon, or maybe . . .

I noticed Aunt Birdie hovering in the hallway behind me, and I introduced her. She nodded curtly in reply. Herman Beckett and his sister were the first visitors we'd had that Birdie hadn't greeted with one of her famous hugs. I could understand why.

"Would you care for a cold drink before we leave?" I asked.

"Thank you, but no. We have a lot to see today, and I think we should get going."

I had dreaded returning to the fair and being reminded of my unsettling visit with Silas McClure, but seeing the fair with Herman Beckett turned out to be a completely different experience. Herman had purchased *Claxton's Guidebook to the World's Columbian Exposition* and he followed it as religiously as Louis Decker followed the Scriptures. He opened to the first page as we rode the streetcar to the fairgrounds and gave us a taste of what was ahead.

"It says here that the fair offers 'the assembled achievements and products from the mind and hand of mankind, such as never before presented to mortal vision.'"

"My word," his sister murmured. She was evidently too overwhelmed to say more. I said nothing. It was going to be a very long day.

We got off the streetcar at the fair's 57th Street entrance and stood in line for our tickets. Herman showed me the guidebook's map as we waited. "This red line shows the recommended route we should take. It's the best way to experience the fair. We'll start here," he said, tracing the line with his finger, "and gradually make our way around from the north end of the fairgrounds to the south. The recommended pavilions and exhibits are highlighted."

"Why see what the author wants you to see, Herman? Why not decide what you're interested in and skip the rest?"

Herman's dark brows met in the middle as he frowned. They reminded me of two wooly caterpillars kissing. "The author made a thorough study of the fair. I'm sure that the advice he gives is very sound. The grounds cover 633 acres, Violet, and there are more than sixty-five thousand exhibits. It would be impossible to see it all in one day. The guidebook has rated the best attractions as 'interesting,' 'very interesting,' or 'remarkably interesting.'"

"Does he recommend that we ride Mr. Ferris' wheel?"

"Certainly not! The wheel is on the Midway." Herman made *Midway* sound like a dirty word.

"What's wrong with the Midway?" My question caused his eyebrows to kiss once again.

"Those amusements cater to the lowest sort of person. I have no interest at all in seeing bawdy attractions."

Herman's sister leaned close to whisper in my ear as we walked through the entrance gates. "Some of the Midway exhibits are very vulgar. One of them features hootchy-kootchy dancers who are indecently clothed! And those women make the most obscene gyrations! Many of the primitive Africans on display are scantily clad as well."

"Oh, I see." I decided not to mention that I had already visited the pagan Midway and had found it "remarkably interesting." But then, a thief like Silas McClure was exactly the low sort of person Herman had referred to.

We strolled around the northern section of the fairgrounds for a while, passing dozens of state pavilions and exhibits. In the center stood a magnificent building with enormous statues of women serving as support pillars. "That looks *remarkably* interesting," I said. "What's inside that building?"

"It's the Palace of Fine Art." Herman said *art* with the same horrified tone that he'd used for the Midway.

"What's wrong with art?"

Mary cupped her hand around my ear again and whispered, "They have *nudes*." I stifled a sigh.

Viewed from the outside, the state pavilions were all very different from each other and seemed very interesting to me, but the only building that Mr. Claxton's guidebook allowed us to enter was the Illinois State Pavilion.

"Why would we waste time here?" I asked. "We live in Illinois. We can see the real thing every day."

Herman stared at me, oblivious to the irony. "The pavilion offers

216

a chance to learn something new about our state. The guidebook says it will be 'very interesting.'"

I dutifully wandered through the Illinois building, longing to see exotic displays that were truly very interesting. I didn't find General Grant's memorabilia interesting in the least, nor the Women's Corn Kitchen featuring one hundred different ways to prepare Illinois' favorite agricultural product—corn. I couldn't imagine that the pavilion had earned even an "interesting" rating, let alone "very interesting." I decided to start my own rating system: "boring," "exceedingly boring," and "I'm-falling-asleep boring." In the "exceedingly boring" category was a huge mosaic of a prairie farmyard, complete with cattle and horses, made entirely out of seeds and grains. Herman stood before it awestruck.

"Look, Mary! Even the frame is made from ears of corn."

"My word," she murmured. I stifled a yawn.

We walked around the fairgrounds all morning, following the approved path as if it would lead us to buried treasure. As Herman narrated the highlights for us, I learned that he was very fond of statistics.

"Did you know that the fair has more than sixty-one acres of lagoons and waterways, and over three miles of intertwining canals?"

"My word . . ." his sister replied breathlessly. I wasn't sure if it was from wonder or the brisk pace Herman set.

Whenever he began a sentence with "Did you know. . . ?" I braced myself for another batch of statistics, invariably followed by another awestruck, "My word . . ." from his sister.

"Did you know," he asked as we viewed the enormous Manufactures and Liberal Arts Building, "that you're looking at the largest building in the world? The fair is comprised of fourteen Great Buildings and more than two hundred others—at a cost of twenty-eight million dollars."

"My word . . ."

"Did you know," he asked as we approached the Electricity

Building, "that each of that building's ten spires is one-hundred-seventy-feet high? The fair uses more than one hundred twenty thousand incandescent lights and seven thousand arc lights."

"My word . . ."

"Did you know," he asked as we viewed the Horticulture Building, "that this building houses the world's largest collection of horticultural products? The gardens feature a half a million pansies and one hundred thousand roses."

"My word . . ."

We spent a considerable amount of time in the glass-domed Horticultural Building, viewing an endless number of plants and flowers. It earned my highest rating for boring. I longed to see something truly exciting.

"Does the guidebook recommend any foreign pavilions?" I finally asked.

"A few, but I'm not sure we'll have time for any of them."

I decided that I would never suffer from insomnia again if I married Herman Beckett. Nelson Kent, on the other hand, might not be faithful to me, but he would take me to Italy and Paris.

"Do you ever feel the urge to see the world, Herman?"

"Not really. If one can't find contentment at home, one is unlikely to find it anywhere else."

Could that be true? Did the fact that I had been discontented living in Lockport mean that I was doomed to a life of discontent? If so, I may as well marry Nelson and be discontented but rich.

Shortly before noon we at last viewed something that was "remarkably interesting." The Fisheries Building featured ten aquariums displaying beautiful, fascinating worlds that I never knew existed beneath the seas. I got so carried away that I found myself asking Herman, "If you could choose to live on another planet or to live under the sea, which would you choose?"

"I wouldn't want either," he replied. "I'm content where I am." His sister nodded.

"Suppose you *had* to choose?" My impatience and frustration must have shown; perhaps in the way I stomped my foot. Herman turned from the aquarium to gaze at me with a look of concern.

"I don't understand why the question is so important to you, Violet."

I didn't know either. I couldn't stop thinking of Silas and how much fun he'd had answering my questions.

On the way out we passed a statue that reminded me of Cupid, and I found myself asking, "Do you believe in love?"

"What do you mean?"

"You know—falling in love, love at first sight, true love, everlasting love. Or do you think it's only found in fairy tales?"

Herman's face turned the color of beet juice. "Honestly, Violet. Does it matter what I think?"

"I would like to know."

"Well, then, I would have to say I believe love exists—although I would be highly suspicious of love at first sight. I believe love is something that grows over time as two people get to know each other."

He whipped open his guidebook and gave it all of his attention, cutting off all further discussion of love. "Let's see, now. . . . What's next?"

"How about a gondola ride on the lagoon?" We were standing alongside one of the many canals, and the boats looked as graceful as swans as they glided over the water. The gondoliers in their colorful costumes added to the illusion of adventure and romance.

"The lines are too long. The guidebook says we would waste too much time waiting. Besides, the admission fee is rather expensive."

But Herman did consent to eat our picnic lunch on the grass alongside the lagoon so we could watch the gondoliers poling more fortunate fairgoers across the water. Mary unpacked her picnic basket and passed around the ham sandwiches she had made.

"What do you want in life, Herman?" I asked. It must have been the Grecian-style buildings with their multitude of pillars that had made me so philosophical.

"I would prefer a simple life with a peaceful home in a quiet town like Lockport," he replied. "I couldn't stand to live in a big city like Chicago with all of this noise and dirt and rushing around."

"Wouldn't you like to travel and see new places?"

"As I said, I believe that we are happiest when we learn to be content at home. We should want nothing more than the life God has given us. Why try to be something we're not?"

Contentment. I didn't have it. In truth, it sounded boring—like the last stage one reaches before falling asleep. House cats were content, and they slept all day.

"I would like to have a happy home," Herman continued. "A refuge I could return to after a day's work."

"What about fun?"

"Well, I enjoy boating in Dellwood Park in the summertime . . . skating in the winter . . . attending church on Sunday. I would like to have children and a family. . . ."

"A family," I repeated. I was suddenly reminded of my father and Murderous Maude. "Speaking of families, have you heard that my father plans to marry Maude O'Neill?"

"Yes. They seem very content."

I tried not to roll my eyes. "I understand you know Maude O'Neill quite well. Tell me, was she content with her first husband?"

"I'd rather not say."

He didn't have to; his face said it all. He not only was blushing, his wooly-caterpillar-eyebrows were kissing as voraciously as Nelson and Katya had. Mary rummaged through the picnic basket as if searching for her ticket out of this conversation.

I suddenly recalled something that I'd learned from Ruth's detective novels: *Sometimes it's not what people say that's important, it's what they don't say.* If Maude and her husband had been happy, why not say so? *"Mr. O'Neill was a wonderful man. They were so happy. She was devastated when he died."* Herman's silence spoke volumes.

"Why won't you tell me, Herman?"

"It isn't right to gossip." He started to rise, but I gripped his arm, stopping him.

"It isn't gossip. She's going to marry my father. She will be my . . . my stepmother." I winced as I said the word. How I hated it. "Listen, I know that my father's first marriage ended unhappily, so I'd like to know if he'll find happiness the second time around."

"I'm not in a position to say." He broke free and stood, then offered me a hand up as well.

This detective business was very hard work. I had read about reluctant witnesses in Ruth's *True Crime Stories*, and now I had encountered one. I decided to try a different approach, hoping that my feminine charm would do the trick. I linked my arm through his as we started walking and mustered all of my feminine weapons: my coy, flirtatious voice; my enigmatic smile; my fluttering eyelashes. I gazed up at him adoringly.

"Listen, Herman, just tell me one thing: do you think Maude loves my father or is she still pining for her first husband?"

"I hardly think she is pining for him! He—" Herman stopped, horrified that he had said so much. "I never meant to gossip."

"I know. I don't think telling someone the truth is in the same category as gossip."

"Maude O'Neill is a wonderful woman," he said, showing more passion than I had ever seen from him. "She deserves a happy life with a good man like your father."

"How did she and my father meet? As you know, I've been away at school for the past three years."

"They've known each other for several years. Mr. O'Neill worked for your father at one time."

His words horrified me. What if Maude and my father had fallen in love before Mr. O'Neill's death? What if I continued to probe and discovered that Father was Maude's accomplice in the murder?

"You'll be home for their wedding, I assume?" Herman asked.

"Huh?"

"When are you coming back to Lockport?"

I wanted to shout, *"Never!"*

"I-I'm not sure," I said instead. Perhaps I should stop my investigation. But how else could I prevent Father's marriage?

I pondered my dilemma for the next hour or so as we journeyed through the fairgrounds. None of the exhibits fascinated me as much as the aquariums had. And many of them, like the display of every type of paper money the government had ever issued, were astoundingly boring. But when we came upon a replica of the Liberty Bell made entirely out of oranges, it was such a ludicrous sight that I had to cover my mouth to keep from laughing out loud. I glanced at Herman to see his reaction and caught him staring at the bell with a look of wonder on his face.

"Isn't that a marvel?" he asked. "It even has the famous crack!"

"My word . . ." Mary breathed.

A giggle that I could no longer suppress sputtered out. Once unleashed, my hilarity bubbled forth until I was laughing out loud.

"Violet? What's so funny?" Herman asked.

"That bell! I think it's the most ridiculous thing I've ever seen!"

"Excuse me?"

"Aren't there better things to do with a couple of crates of oranges? I mean, why not pass them out to the poor children instead of gluing them into the shape of a bell?" Now I sounded like Louis Decker. Herman gazed at me as if I'd spoken blasphemy.

"Sometimes I don't understand you at all, Violet," he said, slowly shaking his head.

"They're oranges, for goodness' sake," I said, still unable to control my laughter. "What do oranges have to do with the Liberty Bell? The founding fathers didn't win our freedom by lobbing oranges at the British, did they?"

"Maybe we should move on." People were staring at us—or more specifically, at me—and I could see that my laughter embarrassed Herman. I couldn't seem to stop.

"Did George Washington cross the Delaware on a raft of orange crates?" I asked. "Did Thomas Jefferson toast the signing of the Declaration of Independence with a glass of orange juice? Did Patrick Henry say, 'Give me oranges or give me death'?"

"I really think we should move on." Herman marched me from the building as if dragging me to the headmistress' office by my ear. Mary scurried behind us with her head lowered.

I was still wiping tears from my eyes when we emerged from the building into the sunlight. Herman paused for a moment to bury his nose in the guidebook, searching for the next marvel on his list, when all of a sudden I saw Silas McClure walking straight toward me. At least I thought it was Silas.

He was dressed like a British lord in a suit that was as finely cut and tailored as Nelson Kent's suits were. He had grown a mustache and a neat goatee since the last time I'd seen him, and he wore a fedora on his carefully barbered head. He even carried a silver-topped cane.

"Mr. McClure?" I said as he approached.

He didn't turn his head at the sound of his name, but continued to stroll straight down the pathway. A moment later he vanished into the crowd. Could I have been mistaken? Did Silas have a twin brother? And if so, was he a thief too? If so, he was a much more successful thief, judging by his clothing.

"Who was that?" Herman asked.

How in the world could I explain Silas McClure? *"Oh, just a thief I met on the train to Chicago. I helped him and his pals pull off a robbery the last time I visited the fair."*

"No one," I sighed. "He resembled someone I know, but I guess it wasn't him." Yet the stranger had the same effect on me that Silas always had. My heart was chugging like an engine at full steam. I had to change the subject.

"I hear there's a walkway on the top of the Manufactures and Liberal Arts building that offers a marvelous view. Does your guidebook recommend it by any chance?"

"It costs extra."

I might have known.

The aroma of exotic food and spices rose to my nostrils in tantalizing fashion from dozens of pavilions we passed. We didn't sample anything. The only food item Herman purchased was water from the Hygeia Water stand, and he complained about that.

"I think it's outrageous to charge money for a drink of water! Water should be free. Just look—there's a Great Lake full of water, right over there. What will they charge us for next? Are they going to make us pay for soil? Or for air?"

"My word . . ." Mary said.

I kept my mouth shut.

By late afternoon, I was relieved to learn that the guidebook scheduled a stop at the comfort station. I went inside with Herman's sister, and as soon as she had me alone she unleashed a sales pitch on behalf of her brother that rivaled Silas McClure's pitch for Dr. Dean's Blood Builder.

"My brother is a fine young man—hardworking, sensible, modest, and upright. Unlike a lot of other men, he has no vices. . . ." And so on, and so forth. I could have added that he also had no sense of adventure, no sense of humor, and no imagination, but Mary barely paused for breath. When her sales pitch ended, she began to interrogate me.

"Do you have a lot of other suitors, Violet?"

"Well, no . . . not a lot . . ."

"How many? Are they seriously courting you?"

"I've only been in Chicago for three weeks. It's pretty hard to form a serious relationship in—"

"Listen." Her face was close to mine as she pleaded with me, begging with the same fervor that Louis might use when asking sinners to repent. "I beg you to be fair to my brother. Don't toy with him. Some girls do that, you know. They make a game out of winning a man's heart just so they can break it. Herman deserves your honesty, Violet. And your loyalty and trust."

"I won't lead him on."

"Thank you."

I had to admit that Herman did exhibit sterling character. And he was neither devastatingly poor nor exorbitantly rich. Maybe Herman would be a compromise between Louis' world of smells and sorrow and Nelson's life of pretentious pretending. Maybe it was my calling to settle down in Lockport and raise a peck of children and hire a housekeeper like Mrs. Hutchins to peel my onions.

Later, as we passed a souvenir stand, I asked Herman if we could stop. "I would like to purchase a packet of postcards with photographs of the fair." The photo on top—the one that had lured me— was of Mr. Ferris' wheel. For a moment I thought Herman might have to check his guidebook to see if the stop was authorized, but he not only stopped, he even paid for the postcards.

"Thank you. This will be a nice reminder of my visit to the fair." I didn't mention which visit.

There were hundreds of interesting exhibits besides the Palace of Fine Art and the enticing Midway that we never had a chance to see. If Herman's guidebook didn't recommend it, we didn't see it. Would he go through life this way, following someone else's agenda and living by the book? I briefly considered launching into a motivational speech: *What about spontaneity? What about fun? Why not ride life's Ferris wheels once in a while?*

Yet I knew that his sister was right. Herman was a good man, kind, thoughtful, well-mannered. He was hardworking; he didn't love money; he wanted a family. In fact, Herman was very much like my father—which led to another thought: If I was like my mother, perhaps boredom was the reason she eventually left him.

We stayed to watch the fireworks display before returning home.

I arrived at Grandmother's door thoroughly exhausted. My feet ached from walking all day, but my head ached even more from holding back all of the outrageous thoughts that had bubbled up in my imagination throughout the day. I had longed to say so much more but couldn't, especially after the Liberty Bell incident.

"When are you coming home to Lockport?" Herman asked as we said good-night in my grandmother's foyer. Once again, I wanted to reply, *"Never!"*

"To tell you the truth, I haven't thought much about Lockport. I'm still enjoying my visit to Chicago very much."

"If I may say so, Violet, I hope you will come home soon." He fumbled for my hand and took it into his sweating one, squeezing it limply before releasing it again.

"Thank you, Herman," I managed to say. "And thanks for an . . . interesting day."

Chapter

18

Monday, June 26, 1893

I happened to be standing in the front hallway on Monday morning when the mailman pushed several letters through our mail slot. The one on top was addressed to me.

It was from Silas McClure.

I dropped the other letters onto the floor and ran upstairs to read it in the privacy of my room. I didn't find his chunky, schoolboy penmanship at all endearing this time. I opened the envelope to find that the stationery he'd used came from a hotel in Chicago. He had put another Dr. Dean's Blood Builder card in the letter, along with a commemorative coin from the Exposition.

Dear Violet,

Please accept my deepest apologies for ending our visit to the fair so abruptly. There were hundreds of things that I wanted to see and do together, and I'm still sulking because we didn't get a chance to do any of them. I never would have asked Robert and Josephine to be our chaperones if I had known they would leave us in the lurch like that. Do you think you can ever forgive me?

I had a great time with you, even though our day was cut short. I can still see the look on your face when we rode the wheel together. I enjoyed every minute that I spent with you, as few as they were.

I'll wager that I'm probably asking too much to expect you to accompany me again, but I sure would love a second chance if you can find it in your heart to give me one. I'll be in town at this hotel for the next few weeks, so if you're willing to give me that second chance, please write me a note. You can send it in care of this hotel, or to my post-office box. You'll find the number on my card, which I'm enclosing.

I'll understand if you still feel shortchanged. To tell you the truth, I feel shortchanged myself. Drat those useless chaperones! I'll find better ones next time. I promise.

> *Yours very truly,*
> *Silas McClure*

The coin was an Exposition souvenir. I turned it over in my hand and a tear rolled down my cheek when I saw the image of Mr. Ferris' wheel on the back. I could still remember what it felt like to hold Silas' hand. And to land in his arms when the wheel lurched the first time. Nor could I forget the way he had looked at me when we halted at the top of the wheel.

"Stop it!" I told myself.

Silas was a thieving elixir salesman. He had been trained to be a smooth talker. I could not—would not—have anything more to do with a thief. Or the friend of a thief. It could only lead to enormous heartache.

I wiped away another tear and shoved the letter under my mattress. I refused to answer it. I was on my way out of the room with the coin in my pocket when I remembered the well-dressed gentleman I had seen at the fair. Had that been Silas? If so, why had he been dressed that way?

The only explanation that made sense was that he had been wearing a disguise. He could have been posing as a wealthy gentleman in order to rob other wealthy gentlemen. I faced the truth that Silas McClure was probably a pickpocket as well as a thief.

I pulled the commemorative coin out of my pocket as if it might set my skirt on fire and laid it on the hall table beside the packet of postcards that Herman had bought for me.

On Tuesday, I decided to go calling with Aunt Agnes. After my muddy afternoon with Louis and my boring tour of the fairgrounds with Herman, I needed a dose of beauty. I had missed the luxurious homes, the gorgeous dresses, the elegant atmosphere—and the cucumber sandwiches. One of the women on whom we called was Nelson's grandmother.

"Where have you been, Violet? I was so afraid you'd left Chicago for good. And without even saying good-bye."

"I would never do that, Mrs. Kent."

"My Nelson would never forgive you if you did. He is so very fond of you." She took my hand in both of hers and added, "I probably shouldn't have told you that. Nelson would be peeved with me for tattling on him. But I've never heard him talk about the other girls the way he raves about you."

We sat in the afternoon room and sipped tea. Everything was lovely but—I hated to admit it—boring. I entertained myself by watching the serving girls flitting in and out with our tea and finger sandwiches, hoping to glimpse the stunning Katya. But when the luncheon ended and the maids cleared away our tea things, I still hadn't seen her. I decided to discreetly ask one of the other servers about her.

"Excuse me, but I haven't seen Katya today. Is it her day off?"

"She no longer works for the Kents, Miss." The maid's cool voice revealed her unwillingness to say more.

I was instantly intrigued. "What happened to her?"

"They hired Sadie in her place."

"Did Katya quit or was she fired?"

"I couldn't say, miss. Will you excuse me, please?"

If someone had seen Katya kissing Nelson the way I had, I could understand why she would be sent away. Far, far away. I pictured her in an igloo in Lapland, shivering with the Eskimos.

Aunt Agnes and I were preparing to leave when Nelson sauntered in.

"Violet! It's wonderful to see you." There was warmth in his voice as he squeezed my hands, but he might have been greeting anyone. "Listen, I'm glad I caught you. I've been invited to a string of gala affairs at the Columbian Exposition fairgrounds. Might you be able to accompany me to some of them? I would like to show you the fair."

"Violet would love to go. Wouldn't you, dear?" Aunt Agnes replied. "You'll enjoy it, I'm sure. The fair is a marvelous, marvelous place."

She and Mrs. Kent gushed on and on, never giving me a chance to reply. Nelson and everyone else simply assumed that I would go.

"Will you be using a guidebook?" I asked him, remembering my visit with Herman Beckett.

"A guidebook? What for?" He appeared amused.

"To see the fair."

"I don't need a guidebook," he said, laughing.

"Then yes, I would love to go."

"Good. I have tickets for a concert in Choral Hall on Thursday evening. Afterward there is a private party I've been invited to attend in one of the other pavilions."

"That sounds nice." I could wear my new gown again. I could listen to beautiful music, enjoy sumptuous food—and pleasing smells.

"I'll pick you up a little before seven."

When I returned home, Aunt Matt stopped me in the front hallway. "Don't make any plans for Wednesday afternoon, Violet. I'm taking you to see the Woman's Pavilion."

And she did.

We got off the streetcar at the 59th Street entrance and walked a dozen yards to the pavilion. The Midway was directly behind us, and I peeked over my shoulder at the wheel, towering above the fair. Then I gave Aunt Matt my full attention.

"First of all, you need to know about this building. It was designed by a woman architect in the Italian Renaissance style. The Board of Lady Managers launched a nationwide search for a woman architect and received twelve submissions. All of the women were under the age of twenty-five, by the way. The winner, Sophia Hayden, was around your age, Violet—twenty-one—and had recently graduated from the Massachusetts Institute of Technology."

I couldn't comprehend it. A girl my age? And she knew how to design a building? I stared at the pavilion for a moment as I tried to take it all in—the lagoon in front, the prolific flowers in the hanging gardens, the graceful staircase to the terrace, the triple-arched entrance. Designed by a woman my age.

"It truly is beautiful, Aunt Matt."

"Keep in mind as we go inside that it was also decorated entirely by women. And The Board of Lady Managers, which is composed of members from every state and territory in the U.S., are in full charge of it all. This is unprecedented, Violet. Women have never been given control of a pavilion at such a huge, important exposition as this."

The first displays we viewed were a model hospital and a model kindergarten. I glanced around as we walked through the exhibits, hoping to see the famous Pinkerton guards, standing in uniform at all of the strategic places. I wanted to ask one of them how much it would cost to find my mother. But I saw very few men, and none in a guard uniform.

"Where are the Pinkerton guards?" I asked Aunt Matt.

"You can't see them—that's the whole point. They purposely blend in so the thieves don't know they're being observed." She pulled her father's gold watch and chain out of her purse and glanced at the time. "We can see the rest of the building after the speech. Come on."

"A speech? What's it about?" I asked as we marched to the lecture hall.

"I believe a woman physician is going to present her research on women's health."

The lecture hall was packed, and we had to take seats in the front row. One of the Lady Managers introduced the physician, and I had to cover my mouth to disguise my amusement. Instead of a proper dress, the good doctor wore a baggy tunic and an enormous pair of bloomers. They looked like the pantaloons women wore beneath their skirts—but without the skirt!

"Ladies," she began, "I'm well aware that the majority of you are, at this very moment, trapped in the confines of a whalebone corset. But you might be shocked to learn that, according to my research, your tightly laced corsets are responsible for more than fifty feminine ailments."

She proceeded to enumerate them, one by one, but my mind began to wander after "heart palpitations, difficulty breathing, and light-headedness." The symptoms sounded suspiciously like a romance novel's description of love. Could it be that thousands of women had married their husbands in the mistaken belief that they were in love, when all along their corsets had been too tight? How disappointing to watch their love mysteriously vanish once their corsets were unlaced. I made up my mind that if I ever felt love's symptoms, I would loosen my corset immediately before accepting a proposal of marriage.

I turned my attention back to the speaker and learned that she not only advocated tossing out our whalebone corsets, but expected us to replace all of our leisure dresses with bloomers.

"Someday, dresses for women will be a thing of the past," she insisted. She bounced around the stage as she talked as if she had taken an overdose of Dr. Dean's Blood Builder, her baggy bloomers flopping like a clown suit. "Women will experience more comfort, better health, and more freedom of movement when they switch to wearing bloomers. Once you try them, every one of you will want to wear them. We'll see bloomers on trains, in the parks, and in every public place. Freedom, ladies! Bloomers mean freedom!"

I had to work hard to stifle my giggles. I was probably the only woman in the audience who thought the lecture—and the doctor's bloomers—were hilarious.

The applause that followed her speech seemed a bit tentative to me. As much as Aunt Matt and her friends might yearn for freedom, I don't think they could picture themselves in bloomers. Nor could I. Admittedly, corsets were uncomfortable. But the unrestrained female form, especially on some of the plumpest dowagers, might yield more freedom than the world was prepared to see.

Aunt Matt and I continued our tour of the Woman's Pavilion after the lecture, and it truly was awe-inspiring. The Women's Christian Temperance Union and Susan B. Anthony's suffragettes both had booths. The sky-lit gallery housed every type of artistic endeavor I could imagine: paintings, sculpture, needlework, pottery. The pavilion overflowed with women's accomplishments in science, health care, literature, education, and exploration. The variety of inventions was staggering—everything from washing machines and surgical bandages to egg beaters and frying pans. All created by women.

"I had no idea that women were doing so many things," I said.

"Yes. While it's still an unfortunate fact that men dominate our culture, we would like our pavilion to show that creativity and inventiveness aren't limited to men. Have you read the novel *Jane Eyre*?"

"Yes, of course."

"We have a copy of it on display written by Charlotte Bronte's own hand. I can also show you an original copy of the law that allowed women to argue cases before the Supreme Court for the first time. This pavilion is going to further women's causes far into the twentieth century."

"Where did the Lady Managers ever find all these things?"

"We sent invitations to women around the world, and even asked queens and princesses for their help. Women in every state and nation gathered together to search for their most outstanding accomplishments in every field. An all-women jury judged the entries and selected the winners."

"I am truly amazed, Aunt Matt."

"Good. But don't stop there, Violet. As you look at all of these achievements, think of what you might accomplish someday."

"Me? It never occurred to me to do anything. I mean . . . no one ever told me that women could do these things."

"That's why I wanted to bring you here. No one ever encouraged me either. But I hope you will begin to dream of more for your life than sipping tea or marrying a wealthy husband."

"This pavilion is like . . . like a celebration!"

"You're absolutely right. That's exactly what this pavilion is—a celebration of women's abilities and talents. The world can no longer dismiss us. You will have so many more opportunities in life than I ever did. Take your time choosing, Violet."

I gazed around at the variety of displays and remembered my grandmother's words about being unique: *"You be exactly who God created you to be, and don't let anyone tell you otherwise."* Where did I fit in? Could I really do something as amazing as all of these women had?

Later, Aunt Matt stopped at a booth that sold silk scarves handmade by women in India. "Pick one," she said, "and I'll buy it for you. I want you to remember your visit."

I came out of the building inspired to accomplish great things. But as we walked back to the streetcar stop, it seemed that everywhere I looked I saw men and women together—strolling the fairgrounds arm in arm; pushing children in baby carriages; sitting beside each other on the streetcar. I realized that in spite of all the wonderful things I'd seen in the Woman's Pavilion, I still longed to fall in love.

More than anything, I wanted to know what it felt like to be kissed the way I'd seen Nelson kissing Katya. I didn't want to spend my life all alone, even if I could accomplish great things.

Did I really have to choose one or the other? Why couldn't I have both?

Chapter

19

⁂

Thursday, June 29, 1893

On Thursday evening, Nelson Kent and I boarded the whale-back steamship *Columbus* in Chicago's harbor and sailed to the fairgrounds. A large group of pea pods and their dates joined us, including Haughty and Naughty. The Grant sisters greeted me like long-lost friends.

"What a fine-looking couple you two make," Haughty said, looking us over.

"Don't we?" Nelson replied. He treated me very possessively, as if letting the others know he had staked his claim. We conversed politely with everyone for a few minutes, then Nelson steered me away.

"I've had enough of them," he said. "It takes forty-five minutes to get there, and I want to enjoy the cruise with you."

"I am enjoying it already." We stood at the rail and watched as the ship steamed along the shoreline. Homes and factories, shipyards and church steeples slipped past us. Soon the fair's domed buildings came into view, its towers and turrets topped with colorful flags and streamers. A little daylight remained in the warm June evening, and the setting sun leaked streams of vivid colors across the western sky.

"What do you think of your first view of the fair?" Nelson asked. I didn't have the heart to tell him that I had seen it three times already.

"It's beautiful from this vantage point. It looks like a magical city with the white buildings all lit up with electric lights."

"It's like something from a storybook, isn't it?"

Indeed, it resembled a scene from an entirely different world, and I couldn't resist asking Nelson the question, "If you could choose between living on another planet or living beneath the sea, which would you choose?"

"I can't imagine either place being more lovely than our own planet."

We got off the ship at the end of the pier, and Nelson paid our ten-cent fares to ride on the "people mover." The moving sidewalk had chairs to sit on, as it transported us all the way down the pier to the fairgrounds. We got off in front of the Peristyle, a long hallway of massive columns that made me think we had arrived in ancient Greece. Nelson took my arm as we walked beneath the arch, and then we paused to admire the scene. The Court of Honor lay ahead of us with a view of the Grand Basin, the Statue of the Republic, and MacMonnies Fountain.

"This is so beautiful, Nelson!"

"And it's only the beginning."

He stopped at a souvenir stand on the way to the concert hall and bought me a beautiful ivory fan with a picture of Columbus on it. "In case it's warm in the theater," he said.

We stopped again to admire the statues of Handel and Bach in front of Choral Hall and the portraits of famous musicians and composers that decorated the building's facade. We found our seats inside, and when the music began, I closed my eyes and lost myself in the magnificent sound. This was a world away from the Gospel Wagon's wheezing organ and muddy streets. We might have been on a different planet altogether instead of the same city.

We went outside for air during intermission. Nelson grabbed my hand. "Come on, we have a few minutes. I want you to see the Electricity Building all lit up at night."

We hurried past a pavilion that looked as though the Moors had built it, with an arched doorway painted in vivid reds and gold.

"What's inside that building?" I asked.

"I wish I had time to show it to you. It's the Transportation Building, and it's amazing, Violet. Every means of transportation you can imagine is inside from the smallest wagon to the largest locomotive."

"It sounds interesting." In fact, it must have been "remarkably interesting" since it hadn't been on Herman Beckett's list.

"There are so many new inventions and ideas at this exposition," Nelson said. "You can really get a glimpse of what the future is going to be like. Someday all of the streetcars will run without horses. And everyone will ride around in their own horseless carriage too."

"How will a carriage get anywhere without horses?"

"They will all have miniature steam engines to power them. And man is going to figure out how to fly like the birds one of these days too. The modern age is just ahead of us. If only I could convince my father to invest in that future."

A statue of Ben Franklin stood guard in front of the Electricity Building. I had never seen so many electric lights in one place.

"I wish I had time to show you Thomas Edison's displays. He has some amazing new inventions. There is a machine that makes music—or rather, reproduces the sound of music from an orchestra or choir. Can you imagine what it will be like to have a music machine in your own home? We'll be able to hear a concert like the one we heard tonight whenever we want to."

"It will put a lot of musicians out of a job." I happened to glance behind me at the Wooded Island and saw thousands of tiny lights twinkling in the dark like fireflies. "Oh, look, Nelson! It's like a fairy-land!"

"Come on, let's go." He took my arm, leading me toward the island.

"What about the concert?"

"This is more fun, isn't it? Besides, I'm pretty sure there's a path that will take us across the island and back to Choral Hall again."

I linked my arm through his and we hurried across the footbridge and onto the island. I was so entranced by the trees and the lagoon and the twinkling fairy lamps that several minutes passed before I realized that Nelson and I were alone.

"We don't have a chaperone!" I said, skidding to a stop.

"It doesn't matter, Violet. You're safe with me."

It annoyed me that America was entering an era of inventions and innovations, yet I still had to live by an old-fashioned set of rules. I was tired of them.

"I want to be a modern woman," I told Nelson, "and go wherever I'd like with whomever I'd like. I can't even get on a streetcar and go downtown without someone to accompany me. I wish I didn't need a chaperone."

"They're for your protection, Violet. Believe me, there are plenty of unsavory rogues and thieves out there who would like nothing better than to take advantage of a pretty young woman like you."

Silas McClure, for one.

"Speaking of change," I said, swiftly changing the subject, "would you support a woman's right to vote?"

"I don't know . . . I haven't given it much thought."

"My aunt Matt reads the newspaper every day, and she believes that women not only should be allowed to vote, but that a woman can do any job that a man can do."

"Surely not manual labor like building railroads and working in coal mines. Why would a woman want to do that kind of work?

Besides, aren't there jobs that only women can do—such as having children? Only a woman can nurture a child properly."

We slowed our pace, enjoying the evening as we strolled down the winding pathway past hundreds of fairy lamps. Neither of us was paying much attention to where we were going.

"I sometimes wonder what it would be like to be able to make my own decisions," I said, "the way men do. Jane Addams defies convention with her work among the immigrants. Aunt Matt defies tradition too."

"But money is a big factor in both instances. If you can support yourself, you can do anything you want. Didn't your aunt inherit her father's estate? And Jane Addams inherited money too, I believe. That's how she started her work."

"I guess you're right. And I'm not likely to inherit any money. My father is comfortable but not wealthy. When he remarries everything will go to his new family. There's not much chance that I could inherit enough to be independent."

"There is another way to inherit money and be independent."

I looked up at Nelson. "There is?"

"Yes, you could marry into it."

I halted in the middle of the path and a group of people walking behind us nearly ran into us.

When I didn't respond, Nelson continued. "Some wealthy, modern-minded men—such as myself—are willing to give their wives a great deal of independence. My wife would have enough money to do whatever she pleased."

"That sounds so . . . so devious—to marry someone for money."

"Women do it all the time," Nelson said with a shrug. "So do men."

"Men do? What do you mean?" We started walking again.

"Well, if a man who is without financial means marries a woman from a wealthy family, all of her property and assets become his. It works in a man's favor to marry well, just as it does for women."

I understood what Nelson meant, but it didn't seem right. "Aunt Agnes told me that your father won't let you get ahead in his business until you settle down and get married. Is that true?"

"Yes, it's true."

"May I ask you a question . . . ? Is that why you're courting me?"

"Would you think less of me if I told you it was? I mean, aren't you and the other young ladies—Haughty and Naughty and all the rest—doing exactly the same thing? Isn't it your goal to marry the richest man?"

"I suppose so. I just don't like the sound of it."

"Hey, we were having fun until the subject of money came up. Can't we simply enjoy this evening?"

We stopped in a clearing and watched the colored floodlights sweep across the sky, lighting up the distant buildings and domes and fountains. I felt as though I had stepped into a storybook.

"This is a beautiful place, Nelson. Thank you for bringing me here at night." He took my chin in his hand and lifted my face toward his. He was about to kiss me. And I was about to let him— until I remembered Katya. I quickly turned away.

"We should probably get back."

"Violet, wait." He captured my arm. "I understand that you have other suitors, but tell me—how can I win you away from them?"

I knew that I couldn't explain the true reason for my hesitation, because it had been wrong to spy on him and Katya. I decided to tell a story instead.

"Years ago, Gilbert Casey fell madly in love with my great-aunt Bertha. He easily obtained her father's permission to marry her, but that wasn't enough for Gilbert. He wanted Bertha to fall in love with him—really and truly in love. And so he set about to win her heart."

"You're quite the romantic, Violet Hayes. Always bringing up the subject of love." He lifted my hand to his lips and kissed it. "But at least I know, now, what it will take."

"We'd better get back," I said again. And quickly too—before my curiosity won the battle with my good sense and I allowed him to take me into his arms and kiss me the way he had kissed Katya.

When we finally got back to the Choral Hall, all of Nelson's friends were standing around outside. "There you are," one of the pea pods said. "We wondered what happened to you two."

"I can guess what you've been doing," Haughty said.

"You would be wrong," Nelson told her. "Our excursion has been entirely aboveboard, I assure you. Miss Hayes is a very proper lady." He offered me his arm and we started walking, along with the whole group, away from the music hall.

"Is the concert over? Where are we going?"

"We've been invited to a private party in one of the other pavilions."

I never did learn the name of the building. The party took place in a rented hall, away from the exhibits and displays. The lavishly decorated room resembled a European casino, complete with a roulette wheel, dice games, playing cards, and other games of chance. I thought they were merely elaborate props until I saw the stacks of real money being exchanged for multi-colored chips. Waiters circulated with trays of appetizers and drinks. Judging by the raucous laughter and loud voices, the drinks were alcoholic.

Nelson took a wad of bills from his wallet and exchanged them for a little tray of chips. He chose a game of dice, and I could see right away that he wasn't gambling for fun. His intent was to win. But the longer he played, the more money he lost, and as his pile of chips dwindled away, he began to grow angry.

"Let's leave, Nelson. This isn't fun anymore." I rubbed his arm to soothe him, but he shrugged me away.

"Not until I win my money back."

"Do you think that's a good idea? You might lose even more."

He turned on me with surprising anger. "You know, women aren't the only ones who lack the freedom to make their own decisions. But if I can accumulate enough money on my own, I'll be able to do whatever I want with it. I'm going to be a self-made man, Violet, like

Turlington Harvey and Marshall Field and all the rest of them."

"By gambling? Didn't you tell me that the lumber baron, what's-his-name, worked his way to the top through hard work? Mr. McCormick invented his machine and Mr. Field built his store, and—"

"What difference does it make how I get it?" He turned back to his dice game.

"That looks like a lot of money," I said as he placed his last few chips on the board. "Why risk it all? Why not just work for your father?"

"It will take too long."

"Too long for what?" But I thought I knew. He could break free from his father's control and marry Katya if he had his own money.

"Too long for my father to trust me," he said. "I want to make my own investments and get in on some of the new inventions from Mr. Edison and the others. New modes of transportation. Father won't try any of them."

"Well, I don't know anything about investments, but it's hardly a good idea to win your father's trust by gambling away all your money."

Nelson seemed to have a moment of sudden clarity. "I suppose you're right. I'm sorry for yelling, Violet."

I sighed with relief. Surely Nelson would scoop up his remaining chips and leave—but he didn't.

"One more throw. Kiss the dice for me, would you, Violet?" He held them up to my lips and I reluctantly gave them a peck. I held my breath as he rolled the dice—and won!

"We can't leave now," Nelson said. He was back in the game with all of the fervor and excitement of Louis Decker and his friends at an evangelistic rally. Every time he made me kiss the dice, he won.

"You're my good-luck charm!" He grinned and gave me a quick hug.

I had to admit that winning was exciting. The Grant sisters and all of the pea pods gathered around to cheer us on. With each roll of the dice, my heart pounded a little faster, and the tension and excitement grew greater and greater—along with the risk. I couldn't help jumping up and down each time Nelson won. We cheered louder as the pile of chips in front of Nelson grew into a large mound. We were on a winning streak! I hadn't felt this alive since Ruth Schultz and I decided to sneak out of the dormitory after curfew.

An hour after I had first kissed his dice, Nelson had won all of his money back along with a little more. He would have continued to play, but the fairgrounds were closing down for the night.

"Too bad we have to go," he said. "Just when we were winning too."

He traded in his chips and stood counting his money as the casino lights dimmed. One of the blackjack dealers offered to escort Nelson and me to the ship for our protection. I thought of Silas' thieving friends roaming the fairgrounds and told Nelson he should accept.

"I would feel much safer," I told him. "People have been robbed here at the fair, you know."

"You're my lucky charm," he told me again as we boarded the ship. "We make a great team, don't we?"

Chapter

20

Friday, June 30, 1893

I managed to forget all about Louis Decker and Folk Night at the settlement house until Friday afternoon. By then, my grandmother was so excited about our evening out that I didn't have the heart to hurt her feelings by staying home. I decided to douse a handkerchief with perfume and carry it in my pocket so I would have a way to defend myself against the putrid smells. I also wore my least favorite dress and oldest pair of shoes.

Louis looked thoroughly bathed, combed, tucked, and spit-shined when he arrived at the house to escort Grandmother and me. Only his spectacles remained smudged, as usual. He really was a nice-looking man when he was all cleaned up. Not as classically handsome as Nelson, perhaps—and certainly not as well dressed—but attractive, nonetheless.

The evening began with a dinner held in the dining room where we had served the soup. Thankfully, the delicious aroma of roasting meat overwhelmed the stench of the neighborhood, and I could relax and tuck my perfumed handkerchief into my pocket. Scores of Bohemian people crowded inside the room, some in their colorful, traditional clothes, but most in much humbler attire. I felt a pang of guilt for enjoying the finer things in life that Nelson could offer. I should like Louis Decker. I should gladly choose him and a life of meaning and purpose and good values. Nelson enjoyed gambling—and I had helped him win. I had joined in. First I'd helped a thief and now a gambler. What was wrong with me?

Grandmother sat with a group of her friends, leaving Louis and me alone—if you can call sitting with hundreds of other people alone. Louis was a very quiet man when he wasn't preaching, and he didn't seem to know how to begin a conversation or keep it going. I did all the work of keeping the tennis ball in the air as plates of roast pork, potatoes, vegetables, and several other things I didn't recognize circulated around our table.

"Have you been to the World's Fair, Louis?"

"Not yet. I've been too busy working with our evangelism team."

"Are you planning to go this summer?"

"Only if the Lord leads me, and if it fits His purposes."

"You wouldn't consider going just for fun?" He looked up at me as if he had never heard of the word. At least I think he was looking at me. His glasses were so smudged I didn't understand how he could see anything at all, including the plate in front of him.

One of the platters that circulated around our table was piled with slices of a mysterious-looking meat. It had a strange, gelatinous consistency and resembled what you might get if you made a gelatin dessert out of random pieces of leftover meat.

"What is this?" I asked.

"I can't pronounce the Bohemian name, but it's similar to what we call head cheese."

"I've never heard of head cheese. What's in it besides cheese?"

"It isn't really cheese. They take the animal's head with all of the unused parts such as the brain, the tongue, and so forth, and boil it together to make a sort of sausage out of it. It's quite delicious."

I quickly passed the plate to the next person. As much as I longed to be as adventurous as Silas McClure, who had eaten rattlesnake, I lacked the stomach for it. And I did not care to sample any body parts from an animal's head. I nibbled a bit of the roast pork and dumplings but was afraid to fill up, remembering the smelly ride home. What I did eat, however, was delicious. Louis had a voracious appetite and devoured everything in sight.

"What is the most adventuresome thing you've ever eaten?" I asked him.

"What do you mean?"

"I once met a person who'd eaten rattlesnake meat. Would you try it?"

"Only if I had a very good reason to." I had hoped to make him laugh, but I was beginning to realize that Louis Decker didn't laugh much. He wasn't as gloomy and boring as Herman was—Louis would become quite animated when he preached or sang. But I had the feeling that he would never laugh unless God instructed him to.

"Suppose you became a missionary and the natives you were trying to convert served you something disgusting, like alligator eyeballs. Would you eat them?"

"That's different. I would do anything for the sake of the Gospel."

Yes, I was quite certain he would. I watched him swipe his bread across his plate to sop up the gravy and asked, "Have you always lived in Chicago?"

"No. Like Mr. Moody, I came to Chicago to get rich. Mr. Moody was a shoe salesman at one time, and his goal in life was to make a lot of money. But then the Lord changed his life and he gave up chasing wealth to serve God. That's basically my story too."

"Where do you see yourself living and working after you finish school?"

"Wherever God sends me."

For dessert we had little cookies with fruit in the middle of them, and there was something about the sight of them, or maybe the flavor, that seemed familiar to me. The Bohemian women pronounced them "ko-latch-key."

"I've eaten cookies like these before," I told Louis. "I can't recall when or where."

Everyone relaxed while we waited for the folk dancing to begin, and some of the smaller children chased each other around the tables, giggling. The sound of their laughter was as lovely as the music I had heard with Nelson Kent. I remembered Herman Beckett saying that he wanted a family, and Grandmother had told me that Louis was wonderful with the children. Yet I suspected that if I asked Louis if he envisioned children in his future, his reply would be something like, "Whatever God plans for me."

"Tell me about your family, Louis."

"My father owns a bakery in Milwaukee. We're just an ordinary family—three sisters, two brothers. I came to Chicago to make my mark in life, and I was doing very well in the business world until I saw the light of Christ. I'm like the man Jesus healed: I once was blind, but now I see." Louis always managed to talk more about God than about himself. I decided to change my tactics.

"If you had to choose between being struck blind and never being able to see the face of your beloved again, or becoming permanently deaf and being denied the sound of music and of a child's laughter, which would you choose?"

"I believe that we're responsible for our own behavior, but the choices you're talking about come from God. Not a hair can fall from our heads unless it's His will. The disciples once asked Jesus about a man born blind and wanted to know who had sinned to cause that tragedy. Jesus said that the man had been born blind in order that God would be glorified. And so, whether deaf or blind, I pray that my life would bring Him glory."

Of the many times I had asked that question, I had never heard

247

an answer quite like Louis'. I decided to ask another one.

"If you had to choose between being rich but disfigured, or poor but handsome, which would you choose?"

"The Bible says, 'Give me neither poverty nor riches; feed me with food convenient for me: Lest I be full, and deny thee and say, Who is the Lord? or lest I be poor and steal, and take the name of my God in vain.' . . . That's from Proverbs."

The moment he mentioned stealing, I thought of Silas McClure. And wealth reminded me of Nelson Kent.

"Is money bad? Should wealthy people give it all away?"

"No, money itself isn't bad. The Bible says that it's the *love* of money that's the root of all evil."

I nodded, pretending to understand what he was talking about. I had never met anyone who talked about the Bible as much as Louis did. He made me ashamed of my shallowness. So I pretended to understand.

Once again, I thought of Aunt Matt's contention that every married woman was an actress. I was beginning to think she was right— and also that all the unmarried women, like myself, were continually auditioning to become actresses. Ever since coming to Chicago I seemed to be playacting. I had to smile enigmatically at Aunt Agnes' parties. I had to pretend not to be bored when I was with Herman Beckett. And now I had to pretend to be nice with Louis Decker. In fact, the only person I had been myself with was Silas McClure— and he was a thief! What did that say about me?

"Do you think it's possible for people to change?" I asked, still thinking of Silas.

"Not on their own. Only God can transform people. But when the Son sets you free, you are free indeed."

"What about real criminals? Have you ever known a hardened criminal, such as a thief or a con man, to change his way of life after hearing Mr. Moody preach?"

"Sure, I've heard plenty of stories where that's happened. And of course there's the example of the thief who was crucified beside Christ. After the thief repented, Jesus told him, 'Today shalt thou be with me in paradise.'"

Talking to Louis Decker was like conversing with Moses or one of the Apostles. I wondered what he had been like before he'd started studying the Bible.

The sound of musical instruments warming up began to drift into the restaurant as we talked—a clarinet, an accordion, a couple of violins, a bass fiddle—and soon a little orchestra began to play outside in the street. The musicians were quite good. Everyone spilled outside to listen and to watch the dancers perform in their colorful, embroidered dresses. As I watched, the same feeling of familiarity that I'd had with the cookies suddenly returned. This dance was somehow familiar to me.

"I've heard this music before," I told Louis. "I can't recall where."

"It certainly is lively," he said, clapping in tune.

For the next dance, the women all produced colorful scarves and waved them joyfully in the air as they whirled in time to the music. That's when it all came back to me: the bright colors, the dancing, the joy—my mother used to twirl a colorful scarf the same way and sing in another language as we danced around the room together. My heart pounded with excitement as the memory returned. It had been a long time ago. I had been very small. And Mother had been very beautiful.

Later, the band played a slow tune, and tears filled my eyes as the immigrants linked arms to sing along. I had no idea what the words meant, but I know that my mother used to sing the same song to me as a lullaby. She would sit on my bed stroking my hair, singing to me until I fell asleep. A tear rolled down my cheek as the song ended.

"That was beautiful, wasn't it?" Louis asked. I nodded. I didn't reveal the real reason for my tears.

By the time the evening ended and people began to leave, many of the smaller children had grown tired and overly excited. I heard a little girl crying, "I don't want to go," and I couldn't blame her. She would have to leave the warm companionship and laughter and music to go home to a bleak tenement building. The child's mother scooped her up in her arms.

"Come to Mama, *ho-cheech-ka*," she murmured. For a moment, the street in front of me seemed to tilt. I had to grip Louis' arm to keep from stumbling as another memory stirred. That was what my mother used to call me. She would hug me as tightly as Aunt Birdie always did and whisper the word tenderly, just as that mother had: *ho-cheech-ka*.

"Are you all right, Violet?"

"No . . . I mean . . . I think my mother might have been Bohemian."

"Why don't you ask her?"

"She . . . she left when I was nine years old. I don't know where she is."

"I'm sorry."

I knew I had discovered an important clue to my mother's past, and like the little girl, I didn't want to go home. I wanted to stay and talk to these people and see what other memories of my mother might spring to life. But the evening had drawn to a close and everyone was leaving.

I felt too emotional to converse much on the way home, so I listened as Louis and my grandmother talked. She had much more in common with him than I did. They spoke the same language, sprinkled with Bible verses and references to God as if He were an old friend.

"Thank you for a nice evening," I told Louis at our front door.

"I hope to see you again soon, Violet."

The moment the door closed, I turned to my grandmother. "May I ask you just one question about my mother?"

"You may ask. I can't promise I'll be able to answer it."

"The songs tonight reminded me of her." My voice trembled with emotion. "She used to sing tunes like that to me. And then I heard a mother call her child *ho-cheech-ka*, and that was what Mother used to call me. Was she a Bohemian immigrant?"

"I believe that her family might have been from that region of Europe, yes."

"So she was poor, like those people, before she married my father?"

"I never saw her house, Violet, and I never met her family."

"Please tell me *something*," I begged as my tears spilled over. "Anything! What does it matter now, since my parents are divorced and Father is going to marry Maude O'Neill?"

Grandmother saw my tears and hugged me close. Then she led me into the kitchen and sat me down at the table while she fixed a pot of tea.

"Your parents met on the night of the Great Fire, as you know. Your father rescued her." I wanted to ask how, but I was afraid to interrupt. "Your mother lost everything she owned. Our church in Lockport took in many of the homeless families—and there were so many of them. More than one hundred thousand people here in Chicago lost everything in the fire. Your father brought your mother home to our church in Lockport. When they fell in love and were married, she didn't return to Chicago. There was nothing to go back for, she said."

"They really loved each other?"

"Yes, at one time, they really did."

"What happened?"

Grandmother shook her head. She wouldn't answer.

"Aunt Birdie keeps telling me that I should marry for love, but that's what my parents did, and look what happened to them. I need to know why their love ended and why my mother left."

"Have you asked your father that question?"

"He told me that she hated her life in Lockport, hated being tied down."

"He would know much more about it than I do."

"But why was she so unhappy? Please tell me *something*!"

Grandmother reached across the table and took my hand in hers. "Violet, I don't know all the details of your parents' lives, but I do know there were huge differences between them. And once Angeline married John, she had new expectations placed on her as his wife. He is a prominent man in the community, as you know."

My grandmother gave my hand a squeeze, then released it. I watched her take a sip of tea and tried to picture my father when he had been young and in love. I couldn't do it. It was like trying to imagine Herman Beckett as Shakespeare's Romeo.

My grandmother set her teacup down and said, "Your mother came from Chicago and your father from tiny little Lockport. Maybe she missed the excitement of the city once in a while. Maybe she missed her own family too."

"I understand what you're saying, but that doesn't explain why she left *me*. Didn't she love *me*?"

Tears filled my eyes again. Grandmother stood and hurried to my side, smoothing back my hair and kissing my forehead. She had tears in her eyes as well.

"She loved you very, very much, Violet Rose. I know that to be true."

"Then why did she leave me? Do you know why?"

Grandmother bent and drew me into her arms, holding me tightly. "I'm sorry, Violet Rose. You need to ask your father that question."

Chapter

21

Saturday, July 1, 1893

I stayed in bed the next morning until long past breakfast. If I kept the pillow over my head to drown out all of the other noises, I could recall the music from the night before and imagine the dancers whirling. I wanted to hang on to the wispy memories of my mother for as long as possible.

It was Saturday, and my grandmother and aunts were at home, but I didn't want to face any of them. They all had such high hopes for me, which I had encouraged by accompanying them on their various pursuits. But I felt very confused. I didn't know what I wanted to do with my life. So I remained in bed.

It was close to noon when I heard Aunt Agnes' silvery voice gilding our front hallway. "*Bonjour*, darlings! How is everyone?"

I made up my mind that I would plead illness rather than endure any social calls with her today. Even so, it was rude of me to remain in bed when she had come to call. I got dressed and went downstairs. All four of the Howell sisters sat in the parlor.

"*Bonjour*, Violet dear. Good news! Nelson simply *raves* about you. His grandmother is *so* pleased. So is his father, by the way. Did you enjoy the concert at the fair the other night? And how was the party afterward?"

I didn't know what to say. Grandmother seemed to be waiting for my reply too. They would be shocked to learn about the gambling. I was still trying to formulate a response when someone knocked on the front door.

"I'll get it," Aunt Birdie sang. She fluttered out to the hallway, and a moment later I heard her say, "Why, it's Johnny!"

I jumped up and hurried to the foyer—and there stood my father on the other side of Aunt Birdie's embrace.

"What are you doing here?" I asked.

"I came for you," he replied, as if stating the obvious. "I'm going to accompany you home and help with your trunk."

"Oh, how nice," Aunt Birdie said.

"Home?" I shouted, forgetting to be ladylike. "I just got here!"

"Violet, you've been here for a month."

"Today is the first day of July," Aunt Birdie said helpfully.

"But I'm not ready to go home!"

Father looked perplexed. "You told me that you wanted to see the World's Columbian Exposition. You've seen it, haven't you?"

"Yes, but—"

"Violet has seen it four times. Isn't that right, dear?" Aunt Birdie gestured to all the souvenirs I had collected, which for some reason had ended up on the hall table: the Ferris wheel coin from Silas McClure, the picture postcards from Herman Beckett, the silk scarf from Aunt Matt, and the beautiful ivory fan with Columbus' portrait on it from Nelson Kent.

"Four times?" Father repeated. "Then you should be more than ready to come home."

"Shall I help you pack?" Aunt Birdie asked.

"I don't want to go home!" I sounded like one of the petulant children at the settlement house last night.

Aunt Matt marched into the foyer. "Lunch is ready," she declared. "Let's sit down and eat like civilized people. It's nothing fancy, Agnes, only vegetable soup, but you're welcome to join us."

"I believe I will," Agnes said. "John and I need to talk "

We all trooped into the dining room and sat down. Aunt Matt filled our soup bowls and Grandmother prayed. The room felt tense as everyone passed the rolls and butter around the table. I stared at my soup, unable to eat.

"I spoke with Herman Beckett," my father began. "He holds you in very high regard, Violet, and is eager for your return. Maude says that he is serious about your courtship. She thinks you should marry him."

"We hardly know each other!"

"That's why he's eager for your return, so he can court you in earnest. He seemed very pleased when I told him that I was coming to fetch you this weekend."

"Maude just wants to marry me off so she'll be rid of me."

"That's very unkind, Violet. Maude has your best interests at heart."

"Wait a minute, John," Aunt Agnes said. "Who is this suitor you're discussing?"

"He's a young man from Lockport. He works as a shipping clerk."

"He's a bore," I mumbled.

"John, dear, never mind some yokel from Lockport. I've found a much better match for our Violet. His father is the business tycoon Howard Kent. His family is swimming in old money. And Nelson's grandmother insists that he has grown very fond of our Violet. She hinted that he might be ready to propose soon."

I nearly choked on a mouthful of lemonade. I coughed a few times, then managed to say, "I like Nelson, but I'm hardly ready to marry him."

"For goodness' sakes, why not?" Agnes asked. "Nelson is eager to settle down and take his place in his father's firm. It's a wonderful opportunity."

"Yes, for Nelson."

"I don't know why you're being so contrary," Agnes said, "but you had better come to your senses before it's too late. Things are going so well with him, and he's a wonderful catch. John, perhaps you could speak with Nelson's father while you're here in the city. I could arrange a luncheon or something so you could meet the Kent family."

"It does sound promising," Father said.

I got my grandmother's attention across the table and pleaded silently with her for help.

"Louis Decker admires our Violet a great deal too," she said, jumping in. I lowered my head in despair. That wasn't at all what I'd wanted from her. "If Louis knew you were in town, John, I'm sure he would want to ask permission to court Violet as well."

"Who is this Louis Decker?" Agnes asked. "Is he any relation to Homer and Nettie Decker on Prairie Avenue?"

"I doubt it," Grandmother said. "But I think John should meet Louis in person, rather than hear about him or his family secondhand from me."

"He must be a religious zealot," my father muttered. "I'm not interested in meeting one of those. I wouldn't let my daughter marry one either." He turned to face me again. "If you aren't interested in this Kent fellow, then I want you to come home. Herman Beckett would make an excellent husband. He comes from a very good family."

"What about love?" I asked. "Shouldn't two people love each other before they marry?"

My father made a face. "Don't be naïve, Violet. There is plenty of time for love to grow once a commitment has been made."

Aunt Matt dropped her soup spoon with a clatter. I thought she had shown remarkable restraint by keeping quiet for as long as she had. "This is nearly the twentieth century, John, not the fourteenth! Arranged marriages are a thing of the past. Violet is a sensible young woman. Shouldn't she be allowed to choose for herself?"

"Violet, dear," Aunt Birdie said, "make certain you marry for love."

Her words gave me an idea. "Do you love Maude?" I asked my father.

"We aren't discussing Maude; we're discussing you. I'm responsible for you. Your future is much too important for you to ruin by making a bad choice."

"Aunt Birdie, help me! Please!" I begged, tugging on her sleeve. "Tell my father how important love is."

Aunt Birdie picked up her spoon and tapped it against her water glass to command everyone's attention. "I think Violet should marry that nice gentleman with the wonderful smile. He's *madly* in love with her."

"Oh no." I covered my face with both hands.

"Which gentleman is that?" Father asked.

"I think Birdie means the man who accompanied Violet on the train from Lockport," Grandmother said.

This was getting worse and worse. If Father learned about Silas McClure, he would never trust my judgment again. I cringed, waiting for Father to angrily declare that no one had accompanied me from Lockport, but Aunt Birdie spoke first.

"I don't recall his name, but he gave us his card. I'll go get it." She rose from the table and headed out to the hall to fetch the silver tray. Thank goodness I had hidden all of Silas' cards inside my diary. How would I ever explain why I foolishly had gone to the fair with a thief who sold Dr. Dean's Blood Builder?

"Don't mind her," I said after Aunt Birdie had left the room. I waited until my father took another slurp of his soup and asked, "What if I'm not ready to marry?"

"Why wouldn't you be ready? You've finished school, you'll be twenty-one next April. What else would you do with yourself?"

"Women are doing all sorts of things. I saw some of their accomplishments when I visited the Woman's Pavilion with Aunt Matt."

"I might have known." He gave Aunt Matt a dark look. I turned to her next, silently pleading for help.

"John knows my opinion on the matter," she said. "Violet doesn't need to marry at all in order to lead a fulfilling life. But if she does choose to marry, it should be to whomever she wants, whenever she wants. And it should be to someone who loves her and appreciates her for herself, not for what *he* stands to gain from the marriage."

"I disagree," Father said. "I think parents are in a much better position than their children are to see the good qualities in a spouse and make a sound choice. Parents have the maturity and experience that young people lack."

"Why, John Jacob Hayes!" Grandmother said. "I'm surprised you would say that, considering your own experience."

"My own experience serves to prove my point. I believe I have made a much better choice for my second marriage now that I'm a mature adult. You'll see that immediately when you meet Maude O'Neill. And that's another reason why you need to come home, Violet. Maude would like to spend some time with you and get to know you a little better since we're going to become a family in a few months."

My stomach seethed in protest. My soup lay untouched. If only I could find my mother and remind Father of the power of true love.

"And it's because of my own experience that I've decided to choose for my daughter as well," Father continued. "I want Violet to avoid repeating the mistakes I've made. Marriages work better if people are from a similar background, a similar social class." I knew he was talking about my mother.

I realized that I didn't have a pattern for a happy marriage. Father was divorced, Aunt Matt was a spinster, Aunt Agnes' husband had affairs, and even Grandmother had admitted that her marriage hadn't been ideal. Aunt Birdie claimed to be happily married, but Uncle Gilbert was dead. Besides, Birdie seemed to tap-dance around reality a great deal of the time.

"I want to know what went wrong between you and Mother," I said boldly.

"I've already explained it to you, and I'm not going to repeat myself." He stuffed a roll into his mouth to avoid saying more.

I refused to give up. "You said she was bored, that she hated living in Lockport and being tied down. That's exactly how I feel! I don't want to settle down in Lockport either, and be bored to death by Herman Beckett."

"Violet is so much like her mother, isn't she?" Aunt Birdie asked as she glided back into the dining room with the empty silver platter.

Her question was met with a long, spine-tingling silence. It was as if she had lit the fuse on a stick of dynamite, and everyone in the room was holding his or her breath, waiting for it to explode. I broke the silence.

"Am I like her, Aunt Birdie? In what way?"

Father cleared his throat, interrupting before she could reply. He held up the empty breadbasket. "Are there any more rolls, Aunt Bertha? I would like another one."

"I'll go and see," she said with a smile.

"You told me that you find Nelson Kent interesting," Aunt Agnes said. "Think of what a wonderful life you could have with him."

Yes, if I was willing to share him with Katya. I had to do something, fast, but I was too panic-stricken to figure out a plan. I had come to Chicago with two goals and had accomplished neither. Now it was time to return home. Why hadn't I figured out a way to find my mother and to stop Father's marriage? Why had I wasted time running around the city with worthless suitors? If I didn't find my mother soon, I would have to marry whomever my father chose.

"It's my life, isn't it?" I blurted. "I don't trust you to choose for me, Father. I hate Maude. Besides, you lied to me all these years about my mother." I knew I sounded childish, but I was desperate.

"I kept the truth from you for your own good. I was protecting you. You can be very impulsive and prone to theatrics, Violet. That's why I want to see you safely married to a good husband who will provide you with a comfortable life."

"Can't you give Violet a little more time with us, John?" Grandmother asked. "July has just begun."

I saw him glance briefly at Aunt Matt. She saw it too.

"He's afraid I'll be a bad influence on you, Violet."

"But if she spends more time with Nelson Kent," Aunt Agnes said, "I'm certain he'll propose."

"Do you want to continue seeing this Kent fellow?" Father asked.

"Yes," I said, gulping. I wasn't ready to marry Nelson, but courting him would buy me some more time.

Father paused for a long time while he thought it over. "All right," he said with a huge sigh. "I suppose you can stay."

"Oh, how nice," Aunt Birdie said.

"Will you be spending the weekend with us, John?" my grandmother asked. "I can make up an extra bed . . ."

"No, I think I'll catch the train home tonight." He pulled out his pocket watch, stared at it for a moment, then snapped it closed again. "Maude will be expecting me this evening. But I'll be back in two weeks, Violet, do you understand? You seem to have no shortage of interested suitors from which to choose. Just don't prolong this, or I'll be forced to make the decision for you."

Chapter

22

I couldn't sleep that night. I needed to know which man I was destined to marry. My only recourse was to perform the Midnight Stairway Ritual.

Ruth Schultz and I had tried the ritual at school with mixed results. According to tradition, if a woman wanted to see the face of her future husband she had to dress all in white, let down her hair, and wait until just before the stroke of midnight. Then, with an uplifted candle in her right hand and a mirror in her left, she had to walk slowly down the stairs, backward, all the way to the cellar. When she reached the final step and the clock struck twelve, her future husband's face would appear in the mirror.

Ruth tried it first and swore that she saw a handsome man's face. "He was someone I didn't know," she'd said, "But I'll recognize him the moment I see him again."

Ruth and I had only one mirror and one candle so I had to wait until the second night for my turn. The ritual had to be performed at the stroke of midnight. Besides, it was easier to walk backward down the stairs with someone helping you. Otherwise, you risked falling down the stairs and breaking your neck and never finding your one true love. No one wanted to marry a cripple.

But when my turn came the second night, a jealous classmate who had gotten wind of what Ruth and I were doing snitched on us. The headmistress caught us and punished us for being out of bed after curfew. The fact that we had "endangered the dormitory" with a lit candle had prolonged our imprisonment. I never did see my future husband's face. Now, in desperation, I decided to try the midnight ritual without Ruth's help.

I borrowed a candle from the silver candelabra on the buffet in the dining room and a box of matches from the kitchen drawer. I didn't have a hand mirror, so I decided to use Aunt Birdie's silver tray. It was shiny enough for me to see my reflection, and besides, it wouldn't break if I fell down the stairs. My luck had been pretty bad lately, so I couldn't risk seven more years of it.

I let down my hair, dressed in my white muslin slip, lit the candle, and crept from my bedroom as midnight approached. My stomach felt as knotted as one of my knitting projects as I stood at the top of the stairs and waited for the case clock in the hallway to begin chiming the hour.

Bong!

The first stroke startled me as it reverberated through the silent house. I quickly recovered and started carefully down the steps, walking backward.

Bong! . . . Bong! . . .

I reached the front foyer and grabbed the silver tray from the hall table.

Bong! . . . Bong! . . . Bong! . . .

I could hear Aunt Matt snoring as I crept backward down the hall past her door. The clock was still chiming as I reached behind me to open the cellar door and start down.

Bong! . . .

My foot touched the last step at the stroke of twelve, and I held up the mirror, waiting for the face of my husband to appear. Instead, a shadowy figure suddenly materialized in front of me at the top of the stairs.

I gasped in fright. I couldn't seem to scream. My mind told me to run, but I didn't know what dangers loomed in the murky blackness behind me. Besides, the only part of me that could move was my heart, which was trying to escape from my chest.

Suddenly a trembling voice called out, "Give me back my silver tray you dirty, rotten thief!"

Aunt Birdie.

My knees gave way and I sank to the cellar floor in relief. Aunt Birdie slowly descended the stairs, brandishing an umbrella like a club. I finally found my voice.

"Aunt Birdie, wait! It's me! Violet!"

She halted, her eyes wide with surprise. "Violet Rose Hayes! Why in the world are you stealing my silver tray?"

"I'm not stealing it. I'm . . . I'm using it to see my husband's face." But the stroke of midnight had long since passed, and his face was lost to me.

Aunt Birdie sat down on the stairs and laid the umbrella in her lap. When my heart finally slowed again, I explained what I had been doing.

"I should have tried the wedding cake method," I said when I'd finished my story.

"Wedding cake?"

"It's another test Ruth told me about. You're supposed to put a slice of wedding cake under your pillow before you go to sleep. She says you'll dream about the man you'll marry that night."

"Oh, how nice."

"But I haven't been to any weddings, Aunt Birdie, and I don't intend to wait for my father's. I have to find my one true love and stop Father from marrying Maude—and I'm running out of time."

"I've never heard of either of those methods for discovering who you'll marry, dear, but I do know one method that works every time."

"Really? What do I have to do?"

"You place two walnuts on the stove, one for your suitor and one for yourself. If your suitor's walnut cracks or jumps, it means he will be unfaithful to you. If it blazes and burns, it means that he loves you. And if his and yours burst into flames at the same time it means you will marry him."

I scrambled to my feet. "I'm going to try it."

"Oh, how nice."

We went upstairs to the kitchen. The fire in the stove was out since it was summertime, but we shoved in a few sticks of kindling along with one of Aunt Matt's newspapers, all crumpled up. I blew on the wood to stoke the flames while Aunt Birdie fetched a bag of walnuts from the pantry.

"I have more than one suitor," I told her. "Will it still work if I test all three?"

"Let's try it and see." She pulled a chair over to the stove and sat down to watch.

"The first one is for me," I said, placing one walnut on the stove. "And this one is for Nelson Kent." I felt the heat from the growing fire as I put the second walnut in place. "The third is for Louis Decker . . . and this fourth one is for Herman Beckett."

"Don't forget that other gentleman." Aunt Birdie handed me another walnut.

"Which other gentleman?" But I knew very well whom she meant.

"You know, that man with the autumn blue eyes and beautiful smile."

"He's not even in the contest, Aunt Birdie." She looked so sad with her lips in a pout and her head tilted to one side that I relented. What could it hurt? Besides, she already had taken Silas McClure's walnut away from me and laid it on the stove.

"Fine. That one is for Silas McClure," I said.

I pulled up another chair and we sat watching for several long minutes. I fully expected Nelson Kent's walnut to crack and jump, proving that he would be unfaithful. Louis Decker's and Herman Beckett's might blaze and burn, revealing that they loved me, but I kept a close eye on my own, hoping it wouldn't burn along with one of theirs and indicate that we would marry. The suspense mounted as the fire roared and the flames grew hotter. I fidgeted nervously. Suddenly Aunt Birdie jumped up, moved behind my chair, and covered my eyes with her hands.

"Wait! What are you doing? I can't see."

"I know you can't," she said sweetly. "So now the question is, which beau are you hoping for?"

I saw the logic in her method.

"Is . . . is that how you discover the answer?"

"It isn't magic. Your heart knows which man is the right one for you. Tell me what your heart sees."

I was still in the dark with my eyes covered, but I thought I was beginning to see. "I would have a meaningful life doing good deeds if I married Louis, and he would consider me his partner in every way. But I don't think I could stand being poor or working with poor people. I know that makes me seem shallow, but I can't help it. I can't do what he does for the rest of my life. He works in such terrible places. Besides, Louis' passion is for God, not me."

"So he isn't the one."

"No, I don't think so. And Nelson would give me a wonderful life with servants and gowns and fine food. I know he would let me donate money to help the poor and everything. But is that enough for a lifetime together? He doesn't love me, Aunt Birdie. Nelson and I are good friends, but I think he's in love with someone else. He looks at her with love in his eyes, and I saw them kissing." I suddenly felt warm, remembering their impassioned kiss—but the heat might have been coming from the stove. "Do you think love could grow after we were married?"

"Every fire needs a spark in order to kindle a flame," she said. I had to admit that the spark between Nelson and me just wasn't there.

"Herman Beckett would be a compromise, neither rich nor poor. He seems to care for me, and he wants a home and a family. He could offer me a life that is safe and stable—but he's so *boring*! My mother was discontented living in Lockport. What if I'll be too?"

"Is he that young fellow who works for the undertaker?"

"Um . . . yes." It was late at night, and I didn't have the patience to explain Herman Beckett to her.

"Well, he's *out*! You can't spend the rest of your life with an undertaker, Violet. They're such dreary people. I despise under-takers."

"Then I guess you can take your hands away now." She didn't uncover my eyes.

"Aren't you forgetting the other fellow?"

"No, Silas McClure is a thief. He's out of the question." I imag-ined his walnut rolling into the flames, proving that he would spend eternity in hell with all of the other thieves and criminals.

"I think you know which husband you want—don't you, dear?"

"None of them."

"Well, then. That says it all, doesn't it?"

She finally uncovered my eyes. The walnuts all sat on the stove, exactly where I had placed them. The newspaper and kindling wood had nearly burned up, and the fire was going out. I opened the stove lid and pushed all of the nuts into the dying flames.

"Let's go to bed," I said with a sigh.

As I walked up the stairs, I wondered which would be the worst fate: to live with a husband who didn't love you, like Aunt Agnes did; to marry a man whose passion was directed toward God, like my grandmother had; or to be like Aunt Matt and never marry at all. But when Aunt Birdie hugged me good-night at the top of the stairs,

I suddenly knew the answer: The worst fate of all was to lose the man you truly loved the way Aunt Birdie had.

I blew out the candle and climbed into bed, burying my face in my pillow. I couldn't hold back the flood of tears any longer. That's when I admitted the truth to myself for the first time: before Aunt Birdie had covered my eyes, I had been hoping that Silas McClure's walnut would burst into flames at the same moment as mine. I could have fallen in love with him if he hadn't turned out to be a thief. But now Silas was dead to me, just as Gilbert was dead to Aunt Birdie.

Then I had another thought. Like Aunt Birdie, my father also had lost the love of his life when my mother left him. Maybe that was why he didn't want me to marry for love. Maybe he wanted to spare me the same heartache he'd experienced.

I wanted to live happily ever after, but I was beginning to believe that true love existed only in romance novels.

Chapter

23

Monday, July 3, 1893

I was desperate. My father had granted me only two more weeks in Chicago, and I couldn't waste another day. I rose early Monday morning determined to take action, any action—yet I hadn't decided what it would be. I found my grandmother in the kitchen flipping pancakes.

"You're up early, Violet Rose. Are you going to the settlement house with me?" She set a plate in front of me and turned back to the stove, humming a hymn.

"Sorry. Maybe another day."

"We could use some help down at the Suffrage Association," Aunt Matt said. She lowered her newspaper long enough to slice into her morning grapefruit. The pungent aroma filled the kitchen.

"Next time," I told her. "I promise."

"Are you going out with Agnes, dear?"

"No," I told my grandmother, "not today."

As soon as Aunt Birdie and I were alone, I yanked the drawer full of photographs out of the secretary and sat down on the sofa to look through them. Most of them were of Aunt Birdie and her sisters and their families. But I stopped when I found one that looked like a younger version of my father. Alongside him posed another young man who looked remarkably like him.

"Is this my father?" I asked Aunt Birdie, who was hovering nearby.

"Yes, that's Johnny. Wasn't he a handsome devil when he was young?" She sank onto the sofa beside me.

"Who is this man with him? A cousin?"

"No—you know. That's his brother, Philip, of course."

"Wait a minute. My father doesn't have a brother."

"Well, he certainly does. Philip and Johnny are two years apart and as loyal as twins."

I held the photo closer, studying it. "No one ever told me he had a brother. I never knew he even existed. Why doesn't anyone talk about him? Where is he?"

Aunt Birdie's wistful smile faded. "He's away at war, just like Gilbert," she said sadly.

Oh no. What Pandora's box had I opened *now?*

"I believe Florence got a letter from him not too long ago. I'll go look for it." She started to rise from the sofa.

"No, that's okay. I'll read the letter later. Let's finish looking at these photos."

The last thing I wanted to do was remind Aunt Birdie of the truth about her beloved Gilbert. But why hadn't anyone ever mentioned Philip? Here was one more secret that my family had kept from me. I tossed the photo of my mysterious uncle onto the pile and went on to the next one. And the next, and the next. When I reached the bottom of the drawer, I exhaled in frustration.

"Why aren't there any photos of my mother?"

"I don't know . . . Do you think someone could have stolen them?"

"Or else destroyed them." I decided to try a different approach. "You said the other day that I was a lot like her. Can you tell me what you meant by that?"

"She was a pretty little thing, just like you. And very imaginative. A free spirit."

I stuffed all the photos back into the drawer, upset that the search had proven fruitless. Trying to pry information from my family was a waste of time. Why not just get on the streetcar and ride down to LaSalle Street and find my mother myself? As Silas had pointed out, we were entering the twentieth century. Women should have more freedom to go places alone. I could find her address on my own, couldn't I?

Yet as I remained seated on the sofa, I realized that it wasn't the fear of the journey or the lack of a chaperone that made me hesitate. I finally came face-to-face with the truth that I had been avoiding for the past month: I was afraid to find my mother. Afraid of what I would discover about her. Afraid to learn that she didn't love me. Afraid that she would reject me all over again.

I now had to weigh those fears against the reality of my father's ultimatum. If something didn't change in the next two weeks, he was going to arrange for me to marry Herman Beckett or Nelson Kent. And my father would marry Murderous Maude O'Neill. Homely and Horrid would become my siblings. The time had come to lay aside my fears and summon some courage.

"Aunt Birdie, how would you like to go for a ride downtown with me?" I didn't quite have the courage to make the journey alone.

"Okay," she said, rising from the sofa. "Where shall we go?"

"To LaSalle Street. To find my mother."

"Oh, how nice."

Unlike her two sisters, Aunt Birdie did not walk briskly and purposefully. A stroll to the streetcar stop with her resembled a leisurely waltz in the moonlight. But Birdie was a cheerful companion and didn't lecture at the top of her voice on the ride downtown. I linked arms with her after we disembarked onto crowded LaSalle Street, feeling as though I was holding on to a balloon that might float away on the breeze if I loosened my grasp.

I located a house number on the nearest building, then turned in circles for a few moments like a blindfolded three-year-old until I got my bearings. When I'd figured out which direction to walk, we finally set off to the south. I noticed that odd and even house numbers were on opposite sides of the street, so we crossed at the first intersection to the west side of LaSalle.

We were getting very close. My feet longed to run as quickly as my racing heart, but Aunt Birdie drifted slowly beside me like a sail-boat on a calm day. She smiled at perfect strangers and greeted any man in a uniform—policeman, bellhop, doorman, streetcar driver. She probably would have hugged them all if I had relaxed my grip on her arm.

And there it was—my mother's building. Except that it wasn't an apartment building at all, but a squat three-story office building wedged between two much larger ones. A sign dangling above the door advertised a dancing school.

"This can't be it!"

"Why not, dear?"

"I don't see any apartments."

Nevertheless, I towed Aunt Birdie into the miniature lobby and read the directory. The first-floor offices belonged to an engineering firm, the second floor to the dancing school, and the third to a law firm.

"Oh no," I groaned. "This must be the lawyer's office that my mother used for her divorce."

"Well, then. That says it all, doesn't it?"

I refused to give up. We trudged up the stairs to the third floor and met an unsmiling clerk guarding the portal to the shabby office suite behind him.

"May I help you?"

I struck a dignified yet flirtatious pose, hoping to penetrate his officiousness with my dignity and his male instincts with my feminine charms.

"Oh, I surely hope so, Mister . . ." I spotted the nameplate on his desk. "Mister Morgan. You see, my name is Violet Rose Hayes, and I'm trying to locate one of your clients, Mrs. John Hayes—who happens to be my mother. Her first name is Angeline. This address was listed on my parents' divorce papers. Would you happen to have the address of her residence?"

"We can't divulge our clients' personal information." His cold voice and lack of interest felt like a slap. It didn't require much for me to summon tears.

"Oh, please . . . you must help me! She's my mother. She left home when I was nine, and I haven't seen her in eleven years."

Mr. Morgan might have been carved from stone. "That's unimportant."

"Unimportant! I've traveled all the way from Lockport by train, and it's vitally important that I get in touch with her immediately!"

"Our clients' confidentiality is also vitally important."

I took a deep breath to calm myself. My feminine charms obviously weren't working. Grumpy Mr. Morgan showed more interest in the papers he was shuffling around on his desk than in me.

"Suppose . . . suppose I wrote her a message? Could you forward it to her?"

"We are not a courier service."

"I realize that, but what if . . . What if I paid to become one of your clients, and then you could give—"

"Our firm only consults on legal matters."

I grabbed Aunt Birdie's arm and stormed away. As soon as we were out of his sight on the stairwell landing, I started to cry. Aunt Birdie offered me her handkerchief and a hug.

"There, there . . ."

"I need to find my mother, Aunt Birdie!"

"Well, then, we'll just have to keep looking, won't we?"

We went outside and started to walk again. I was too upset to care which street we were on or which direction we were going. We had stopped at an intersection and were waiting for the traffic to clear, when Aunt Birdie suddenly pointed to a group of men standing in front of the Municipal Court Building across the street.

"Oh, look. Isn't that the young man with the lovely blue eyes who came to call on you? What was his name?"

"Silas McClure . . ." I breathed. He was unmistakable, even from this distance. I whirled around so quickly to walk the other way that Aunt Birdie broke free. Before I could stop her, she waved her arms like a drowning victim and called to him.

"Yoo hoo! Mr. McClure!"

"Hey there!" he shouted when he saw her. He waved in return, then left the other men and hurried across the street, weaving expertly between horses and wagons and carriages. "Miss Hayes! And Mrs. Casey. Hey, it's great to see you!" Aunt Birdie greeted him with an enormous hug.

My pulse began to race, and I didn't want it to, but Silas' face had lit up like the White City at night when he saw me. It was so seldom that someone looked that pleased to see me. Nelson greeted me coolly, Louis was cordial, and gloomy Herman might have been comatose. I told my heart to slow down, reminding myself that Silas was a thief and a criminal—he had just come out of the courthouse, hadn't he? But the element of danger only made my heart beat faster.

"What brings you ladies down here?"

"Violet is looking for her mother," Aunt Birdie said. "Have you seen her?"

He blinked. Then I saw understanding dawn in his eyes.

"Hey, that's right! On the day we arrived in Chicago you asked me to take you to LaSalle Street, and then—" He halted. His blinding smile disappeared. "I am really, really sorry, Violet. I was supposed to bring you here after the fair, wasn't I? I really let you down that day."

"It doesn't matter," I said, sniffing away my tears. "The address turned out to be a lawyer's office. They're the ones who drew up my mother's divorce papers, but they won't tell me where she lives."

"Your mother loved the theater," Aunt Birdie said. "That's probably where she went. Why don't we look there?"

I grabbed Birdie's arm in time to stop her from leaving. "I don't think she went to the theater, Aunt Birdie. She's been gone for eleven years."

"And there are dozens of theaters in Chicago," Silas added.

"Well, there was a wonderful production of *Romeo and Juliet*. She would enjoy that. She and Johnny were just like them—star-crossed lovers."

"Gosh, I can't tell you how bad I feel for letting you down," Silas said. "I'd like to make it up to you, Violet, and help out. If you give me your mother's name, maybe I can help you find her."

"How? I don't even have an address."

"I've . . . uh . . . I've got ways."

I imagined him using the seedy underworld of thieves and pickpockets, whispering her name from one den of criminals to the next. I knew Silas was a thief, yet I didn't feel at all afraid of him. Besides, as far as finding my mother was concerned, I was at a dead end and facing my father's deadline. How could it hurt to tell him? I needed all the help I could get.

"If I give you her name and you do find her, will you promise not to say anything to her until I've had a chance to talk to her? I don't want to frighten her off."

"How could he frighten her, dear?" Aunt Birdie asked. "He wouldn't hurt a fly. Would you, Mr. McClure?"

"A mosquito, maybe," he said, winking at her, "but never a fly. Listen, Violet, don't worry about a thing. Tell me her name and I'll see what I can do for you."

He reached into an inner pocket of his jacket to pull out a wad of folded paper and a stubby pencil. But as he did, I noticed a large bulge in another inside pocket and saw something metallic poking out.

Was that a gun?

I had never seen a pistol up close before, but from the brief glimpse I caught before he buttoned his suit coat closed, I feared that's what it was. My heart started thudding so loudly that Silas' friends probably could hear it across the street. Now I *was* afraid of him! I opened my mouth but nothing came out.

"Her name is Angeline," Aunt Birdie said. "Angeline Hayes."

"An-ge-line . . ." he repeated as he scribbled it down. "Anything else you can tell me that might help?"

"She was a pretty little thing," Aunt Birdie added. "Just like Violet. And she loved the theater."

"I think . . . I think she might be Bohemian," I finally managed to say. Desperation had won the battle over fear. "I-I heard some Bohemian folk music the other night, and the language and the songs and everything sounded very familiar to me. I don't remember much about my mother, but I remember that she sometimes sang in a different language."

He finished writing everything down and refolded the paper. I held my breath, waiting for him to open his jacket again, but he shoved the paper and pencil into an outside pocket.

"Okay then, Violet. I'll see what I can do."

"Can you hurry, please? I have less than two weeks to search for her."

"Two weeks? And then what happens?"

"Then my father is going to make me go home to Lockport."

"Hey, McClure. Come on," one of the men called from across the street. "Court is back in session." I tried to get a look at their faces and see if I recognized "Josephine" or Robert, but the men had already turned away.

"Sorry, but I gotta run." He squeezed my arm. "I'll let you know as soon as I find out something, okay?" He gave me a long, lingering look, like he was memorizing my face. His candelabra grin had returned. "It was great seeing you ladies again. Bye."

I watched as he dodged around the traffic again and bounced up the courthouse steps. He turned and waved before disappearing inside. I couldn't seem to move. There was something terribly wrong with my heart. It was out of rhythm and pounding wildly. *It's because of the gun,* I told myself. *He has a gun!*

Aunt Birdie tapped me on the shoulder, breaking the spell. "He's in love with you," she said.

"No. Th-that's impossible. He's . . . he's completely unsuitable!"

"Your cheeks aren't pink this time, dear, they're bright red."

I covered my cheeks with my hands and felt the warmth. Aunt Birdie cocked her head to one side and smiled at me.

"Make sure you marry for love, dear."

Chapter

24

By the time Aunt Birdie and I arrived home, I had finally stopped shaking from my encounter with gun-toting Silas McClure. But I battled tears of bitter disappointment because I hadn't found my mother. I wished I'd gone to LaSalle Street four weeks ago instead of wasting all this time. Now less than two weeks remained in which to find her, and my best hope of doing so was with the help of a thieving elixir salesman. I wanted to push past Aunt Birdie and run upstairs to my room and weep.

"It looks like you got another letter," Aunt Birdie said. She had stopped in front of me to scoop up the mail that lay waiting for us on the foyer floor.

"From whom?" I asked wearily.

"It says, 'Mrs. Charles Crane' on the return address. 'Riverside, Illinois.'"

It took me a moment to realize it was from Herman Beckett's

sister—whom I had dubbed Misery Mary. I took the letter from Aunt Birdie and ripped it open.

Dear Miss Hayes,

I am writing to invite you to a family picnic on July the fourth here at our home in Riverside. Herman will be coming by train from Lockport along with our mother, so you will have the opportunity to become better acquainted with our family. I know this is short notice, but I do hope you will be able to attend. Herman and my husband, Ernest, will call for you around ten o'clock in the morning. I look forward to seeing you again.

Sincerely,
Mary Crane

"Is it from one of your beaus?" Aunt Birdie asked.

"From his sister. She invited me to her Fourth of July picnic."

"Oh, how nice. And tomorrow is the Fourth."

"It is? Oh no," I moaned. "That means there won't be time to write back and send my regrets."

"Don't you want to go, dear? I do love Fourth of July picnics with the parades and the fireworks and everything. Don't you? And everyone is so patriotic now that our country is at war."

"It's just that I can't afford to waste another day, Aunt Birdie. I need to find my mother before the two weeks are up, and I have no idea where to look."

"Well, you could always ask Philip. He would know where she is."

Philip? My father's missing brother? A strange, tingling sensation rippled through me—the kind I used to get when one of the detectives in *True Crime Stories* unearthed an important clue.

"Did my Uncle Philip know my mother?"

"Well, I'm sure he did."

I hesitated before asking the next question. "Where . . . um . . . where can I find Philip?"

"Well, he's . . . I mean . . . Oh, that's right. Philip is off fighting in the war like my Gilbert. He . . . they . . ."

Her gray eyes clouded over with tears. She looked down at the pile of mail she was holding and her frail hands trembled as she leafed through the letters again.

"I can't imagine why Gilbert hasn't written. He must be so warm down in Virginia this time of year—the poor dear. Those uniforms are ever so hot. And the Virginia Peninsula is such a muggy, buggy place. And it looks like Philip hasn't written either. . . ."

She dropped two letters as she shuffled clumsily through the mail. I picked them up, then gently took the rest of them out of her hands and laid them on the hall table.

"Let's go make some lemonade and you can tell me all about my Uncle Philip, okay? What's he like?"

"Full of life," she said with a smile. "But headstrong. He and his father are always butting heads, you know. Isaac didn't want his boys to fight, but as soon as Philip turned eighteen, he ran away to enlist. Is that a letter from him?" she asked, pointing to the invitation from Mary that I still held.

"No. I've been invited to a picnic tomorrow."

I decided not to ask any more questions about Philip. I feared that he also had perished in the war, and I worried that my probing would hurt Aunt Birdie. We made lemonade and a light lunch. Afterward, I went upstairs to my room to devise a new plan.

I couldn't afford to waste time crying helpless tears of disappointment. My future was at stake. My father seemed determined to marry me to Herman or to Nelson. I had been taught to be well mannered and compliant, trusting that men were more knowledgeable than women and better able to make choices for me. But that was before I'd seen for myself what women could accomplish; before I'd visited the Woman's Pavilion and the suffrage headquarters and seen the work that my grandmother and Jane Addams did.

Yes, I needed to take matters into my own hands. My two goals would now become three: find my mother, stop Father's marriage, and—did I dare believe it?—decide my own future.

I had no idea what that future might be, but I knew that I did not want to marry Herman Beckett. Tomorrow I would make certain that he saw a side of me that he would find unacceptable. But first, I would use the picnic as an opportunity to glean more information from Herman's mother about Murderous Maude O'Neill. I needed something so damning it would prevent my father from marrying her.

While rummaging through my wardrobe in search of something to wear to the picnic, I came upon an idea that was pure genius. I had found the outfit that Madame Beauchamps made all of us girls wear for physical exercise classes at school. It consisted of a baggy pair of light blue pantaloons with elastic around the ankles and a tunic-style blouse with short, puffy sleeves and a sailor collar. It even had a navy blue sailor tie. I had tossed the exercise outfit into my trunk on a whim, and now I was glad that I had. Herman would be so scandalized to see a woman wearing bloomers that he would probably cancel the picnic as well as the courtship. Yes, my idea was ingenious. Ruth Schultz would have been proud of me.

When the time came the next day to button on my bloomers, I nearly lost my nerve. In truth, I felt naked without my usual layers of petticoats and skirts. I couldn't imagine all women everywhere throwing away their skirts and dressing in pants someday, in spite of the lady doctor's predictions. Fortunately, the Fourth of July had dawned cloudy and gloomy. I drew courage from the fact that we weren't likely to be viewing parades on public thoroughfares or picnicking in a city park in such weather.

In the end, the hideous prospect of becoming Mrs. Herman Beckett strengthened my resolve. I climbed into my bloomers and stood at my bedroom window to wait for Herman. For my plan to work, I needed to watch for his arrival and make a quick escape from the house. I couldn't let my grandmother see me dressed that way, or she would never let me out of the door.

As soon as Herman's carriage drew to a halt out front, I raced downstairs to make my escape—and nearly collided with my grandmother, who was in the foyer pinning on her hat.

"Violet Rose Hayes! What in the world. . . ?"

"Herman's here, I'm going to be late, bye," I said breathlessly.

"Wait a minute!" she said, snagging my arm. "Where are you going? You can't go outdoors that way! You aren't dressed!"

"Yes, I am. These are called bloomers." I twirled around in the hallway to demonstrate my freedom of movement. "All the girls at Madame Beauchamps' school were required to purchase a pair. And according to a very distinguished female doctor, it is much better for a woman's health to wear bloomers in place of a stifling corset."

"Where did you hear such a thing?"

"I heard the doctor speak at the Woman's Pavilion."

"Matilda!" I had never heard Grandmother raise her voice, let alone yell so loudly. "Come out here right now!"

Aunt Matt's bedroom door burst open. "What? What's the matter?" She had a look of startled fear in her eyes, as if the Great Fire had just been rekindled.

"Look what you've done!" Grandmother said, pointing to me. Someone knocked on the door.

"That's Herman Beckett," I said sweetly. I turned to open it, but Grandmother blocked my path.

"Oh no, you don't. I'll answer it. You go straight up those stairs, young lady, and put on some clothes."

"What's wrong with her clothes?" Aunt Matt asked. She had folded her arms across her chest, ready to do battle. "Those are called bloomers, Florence, in case you don't know. Many of our suffragettes are already wearing them. And I dare say that all women will wear them someday."

"They're indecent! She looks like she's in her undergarments."

"Don't be absurd. She's covered all the way to her ankles."

I heard Herman Beckett knock again, louder this time. Aunt Birdie glided into the hallway.

"Isn't someone going to answer the door?"

"In a minute, Birdie." Grandmother held out her arms to bar the way as if guarding against my escape.

"What's the difference between a baggy pair of bloomers and a long skirt?" Aunt Matt demanded.

"Well . . . well, for one thing," Grandmother stammered, "everyone can tell that Violet has a derriere! And legs!"

"Of course she has legs. And I'm sure people are just as aware of that fact when she's wearing a skirt."

"No, Matilda. Her backside is much more . . . more *apparent* . . . in bloomers."

"Violet, dear," Birdie asked, "why are you wearing your underwear?"

"See what I mean?" Grandmother asked. Herman knocked a third time.

"Someone better answer that," I told my grandmother.

"Go on, Violet," Aunt Matt said. "You go and have a nice time at your picnic. And good for you!" She applauded quietly.

"Matilda!"

I ducked beneath Grandmother's arm and opened the door. I had taken a daring step, but if Herman and his mother reacted the way my grandmother had, the courtship would be called off before noon.

Herman's eyes boggled when he saw me. He never had been overly talkative, but my bloomers turned him into a stone mute. I took his arm, chattering enough for both of us as we walked down the front steps to the waiting carriage. Misery Mary's husband, Ernest, would be driving us to Riverside. He caught himself staring at me, then carefully averted his eyes from my shocking costume, staring at my toes as Herman introduced us.

"Violet—Ernest. . . . Ernest—Violet," Herman said curtly.

"How do you do, Ernest? It's so nice to meet you. I'm so sorry you were unable to join us for our day at the fair, but it's kind of you to invite me to your holiday picnic."

"Um. Yes."

I climbed into the back of the carriage and sat cozily by Herman's side as I continued my monologue.

"How have you been, Herman? Do you have the holiday off from work? Too bad the weather is so gloomy. It's not a very nice day for a picnic, is it? Do you think it will rain? How far is it to Riverside? Will the ride take long?"

His mouth opened and closed in response to each of my questions, but nothing came out. His caterpillar brows had crawled halfway to his hairline in surprise and seemed to be trying to hide in his hair. He slowly blinked after each of my questions, as if hoping he would open his eyes and discover, to his great relief, that he had been having a nightmare.

It seemed to take forever to ride the nine miles to Riverside. In Herman's muted condition, our conversation resembled a one-woman tennis match in which I was required to lob the ball over the net, then run over to the opposite court to retrieve it. I reached our destination verbally exhausted.

The Crane home was a sprawling, three-story residence with a turret and a wide front porch adorned with wooden gingerbread. It was in a lovely neighborhood of winding streets and stately homes near the Des Plaines River. The grassy front yard would have made a splendid spot for a picnic, but the damp day and misty rain would drive us inside.

Our carriage pulled beneath a covered entryway on the side of the house where Herman's mother and sister awaited our arrival. I watched their faces transform as I stepped from the carriage. I had seen expressions like theirs before in a crowd that had witnessed a spectacular buggy crash in which horses and wagon wheels and bloodied victims had become hopelessly entangled.

Mrs. Beckett stuttered incoherently in a brave effort to be polite.

Misery Mary couldn't seem to look at me, as if I had arrived stark-naked. Her two daughters, four-year-old Emily and six-year-old Priscilla, stared and stared and stared, their eyes frozen open, unblinking. I expected one of them to declare *The Emperor has no clothes!*"

When I finally realized that Herman's family was too well mannered to comment on my attire, I took the first step. "What do you think of my bloomers? They're all the rage in Paris this season."

"My word . . ."

"According to all the fashion experts they are *de rigeuer* for leisure events such as boating or bicycling—and very appropriate for picnics." I held the material out to the sides as if I were about to curtsy, then twirled around like a ballerina to demonstrate my freedom of movement. The silent pause that followed was big enough to drive a streetcar through.

"They . . . they are . . . interesting," Mary managed to say. "If you'll excuse me, I'll fetch us something to drink."

"I'll help you," Herman's mother added. They scurried from the room, herding the two little girls ahead of them as if shielding them from an appalling sight. Herman led me into the front parlor, where we sat opposite one another on the overstuffed furniture.

"Your nieces are lovely girls. Too bad they couldn't have accompanied us to the exposition."

"Mary feared it would be too much excitement for them."

I nodded, trying not to giggle. The gigantic bell made from oranges might have kept them awake all night.

"Is there a parade today?" I asked.

"A small one. Riverside isn't a very large town."

"Oh, good. I do love parades." But when Mary returned with our beverages, she and Herman had a quick, whispered consultation.

"We've decided not to watch the parade after all," she told me. "The day is much too damp. It wouldn't be good for the girls. I would hate for them to catch a fever."

"Will we be picnicking in a park, perhaps?" I asked.

Mary shook her head vigorously. "No. Here at home. Inside."

They were embarrassed to be seen with me. Good. My plan was already working.

We ate our picnic lunch at precisely two o'clock, seated around the dining room table. With my future at stake, I made up my mind to ignore all of Madame Beauchamps' diligent instructions and do the opposite of everything I'd ever learned about table manners. I started eating before the hostess sat down. I didn't use my napkin, much less place it on my lap. I reached across the table for my food instead of asking someone to pass the serving dishes. I ate Mary's fried chicken with my fingers, when the proper way was with a knife and fork. I buttered the entire dinner roll instead of breaking it into small pieces. I slurped my iced tea. I didn't have quite enough nerve to belch when I'd finished eating, but I considered it.

Not one of the Becketts or Cranes uttered a word about my behavior. In fact, Herman's family was so quiet and reserved that I could hear the silverware scraping across the plates while we ate.

Afterward I joined Herman's mother outside on the front porch, determined to use all of my detective skills to learn the truth about her good friend Murderous Maude. I was quite certain that my courtship with Herman was about to end today, so this might be my very last chance to interrogate Mrs. Beckett.

"I understand that you and Mur—um . . . Maude O'Neill are good friends."

"Yes, she is such a sweet person. You'll love her."

I doubted that. I leaned closer, as if we were conspirators.

"Listen, I know the truth about her first husband," I bluffed. A detective in one of Ruth's novels had used this method with excellent results. He had pretended to know the truth, then waited for a response. If it worked, Mrs. Beckett would either say, "I don't know what you're talking about," or else confess that Maude had murdered him, believing that I already knew the truth. I waited, holding my breath. Mrs. Beckett glanced all around, as if expecting eavesdrop-pers.

"You know the truth?" she finally asked in a hushed voice.

"Yes. About his death." She stared at me, as if waiting for an explanation. "Mrs. O'Neill is marrying my father, after all. And of course I'm holding her secret in strictest confidence. But you must agree that I had a right to know everything since Maude is going to be my . . . s-stepmother." I almost choked on the word.

Mrs. Beckett nodded and glanced all around again. "Maude was very courageous throughout the ordeal."

"Of course."

"It happens more often than people know . . ." Her voice dropped to a whisper again. "Behind closed doors."

It happens often? Was she talking about women murdering their husbands? I stumbled to find an appropriate response.

"Y-yes. I-I'm sure that's . . . true."

"Your father was such an enormous help; bless his soul. I don't know how many times he traveled to Chicago to the Jolly Roger. He said he wanted to do it for his brother's sake."

The Jolly Roger? For his brother's sake? Was my uncle a pirate? Blast my secretive family!

"Y-you mean my father's brother, Philip?"

"Yes, I believe that was his name. Still, it was kind of your father to help Maude."

Yikes! My father had helped Maude?

Fortunately, my hours of practice at school holding an enigmatic smile in place kept my mouth from dropping open in horror and shock. How could my father do such a thing?

"Now that Lloyd O'Neill is gone, Maude's life has been blessedly peaceful," Herman's mother continued. "And it's good that the truth was never revealed. . . . For the children's sake," she added in a whisper.

Ah-ha! She practically had admitted it was murder!

"Much better to have it ruled an unfortunate accident," she said, "instead of . . . well, you know, Miss Hayes."

I nodded mutely, realizing that I faced a troublesome dilemma. How could I expose Maude as a murderer if my father had helped her?

Herman chose that opportune moment to join us on the porch. "Would you care for a game of croquet on the back lawn, Violet? It's no longer raining, as you can see, and the grass has dried out."

"That would be lovely," I said, struggling to regain my composure. "Would you excuse us, Mrs. Beckett?"

I was badly shaken by what I had learned, and I used my mallet to vent my emotions. I played cutthroat croquet. It was very unfeminine of me to be so competitive, but I was trying to absorb the fact that my father might be an accomplice to murder. At the same time, I had to be mindful of my plan to discourage Herman from courting me. I was prepared to swing from the trees and howl at the moon to accomplish that goal.

Herman played croquet very slowly and patiently, helping his two little nieces, who were playing with us. None of them was prepared for my ruthlessness. Priscilla pouted when I whacked her ball into the shrubbery, yards and yards from the nearest wicket. Emily ran into the house, crying, when I sent her ball rolling down the driveway. My bloomers gave me an amazing degree of freedom as I attacked my opponents' balls.

"Aren't you being a little hard on the children?" Herman asked. "After all, it's only a game."

"The world is a cutthroat place, Herman. I don't believe it is wise to raise one's children in a sheltered environment." I sent his ball bouncing behind the tool shed and won the game. Afterward, I decided to shock him further with one of my grisliest questions.

"If you could choose, Herman, would you rather perish in an appalling cataclysm such as a mine explosion or a train wreck and die amid twisted iron and tons of rock, listening to the screams of trapped and suffering humanity—or would you prefer to linger at home in your bed from a long, agonizing illness, your helpless body growing weaker, your every breath a painful gasp?"

"It's quite distasteful to discuss death, Violet."

"I know that. But it's a game, Herman. The point is to think about what you would do if faced with two impossible choices. So which would you choose?"

"I really don't know."

I sighed and gave up. Herman Beckett was never going to play. But with any luck, I had shocked him right out of my life today.

Later, under the cover of darkness, we ventured out to the public park to watch the fireworks. Most of the rockets had gotten damp and they fizzled dismally. I couldn't wait to return home. The day had seemed twenty-four years long, but when it finally ended, Herman stopped me on our front doorstep before bidding me good-night.

"Violet, there is something I need to say to you."

Here it comes. It's good-bye forever to stuffy Herman Beckett.

"I believe that you are the wife for me."

"W-what? But—"

"No, let me finish. I understand from your father that you have other suitors, but I want you to know that I intend to continue my courtship in all earnestness and sincerity once you return to Lockport, with the hope of winning you. I wanted you to get a glimpse today of the simple contentment we could share if you married me."

I almost blurted *"You still want me—in bloomers?"* But I didn't. His speech reminded me of my Uncle Gilbert's touching pursuit of Aunt Birdie, except that Herman hadn't mentioned love.

"To be honest, Violet, I have worried in the past that you were out of my reach. You attended such a fancy school, where you learned proper manners and how to speak French and all the rest. My mother didn't think you could be content with an ordinary family like ours. But today I saw a different side of you. You aren't pretentious or high-class at all. Now I'm more certain than ever that we could be happy together."

"Your mother approves of me?"

"She thinks you're vivacious. She said you would be a good balance for me in that regard. And I must say I believe she is right. You're an unusual woman, Violet. I find you . . . *exciting!*" His eyes met mine, and even in the dark I could see an uncharacteristic gleam in them. "The way you whacked those croquet balls! My word! And you looked so attractive in those . . . in your . . . in that attire!"

Now I was the one who was mute. My plan had backfired! Why hadn't these stupid bloomers come with a warning? *Caution: Stodgy men may find this garment attractive. Bloomers have been known to precipitate a proposal of marriage!*

"You don't need to answer me tonight, Violet. I know that you'll be coming home in less than two weeks' time. It will seem like an eternity to me, but I'll wait. Until then . . ." He gripped both of my hands in his and gave them a determined squeeze. "Good night."

Good grief!

I fled up the steps and into the house. Grandmother met me in the foyer as if she had been standing there since I'd left. She heaved a weighty sigh.

"Violet Rose. I have been sick at heart all day, just knowing that you've been running around in public dressed that way."

"I'm sorry. I didn't mean to upset you—"

"Believe me, if I had been strong enough to bar your way I would have. Your father—"

"My father wants me to marry Herman Beckett, and I don't want to. Wearing bloomers was part of my plan to discourage him—but it backfired! It seems I've enflamed his passions. He thinks I'm exciting."

"I shouldn't wonder. You could awaken a dead man in that outfit with your backside so . . . so . . . prominent. If your father hears that

I allowed you out of this house in bloomers, he'll never speak to me again."

"I'll tell him it wasn't your fault. You tried to stop me, but—"

"Oh, Violet! Thank goodness you're home!" She pulled me into her arms for a fervent hug. I hugged her in return.

"Do you think there is really such a thing as true love?" I asked.

She drew back to gaze at me. She seemed taken aback by my question. "Of course there is."

"Do you know anyone besides Aunt Birdie who has ever found it?"

She closed her eyes and exhaled. "You are more than I can handle, Violet Rose. No wonder your father wants to see you safely married."

Chapter

25

Wednesday, July 5, 1893

When a deliveryman brought a dozen red roses to our door the next morning, I feared they were from Herman. Why hadn't Madame Beauchamps ever taught us that bloomers unlocked the door to romance? I would at least have expected *True Romance Stories* to have mentioned it. I tore open the attached card with dread.

Roses for my Violet—
    Will you attend a gala dinner with me at the fairgrounds tonight? I promise to woo you with a romantic gondola ride in the moonlight.

                                                    Yours,
                                                    Nelson

I sighed with relief.

"From your beau?" Aunt Birdie asked. I could only nod. I felt as though I had stepped onto the pages of one of Ruth's romance novels. A proposal of marriage one day, roses and moonlit boat rides the next.

"Gilbert charmed his way into my heart with flowers too," Aunt Birdie said.

"Nelson Kent is going to take me on a gondola ride in the moonlight," I said, showing her the card.

"Oh, how nice. Will you be going out in your underwear again?"

My smile vanished. "No. That turned out to be a huge mistake."

"Well, then. That says it all, doesn't it?"

As I carried the flowers into the kitchen to look for a vase, I suddenly remembered Katya and the impassioned kiss I had witnessed. How could he kiss her that way, then turn around and woo me? Nelson Kent obviously was deceiving one of us. I had the sinking feeling that it was me.

Nevertheless, the roses were beautiful. I bent to inhale their rich, velvety scent, and the aroma brought another memory to mind. My mother had smelled like roses. I closed my eyes and inhaled again, remembering how she would give me her handkerchief, sweetened with her scent, to sleep with at night.

Where was she? How could I find her? If only there was something I could do instead of waiting for Silas McClure and his unsavory friends to locate her.

I debated all day whether or not I should accompany Nelson to the gala dinner. In the end I decided to go. But I made up my mind to learn the truth about Katya before I allowed him to pursue me any further.

Nelson and I sailed to the fair by steamship once again. It was crowded with all of the regular members of his social circle, including his grandmother and my Aunt Agnes. I saw the two ladies whispering like thieves as Nelson and I stood side by side at the ship's rail, gazing at the distant silhouette of Chicago. Tonight the harbor resembled an overstuffed pincushion with dozens of ships' masts poking into the sky. They brought to mind the intriguing clue that Herman's mother had let slip yesterday: *My father traveled to Chicago . . . to the Jolly Roger . . . for his brother's sake.*

"Have you ever heard of a ship named the *Jolly Roger?*" I asked Nelson.

"Is this one of your amusing questions?" he asked, smiling. "I think we already discussed the fact that I'd rather be the captain of a warship than a pirate ship, didn't we?"

"No, I'm serious. Someone mentioned that my father used to come to Chicago to the Jolly Roger. I thought it sounded like a pirate ship."

"Or a saloon. There aren't many pirate ships in Chicago these days, but there are plenty of saloons—" He must have noticed the surprise on my face because he quickly added, "But I'm sure your father wouldn't frequent a saloon. Perhaps it's a restaurant?"

Little did Nelson know that my father had indeed frequented saloons when he'd worked with Mr. Moody's Yokefellows. Maybe I had found another important piece of the puzzle.

"How would one go about finding an establishment by that name?" I asked.

"I don't know. I'm sure the city must keep records of all the businesses and so forth. Maybe in the city administration building?"

I gazed into the distance, trying to add up all the clues—and trying not to think about the fact that my mild-mannered father may have been an accomplice to murder. Nelson took my chin in his fingers and turned my head to face him.

"You're a million miles away, sweet Violet."

"I'm sorry."

"I'm trying to romance you. Aren't you the lady who craves romance?"

"Yes, I know. And I forgot to thank you for the flowers. They were beautiful, Nelson."

"I sent them to remind you of the first day we met. Remember our stroll through my grandmother's flower garden?"

"Of course. How could I forget?"

What game was he playing, making sweet talk and gazing into my eyes? I needed to find out if he was still in love with Katya before I succumbed to his considerable charms. Though she no longer worked for the Kents, it didn't mean that Nelson no longer loved her. Maybe he had hidden her away somewhere as his mistress, like my Uncle Henry hid his mistresses. I had to figure out a way to bring Katya into our conversation.

"I remember our first meeting very well," I said. "Your grandmother sent that beautiful young serving girl to fetch you, and I had no idea what to expect or what you would look like. I was very pleasantly surprised, by the way, when I met you." I smiled flirtatiously.

Nelson glowed at my compliment. "I was surprised too."

"I also recall how lovely that little serving girl was. What was her name? . . . Katy? . . . No, it was foreign sounding . . . Katya! That was it. Katya always serves the tea when I come to visit with my Aunt Agnes, and I love watching her. Such natural grace and poise. But come to think of it, I didn't see her the last time I called. Some clumsy oaf of a girl served us instead. She dripped tea all over my shoes."

"I'll have her fired."

"No, don't do that. Just make sure Katya serves us the next time."

His smile vanished. "She no longer works for us." I found it very revealing that Nelson knew exactly who I was talking about. And that she was gone.

"What happened to her?"

"Servants come and go all the time, Violet." He waved as if dismissing the topic, but his cool, blasé facade had slipped from its usual place. "It's the housekeeper's job to keep track of them, not mine."

So Katya really was gone. Maybe the affair between them had fizzled. Maybe that was why he had decided to pursue me in earnest.

We arrived at the fair and rode the moving sidewalk once again to the Peristyle. I fell into step with all of the other partygoers when I got off, but Nelson drew me to a halt.

"Wait. You need to stop and look at this magnificent view. Can you even imagine a more perfect spot for romance?" Once again, sparkling lights lit up the lagoon and water splashed from the fountains. Electric lights twinkled from the whitewashed pavilions and reflected off the water like diamonds.

"I feel like a princess in a fairy tale," I murmured.

"And it's just the beginning."

We dined on quail and truffles in the garden restaurant on the rooftop of the Woman's Pavilion. Our hosts had rented the entire dining room, along with a thirty-piece orchestra so we could dance afterward. The scent of flowers filled the air and stars shone in the night sky as I waltzed in Nelson's arms. The evening was designed to make any woman fall in love.

"Do you have any idea how fortunate you are?" Aunt Agnes whispered when Nelson left to replenish my punch cup. "There isn't a woman in this city who wouldn't give her right arm to marry a young man like him."

"Yes. I know." But I wasn't in love.

The moon had risen above the horizon when Nelson took me for a gondola ride on the lagoon. Colored searchlights and fireworks blazed above our heads as we glided gently across the water. Nelson pulled me close on the seat beside him.

"A beautiful night . . . for a beautiful woman," he murmured. "Who could ask for more?"

He bent his face toward mine, and I was certain he was going to kiss me. Instead, he pressed his warm cheek against mine and said, "If you marry me, you can have this life from now on."

I pulled away and looked up at him in surprise. "Are you proposing?"

"Isn't this the most romantic place in all of Chicago for a marriage proposal? Must I do something more? I was certain you told me that romance was the way to win your heart."

"It is, but . . . it's just that we haven't known each other very long."

"That's what engagements are for. Listen, I understand that your father is coming back to Chicago for you soon, and I plan to ask him for your hand to make it official. We can be engaged for as long as you like—but I hope it isn't for too long. I'm dying to kiss you, Violet."

I couldn't seem to reply. But I wasn't considering his proposal; I was analyzing my symptoms. My pulse seemed disappointingly normal, my palms were dry, I could draw great, hearty breaths, and I didn't feel the least bit shivery or feverish. A handsome, charming, wealthy man had just proposed to me and . . . nothing! Even with my corset tightly laced! Maybe there was something wrong with me.

"I'll give you anything your heart desires," Nelson said. "Beautiful gowns, jewels, the finest home, dozens of servants . . ."

Servants. Katya suddenly materialized in the boat with us. Nelson hadn't hesitated to kiss her before their engagement. If I hadn't spied on them that night, I might be accepting his proposal this very minute.

"And I promise to give you independence as well," he said.

"Independence? What do you mean?"

"What you do with your free time will be entirely up to you, Violet. For instance, Potter Palmer's wife is the director of the Woman's Pavilion. Mrs. McCormick works for several charities. You could do whatever you wish."

"Suppose I decided to march with the women's suffrage movement—in bloomers?"

"Well . . ." His smile wavered slightly before returning to its place. "As long as you don't disgrace me by getting arrested, I suppose that would be okay."

He hadn't declared his love. Should I ask him if he loved me? Would I believe him if he said that he did? He had dismissed love as unnecessary when I'd mentioned it before. But if he didn't love me, why was he working so hard to woo me? Was it for money and a position in his father's business?

I shook myself. What was wrong with me that I was questioning Nelson's motives? The heroine of every romance novel I'd ever read would have gladly lived happily ever after with someone like him—especially if he wooed her with roses and moonlit gondola rides.

Our gondolier returned us to the dock, and Nelson and I returned to the party. I wondered if he'd noticed that I hadn't answered his proposal.

He waited on my every whim, charmed me with his wit, and held me close as we waltzed to the glorious music. I saw his grandmother and Aunt Agnes watching us, smiling in approval.

"My friends and I are going to the private casino again tonight," he said when it was time for us to leave. "I'm hoping you'll come with me and be my good luck charm again."

"I-I'd rather not. I really don't like gambling, and besides, I got terribly carried away the last time." I continued walking as we came out of the pavilion, following my aunt and all of the others as we headed toward the pier.

"Please?" he begged. "I'm not ready to call it a night yet."

"It scares me to think that you could lose all your money."

"But I'll win if you're with me. Please stay."

I shook my head. "I don't want to spoil your evening, Nelson, but I would like to go home. Why don't you go with your friends, and I'll ride home with my aunt Agnes?"

"You won't feel like I'm deserting you?"

"Not at all. It was a wonderfully romantic evening. I'll remember it for the rest of my life. Thank you so much." I stood on tiptoe and quickly kissed his cheek. "Good night."

The kiss was a test, of sorts. I had hoped that my heart would send off a few fireworks, but nothing happened. Nor did anything happen when Nelson lifted my fingers to his lips and kissed them.

"Good night, my beautiful Violet."

I followed the others to the pier and boarded the steamship back to the city. Aunt Agnes pulled me into a quiet corner and sat me down as soon as we left the dock.

"My stars, Violet, why did you leave Nelson? Did something go wrong between you two? It looked like things were going so well."

"They were . . . I mean, they are going well. Nelson asked me to marry him."

"That's wonderful! So why are you sitting here with the face of doom, twisting your gloves into a knot?"

I dropped my gloves onto my lap and sighed. "I don't know . . ."

"You didn't refuse him, did you?"

"No . . ."

"Well!" She exhaled. "Thank goodness for good sense! Do you want to tell me what's wrong, then?"

"Nelson never said that he loved me. I know you don't think love matters, but I-I want to fall in love. And I want to be loved."

"And you're too impatient to wait for it to grow?" She caressed my cheek with her sparkly fingers.

"What if it doesn't, Aunt Agnes?"

"Listen, it's probably no secret that Henry and I weren't in love when we married. But over time, living together, raising our sons, our love grew to become very deep."

"It did?" I remembered my uncle's mistresses. "How long did it take? And when did you know?"

"I found out on the night of the Great Fire," she said matter-of-factly. "Sometimes it takes a tragedy such as that one to make us realize how we really feel about someone."

I immediately thought of my parents, falling in love during the fire. I wanted to hear everything that Aunt Agnes knew about that night. I perched on the edge of my chair and leaned toward her.

"Were you living here in the city during the fire?"

She nodded. "Henry and I had a Terrace Row townhouse, right on Michigan Avenue and Congress Streets. Michigan Avenue used to be on the lakefront, you know, but after the fire they dumped all of the rubble into the lake and created Grant Park and a new shoreline. But anyway, that's where we lived."

"Grandmother said that my parents met that night."

"She would know more about that than I would. Henry and I were sound asleep when our son Michael woke us up at around two o'clock in the morning. He was the only one of our children still living at home at the time.

"'I think the city is on fire,' he said. 'You'd better get dressed.'

"All the alarm bells were ringing, and the great courthouse bell was tolling like it was doomsday. Henry opened the bedroom curtains, and the sky to the southwest of us was an eerie shade of orange. It made the lake across the street glow like molten lava. The wind howled around the eaves like a hurricane and rattled the panes. I thought I had awakened in hell itself.

"Henry decided to go out and see where the fire was and in which direction it was spreading. He had important papers and ledgers and things that needed to be rescued if the fire was spreading toward his downtown office. He told me not to worry, but I got dressed and proceeded to pack, just in case.

"'It's so hard to choose which things are important and which ones aren't when it comes to fleeing for your life. I didn't really believe that the fire would spread all the way to the lake. It seemed to be across the river. But I decided to take precautions.

"Henry was gone for a very long time. He came back with a cartload of documents and descriptions of the inconceivable damage he'd seen—the courthouse was burning, as was the main post office and several grand hotels, including one that Henry owned. The fire seemed to be spreading out of control, heading toward his office building and all of the others on LaSalle Street. I couldn't imagine it. But I could see how badly shaken Henry was. He described the panic in the streets, all the frightened people running in every direction, carrying their belongings—the silliest and saddest things: an oil painting, a birdcage, a chair. Others dragged screaming children by the hand as burning cinders rained down from the sky. I asked Henry if we needed to evacuate.

"'No,' he assured me, 'the fire seems to be heading in the other direction for now. I believe you'll be safe here.' But he took Michael and they went back to retrieve more things from his office.

"The servants and I continued to pack everything of value, and we piled it all in the foyer. Every time I looked out the window, the sky seemed brighter with flames. I could hear the wind howling and whipping ashes and cinders against the panes as if we were in a sandstorm.

"Hours passed. I became sick with worry for Henry and Michael's safety. I could see that the fire was moving closer and closer, and I feared we would soon lose our home. I decided to haul our belongings out of the house and across the little parkway that was on the other side of Michigan Avenue to the beach. Our neighbors were all doing the same thing. It proved extremely difficult. All manner of vehicles and panic-stricken people jammed the avenue, trying to escape the flames.

"The servants helped me save a great deal of our furnishings and household goods and valuables. We rescued most of Henry's books. Our eyes burned and watered and stung from the smoke, and our faces turned black with soot.

"Believe it or not, there were unscrupulous men who took advantage of the disaster to help themselves to our personal effects through the open door. One neighbor had an entire wagon full of his salvaged goods driven away by a stranger, never to be seen again. I found a thief in Henry's dressing room, helping himself to his clothing and cigars. He laughed at my outrage and said, 'Go ahead and holler for the police, lady.'

"We continued to work, trying to empty the house, while fear for my husband and son grew with every passing hour. The approaching flames seemed to ride through the sky in the clouds. It would have been beautiful if it hadn't been so horrifying. And the noise! I could hear rumblings and explosions as buildings crumbled in the distance. And always, the roar of the flames and the sound of screaming.

"When the heat became too strong and we'd carried the last load that we dared to the beach, I sat down on my pile of belongings and watched my home burn. The flames leaped to the roof, then spread down through the interior, hollowing it out and devouring everything inside until only a blackened shell remained. Everyone on the beach was weeping, but I felt little sorrow for my home compared to the terror I felt for Henry and our son. They had been away for too long. I wept for them, not our home.

"That was when I knew how very deeply I loved Henry—when I was faced with the prospect of losing him. We weren't in love when we married, of course. But we'd lived together all those years, raised our family, built a life with one another—and I couldn't bear the thought of living without him.

"Meanwhile, Henry and Michael had been forced to take a wild, circuitous route back home in order to avoid the flames and the mobs of fleeing people. One of the drawbridges they'd tried to cross had to be raised just as they reached it in order to allow several ships to get out of harm's way. Henry walked for miles and miles and made it home in time to see the rear wall of our townhouse topple to the ground. He had been terrified for my safety as well and had been trying desperately to escape the fire's relentless path and return home for me. All the while, he'd had to fight the current of humanity fleeing in the opposite direction.

"When we were finally reunited, we stood on the lakeshore clinging to one another for a very long time. Henry's face was black and tear streaked, his clothing stank of smoke, his entire body trembled from all of the horrors he'd witnessed. But he held me tightly and whispered, 'I love you, Agnes.'"

My aunt Agnes paused as her voice choked. She wiped away the tears that had rolled down her cheeks. Her story had moved me deeply, and I couldn't speak. I took her hand in mine.

"Henry and I lost our home, several other properties, and his brand-new office building. But we had each other, and that was all that mattered.

"Love will grow, Violet. It comes from mutual respect and from building a life together, one day at a time. Romance is fine when you're young, but you can't always trust the emotions that seem so strong in the beginning. Those feelings often fade, and you wake up one morning to find you have nothing in common with each other. Marriage is about maturity and creating a future together. It's not about romance."

I nodded, thinking about my parents.

"Yes, Henry's family was wealthy when I married him. But I helped him prosper and gain stature in Chicago. I played hostess for his business and social contacts. I volunteered in countless charitable causes to help build his good name. We are Mr. and Mrs. Henry Paine, and that's so much more important than fleeting feelings of romance."

She met my gaze for a long moment; then her voice grew very soft. "I know that Henry loves me. His dalliances don't mean anything, Violet. They allow him to believe that he is still young and indestructible. I'm the one who shares his name and his home—and his life."

I nodded, too moved by her confession to speak.

"Nelson Kent is a fine young man from a lovely family. In many ways, he is still young and unformed. You could be the woman behind the man. With your grace and intelligence and wit, you could help him make a name for himself and find his rightful place in this city. Every man needs a good woman to believe in him. And in time, love and affection will follow."

I thought of Nelson's passion for new inventions. I could encourage him, cheer him on, and be his source of inspiration. As my aunt had said, Nelson could make a name for himself and find his place in life.

But what about my name and my place? I would no longer be known as Violet but as Mrs. Nelson Kent. If I joined my life to his, would I find myself—or become swallowed up in him and lost?

I still wasn't sure if I wanted to accept Nelson's proposal. But if my father forced me to choose, I would rather marry Nelson Kent than Herman Beckett.

Chapter

26

Thursday, July 6, 1893

Only three days had passed since Silas McClure had offered to help me find my mother, but it seemed like three weeks. As my father's deadline neared, I thought I understood how Aunt Agnes had felt on the night of the Great Fire, watching disaster creep closer and closer and being helpless to stop it. It should have been a relief to know that I had an alternative to marrying Herman Beckett, but it wasn't. I didn't love Nelson Kent, and the idea of marrying him for his money made me feel very shallow, even if I believed that love would grow over time.

I had to do something. It was already Thursday morning. Since my efforts to find my mother had reached a dead end, I would renew my efforts to stop Father's wedding. I needed to learn the truth about Mr. O'Neill's death, and that meant following the clue that Herman's mother had given me: the Jolly Roger.

I waited until my grandmother and Aunt Matt were both gone,

then I approached Aunt Birdie, who was rubbing furniture polish onto our dining room table.

"Would you like to take a little trip downtown with me?" I gently took the polishing cloth from her and handed Birdie her straw hat.

"All right. Where shall we go? To the theater?"

"Well . . . maybe another day. I need to visit the city administration building today."

Nelson Kent thought that I might be able to locate the Jolly Roger by asking for information there. I had no idea where that building was, but I had graduated from charm school—it was my only natural resource—so I would spread my charm liberally until I found the place. I towed Aunt Birdie to the streetcar stop on the corner and boarded the first car that arrived. I greeted the driver in my sweetly charming voice.

"Good morning, I wonder if you could help me? Do you know where the city administration building is?"

"Not exactly, miss. But if I were you, I'd get off downtown at State or LaSalle or maybe Michigan Avenue. From there, I'm sure you can find a patrolman to help you."

It sounded like a good plan. But Aunt Birdie and I wandered up and down LaSalle for quite a while before locating a patrolman. When we tried to follow his directions, we got lost and had to consult a second patrolman. He sent us in the wrong direction entirely. But the third patrolman was very young and obliging; he walked us right to the door of the administration building.

"Good luck to you, Miss." He held open the door for us and tipped his hat.

By that time Aunt Birdie was so weary she seemed to be dragging a ball and chain from each ankle. I felt guilty for using her this way, but I couldn't run around alone in the city. We wandered through the building, asking for information, and eventually found the department of records. I had learned my lesson after trying to pry information from my mother's lawyer. I would have to use deceit if I wanted to get anywhere in the detective business.

An apathetic-looking clerk with a handlebar mustache met us at the information counter. His eyelids drooped at half-mast as if I'd awakened him from a long nap. Even my dazzling smile didn't seem to move him.

"May I help you?" he asked wearily.

"Yes. I plan to open a restaurant—"

"Oh, how nice!" Aunt Birdie interrupted. "I didn't even know you could cook, Violet."

I patted her hand and continued. "I was told that I could come here to learn if another business is already in possession of the name I've chosen."

His bored expression remained firmly in place. "What is the name?"

"The Jolly Roger."

His drooping eyelids narrowed in suspicion, as if I were playing a prank. "The Jolly Roger?"

I nodded.

"That says it all, doesn't it?" Aunt Birdie asked.

The clerk eyed the two of us as if we had recently escaped from an asylum. "One moment."

"What a lovely surprise," Aunt Birdie said as the clerk trudged away. "A restaurant! I had no idea you possessed culinary aspirations. And to think I knew you when."

The man returned with a large ledger book and set it on the counter between us while he paged through the alphabetical entries. He either was paid by the hour or he was quite unfamiliar with the alphabet, because his search took a very long time.

"You're out of luck, miss," he finally grunted. "There's already an establishment named the Jolly Roger."

"Oh, dear. I'm so disappointed," I said, masking my excitement. "How do they spell it? Perhaps if I varied the name a bit . . ." He turned the ledger around so I could read it. I not only saw the address on Bishop Street but the name of the proprietor as well: Lloyd O'Neill. My mouth dropped open in surprise. He was Murderous Maude's first husband!

I was so shocked that I took Aunt Birdie's arm and left the office without thanking the clerk. I wanted to hail a cab and go to the Jolly Roger right away, but I had no idea where Bishop Street was or how to get there. What if it was in a disreputable part of town?

I was looking all around for the helpful young patrolman when Aunt Birdie said, "Can we go home, dear? I must make lunch for Florence, and besides, my bunions are killing me."

"My grandmother is coming home for lunch? I thought she was going to be gone all day."

"No, she and Matt said they both would be home by lunchtime."

"Then I guess we'd better go." I didn't want my grandmother to know that I had been out searching for my mother.

I felt as though I had the ball and chain on my ankle as I dragged Aunt Birdie home. Once again I was bitterly disappointed, but at least I had made some progress in my search. I not only knew where the Jolly Roger was located, but I'd discovered a connection to Murderous Maude.

We arrived home the same time as my Aunt Matt. "Where have you two been?" she asked.

I answered before Aunt Birdie could. "I had an errand to run, and I thought Aunt Birdie could use some fresh air. Exercise is good for women, you know."

"Well, I came home to see if you wanted to accompany me this afternoon. We're marching on a factory in the garment district."

Marching on a factory? I had no idea what she was talking about and no desire at all to find out. But Aunt Matt knew her way around the city pretty well. She probably could tell me where Bishop Street was and therefore the Jolly Roger. At the very least, I could ask her about my mysterious Uncle Philip.

"I would love to go with you. How does one march on a factory?"

"Let's have lunch first, and I'll explain on the way there."

"We should let Violet prepare lunch," Aunt Birdie said. "She's opening a restaurant." Fortunately for me, Birdie's sisters were in the habit of ignoring most of the things she said.

"By the way, Aunt Matt," I said as we sat in the kitchen, "I never thanked you for supporting my decision to wear bloomers the other day."

"You're welcome. You looked ridiculous in them, but it was the principle that mattered."

"Oh. Well, thanks anyway."

Having heard the word "march," I chose the largest, widest-brimmed hat that I owned, hoping to hide beneath it. As usual, Aunt Matt's thundering lecture began as soon as we boarded the crowded streetcar.

"This has been a landmark year for legislation that protects women and children," she began. "Our lawmakers down in Springfield just passed the Illinois Factory Act. It bans labor for all children under the age of fourteen and regulates work for children between the ages of fourteen and sixteen. The law also forbids garment-making in the tenements. Work must be done in a factory with certain safety guidelines in place. And the law states that women and minors can't be made to work more than eight hours a day. In other words, factory owners will no longer be allowed to exploit women and children in order to boost their profits."

"That sounds like a very good law."

"It is indeed. Some of us have lobbied very hard to get it passed. Unfortunately, there are factory owners who simply ignore it. We've been gathering the names and locations of the most offensive places so that we can stage demonstrations and read them the law."

"That sounds . . . confrontational."

"It is."

I suddenly felt very reckless and brave. My father might force me to move back to Lockport and settle down next week, but at least I would have an adventurous story to tell my children at bedtime.

Aunt Matt and I rode a very long way and changed streetcars three times before meeting up with the other women who were marching with us. Quite a mob of us showed up. The neighborhood near the river where we gathered stank of fish. It was every bit as ugly and unpleasant as the area near the settlement house, but since none of the other women covered their noses, I decided not to cover mine. I hoped that the women we'd come to rescue appreciated our sacrifice.

No one carried signs this time, so I had nothing to hide behind except my floppy hat. I decided that it didn't matter. I felt proud to be making a difference in the world. We lined up in the middle of the street a few blocks from the factory and began to march toward it. Several women had brought pots and pans, which they banged together as we chanted, "Unfair to women and children! Unfair to women and children!"

People came out of saloons and tenements to see what was going on. Pedestrians turned to watch. Little children skipped alongside of us. As we neared the river, dockworkers stopped loading their ships to stare. One group of men pointed and laughed and called us unrepeatable names.

"Get out of the road!" an ice vendor yelled. "My ice is melting!" He and several other deliverymen grew irate because our march blocked the street. It was such fun. I wished Ruth Schultz were with me.

"If all of these factories are breaking the law," I asked Aunt Matt, "shouldn't the police be raiding them instead of us?"

"Of course they should. But the police have been known to take a bribe to look the other way instead of enforcing the law. Or else they plead ignorance. In the end, it's usually up to women like us to protect other women and children."

The door to the low-slung brick factory stood open on this sweltering July day, and we poured inside as if storming a castle. The interior was so dark and dingy that I could hardly see where I was going at first. The dusty, lint-filled air made me sneeze. I heard the clatter of hundreds of sewing machines before I saw them—row after row of them, stretching into the dim workshop, with a woman bent over each one, sewing as if in a race against time.

As my eyes grew accustomed to the light, I realized that most of the seamstresses were teenaged girls, younger than I was. Each had a towering pile of clothing pieces by her side, waiting to be stitched. Small children scurried around between the rows, carrying more bundles of cloth. The workers glanced up when we entered, then quickly resumed sewing. A man I assumed to be the factory manager hurried over to us.

"Hey, now, see here! What's going on? You're trespassing on private property!" The woman who had led our march launched into a heated debate with him, enumerating the details of the new Illinois Factory Act.

Meanwhile, the other women in our group quickly fanned out in every direction, weaving up and down the rows, informing the workers of their rights. I followed my Aunt Matt.

"A new law has been passed, and this factory is violating it," she announced in her commanding voice. "You no longer have to work more than eight hours a day. You have the right to refuse to work longer. The owner must provide safe working conditions." And so on.

Three men, who I assumed were foremen, started running up and down the aisles trying to round up the marauding marchers like so many stray cats.

"You're trespassing! Get off our property."

"Go ahead and summon the police," Aunt Matt told one of them. "They'll arrest you for being in violation of the Illinois Factory Act."

It turned into quite a circus. In fact, it would have been comical if it hadn't been so exhilarating. Through it all, the teenaged girls kept right on sewing as if their lives depended on it. Maybe they did.

Eventually, everyone grew tired of the chase. Aunt Matt and I marched from the factory with the other women, cheering in victory. Sweat rolled down Matt's stern, flushed face as I fell into step beside her. Then I remembered my grandmother's friend Irina.

"Um . . . Aunt Matt? What about all the women with little children who work at home? How will they make a living from now on if it's against the law to work in the tenements?"

"Those women are being taken advantage of at the moment, and they don't even know it." We were parading back down the street in triumph, and Aunt Matt and I had to shout in order to be heard above the sound of cheering and banging pots. "The point of the law is to make factory owners hire those women to work decent hours for a fair wage in a safe environment, instead of paying them mere pennies for hours and hours of labor at home. Children shouldn't be working at all. If women ran the world, all of the children would be in school where they belong. Education is the only way that the working poor will ever get ahead in this world. If factories paid their mothers a fair wage, indigent children could attend school."

"When I visited the tenements with my grandmother, it seemed like there were thousands of children—most of them working. And the women seemed little better than slaves."

"I know. And it's very difficult to change the status quo, especially if you're a woman. Without the right to vote, women in our society are powerless. They are forced to work for slave wages in poor working conditions, or else get married and have too many children. The prettier women can make money in bawdy houses, I suppose. Mind you, I don't condemn women who make that choice. But I would like to give them a better alternative."

"Thank you for taking me today," I said when we reached our first streetcar stop. "I found it very invigorating to do something worthwhile."

"We'll be marching to other factories in the coming weeks if you want to join me again."

"I'd love to—but I'll only be in Chicago for another week, remember? My father is taking me home. And I don't want to go."

We sat on the streetcar in companionable silence, heading toward home again. The more I thought about returning to Lockport without finding my mother, the more anxious I became.

"Aunt Matt, will you talk to my father? Will you help me convince him to let me stay?"

"I would be happy to, but I'm sorry to say that he's not likely to listen to me. He thinks I'm a bad influence on you."

"No, you've been a wonderful influence, Aunt Matt. I've learned so much from you." I waited until we'd disembarked from the first car and boarded the second before saying, "I've had two marriage proposals this week. One from Nelson Kent and one from Herman Beckett."

"You don't sound very pleased."

"I'm not in love with either of them. But Father wants me to get married, and I'm afraid that if I don't choose one of them he'll decide for me."

Aunt Matt's fists seemed to clench a little tighter. "Someday fathers won't have that kind of power over their daughters."

"I wish 'someday' would come soon. . . . Can I tell you a secret, Aunt Matt? The truth is that I came to Chicago to find my mother. Father told me she was ill all these years, and when I finally learned that she wasn't, I decided to find her and ask her if I could live with her. I've been trying to learn more about my parents and their past, and one of the clues I discovered is this address." I pulled the paper from my pocket and showed it to her. "Do you know where Bishop Street is? Would you be willing to take me there?"

"If it's where I think it is, it's out of the question. That's not a very nice part of town, Violet." She handed the paper back to me and said, "What makes you think your mother is at this address?"

"I don't know whether she is or not, but someone told me that my father used to go there. It's connected with Uncle Philip, somehow.

And Aunt Birdie said that Philip knew my mother."

"You've lost me, Violet."

"I didn't even know I had an Uncle Philip until Aunt Birdie showed me his picture a few days ago. Why doesn't anyone ever talk about him?"

"It's Florence's place to tell you about Philip, not mine."

"But I want to know—"

"I won't talk about him, Violet. But I will tell you that Birdie imagines things. Philip has nothing to do with finding your mother."

I groaned in frustration. "Don't you understand? If I don't solve this mystery I'll have to choose a husband."

"I honestly don't believe that your father would force you to marry against your will. You don't have to marry at all, you know."

"I know. But I want to find out what it's like to fall in love, and to be kissed. No one has ever kissed me, Aunt Matt, and it looks so . . . so wonderful." I drew a breath for courage and decided to take a chance. "Aunt Birdie also told me that you were engaged once. Do you mind if I ask why you broke it off?"

Aunt Matt was quiet for so long that I was afraid I had offended her—or else hurt her feelings. According to Birdie, Aunt Matt had loved her beau deeply.

"I didn't marry Robert," she finally said, "because he didn't love me." She was speaking very quietly for once. "When he asked me to marry him, he had ulterior motives."

I waited for her to say more, but she didn't. After we'd boarded the last streetcar, I decided to probe again.

"Aunt Birdie said that your beau turned out to be a thief." I hadn't thought about Silas McClure all morning, but he suddenly sprang to life in my mind with his bright, candelabra grin.

"A thief?" Matt repeated. "I'm not sure what she meant."

"Well, what did happen to him?"

"My sister Agnes threw an engagement party for us," she said with a sigh. "Everything was going well until Robert and a friend went outside to smoke cigars. They were gone for quite a while, so I went outside to find him. That's when I accidentally overheard him talking." Aunt Matt was usually so stern and abrupt, but now her voice grew soft with emotion.

"I heard him saying unkind things about . . . about my physical appearance. He and his friend were laughing at me because . . . because I had been foolish enough to fall in love with him. He told his friend that he didn't love me. He had been lying to me when he'd said that he did. I don't think he even liked me. His friend asked Robert why he'd proposed to me, and he said it was because my father was going to die soon, and I would inherit the house and all of Father's estate. By law, a woman's inheritance transferred to her husband the moment they were married."

I didn't know what to say. No wonder Aunt Matt distrusted men. "Aunt Birdie was right when she called him a thief," I finally murmured.

"Yes. I suppose she was." Her voice quavered with emotion—even after all these years.

I was no longer sure that I wanted to fall in love if it hurt this much. Aunt Birdie was still devastated after losing Gilbert. My father had become emotional when he'd talked about my mother. And now I'd learned that Aunt Matt still felt the pain of rejection after all these years. Romance novels never warned about this side of love—the not-so-happily-ever-after part.

"Now, Violet," she said, clearing her throat. "I don't want to sound critical, but is what Robert Tucker planned to do so different from what Agnes did, marrying Henry Paine for money and social privilege? Would it be so very different from your choosing a husband you didn't love for no other reason than because he's wealthy?"

Ouch!

"But . . . but there are a lot of women like me who have no way of supporting ourselves. We have to marry a man who can support us."

"He doesn't have to be wealthy, does he? Any decent, honest, hard-working man can support you. The point I'm trying to make is that everyone—man or woman—should marry because they are in love, not for what they stand to gain. And I hope that you'll do the same."

"Do you believe in love?" I asked after we stepped off the streetcar near home.

"Yes, of course," she said sternly. "The problem is, most of us are selfish. And so we often choose a mate for selfish reasons. That's my advice as far as your two proposals are concerned. Don't marry either man for selfish reasons. And make sure they aren't marrying you for selfish reasons either."

I now had one week. And two marriage proposals.

I had to find my mother.

Chapter

27

That evening the house felt so warm and stuffy, even with all of the windows open, that I could scarcely breathe. Part of it might have been panic. My life seemed headed on a course that I couldn't control.

My bedroom was especially hot, so I went outside after supper and sat on the front steps, hoping to find a cool breeze—and a plan. I needed to make sense of the various clues I had been given and find a way to solve all the mysteries I'd unearthed. Maybe they would lead to my mother.

Daylight was fading and the lamplighter was making his way along our street, lighting the gas lamps, when I saw Silas McClure striding toward our house from the streetcar stop. I recognized him by his smooth, boneless stride. When I'd seen him on the train that first day I had described his movements as slippery, but I viewed Silas differently now that he no longer oiled his hair and wore his cheesy suit. His athletic stride was smooth and panther-like, and he carried himself as if every muscle was so well greased he could break into a run at a moment's notice. No doubt he needed to stay fit in order to make quick getaways.

He saw me as he approached and waved. I sprang to my feet, longing to run to him and ask if he'd found my mother. But I noticed that his grin wasn't as bright as usual, and I feared bad news.

"Good evening, Violet." He swept off his hat, revealing clean, wavy hair.

"Good evening, Silas. Do you have news of my mother?"

He exhaled. "I'm sorry to say that I've had no luck, so far. I haven't been able to locate anyone by the name of Angeline Hayes here in the city."

I slapped my fists against my thighs in frustration. For the first time I began to wonder if she still lived in Chicago. Perhaps she had come to the city only to sign the divorce papers. Silas must have seen my reaction, or perhaps the tears that filled my eyes, because he quickly said, "I'm not giving up, yet, Violet. I have another idea."

"Would you care to come inside?"

"Actually, it's such a nice evening I'd rather sit out here, if you don't mind."

"All right." I sat down again, moving over to make room for him on the steps beside me. His face looked freshly shaved, and he smelled as though he had lavished a great deal of aftershave on himself. I wondered if his efforts were for my sake. Might he propose marriage to me too? The steps were not very wide, and I felt his shoulders brush against mine when he sat down.

"How did you know where to look for my mother?"

"I know a lot of people in this city who get around . . . if you know what I mean." He gently nudged my ribs for emphasis. "I have my ways. "

"I would love to hear about them. Solving mysteries fascinates me. I used to read *True Crime Stories* and *The Illustrated Police News*."

"That's pretty unusual reading material for a proper young lady like yourself. I'm surprised you'd go for that sort of thing."

"One of my favorite books was Allan Pinkerton's biography."

"Is that right?"

I tried to read his expression, but his face was turned away, and I couldn't see his features in the fading twilight. "Have you heard of Mr. Pinkerton's detective agency, Silas?"

"Who hasn't? I'll wager they're the best crime-fighters in the country. But back to your mother . . ."

His reluctance to discuss Mr. Pinkerton seemed highly suspicious and should have served as a warning to me to have nothing more to do with him. No doubt Pinkerton's men were hot on Silas' trail at this very moment. They were famous for tracking down notorious criminals. But I needed Silas' help.

"Yes? What about my mother?"

"Sometimes women take back their maiden names after they're divorced. I just thought that your mother might have done the same thing. Do you know what her maiden name was?"

"I have it written down. It's upstairs. Shall I go get it?"

"It might help."

He stood, offering me his hand to help me up. A jolt passed from his hand to mine as I gripped it, traveling up my arm and giving me the same sensation I'd once had after accidentally striking my funny bone. I raced upstairs, my arm tingling, and dug out my journal from beneath my mattress. Thank goodness I'd had the good sense to copy down my mother's full name from her signature on the divorce papers along with the now-worthless address. I ripped out a blank page and copied her full name on it then carried the paper down to Silas.

"Her maiden name was Cepak. Angeline Cepak."

"Good. That might help. But keep in mind . . ." He hesitated.

"What? Please tell me."

"She might have remarried. That might be why we haven't found an Angeline Hayes. And in that case we won't find an Angeline Cepak either."

I sat down on the steps again and motioned for Silas to sit beside me. His shoulder seemed to press closer to mine this time, as if the stairs had mysteriously shrunk while I was gone.

"You seem very knowledgeable about this sort of thing, Mr. McClure." I was fishing for more information, perhaps even a confession. I wanted to know the truth about Silas and his mysterious friends.

"I have friends who know a lot about the goings-on in Chicago."

Thieves and murderers, no doubt. I suddenly remembered my second goal: to stop father's wedding.

"Would any of your friends know how to investigate a murder?"

"A murder?"

"I read about an intriguing case in my hometown, where a man fell down the cellar stairs and died. There are some people"—I didn't mention that it was me—"who suspect that he may have been murdered. Do you have any idea how someone would go about proving that?"

"Wow, you really are into crime-fighting, aren't you?"

"I find it fascinating, don't you?"

He shrugged. "I like a good mystery now and then."

"You seem to have friends in the world of crime, so I just wondered if you might know how the police would go about proving that a suspicious death was murder and not an accident."

"Well, I once read a real good book about solving crimes called *The Adventures of Sherlock Holmes.*"

"I love that book!"

"You do? Where in the world did you run into it?"

"A friend at school had a copy. It was fascinating."

"Then maybe you recall that Sherlock Holmes always looked for two things: motive and opportunity. First of all, did the suspected killer have a reason for wanting the victim to die—that's motive. And second, did he have a way to do it—access to the crime scene or to the weapon that was used. The knife or the poison or the gun, for instance. Or maybe they knew about one of the victim's weaknesses—he couldn't swim or he needed a certain medicine—and therefore had opportunity."

"I know she was at the scene of the crime when it happened."

"She? Your suspect is a woman?" I nodded. "Then I'll wager that it's highly unlikely that she's a murderer. The vast majority of convicted murderers are men."

A shiver of horror rocked through me. It couldn't be my father! I didn't want to believe it of him.

"After all, how many women's prisons do you know of?" Silas continued. "Most women are much too delicate and sensitive to do such a grisly thing."

"You don't know Murderous Maude. She—"

"Murderous Maude?" he asked with a wide grin. "Is that her alias? Is she on a wanted poster somewhere?"

"No, that's what I call her. Anyway, she was home at the time of her husband's death. He supposedly fell down the cellar stairs, but isn't it possible that she pushed him?"

"What about motive? Why would she push him?"

"She wanted his money, I suppose?"

"Not good enough. Too hard to prove unless he was exceptionally wealthy. Was he?"

"No," I admitted. "They have two small children, and—"

"Children? See, that's why I don't believe she did it. If she kills her husband and goes to prison, who's going to look after her kids? Women think about these things, and it keeps them from committing murder."

What Silas said made sense. Yet Herman's mother had seemed to imply that women murdered their husbands more often than people realized. Perhaps I should raise that possibility.

"A close family friend dropped a hint about suspicious things going on behind closed doors."

"You mean husbands who beat their wives?"

"W-what?"

"I'm sorry. I probably have no business talking about this stuff with a lady of your sensitivities and all."

"I'm the one who raised the subject, Mr. McClure. I would like to know the truth."

"Okay. But usually when I hear people talking about what goes on 'behind closed doors,' they're talking about men who get drunk regularly and beat their wives and kids. It happens more often than people realize in the poorer parts of town—and especially in the tenements."

I remembered my grandmother's friend Irina—her bruised face and broken leg.

"If I were one of these women, I'd leave my husband," I said.

"Well, once again, wives usually stay because of their kids. From what I understand, it's very hard for a woman to get by on her own, especially if she has children. Some women stay because they're religious, and the church believes that marriage is sacred. And most of these husbands keep promising to change, and their wives keep hoping that they will."

"What if Murderous Maude pushed her husband down the stairs because he was a drunkard who beat her? Would the police still charge her with murder?"

"They might look the other way and rule it self-defense . . . unless there were other circumstances."

"What do you mean?"

"Well, suppose the police found out that she was—how can I say this delicately?—stepping out with another man while her husband was alive. Now *that* would be motive. It proves that she wanted her freedom so she could marry someone else."

His words horrified me. The deeper I dug, the more I seemed to implicate my father! I didn't want him to go to jail. He wouldn't hurt a flea. All I wanted to do was stop his marriage to Maude. Silas must have seen my shocked expression.

"Sorry. I didn't mean to embarrass you with such indelicate stuff. Maybe we should change the subject."

I shook my head. I had to uncover the truth. "Have you ever heard of a place called the Jolly Roger?"

"No, can't say that I have."

"It's on Bishop Street. Do you know where that is?"

"I have no idea."

"Could you ask around? Maybe one of your friends has heard of it or knows where Bishop Street is. It might be connected to finding my mother."

"Sure. I could try."

He pulled out a pencil and scribbled *Bishop Street* and *Jolly Roger* beneath my mother's maiden name. He had to lean even closer to me as he tucked the paper and pencil back into his pocket.

We both fell silent for a few moments as crickets chirped in the bushes. My mind raced with thoughts of murder and mayhem and my mother, but Silas' thoughts had obviously drifted elsewhere.

"Did I mention how pretty you look tonight, Violet?"

"I don't believe so—but thank you."

"And isn't it a beautiful night? Look at those fireflies winking like stars. And that moon!"

Silas might have been talking about the moon, but he wasn't gazing at it. He had shifted around until he was looking right at me with the same dreamy expression that Aunt Birdie always wore on her face. My heart started thumping like a three-wheeled carriage. I needed to distract him—fast!

"H-how did your trial turn out?"

"My what?"

"You were at the courthouse when we met downtown on Monday, remember? Your friend called to you and said that court was back in session."

"Oh, that. It wasn't my case. It was . . . I mean, I was there with . . . I can't explain it."

"Guilty or innocent?"

"Huh? Oh the, uh, thief was found guilty. Sentenced to three years."

"Was he your friend?"

"No, the thief wasn't my friend. I mean . . ." He exhaled. "I don't want to waste time talking about this stuff. I came here to ask if you would please consider going to the fair with me again. I promise I'll find a better chaperone this time. I'd like to make it up to you, Violet. And there's so much more to see."

That was true. I'd seen the fair's elegant side with Nelson and the boring side with Herman and the educational side with Aunt Matt. It would be fun to explore some of the exotic foreign pavilions and of course the Midway. And if I went with Silas—

But no. Silas was hypnotizing me again, dangling adventure and excitement in front of my eyes, hoping I would fall under his spell. I shook myself.

"I'm afraid I don't have time to return to the fair. My father is coming to take me home to Lockport one week from tomorrow, and—"

"One week?"

"Yes. So you see, Mr. McClure, I have to find my mother. Right now the Jolly Roger on Bishop Street is the only clue that I have. It's connected to my Uncle Philip somehow, and Aunt Birdie says Philip might know where my mother is. I'm prepared to go there myself, even though my aunt Matt said it's probably not in a nice part of town, but—"

"I'll take you. I'll find out where Bishop Street is and I'll take you there."

"You will?" I breathed an enormous sigh of relief. I would be safe with Silas. He carried a gun.

"Would I still need to find a chaperone?" he asked.

"Not this time. I'll provide one." I would sooner drag poor Aunt Birdie along than go out with another one of Silas' chaperones.

"Suppose I took some time off on Monday afternoon?" Silas said. "Would that work for you?"

"That would be wonderful!"

"I'll try to find out where Bishop Street is in the meantime. And if I may make a suggestion, Violet—don't dress too nicely."

"You want me to wear a disguise?"

Silas laughed out loud. "No, I was thinking that I would hate to be robbed."

"Oh. I see." I was disappointed. I had liked the idea of traveling incognito.

"I guess I'd better go," he said, rising to his feet. "But one more question: If we do find your mother before next Saturday, then will you go to the fair with me?"

I gave him my famous enigmatic smile. "Perhaps."

As I was writing in my diary later that night, I realized how much fun it had been to piece together clues and discuss crimes with Silas. Of all the things I had done since coming to Chicago, tonight's conversation had made me feel more alive and invigorated than I'd felt since . . . since . . . riding Mr. Ferris' wheel—with Silas.

What in the world was wrong with me?

Chapter

28

Friday, July 7, 1893

Silas McClure had given me an idea when he'd asked for my mother's maiden name. The women who had danced at the settlement house on Folk Night had all been Bohemian like my mother. Perhaps one of them knew her or had heard of her family. I needed to go back and talk with them. I would ask for my mother by her maiden name. Somebody might have heard of her. I made up my mind to get out of bed early for once, overcome my loathing for horrific smells, and go to work with my grandmother.

"Are you going to the settlement house today?" I asked her on Friday morning. She was bustling around the kitchen making breakfast, but she stopped to stare at me in surprise, a frying pan in her hand.

"Why, Violet Rose. You're up very early this morning. Would you like some eggs? They're fresh."

"No, thank you." I couldn't risk returning to that neighborhood with a full stomach. "But I would like to go with you today, if that's okay."

"I thought you didn't like working at the settlement house?"

"I have a hard time with the stench. But Father is coming for me next week, and . . . and so I would like to go with you." I was deliberately vague about my reasons. It was hard to lie to a woman who was as kind and good as my grandmother was. Even so, I couldn't risk telling her about my search for my mother. I didn't know how she would react.

I wouldn't have believed it possible for the neighborhood to smell any worse than it had the last time I'd visited, but it did. The first week of July had been scorching, and all of the decaying, molding, putrefying odors had intensified tenfold. From the looks of things, the garbage hadn't been collected since the last time I'd visited either. I nearly swooned the moment I stepped off the streetcar. I clutched my perfumed hankie to my nose, longing to run to Miss Addams' house for refuge.

"Let's go inside the main house," my grandmother said, "and see if we can find a job for you in there. The soup kitchen will be much too hot today."

I pushed open the heavy front door and rushed inside like a sprinter reaching the finish line. I could hear the chant of children's voices in the distance. The massive beauty of the home's woodwork struck me once again, each window and door framed with ropy carving that resembled thick braids. How did the immigrants handle such loveliness when their own lives were so stark?

"Would you like to work with the kindergarten children today?" my grandmother asked. "I believe I hear them in the parlor."

"Where will you be working?"

"I'll go wherever I'm needed, dear."

"I guess I could try it."

"Good. Then if it's okay with you," my grandmother said, "I'll leave you here and see if Magda needs help in the soup kitchen."

"Yes, of course. I'll see you later."

I found the children in the parlor, sitting on the floor in a circle while their teacher read a book to them. Louis Decker sat cross-legged on the floor with them. The children were very young, no more than five or six years old, but they looked more like shrunken old people to me than children. The hard life they'd endured was deeply etched on each somber, careworn face. Every one of them looked hungry.

I couldn't do this job either. I couldn't get involved with these little ones and let them into my heart, knowing that some of them would die of polio or typhus or dysentery before the year ended. How did gentle, kindhearted women like my grandmother and Miss Addams ever cope?

I stood in the doorway and leaned against the jamb to watch. The teacher held up a picture book with drawings of farm animals. She pronounced the name of each one carefully—cow, pig, goose—and then the children repeated it after her. My heart nearly broke. She may as well have been showing them unicorns and fire-breathing dragons. The only farm animals they were likely to see would be hanging in the window at the butcher shop.

When the teacher closed the book, Louis Decker glanced up and saw me. He scrambled to his feet. "Miss Hayes! It's so nice to see you!"

"I-I've come to help."

"That's wonderful!" He introduced me to the teacher, Miss Dow. "Violet plays the piano beautifully," he told her. "Maybe the children would like to hear a song?"

"Yes, please, Miss Hayes. I'm sure they would enjoy that."

It was the very least I could do. I made my way over to the small spinet piano in the corner and rifled through the sheet music that lay on top of it. I found a few pieces that I could sight-read and pounded my way through them, then finished with a lively etude that I had memorized for a recital at school. The children applauded my efforts.

The sound of their tiny, clapping hands brought tears to my eyes. I stood and bowed.

"Thank you."

For the next hour or so I assisted Louis with the children as Miss Dow led them in a variety of educational chores: learning to tie a bow, learning their left hand from their right, recognizing shapes such as triangles and squares. Each time I helped a child I would ask, "What's your name?" Most replied with only a first name. "And can you tell me your family name?" I would ask. None of their nearly incomprehensible replies sounded like Cepak.

Eventually, it was time to take the children outside to play. I had no desire to leave my stenchless sanctuary, so I remained indoors. I wandered into Miss Addams' library and greeted a woman who seemed to be working there.

"Do a lot of people in the community borrow books from you?" I asked.

"Quite a few. Especially the ones who are trying to learn English. But our neighbors work very hard, you see, and don't have much time for reading and other leisure pursuits." I spotted what appeared to be a list of names lying on the round wooden table where she was seated.

"You probably see a variety of ethnic names, working here," I said. "I find foreign names fascinating. May I?" I gestured to the list.

"Those are some of our regular borrowers," she told me. I read through the list twice. There was no one named Cepak.

I browsed around the library for a few more minutes, pretending to show an interest in the book titles and in the artwork on the walls. The sound of childish squeals and laughter drifted through the open windows along with the muted odors of the neighborhood and Louis' booming bass voice.

I explored more of the house and found a friendly, middle-aged woman named Miss McPhee working in a cramped office. I took out my verbal tennis racket and engaged her in a conversation about Folk Night.

"I especially enjoyed watching the Bohemian ladies dance," I told her when we'd chatted for a while. "I would love to meet some of them. Might you know their names or where they live?"

"I know, generally speaking, where they live. The area between Halsted and the river is made up mostly of Italian immigrants. To the south on 12th Street you'll find the Germans. Those side streets are where the Poles and Russians live. Still farther south is where you'll find the Bohemians."

"That's very interesting."

"And if you're looking for the Irish, they're mostly north of us."

"Thank you."

A few minutes later, Louis returned with the children. He was as sweaty and red-faced as they were. "It's lunchtime, Violet. Want to help me feed this gang?"

The children gobbled down their meal as if it might be their last. I nibbled on a slice of bread, balancing my need for sustenance with the necessity of walking to the streetcar stop. When the school day ended, Louis invited me to walk to Irina's tenement house with him.

"This is Irina's daughter, Nessa," he said. The little girl gripping his hand had wispy blond hair and pale blue eyes. "Irina still can't get around very well, so I've offered to pick up Nessa in the morning and walk her home whenever I can." I recalled my real goal and drew a deep breath—perhaps my last comfortable one—for courage.

"Sure. I'll go with you." I reached for her other hand. "How old are you, Nessa?" She lowered her chin and stared at the floorboards.

"She doesn't say much," Louis whispered.

We stepped outside. The afternoon had grown oppressively hot, and the sun was a glaring fireball in the hazy sky. I wished I had brought my parasol, even if it would have looked out of place in a slum.

"Do you know many of these neighborhood people's last names?"

I asked. I couldn't afford to waste time easing my question into the conversation.

"Some of them. Why?"

"I'm mainly interested in the Bohemian ones who danced last week. Do you know if anyone has the family name of Cepak?"

"It doesn't sound familiar. I'm sorry."

"Is Irina a Bohemian?"

"No, she's Polish." I would have huffed in frustration, but I couldn't risk inhaling that deeply.

When we reached her tenement, the area around the water faucet was littered once again with a variety of pots and containers. This time, the child patiently filling them was a small girl.

Nessa raced up the stairs ahead of us and into her apartment. When I reached the door, she was hugging her mother's skirts. I felt a pang of longing as I watched Irina caress her daughter's feathery hair. My mother's hands had been beautiful and graceful with long, tapered fingers. The nannies that Father hired had taken care of all my needs, but none of them had held me and loved me the way that my mother had.

"Tank you. Tank you," Irina said, "for bringing my Nessa."

Louis took a moment to bow his head with Irina and pray for her and her family. I watched, moved by his compassion and faith. When he finished I felt Nessa tugging on my skirt. I bent my head toward hers. "Yes?"

"I am five," she whispered.

"That's the very best age to be," I whispered back. If I could have hidden her in my trunk and taken her back to Lockport with me, I would have.

"Irina looked much better than the last time I saw her," I said as we descended the tenement stairs. "I hope her leg is healing well."

"It seems to be . . . until the next time."

"Do you think her husband will beat her again?"

"Undoubtedly." Louis' gentle face tightened with anger. "So many immigrant men feel frustrated and disappointed with the hard lives they find in America. The only way they know to drown their sorrow is at the saloon. They're good men, for the most part, until Demon Liquor takes over their life. It causes them to lose control and take out their frustration on their families."

His words reminded me of what Silas had said. Was it possible that Maude O'Neill's husband had done the same? It made sense, especially if the Jolly Roger turned out to be a saloon. If Lloyd O'Neill had beaten Maude, she might be very glad he was dead. But did that prove she had killed him? I remembered how Irina had looked the last time I had visited: the bruises, the terror in her eyes. And the shame. Her husband deserved to go to jail.

"Isn't it against the law for a man to beat his wife?" I asked.

"Of course it is. But the law isn't always enforced. There's an attitude that a man's wife is his property, and what a man does inside his own home is his business. Only the Gospel can change people and break the power of alcohol. That's why it's so important to preach Christ's love in these neighborhoods."

Would I blame Irina if she pushed her husband down the stairs? But even if it turned out that Maude had pushed Lloyd O'Neill in self-defense, I still didn't want my father to marry her, no matter how much O'Neill may have deserved it.

As I walked, I wondered where my Uncle Philip fit into the picture. He seemed to be connected to Maude and her husband. Herman's mother had mentioned something about the war. But was Uncle Philip connected to my mother? I had to solve this!

"I need to talk to some of the Bohemian women who danced the other night," I told Louis. "Is that possible?"

He stopped walking. He touched my elbow to stop me as well. "Slow down, Violet. It's much too hot to keep up this pace."

"I'm sorry. . . . But could you take me to visit some of those women? Miss McPhee in the office says that many of them live south of 12th Street."

"May I ask why?" When I hesitated, he said, "I can see that this is really important to you, Violet, and I want you to know that you can confide in me. I promise I won't betray your trust."

"I don't want my grandmother to know, but I'm trying to find my mother."

"I see." He gestured to Miss Addams' front porch a dozen yards away. "Let's sit down and talk, okay?"

"My mother left home when I was nine," I said when we'd reached the shady front steps. "She abandoned my father and me."

"That must have been very hard for you."

"I didn't know she was abandoning me at the time. My father told me that she went away because she was sick. It was easy to believe. She had become so sad before she left. It was like she was in a boat that was slowly drifting away from me on the tide. I kept begging her to be happy again, to dance with me—but she wouldn't. I felt so lonely after she left. I missed her hugs. She gave the best hugs. . . ." I couldn't continue.

Louis gently patted my shoulder, the way I'd seen him soothe Irina. "I'm so sorry," he murmured, handing me his handkerchief. He was easy to talk to, kind and sympathetic. I found myself opening up to him, sharing things I'd never talked about before.

"When I was Nessa's age, my mother was a lively, vibrant woman who sang to me at night and danced the way those Bohemian women danced. She smelled wonderful, like roses. She would tell me stories— marvelous, magical adventures with flying horses and talking cats. She made up tales about a princess who battled evil sorcerers and monstrous dragons and finally married a handsome prince. She was like the sun to me, full of brilliant light and warmth. But then her light began to dim. Our house seemed to grow darker and colder as time went on. When she left, our house was always shadowy and cold, no matter how many lamps or fires we lit. I kept believing that if my mother was sick, she would get better and come home again. But she never did."

Louis had removed his glasses while I was speaking. I looked up into his moist, gentle eyes and said, "I need to find her, Louis. Won't you please help me?"

"Of course. What can I do?"

"Could you take me around the neighborhood so I can talk to the other Bohemian immigrants? My mother's maiden name was Cepak. Maybe someone knows her, or knows where I can find her family."

"I would be happy to."

"Can we go today?" I sprang to my feet.

"I'm sorry," he said, rising slowly. "I promised to help out at a rally this afternoon, but maybe you can meet me here next week sometime?"

"I'll only be in Chicago one more week—"

"One week?"

"Yes. Then I have to go home."

"Meet me here on Monday, then."

"Tuesday would be better," I said, remembering my plans to go with Silas to Bishop Street.

"Violet . . ." Louis cleared his throat and shuffled his feet, as if struggling to say something important. "Violet, I feel as though I've known you much longer than one month. I know this is sudden, and that we haven't spent a great deal of time together, but your grandmother told me so much about you that I feel as though I met you long before I actually did. And . . . and she is such a devout woman of God that I feel that you . . . you're obviously a wonderful woman too, Violet. I would feel diminished if you walked out of my life forever next week. I want so much for you to be part of what I do."

"You mean—work with you on Mr. Moody's campaign?"

His face reddened as he stared at his feet. "Well, yes . . . Well, not exactly." He had been fiddling nervously with his glasses and finally dropped them onto the grass. "What I meant," he said as he scooped them up, "was that . . . I mean, I had in mind the possibility of . . . of marriage. In the future, of course."

Three proposals in one week. I couldn't reply.

"I'll be finished with my studies at the end of the summer," he continued, "and there is a church here in Chicago that is considering me for their pastor—" He halted, perhaps stopped by the look of surprise and dismay that was probably on my face. "I'm sorry. I can see that I'm pushing you too fast. Is there some way you could stay longer than a week? We could spend more time working together and see if we wanted to have a future together. July has just begun. We have Mr. Moody's summer campaign ahead of us, and you could play the piano for me."

"I want to stay, Louis. It's my father who is making me leave. I have a suitor back home in Lockport—but I don't want to marry him," I added quickly when I saw Louis' expression.

"That's good news for me. Suppose I spoke with your father and asked for permission to court you?"

I hesitated, recalling my father's mumbled words about religious zealots. "You could ask him."

I wasn't sure I wanted the life Louis was offering me, but courting him meant I could stay in Chicago longer. And that meant more time to find my mother. I knew it was wrong to use Louis for selfish reasons the way Aunt Matt had warned. But wasn't Louis using me to play the piano? I felt so mixed up! Would I ever unravel the mysteries of love?

My grandmother noticed how perturbed I was on the long ride home. "What's wrong, Violet? I can see that you're not yourself today. In fact, you haven't been yourself all week."

"It's been quite a week, that's for certain." I sighed and slouched lower in my seat. Madame Beauchamps had called girls who slouched "jellyfish" and made us balance a book on our head for a full hour as punishment. But Madame Beauchamps never had a week like the one I'd had.

"Herman Beckett proposed to me on Tuesday," I told my grandmother.

"Is he the gentleman from Lockport that your father wants you to marry?"

"Yes. Then Nelson Kent proposed to me on Wednesday night. He's Aunt Agnes' choice."

"You have had a busy week."

"That's not all. Louis just proposed to me this afternoon."

"That's wonderful!" She clapped her hands. Then her shoulders sagged. "It seems I'm happier about it than you are. Are you trying to decide which proposal to accept?"

"I don't want to accept any of them right now. I'm not ready to get married. And even if I was ready, none of the three ever said that he loved me. Father is the one who's in a hurry for me to marry. I'm so afraid he's going to choose for me, and he favors Herman Beckett. Herman is so boring! Nelson Kent could give me a comfortable life, but he . . . And now Louis . . ."

"Louis is a fine young man, Violet. You would have a very fulfilling life with him, serving God. And plenty of excitement too, I would think."

"May I ask you a question, Grandmother?" After a slight hesitation, I continued. "Aunt Matt said something about having the blinders off when it comes to marrying a minister. What did she mean?"

Grandmother gazed into the distance. Her eyes looked sorrowful to me. "Being a minister is not like having a job with regular working hours. Louis will be gone a lot, tending to the needs of his flock. His passion is first and foremost for God, and that's a good thing. When you serve your husband, you'll always know that you are serving God and helping Louis to do the same."

Her words reminded me of what Aunt Agnes had said about supporting and encouraging Nelson in his work.

"Of course, there are unfair pressures on the pastor's family— people who expect them to be perfect," Grandmother continued. "That's not always a good thing. And pastors often make the mistake of putting their congregation's needs ahead of their family's needs.

There will be times of sorrow. But also times of great joy."

"Did you and my grandfather love each other?"

"People didn't talk much about love back when I was a young woman. My father had four daughters, much to his sorrow. He wanted to find decent, honest husbands for each of us. Isaac was a good man. He chose me because of my devotion to the Lord. Love does grow, in time, as you make a life together and raise a family."

Again, I was reminded of what Aunt Agnes had said. I wanted to ask my grandmother about Uncle Philip, but I was afraid that I would have to explain how I had heard of him in the first place. I didn't want her to know that I was digging into my family's past and searching for my mother.

"Did my father fight in the war?" I asked instead. She seemed surprised by the sudden change in topics.

"He had just turned eighteen and was old enough to be drafted when the war ended—thank heaven." She took my hand in hers. "Violet, what is it that you really want in life?"

I thought for a moment, then said, "I want to be loved. I don't want to spend my life all alone like Aunt Matt. I want to find someone who loves me for myself, just the way I am, not for what he'll gain by marrying me. Is that too much to ask?"

"Not in the least." She slid her arm around my shoulders and gave me a hug. "I know someone who loves you that way right now."

I sat up in surprise. "You do? Who?"

"God."

"He doesn't count."

"Of course He counts! I know you're facing some very important choices in your life. And that you're trying to understand all the new things you've experienced this summer. You're trying to figure out how they fit with the experiences you grew up with and what you learned at school. Ideally, you will be able to bring everything together—and find God's purpose for your life in the process. He allows tragedies such as losing your mother in order to shape us into better people. It's not His will that we suffer, but He can bring good from it if you'll allow Him to."

"I can't see any good in it. And now I feel like I'm trapped. Father is going to choose a husband for me if I don't make up my mind."

"When my husband died, I couldn't see any good in it either. I didn't know which way to turn. But all the loose ends came together when I sought God. I pray that you'll do the same. And that you won't marry for the wrong reasons."

"Will you talk to Father for me?"

"Yes, of course I'll talk to him. I'll tell him that I disagree with him, and that I think you should wait a little longer before getting married. But talking is all I can do, Violet. You are his daughter."

"What would you do if you were me?"

"I would pray."

Chapter

29

Monday, July 10, 1893

I fretted all weekend about my trip with Silas on Monday to the Jolly Roger on Bishop Street. I wanted to dress nicely and look my very best in case this rabbit trail led to my mother, but I remembered Silas' advice about wearing plain clothes so that we wouldn't get robbed. I was pacing the floor, wearing a bare spot in the bedroom carpet, when Silas finally arrived on Monday afternoon.

"Any news about my mother?" I asked as I thundered down the stairs. He was in the front hallway, returning Aunt Birdie's hug.

"No, sorry. I've been asking around, but I haven't found anyone named Angeline Cepak. I'm still looking though."

"Thank you. I appreciate your help." I exhaled and took Aunt Birdie's arm. "Come on, Aunt Birdie. We're going out this afternoon with Mr. McClure."

"Oh, how nice. You know, Violet, out of all your beaus, he is my favorite. Too bad his walnut didn't burn up with yours." She beamed at Silas and he grinned in return. I couldn't speak. I felt my cheeks grow warm.

"And out of all of Violet's aunts," he said, "you're my favorite." He offered her his arm and led her outside. "I borrowed a horse and a runabout," he said, gesturing toward the street. "To make things easier on you ladies."

I looked where he was pointing and saw a skinny, swaybacked horse tethered to our hitching post. The horse looked so weary with its head drooping to the ground that I feared it would keel over and die before Silas could untie it. It was harnessed to a rickety runabout that was in even worse condition than the horse. I didn't think either one could make it to the end of the block, let alone to Bishop Street.

I watched Silas help Aunt Birdie onto the rump-sprung seat and wanted to ask if he had resurrected the rig from the garbage dump. Silas offered me his electrified hand so I could climb onboard, then he untied the reins and settled onto the carriage seat between us. He made a clucking sound and jiggled the reins. The horse started off, meandering down the street as if sleepwalking. I tapped my foot impatiently.

"I do believe we could get there faster on foot," I finally said.

"You might be right. But this rig does have one advantage for where we're going."

"Oh? What's that?"

"It's not likely to be stolen while we're inside."

I couldn't help smiling. "I'll be more worried that the horse will die of old age while we're inside."

Silas laughed out loud. He had a wonderful laugh.

I cleared my throat. "So. I gather that you found out where Bishop Street is?"

"I got directions. Do you think your mother might be there?"

"I'm not sure, but here's what I do know: Aunt Birdie said that my Uncle Philip would know where my mother is. Someone else told me that my father used to come to Chicago to the Jolly Roger for his brother Philip's sake. So I thought perhaps I would find my uncle there, and I could ask him about my mother." I didn't mention that my Aunt Matt had said Philip had nothing to do with my mother.

"That makes sense, I guess," Silas said with a shrug.

"But here is where it gets mysterious—when I checked the records at the city administration building, I found out that the proprietor of the Jolly Roger is listed as Lloyd O'Neill."

"Who is he?"

"He's the man who I believe was murdered."

"The guy whose wife pushed him down the cellar stairs?"

I nodded. "If O'Neill owned a saloon," I continued, "perhaps he really was a drunkard who beat his wife."

"That makes sense."

I couldn't tell if Silas was taking me seriously or not, because he hadn't stopped grinning since Aunt Birdie let him through our door. I had to admit that when I added up all the clues—my mysterious uncle, my missing mother, the murdered alcoholic, and the ridiculous name Jolly Roger—the story did sound like a corny plot from a dime novel.

The horse trudged slowly through the city streets as if on its way to the glue factory. We finally reached a neighborhood that was very much like the one where I'd played the piano for Louis. Saloons and burlesque theaters crowded both sides of the street, and there might have been bawdy houses too, but I wasn't brave enough to look for them. I didn't look up at all until I heard Silas say, "Whoa." The runabout rattled to a stop in front of a tawdry-looking saloon.

"I think this is it," Silas said.

My body began to tremble as if I had caught a chill. "H-how do you know?"

He pointed to the sign hanging above the door: *Jolly Roger*. Aunt Birdie had been silent throughout our journey, but she suddenly piped up.

"I certainly hope this isn't your new restaurant, Violet. I wouldn't step one foot inside that place."

"She's right," Silas said. "A classy woman like you should think twice about going in a dump like that."

I drew a breath for courage—or as deep of a breath as I dared, considering my odiferous surroundings. "It's broad daylight," I said. "And I have you for protection." I could see his inside pocket sagging with the weight of something heavy. He had his gun.

"So what's your plan?" Silas asked.

"I brought along a photograph of my Uncle Philip. I thought I would show it around and ask if anyone knows him."

"That's a great idea, Violet. Let's go." He climbed down to tether the horse, then offered Aunt Birdie his hand.

"I don't think I care to eat here," she said. "This isn't a very nice place at all. We need to find a different restaurant."

I hated taking her inside the saloon against her will, but I couldn't leave her alone in the carriage either. She seemed to dig in her heels as I dragged her reluctantly through the open saloon door.

"You want me to do the talking?" Silas whispered.

"No. I appreciate your help, Silas, but I need to take charge of my life. I can do this."

I had learned to be brave this summer, going to neighborhoods like this with Louis, visiting tenements with my grandmother, confronting abusive factory owners with Aunt Matt. I'd received an entirely new education in a few short weeks, learning things that Madame Beauchamps never dreamed of putting in her curriculum.

The Jolly Roger was as dark as a mausoleum inside. I saw a lump in a corner booth that might have been a sack of rags or a customer— it was hard to tell in the grimy light. No one sat at the bar, thankfully, but a distasteful-looking man with entirely too much facial hair stood behind it, wiping a beer mug with a gray rag.

"Good afternoon," I began in a quivering voice. "My name is Violet Rose Hayes, and I'm looking for information."

"You the police?" he asked, glancing at Silas.

"Hardly!" I blurted.

"Then give me five good reasons why I should talk to you."

I couldn't reply. I was unable to think of a single one, let alone five. Silas slipped his hand inside his jacket, and for a horrible moment I feared he was reaching for his gun. But when his hand came out it held a folded five-dollar bill. He slid it smoothly across the bar and beneath the man's fingers. It disappeared into the bartender's pocket.

"Those are very good reasons," he said. "What do you want?"

"I'll have a cup of tea, please," Aunt Birdie replied. She had seated herself on one of the wooden barstools. "And some scones, if you have them."

The man bellowed with laughter. "That's rich, lady! I can probably fix you some Irish coffee but no tea."

"Well, I don't care for coffee. Let's go someplace else, Violet." She slid off the stool and turned toward the door.

"We'll leave in a minute, Aunt Birdie, I promise. I just need to ask this man some questions first."

Silas linked his arm through Aunt Birdie's and hung on to her as if she were made of smoke and might blow away. I turned back to the bartender.

"I understand that this establishment is owned by Mr. Lloyd O'Neill?"

"You understand wrong. O'Neill sold it to me more than ten years ago."

"Oh. I see."

"O'Neill got married and moved to some little one-horse town— Lemont or LaGrange or Lockport . . ."

"Yes, Lockport."

"Why're you asking me if you already know?" He picked up his greasy rag and swiped it across the top of the bar.

"There are still a lot of things I don't know," I replied. "I'm trying to locate a friend of Mr. O'Neill's named Philip Hayes."

"Never heard of him."

Silas bent close to me. "Show him the picture," he whispered. I pulled out the photograph of my father and his brother and laid it on the bar, facing the man.

"I don't remember this guy," he said, pointing to Philip, "but I certainly remember this one." He pointed to my father. "He was a real troublemaker. Tried to break up the act, if you know what I mean. After O'Neill sold this place to me, he would show up every couple of months, begging to buy it back. This guy in the picture would show up soon after and insist that O'Neill come home to Lockport and be respectable. Got him all screwed up with religion, telling him to quit Demon Rum and so on. Had the poor guy on and off the wagon more times than a deliveryman. I gotta admit that O'Neill was good for business, with his leg and all. He could really tell a story, and all his buddies from the war would come in to hear them."

"What do you mean, with his leg. . . ?"

"Lloyd O'Neill has a peg leg. Made out of wood. That's why he called this joint the Jolly Roger in the first place. Thought it fit in with the whole pirate theme, if you know what I mean."

"Was he a pirate?"

"No, lady. There aren't any pirates in Chicago." He gave the bar another swipe. "O'Neill lost his leg in the war. Used to brag that he got hit while saving some other fellow's life. Don't know if that's true or just drunken swagger."

"Was the man he saved named Philip Hayes?" I asked.

"No idea. I'd tell you to ask O'Neill yourself but I heard he died. Can't say if it's true, but I haven't seen him in more than a year."

"Was O'Neill ever involved with a woman? She would have been Bohemian. Very pretty. Dark-haired."

"Don't know nothing about a woman," he replied, shaking his head. "But if she's as pretty as you are, I'd give her a job. I could use a good-looking barmaid, if you're interested. And I've got another business going on upstairs, if—"

"She's not interested!" Silas yelled. "Come on, Violet. I think it's time for us to leave. Unless you want to ask him something else."

"I-I can't think of anything else."

"Thanks for your help," Silas said.

The sunlight seemed blinding when we stepped into the street again.

"Well!" Aunt Birdie huffed. "That says it all, doesn't it?"

My knees shook so badly that I couldn't negotiate the carriage step. Silas had to put his hands on my waist and lift me onto the seat. It would have been very dramatic and appropriate to gallop away, leaving the Jolly Roger behind in a cloud of dust, but the horse wasn't up to the challenge. Neither, I suspected, was the runabout.

I couldn't speak for several long minutes for fear I would burst into tears. Silas seemed to understand my silence and didn't say anything either, until we finally reached a more pleasant neighborhood.

"Do you mind telling me what you gathered from all that?" Silas said, "Or is it none of my business?"

"No, I don't mind. I'm grateful that you came with us." I paused to swallow the lump in my throat and wipe a tear.

"I'd really like to help you find your mother, Violet. I sure hated seeing a classy lady like you in place like that. I think you were very courageous for venturing there—foolish, perhaps, but courageous just the same."

"I knew you could protect us, seeing as you carry a gun and—"

"A gun?" he asked in surprise. I clapped my hand over my mouth. How had I let it slip out?

"I saw it in your pocket the other day when we met on LaSalle Street," I explained. "And if I'm not mistaken, it's in your pocket today too."

"You mean this?" I shrank back as he reached inside his jacket. He pulled out something and laid it on my lap.

"It's . . . it's a harmonica! I feel so foolish."

"No, you made an honest mistake. I'll wager most people would agree that a mouth organ is an unusual thing to carry around."

"Good thing we weren't in any danger," I said, exhaling.

"Well, if we had been, I could have played a jig for the rogues before they robbed us." Silas scooped up the harmonica and played a few bars of "Yankee Doodle." I couldn't help laughing.

"You're lucky nobody stole it from you in that neighborhood."

He shrugged, as if money wasn't an issue. I wondered if Silas had stolen the harmonica to begin with.

"Well, thanks again for taking me."

"I admire you a great deal, Violet. You were amazingly brave in there. Now, do you want to explain to me what that was all about?"

"I'm trying to find my mother."

"I know that."

"All I have are a bunch of clues, and I'm trying to connect them. I've read hundreds of detective stories—but this is so much harder. My family is so secretive. All I know is that my father used to travel to Chicago to the Jolly Roger for his brother Philip's sake. I'm guessing that O'Neill saved Philip's life during the war, which is why my father tried to help him. Even if O'Neill was a drunkard who may have beat his wife, my father probably brought him home to Lockport for Philip's sake."

"That sure makes a great story. Too bad there's no way to find out if it's true. Is this Philip guy missing too? Where is he?"

"I don't know."

"Philip is away, fighting in the war," Aunt Birdie said. "My husband, Gilbert, is fighting too. He's quite determined to help free all of the slaves." Silas smiled at her and patted her hand.

"You know," Silas said, "if this O'Neill had only one leg, I can see where he might have taken a tumble down the cellar stairs—especially if he was drunk. Cellar steps are usually pretty narrow and steep. Maybe his wife didn't murder him after all."

"Oh. I see what you mean." I didn't know whether to be happy about that conclusion or not. It meant that my father was innocent, but it also meant that Maude was too. I would have to find another way to stop their marriage.

"How does your mother tie into all of this?" Silas asked.

"I guess she doesn't," I admitted. "Aunt Birdie told me that Philip knew her, so I thought—"

"Philip loved the theater too," Aunt Birdie said.

"Are you sure my mother didn't go to the theater with my father?" I asked.

"Certainly not! Your father is dead set against theaters and saloons and all those other worldly amusements. Just like his father is."

"I hate to be the one to suggest this," Silas said carefully, "but is it possible that your mother and Philip . . . you know . . . that we'll find them in the same place when we finally find them?"

I gasped. "You think they ran off together?"

He shrugged. "It happens."

"No . . . no, I-I can't believe that!"

Silas laid his hand on my arm. "Hey, I'm sorry. I didn't mean to upset you. It was a wild thought. . . . It's just that they're both missing and . . . Just forget I brought it up, okay?"

But it explained why no one would discuss either one of them. I didn't want to believe something so scandalous could happen in my family, that one brother would steal the other brother's wife. Most of all, I didn't want to believe that my mother would choose to leave me behind in order to run away with my uncle. I preferred to believe what Aunt Matt had told me: *Philip has nothing to do with finding your mother.*

I was quiet for the remainder of the ride home, thinking about my parents and everything I had learned. I wished I had never raised the ugly suspicion that my father and Maude had killed Lloyd O'Neill. I wished I had never heard of Uncle Philip. I had been much better off believing that my mother had left me because she was ill.

If only my father had lied to me at Maude O'Neill's house. If only he had told me that my mother was dead.

Chapter
30

Tuesday, July 11, 1893

Violet Rose? You're up early again," my grandmother said when I appeared at breakfast the next day.

"I'm meeting Louis down at the settlement house this morning."

"He's such a fine young man. And already like a son to me." She looked so pleased and so hopeful. I felt guilty for misleading her. But maybe I would fall madly in love with Louis as he gallantly helped me search for my mother. Things like that happened sometimes in romance novels.

Louis had arrived at the settlement house even earlier than I had, and he'd begun asking questions to find out which of the Bohemian women would be our best source of information. Everyone at the settlement house adored Louis, and I saw how indispensable he was. Miss Dow wanted him to help with the kindergarten children again. Magda said he was needed in the kitchen. Miss McPhee had a list of repairs she hoped he could attend to. If only I liked him as much as they did.

"Another day," he told them all. "I promised Miss Hayes I would help her. Are you ready?" he asked me. I nodded, dreading the walk outside.

"Is it far? Where are we going?"

"I have the address of the woman who helped organize all the food and the dancing on Folk Night. She's sort of the matriarch of the Bohemian community. I'm told that she knows all of the families."

We walked several blocks south, then wove through a warren of back alleys and side streets to a cluster of tenement buildings similar to Irina's. The four-story brick structures were built right up against each other in the shape of a U, with a bleak patch of dirt for a courtyard. More brick tenements towered across the alley and stretched down the block, until there was no way that fresh air or a cooling breeze could penetrate the apartments.

Children swarmed all over the place, tussling in the dirt, leaning from open windows, playing on the landings and on the open-backed wooden stairs that led up the outside of the structure to each floor. The children reminded me of myself at that age, with their dusky skin and dark curly hair, but I glimpsed sorrow and hopelessness in their expressions in spite of their playful laughter. I recalled Louis saying that for many of these people, the reality of life in America had not lived up to their dreams.

Back home in Lockport, children like Horrid and Homely could spend the hot summer days playing in Dellwood Park, where there were trees and grass and a refreshing breeze from the canal.

"The woman we're looking for lives up on the fourth floor," Louis said, pointing to the rickety wooden stairs. "Are you ready to climb?"

I could feel the steps wobbling and the handrail shaking as I began to ascend. The stairs were so steep—and there were so many of them—that I had to stop for breath on every landing, even though I was in a hurry to escape the neighborhood's horrid smells. The door to the Bohemian woman's apartment stood open, and she and her children recognized Louis immediately.

"Is good to see you, Louis. Come in, come in. You are always so kind to help all the people. So kind." She motioned us inside. The apartment was clean but cramped and crammed with too many beds. A very old woman with skin like crumpled paper sat in a wooden chair by the window.

"Thank you," Louis said. "Do you know Mrs. Hayes who works in the soup kitchen with me, ma'am?"

"Yes, yes, of course. She is a kind woman."

"This is her granddaughter, Violet Hayes. She wants to ask you some questions about the Bohemian community, if you don't mind."

"Yes, yes, I try to answer. But you must sit down, please." She pulled out two splintery chairs from beneath the kitchen table. "Let me fix you something," she said, opening a crude wooden cupboard beside the stove.

"We really don't need anything," I said. "You don't have to—"

"Yes, yes, you are my guests. It is important to give you . . . how do you say it? To make you at home." She removed a greasy, cheesecloth-wrapped lump and set in on a cutting board.

"I'm really not hungry—" I began, but Louis elbowed me.

"It's rude to refuse," he whispered. "These people have so little, and they are honoring us by offering it."

She unwrapped the cloth to reveal a jiggling lump of headcheese, just like the one they had served us on Folk Night. Our hostess sliced off two sizeable pieces, carefully transferring them to two mismatched plates, then set them in front of us. My stomach flipped like a pancake. I was certain that my portion contained an eyeball.

"Excuse, please, while I get water for tea." She lifted a kettle from the stove and disappeared through the door.

"I don't think I can eat this," I whispered to Louis. "Can't we tell her I'm allergic?"

He looked horrified. "We can't *lie*, Violet."

The meat was every bit as slimy and gelatinous as the dish they'd served on Folk Night, with varying-sized chunks of things imbedded in it. My choosing game had sprung to life. I was living one of my questions: *If you had to choose between eating something disgusting in order to find your mother, or refusing to eat it and never seeing her again, which would you choose?* The next time Ruth Schultz asked about the most disgusting thing I'd ever eaten, I would win the prize.

I reminded myself that I had eaten snails at Madame Beauchamps'. This was no worse, was it? I could always just gulp it down without chewing or tasting it. But in retrospect, the slippery garlic butter had helped expedite the snail's passage down my throat. Garlic can disguise the most obnoxious of flavors.

I decided against gulping down the headcheese. If I finished it too quickly my hostess might offer me more. She returned with the kettle of water and proceeded to brew tea for us. The finished concoction smelled and tasted as though she had used a clump of weeds from alongside the road instead of real tea leaves.

"I'm trying to find my mother," I began, swallowing the first tiny nibble of meat. "She was Bohemian, I believe. Her maiden name was Cepak. Angeline Cepak. Do you know any other families in this neighborhood by that name?"

"No, I cannot think of any. But I have heard this family name in the old country. Is not so unusual there."

I swallowed a second bite along with my disappointment. "Do you know of any other places in the city where other Bohemian families live? Or do you know someone else I might ask?"

"No, I know only the families around here. I am sorry."

"How long ago did you immigrate to Chicago? Were you here during the Great Fire?"

"No, we are coming here nine years ago. I am sorry I am not helping you find your mother. I wish I could. When did you lose her?"

"Eleven years ago." I ate a third bite and chased it down with a sip of tea. Both tasted terrible.

I had to think! What other clues had I gathered about my mother? Aunt Birdie kept mentioning that she'd loved the theater— but my aunt often got her stories mixed up. Was it possible that my mother *worked* in the theater as an actress instead of merely attending the shows? I knew she had loved to dance. I took a chance. I had nothing to lose.

"Have you heard of anyone named Cepak who worked in the theater? An actress, maybe? Or a dancer?"

"No, I don't think so. . . ."

All of a sudden the little old grandmother in the corner began talking a mile a minute in another language. She pointed to me and gestured with her twig-like hands as she talked.

"What is she saying?" I asked.

"My husband's mother says there are Cepaks in the old country who are married with gypsies. They are thieves." She turned to her mother-in-law and said loudly, "They cannot be her family. She is nice girl." The old woman babbled even louder, waving her arms.

"What did she say? Please tell me."

"She said in America the gypsies perform in the shows. But it cannot be the family you look for. The shows are . . . how do you say? . . . Not so nice." She lowered her gaze, brushing crumbs off the table.

I knew that the old woman was talking about burlesque shows, not the legitimate theater or even vaudeville. The thought made me feel ill. But then, I already felt queasy from the headcheese and bitter tea. I choked down the last bite of meat and stood.

"Thank you so much for your help," I said. "We need to be going." I wondered if I should offer to pay her for the information the way Silas McClure had paid the bartender.

Louis took my arm to help me down the steep flight of stairs. My head reeled from the heat and from this new information.

"I'm sorry we didn't learn more, Violet. Is there someplace else you want to go?"

"No—back to the settlement house, I guess. I'm all out of ideas."

When we reached the main street, I suddenly heard a terrible squealing sound, like a child being tortured. We rounded the corner and Louis halted abruptly.

"Violet, wait!" He tried to hold me back and block my view but his warning came too late. In the middle of the filthy, littered alley, someone was butchering a pig. The man had hoisted the animal up on a scaffold by its rear legs, and he proceeded to slit the pig's throat, right before my eyes. The screeching halted abruptly. The amount of blood that gushed out was unbelievable. I bent over by the side of the road and vomited.

"Violet? Are you okay?" Louis asked, squatting beside me.

"Yes," I lied. I wanted him to go away. Being sick was bad enough, but I was horrified to have him see me this way. I tried to stand up and walk and felt my gorge rise again. I turned away and threw up a second time.

Louis offered me his handkerchief. His kindness and sympathy only added to my humiliation. Every time I was with Louis something degrading seemed to happen. First I had encountered the horrid onions and beets, then the drenching rain and mud, now this. This humiliation was by far the worst.

"I need to go home."

Louis let me lean on his arm as I staggered back to the settlement house. Someone brought me a cool cloth to wash my face. Louis brought me a glass of water.

"I'm sorry for forcing you to eat," he said.

"No, it wasn't your fault. It was the sight of . . . you know."

"I think you should go home."

Home. I would have to go home to Lockport in four more days. I couldn't stop my tears. Could my mother's family really be involved in those horrible shows? Visiting the Jolly Roger had been bad enough, but going to a burlesque theater to search for her would be much, much worse. Nevertheless, I had to do it.

"I need to find my mother, Louis. I need to find the family of gypsies named Cepak who are involved in the theater."

"But the woman said—"

"I know. You don't have to help me anymore. But you've been to some of those neighborhoods—if you have any advice . . ."

"I don't know what to tell you. Mr. Moody sometimes rents theaters for his rallies, but not those places. He's holding a rally on Thursday, in fact, but it's in a respectable theater—"

"Maybe we could talk to the theater manager and ask if he has heard of the name? Or maybe one of the other actors at the theater has heard of her."

He looked very dubious, but he said, "I guess it's worth a try."

"Thank you."

I heard a babble of excited voices in the front hall. The house seemed to be filling with young women my age.

"What's going on?" I asked Louis.

"I think they're registering new girls for the Jane Club. Miss Addams started a boardinghouse for single women using several of her vacant bedrooms. Many of these girls don't have families in the city, and they need a safe place to live that won't use up all of their meager wages."

I nodded, thinking of all the vacant bedrooms in our house in Lockport.

"We should go find your grandmother and tell her you're not well," Louis said. "You need to go home."

My stomach rolled at the thought of venturing outside. "Would you mind if I stayed here while you fetched her? The smells in the street . . ."

"Sure. I'll be right back."

The sound of laughter and babbling voices grew louder as the girls spilled into the other rooms from the front hall. One of them looked very familiar to me. It took me a moment to realize that it was Katya. She looked bedraggled without her crisp maid's uniform and starched white apron. Her skirt was patched and threadbare, her shoes scuffed and worn. My strength had returned, so I stood and made my way toward her, calling her name.

"Katya . . . Katya . . ."

Her eyes widened when she saw me. She whirled around and hurried away, plowing a path through the crowd and out of the house.

"Katya, wait!" I called. "Come back!"

Why was she running from me? I braved the terrible odors outdoors and chased her down crowded Halsted Street, weaving between the other pedestrians. Katya was very fast, and I was still feeling light-headed after being sick, but I kept running. I caught up with her at the corner when she encountered too much traffic to risk crossing the street.

"Don't run, Katya. I'm your friend!" Both of us were breathing hard, and I could taste the terrible odors as well as smell them. "What's wrong? Why did you run?" When she didn't reply, I said, "Listen, I know that you're in love with Nelson—and that's okay with me."

"No, please . . ." I saw her surprise and fear. She had no idea what I would do with that knowledge.

"It's okay. I won't tell anyone."

"But you are the woman Nelson is going to marry."

Now it was my turn to be surprised.

"How do you know that? He only proposed to me a week ago. And that was after you left the Kents. Besides, I haven't agreed to marry him."

Tears filled her eyes. "But he must marry you or he will have nothing."

"Listen, can we go back to the settlement house and talk this over? I want to help you."

"Why? Why will you help me?"

"For Nelson's sake. He's my friend."

"I do not understand."

I took a chance and told her the truth. "I saw you with him. I saw the way he looks at you and the way you look at him. Nelson is in love with you, not me. And I saw him kissing you."

Her hands flew to her face. "Oh no. He will get into trouble. . . ."

"I'm not going to tell anyone. Listen, I came to the settlement house to help women like you, not harm them. Let's go back and talk, okay?"

"You won't tell anyone—about Nelson and me?"

"No. I promise."

We walked back to the house and pushed our way through the crowd of girls. I led Katya into the library and sat down to talk with her at a table in the corner. She seemed very nervous, glancing all around as if she might get into trouble. She spoke so softly I had to strain to hear her above the noise.

"Tell me what happened. Why did you stop working for Mrs. Kent?"

"Because Nelson must forget about me. It is too hard for him, seeing me every day. He was so unhappy. So I quit."

"You mean, nothing happened? No one caught you two together?"

"No. No one knows about us. I leave because I love him." Tears flooded her eyes.

"I don't understand. Why would you leave if you loved him?"

"Nelson loves me too. He tells me over and over. He says he will find a way for us to be together, a way for us to get money. But I know that he is better without me. His family will be very angry about me. They will never want him to marry me. They will throw Nelson out of the family if he does, and he will have nothing. He is better with someone like you. I love him so much . . . and I want him to be happy."

I stared at Katya in amazement as she wiped her tears. Her love was genuine, self-sacrificing. She loved Nelson so much that she was willing to give up her own happiness for his. I envied her. And I wanted to help her.

My mind raced with plans. I could loan her some of my gowns and teach her everything I knew about proper manners. Nelson could break away from his father's business, and they could start a new life together on their own. There had to be a way to make this work.

"Listen, if you and Nelson love each other, then you should be together. I want to help you. Will you trust me?" She nodded slowly, as if afraid to hope. "Where are you staying? How can I contact you again?"

"Miss Addams is very kind to rent me a room here."

"Good. I'll be in touch with you after I talk to Nelson."

"Thank you." Katya stood and hurried away just as my grandmother walked into the library, her face creased with worry.

"Violet Rose! You're as white as a ghost. Louis told me you were ill." She felt my brow for a fever as she smoothed my tangled hair off my face.

"I'm feeling better now."

"I'm taking you home."

We walked to the main street, and for once my grandmother hailed a cab instead of waiting for the streetcar. I was grateful. I couldn't leave that stinking neighborhood quickly enough. When we had traveled a short way, my grandmother sighed and said, "Violet, dear, I know you've been looking for your mother."

"Did Louis tell you?"

She shook her head. "I've been trying to find her too."

"My mother? You've been searching for my mother? For how long?"

"Since coming to Chicago. It was one of the reasons I came here after Isaac died. And one of the reasons I started working down here at the settlement house. Hundreds of Bohemian people live in this area, so I decided to start here and do the same thing you're doing.

But I've had no luck, Violet, in all these years. I haven't found anyone who knows her or her family."

"What were you going to do if you found her?"

"Ask her to come home to you and your father."

I closed my eyes in disappointment and defeat. I wasn't going to find my mother. Grandmother had been searching for seven years and I had only three more days.

"While I was trying to find Angeline," Grandmother said, "I met so many women like her who needed my help. That's how I started working with the poor. So you see, something good can come from our sorrows and disappointments if we give them to God. And when I heard that D. L. Moody was preaching in theaters all over the city, I volunteered to help him too. I still hoped to find your mother—but I also hoped that other women like Angeline would have a chance to hear the Gospel."

I wondered if my grandmother realized that she had dropped a valuable hint. Once again, I pretended that I knew more than I did, hoping she would offer new information.

"You mean other actresses like my mother?"

"Yes. I'm sorry I couldn't find her for you, Violet, but I tried."

I was familiar enough with the neighborhoods by now to know that we were halfway home. I had to keep Grandmother talking and unravel more of the mysteries before we arrived.

"Did my mother run away with Uncle Philip?" I asked.

She drew a startled breath. "With Philip? Who has been talking to you about Philip?"

"Aunt Birdie showed me a picture of him and my father. She said he was away at war. I never even knew I had an uncle. Why won't anyone talk about him? Where is he?"

She turned away, gazing out of the window as if reluctant to answer. I continued talking.

"I came to the conclusion that Uncle Philip must have run away with my mother since nobody will talk about either one of them, and—"

"No, Violet," she said, shaking her head. "No. That isn't what happened." I waited for more, but she was quiet for a very long time. I was about to ask another question when she finally spoke. "No one talks about Philip because it's too painful—for your father as well as for me." Again, I waited.

"Your grandfather tried to control everything his sons did and said and thought. He forgot that God was in charge of the world, not him. He meant well, but he was much too strict. I didn't go against him, I'm sorry to admit, and we did a great deal of harm to our sons. Isaac wanted Philip and John to become ministers, like him. I got caught up in it, and I wished them to be preachers too. But that choice wasn't up to us.

"One day Philip had enough. There were too many rules in our household and not nearly enough love. Too much law and not enough grace. When Isaac tried to discipline Philip, he rebelled and left home. He had just turned eighteen, so he went off to war. He was nearly killed at Cold Harbor, but a good friend saved his life."

"Was his name Lloyd O'Neill?"

She nodded. "Philip returned home from the war filled with bitterness and resentment. He was angry with God. He had seen too much suffering and bloodshed to ever believe in God's mercy. He lived the reprobate life of a prodigal. The only thing that he and your mother had in common was that Philip was also involved in the theater."

"Are . . . are you still searching for Philip too?"

"No," she said quietly. "Philip died more than twenty years ago."

I leaned my head against her shoulder. "I'm so sorry."

"I know. No one talks about Philip," she said, wiping a tear, "because it hurts too much. None of us ever had a chance to reconcile with him."

"It must have been very hard . . . but at least you know why Philip left home and where he went. No one will tell me why my mother left me."

"Violet," she said with a sigh, "you know that I promised your father I wouldn't talk about her."

"Isn't there anything you can tell me?"

She sighed again. "Try to imagine a woman like Irina or one of the other women we met in these tenements. . . . Imagine her suddenly moving to your house in Lockport and having Mrs. Hutchins to cook and clean for her and a nanny to help take care of her children. Can you see what enormous changes she would face?"

"I guess so."

"Suppose Irina had to attend dinners and social functions in Lockport, and she didn't know anything about fine manners or social customs. Think of all the years of training you've had in school about proper etiquette. How would a woman like Irina ever learn those things? And do you think that the women in Agnes' crowd, for example, would ever accept Irina into their social circle?"

"No. They would make her life miserable."

I suddenly thought of Katya. She would never fit into Nelson's world or be accepted by his family and friends, even if I dressed her in my finest gown. If she were to rise from mere servant to lady of the house, Haughty and Naughty and their crowd would have nothing to do with her. Neither would Nelson's family. Could true love conquer all of those obstacles? It hadn't in my parents' case. And Nelson Kent was much wealthier than my father was.

"Can you understand the enormous strain on your mother?" my grandmother asked.

"Yes. I think I can. . . . Thank you." I had gained a little more understanding of my mother, even if I hadn't found her.

Then I recalled offering to help Katya live "happily ever after" with Nelson. I hadn't known what I was getting myself into.

Chapter

31

Wednesday, July 12, 1893

I needed to talk to Nelson. With only three days remaining until my father arrived, it looked as though I wasn't going to find my mother. But if I could help Nelson and Katya find the happiness that had eluded my parents, then at least I would have accomplished something this summer.

"I need to make social calls with Aunt Agnes this afternoon," I told my grandmother on Wednesday morning. She was bustling around the kitchen stove, trying to kindle a fire to brew coffee.

"What time is she coming for you?"

"That's the problem; Aunt Agnes doesn't know that I want to go with her. I'll have to call on her first."

Grandmother turned to face me, still holding a piece of firewood in her hand. "How can you do that? You can't go out alone."

"I think it's time that I did go out on my own, don't you? I can't lean on other people for the rest of my life. Aunt Agnes doesn't live very far, and I know the way. You and Aunt Matt travel all over the city by yourselves. I can too."

She studied me for a long time, a look of sorrow and concern on her face. "You've grown up a lot this summer, Violet."

"Yes, I know. But I needed to grow up."

Grandmother turned back to the stove, shoving the wood inside and closing the cast-iron lid. "I want you to hire a cab, then. I don't want you getting lost on the streetcars."

When I arrived at Aunt Agnes' home, she was surprised and pleased to see me. "Of course you can go calling with me, Violet; that's a wonderful idea. The other ladies have been so disappointed that they haven't seen much of you lately, and—"

"Can we pay a visit to Nelson's grandmother?"

"Certainly. She is more eager than anyone to get to know you better."

Her words were an unwelcome reminder that Nelson had indeed proposed to me—in spite of the fact that he loved another woman. I couldn't imagine what he was thinking or why he would do such a deceitful thing, but I intended to find out.

"We're all thrilled about the engagement, Violet. Just thrilled!"

Her words horrified me. "Y-you didn't tell anyone else about it, did you? Our engagement isn't even official."

"Now, Violet. Nelson's grandmother and I are very good friends."

"I know, but please don't say anything to the other women. Nelson should be the one who makes the announcement, don't you think?"

I could tell by her pursed lips and woeful frown that she was disappointed. She would have loved to stand on the tallest building in Chicago and announce the good news. I couldn't break her heart by telling her that I thought Nelson was using me or that I wasn't going to marry him.

"Well, it will be very difficult to remain quiet about something this momentous, Violet, but I shall respect your wishes. Just tell Nelson not to wait too long."

Making social calls that afternoon seemed almost as boring and tedious as spending an afternoon with Herman Beckett, but I made up my mind to get through it and leave a note for Nelson. For the first time, I found it difficult to paste on a phony smile and pretend that I enjoyed this life of social politics and gossip. I felt awkward making inane conversation with Nelson's grandmother and the other women as we sipped our tea and nibbled dainties.

I knew Aunt Agnes had told Mrs. Kent about Nelson's proposal because she gazed at me the entire afternoon as if it were her birthday and I was a chocolate cake. Meanwhile, I couldn't seem to forget that my father would arrive on Saturday to haul me back to Lockport and into Herman Beckett's stiff, black-suited arms. I felt like an actress— like my mother. I was still trying to adjust to that truth.

"Might I leave a message for Nelson to call on me?" I asked when the afternoon mercifully ended. Mrs. Kent beamed with delight.

"Why, Nelson is here, Violet. Shall I have one of the servants fetch him?"

I was prepared to confront him angrily, telling him that I knew the truth about his love for Katya and demanding an explanation for his marriage proposal—until I saw how terrible he looked. He hadn't shaved. His clothes looked as though he had worn them for days. His golden hair stood on end. Deep worry lines etched his handsome face, making him appear several years older. He hurried me outside to the garden, away from the scrutiny of the other women.

"What's wrong, Nelson? You look unwell."

"I lost it all, Violet. Everything!"

I wondered if he meant Katya. If so, I knew where he could find her. "What did you lose?"

"My luck was terrible the other night. I didn't have you for my good-luck charm and I lost everything!"

"Oh, money," I mumbled. "I might have known. Look, I'm sorry, but I was afraid that would happen. That's why I didn't want to come with you the other night."

"You don't understand. I borrowed the money from my father's business. I was supposed to deposit it in the bank but I . . . I diverted it. And now I've lost it all. I stayed home from work today so I could figure out what to do. It wasn't hard to play at being sick because I am sick. I have to pay the money back before he finds out, but I can't because I'm broke!"

I sank down on a stone bench in the garden to ponder this news, but Nelson couldn't seem to sit. Nor could he stand still. He paced in front of me, running his hands through his hair—which explained why it stood on end.

"If I could just scrape a couple of hundred dollars together, I could go back to the fairgrounds on Friday night and win it all back before my father finds out."

"Or you could lose even more," I pointed out.

"I don't know what to do."

"What about a bank loan?"

"Every banker in the city knows my father. Besides, I have no credit and nothing for collateral. I've heard there are loan sharks I could go to, but they charge high interest rates. It wouldn't matter, though, because I can win it all back on Friday night. . . ." He seemed to be talking more to himself than to me. I decided to confront him after all.

"You were gambling because of Katya, weren't you?"

His pacing stopped abruptly. "What did you say?" I didn't think it was possible for Nelson to look more unwell, but he did.

"I know about her, Nelson. Whenever I was at your house I watched the way you gazed at each other from across the room and saw how you followed each other with your eyes. I also saw you kissing her."

"It's not what you think, Violet."

"What do I think?"

"That it was a seduction. The rich, spoiled son seducing the innocent immigrant girl. It happens all the time in our circle and usually ends with paternity suits and payoffs and covered-up scandals. But this isn't like that. I haven't touched Katya—well, aside from a few stolen kisses. I love her. But she left. She quit. And I have no idea how to find her."

"I know where she is."

He grabbed my shoulders, gripping them tightly. "Where? Tell me, Violet. I have to see her."

"Why? What are you going to do when you find her?"

"I-I don't know . . ." He released me and his head sagged as he started pacing again. "Remember when you asked me whether I would choose true love with poverty or wealth and success without love? I'm living that dilemma, Violet. I love Katya . . . but I'm too much of a coward to give all this up." He gestured to his grandmother's mansion behind me.

"And where do I fit in?"

"You came to Chicago to marry a rich husband, so I thought that . . . Oh, never mind," he said, waving his arms. "It doesn't matter. I couldn't make up my mind what to do about Katya, and so she left, and I don't know where she went. She said it was better this way. We could never marry."

"Why not?"

"Don't you see? It's not just the money—it's my family. Their hold over me is very powerful. I have three sisters. I'm the only son. My father is counting on me to take over his business, but if I choose Katya, I'd have to turn my back and walk away from them forever."

"I understand," I said quietly. "But I talked to Katya, and do you know what she told me? She said she left you because she loves you. What a thought! She was willing to give up what she loved the most in the world—you—so that you could be happy and have all of this. That sounds like genuine love on her part, doesn't it? So the question is, would you be willing to do the same for her? To give up everything—even your family—in order to be with her?"

Nelson sank down on the bench beside me as if he had suddenly run out of strength. "I don't know," he said, shaking his head. "I don't know."

"There is a way out of your dilemma. You could make your own fortune. You're certainly smart enough. Isn't your love for Katya motivation enough? You told me all those other rags-to-riches stories about Mr. Fields and Mr. Harvey. Didn't you say you wanted to invest in some of the modern inventions you saw at the fair, like Mr. Edison's music-making machine?"

"Yes, but I have no capital to start my own business. That's why I started gambling. If I make my own wealth, I can marry whomever I want."

"Where do I fit into this picture? You asked me to marry you, remember?"

"It was never my intention to hurt you, Violet. You wanted a rich husband and I wanted Katya. I thought we could both get what we wanted."

"So I was supposed to share you? That isn't fair to me or to her."

"I wasn't thinking clearly. I was desperate. As long as my father thought I was settling down and was about to be married, he would give me access to his money. So I borrowed some, hoping to gamble with it and win more. You seemed reluctant to get married right away, unlike all of the other girls I know, so I hoped we could delay the wedding long enough for me to make my own money."

"You never intended to marry me?"

"I thought about it. I'm ashamed to say that I thought about marrying you and having Katya for my mistress. But I couldn't go through with it. Besides, Katya kept telling me that it was wrong to deceive you. I like you, Violet. That's why the only solution was to win my own fortune."

"But you lost."

"Yes. And unless I can get a loan, I'm going to be in enormous trouble. I've been trying to locate a loan shark, but I don't know anyone in the world of crime."

I felt sorry for him. And sorrier still for Katya. But after discovering some of the truth about my mother, I wanted to help them, for her sake.

"I might know someone who could help you."

"You do? How on earth do you—?"

"Don't ask. Mr. McClure is an . . . an acquaintance. I don't know him very well, but he seems to have a lot of connections in the criminal world. He might know how you can contact a loan shark."

"I'm starting to think that it's true what they say—that money is the root of all evil."

"Actually, a preacher friend told me that money itself isn't evil. It's the love of money that's at the root of all evil." I was about to ask him if he loved Katya more than he loved money when he interrupted.

"Listen, how can we contact this acquaintance of yours?"

"He's staying at a hotel here in the city. We can probably reach him there."

"How? When?"

"Let me think . . ." I had learned a lot during these past six weeks about detective work and stealth and getting around town. Before I arrived in Chicago it would have taken me hours or even days to figure out what to do. Now I was able to quickly concoct a plan.

"We'll tell my aunt that you want to escort me home. She'll agree because she's very eager for us to get together. We can go to Mr. McClure's hotel on the way—even though it's actually out of our way—and we'll leave him a note asking him to contact you."

We proceeded with my plan. Mrs. Kent and Aunt Agnes were indeed very obliging, imagining that we were in love and longing to spend every moment together. I borrowed paper and a pen to compose the note we would leave for Silas while Nelson returned to his room to attend to his appearance. He called for his grandmother's carriage and driver, and we set off downtown.

I had imagined Silas' hotel to be a shabby flea-bitten place, but the modest establishment had a quiet, understated elegance—and wasn't at all what I expected from an elixir salesman. I glanced around at the bright Turkish carpets, the gleaming brass fixtures and fresh flower arrangements, and wondered if Silas was staying here in order to rob the other hotel patrons. Nelson and I strode up to the front desk together, and I handed the clerk the envelope.

"Good afternoon. Would you please give this note to Mr. McClure when he returns?"

"Mr. McClure returned just a few minutes ago, miss, if you'd like to give it to him yourself. I just gave him his room key. Shall I send a bellboy upstairs for him?"

"Yes, thank you."

I gave the bellboy one of my calling cards and sat down in the lobby with Nelson to wait. I was remarkably calm compared to Nelson, who rapped his fingers on the armrest of his chair as if auditioning to be a drummer at the Javanese Village. I had a view of the elevator doors and I watched as they opened and Silas stepped out. To say that he looked pleased to see me would have been an understatement.

"Violet! What are you—?" He never had a chance to finish.

Nelson leaped from his chair and thrust out his hand to introduce himself. "Good afternoon. I'm Nelson Kent. I understand that you are acquainted with my fiancée, Miss Hayes?" Silas' customary grin vanished. He looked as though Nelson had punched him in the stomach. He glanced at me as if to ask if it was true, but I looked away.

"Yes . . . Miss Hayes and I are acquainted," Silas finally said.

"Look, I'll get right to the point. I need a loan, and for reasons that I'd rather not explain, I can't go to a bank. It would be a short-term loan, but I'd need the money by Friday night. Can you put me in touch with someone?"

"Possibly. Why don't you sit down, Mr. Kent?" He gestured to the chair beside mine and then sat down across from us on the sofa. "I'll be blunt, Mr. Kent. Most men of your obvious wealth don't go around asking for loans unless they're in trouble. I'll wager it's a gambling problem—am I right?"

"It's none of your business. Can you arrange a loan or not?"

"I'll need a few details about the casino first."

Nelson's gray pallor returned. He looked even worse than when I had arrived at his house. He ran his hands through his hair and leaned forward in his chair, staring at the floor as if he might need to vomit.

"Go ahead and tell him," I urged. "What do you have to lose?"

Nelson exhaled. "It's a private game in a rented hall at the World's Fair. By invitation only."

"Hmm. I heard rumors that there was a game going on there. . . . Let me guess—at first you lost, but then your luck changed and you won back all the money you'd lost and a little bit more. But it was closing time."

"That's right," I said. "How did you know?"

"That's the scam, Miss Hayes. The dealers can spot someone who's desperate a mile away. They'll let you win a little money so you'll come back another night and play for even bigger stakes. I gotta tell you, Mr. Kent—you'd be a fool to gamble away any more money at that place if it isn't legitimate."

"Look, I don't need a lecture," Nelson said. "Can you help me get a loan or not? I'll take my chances on winning. I have to."

"I'll tell you what." Silas leaned forward, his manner surprisingly sympathetic. "I have a friend who knows a thing or two about rigged games and weighted dice and marked cards. We'll meet you at this place, and he can check it out for you before you lose any more money."

"I told you it's private. Invitation only."

"Just get us in, okay? If my friend says they're not scamming, then we'll talk about a loan. Why throw away more of your money—not to mention a loan shark's—at high interest rates? Can you get us in?"

Nelson hesitated.

"I think you'd better take his advice," I told him. "What if you borrow money and lose it?"

"Okay, fine," Nelson said. "Just bring the money with you. And wear a tuxedo, if you can get one. The game is for high rollers only."

We all agreed. Nelson would pick me up on Friday night, and we would meet Silas and his friend at the fair.

"Tell me where I can find Katya," Nelson said as soon as we climbed back into his carriage.

"I think you need to decide a few things first. Don't lead her on, Nelson, if you have no intention of marrying her. It isn't fair to her. And you need to figure out how your marriage is going to work since you come from such different backgrounds. Katya doesn't know all the social rules that you take for granted. She would never survive the scrutiny of your grandmother and her friends. They would never accept her. And what are you going to do about Katya's family? Are you going to ask her to give them up along with all of her traditions? Would you be comfortable with her family, visiting their home, eating their food?"

"I told you, I don't know what to do. How do I separate my duty and loyalty to my family from my right to live my own life?"

"I'm sure your family only wants what's best for you. They're thinking of all the problems you would face if you made a bad choice."

As soon as the words were out of my mouth, I recalled my father saying something very similar to me. He wanted to prevent me from making a huge mistake and being hurt, as he had been.

"Why is it any of their business whom I marry?" Nelson asked.

I started to reply when I suddenly thought of Murderous Maude. I had been intent on preventing Father from marrying her, but was it any of my business whom he married? If I didn't want my father to choose a partner for me, what right did I have to choose one for him?

"If you decide to marry her, Nelson, I'll help you. I can teach Katya proper manners and social customs and things like that. It's all an act anyway, isn't it? But you'll have to be prepared to make it through life on your own, without any money from your father—and not from gambling either. So how badly do you want her?"

"I love her, Violet."

I believed him.

And I envied him.

As soon as I arrived home, I wrote a letter to Katya, inviting her to come home with my grandmother on Friday afternoon. I assured her that she could trust me. I asked Grandmother to deliver the message to Katya when she went to the settlement house tomorrow morning.

As for my own problems, I was nearly out of time.

Chapter

32

Thursday, July 13, 1893

I had agreed to meet Louis in the theater district on Thursday afternoon. Mr. Moody was holding a rally there, and I wanted to ask the theater manager for advice on finding my mother. Once again, I wasn't quite courageous enough to venture downtown alone to an unknown part of Chicago, so I dragged Aunt Birdie along as my companion. Louis was waiting in front of the theater with our tickets, pacing nervously and checking his pocket watch as hundreds of people streamed past him into the auditorium.

"I'm sorry I'm late," I told him. "I stopped to read all of the show bills we passed, hoping to see my mother's name on one of them, but I didn't see it."

"That's okay, but we'd better hurry." I introduced Louis to Aunt Birdie as we shuffled into the lobby with the crowd.

"I'm afraid we won't have much time to talk to the theater manager," Louis said. "The rally is about to begin, and I have responsibilities backstage."

"I understand. I just need to ask him a few questions. It shouldn't take long."

"And after Mr. Moody preaches, it'll be my job to pray with the people who come forward for the altar call."

"Okay." I had no idea what he was talking about.

"Just wait in your seats after the rally ends, and I'll find you," he promised.

"Oh, how nice!" Aunt Birdie said when we walked into the ornately decorated theater. I thought it was an outrageously elegant setting for a religious rally, with gilded woodwork, an elaborately painted ceiling, and maroon velvet seats, but I kept my thoughts to myself.

"Are we seeing one of Mr. Shakespeare's plays?" Aunt Birdie asked.

"It isn't a play, Aunt Birdie. We're here for a church service."

"Well, that's odd."

"Yes ... well ..." I didn't quite understand it myself, so how could I explain it to her?

Louis found our two seats along one of the aisles in the rapidly filling hall, and I left Aunt Birdie there while we hurried away to talk to the theater manager. My hair grew faster than she moved, and I didn't have the time or the patience to tow her any farther.

The backstage area resembled an anthill, with people darting around chaotically, shouting last-minute orders about lighting and curtains. Choir members milled around as they tried to find their places and their music. The male soloist sounded like Marley's ghost as he warmed up, moaning his way up and down the scale with eerie-sounding "Ohhs" and "Ooohs."

We found the theater manager sitting behind a desk in his tiny office, calmly reading a newspaper. "How can I help you?" he asked after Louis introduced me.

"I'm trying to find my mother. She's an actress. Her name is Angeline Hayes, but she might also go by the name Angeline

Cepak." I had written down the names for him on a piece of paper, and I handed it to him.

"Sorry. Never heard of her. Do you know which show she's in?"

"No, I'm not even sure she's in a show at the moment, just that she's an actress."

He tossed the paper onto his cluttered desktop. "Look, we've got people running all around town thinking they want to act. Most of them never end up in the business at all."

"Well, if she is in the business, then someone must know her, right? How would I go about finding her? Is there a list of actresses somewhere?"

"I don't know of any list." He must have seen my disappointment—or perhaps the tears that filled my eyes, threatening to spill over—because his manner suddenly softened. "Look, Miss Hayes. If I were you I'd hang a notice in all the places where they're holding auditions. Maybe she'll see it. Or maybe another actor who knows her will see it. And it wouldn't hurt to offer a reward. There're plenty of actors on the lookout for their next dollar."

"I see. Well, thank you for your help." I turned to Louis as soon as we left the office. "I don't have time to post notices in every theater. There must be dozens of them. My father is coming the day after tomorrow. And I don't have any money for a reward either."

"I guess it just wasn't the Lord's will that you find her," Louis said. "I'm sorry, Violet."

"Hey, Louis," someone shouted. "Come on, we need you."

"I have to go, Violet. Can you find your way back to your seat all right? I'll meet you there afterward and take you home."

I was deep in thought as I wandered back out to the auditorium, wondering how I could hang posters in at least a few of Chicago's theaters before my father arrived on Saturday. I could list my grandmother's name and address as the person to contact. Hadn't she told me that she was searching for my mother too?

By now, nearly everyone in the audience had found their places.

I hurried up the aisle before the lights dimmed—and found two empty seats. Aunt Birdie was gone.

Panic gripped me as I quickly scanned the theater. I couldn't breathe. Why had I left her alone? What was I thinking? Several hundred people filled the huge auditorium. Hundreds more filled the balcony. How would I ever find her? I turned to the people in the row behind mine.

"Excuse me. D-did you see my aunt? She's an older woman . . . w-with her hair in a bun and a dreamy smile on her face. I left her sitting right here."

"I saw her get up," the woman said. "I think she went that way." She pointed behind her toward the rear auditorium doors.

Oh, God, help me! I prayed as I raced up the aisle. "Aunt Birdie!" I called. "Aunt Birdie, where are you?"

People turned to stare at me, scowling at my rudeness. I didn't bother to beg their pardon. My voice grew louder and louder as my panic escalated. I knew I looked foolish running in useless circles, shouting her name, but I didn't care. I had to find my aunt. One of the ushers hurried over to me as the house lights dimmed.

"Miss, you have to stop shouting and take your seat. The program is about to begin."

"Please help me. I lost my aunt! She's an older woman with a gray dress and she wears her hair in a bun—and I have to find her!"

"Have you tried the lobby? Or the ladies' room?"

The ushers closed the auditorium doors behind me as I raced out to the lobby, calling her name. She wasn't there. One usher pointed to the ladies' room and I ran inside, my voice echoing in the empty space.

"Aunt Birdie? Aunt Birdie, are you in here?"

She wasn't. I could no longer hold back my tears as I ran out to the lobby again. That's when I began to bargain with God.

Please . . . I'll stop looking for my mother. I'll gladly welcome Maude and her children into our family . . . I'll even marry Louis Decker, if that's what you want. Anything! Just please, please, help me find Aunt Birdie.

I could hear the muffled sound of applause inside the auditorium. Across the lobby from me, the doors to the street stood open. I ran outside, praying that she hadn't walked in front of a streetcar.

"Aunt Birdie!"

Pedestrians crowded the sidewalk, calmly going about their affairs, oblivious to my distress, while traffic streamed in both directions on the bustling thoroughfare.

"Aunt Birdie!"

Madame Beauchamps would have been horrified to hear me shouting like a fishmonger on a busy Chicago street, but I didn't care. How could I ever face my grandmother? How could I tell her that I'd lost her sister?

Please, God!

That's when I noticed a commotion down the block in the middle of the street. Traffic had halted, and people were craning their necks to see what was going on. I ran out into the middle of it all, certain that a team of horses had trampled poor Aunt Birdie. I pleaded with God to spare her life.

And there she was in the middle of the road, hugging a policeman who had been directing traffic.

"Ma'am . . . ma'am . . ." he pleaded as he tried to pry off her arms. "You have to let go of me, ma'am. You're obstructing traffic." I wept with relief as I ran to her.

"Your family must be so glad to see you safely home from the war," I heard Aunt Birdie say. "My husband, Gilbert, is fighting in Virginia to help free the slaves. Is that where you were fighting?"

"Ma'am, I don't know what you're talking about, but you have to let go of me."

"Aunt Birdie!" I called. "Thank God I found you!" She released the policeman to give me a hug. I had never been so happy to feel her arms around me. "I'm so sorry for the disturbance," I told the policeman.

"Next time, lock the asylum door," he replied. I wanted to upbraid him for his unkind remark, but we had caused enough trouble.

"Come on, we need to go back to our seats, Aunt Birdie. The program is starting."

"I thought that soldier was Gilbert at first," she explained as I pulled her out of the road. "He bears a remarkable resemblance, don't you think?"

"Yes," I told her, but in truth, I couldn't have said what the policeman had looked like. My knees were so weak from fright that I could barely walk. I dragged her back to the theater and through the lobby doors.

"I haven't seen this many soldiers since the war began," she said, gesturing to all of the ushers. They smiled and nodded at us.

"Glad you found her, miss," one of them said. "I'll escort you to your seat."

"Is this one of Shakespeare's plays?" Aunt Birdie asked loudly as we walked down the aisle. "I do love *Romeo and Juliet.*"

"Shh . . . It's a church service," I whispered as I helped her sit down.

"Well, it certainly doesn't look like a church!"

I collapsed into my seat beside her, but it was a long time before my pulse returned to normal. What if I hadn't found her? I shuddered at the thought and vowed never to involve her in my adventures again.

The choir sang several songs, as did the soloist I had heard warming up backstage. I was oblivious to all of it as I sat thanking God and waiting for my panic to subside. I remembered all the vows I had made during the crisis and wondered if God would hold me to them. I had promised to stop searching for my mother and to accept Father's marriage to Maude. And I had promised to marry Louis Decker. I deeply regretted making that last vow now that Aunt Birdie was safe.

When I finally drew my thoughts back to the stage, a woman was playing a solo on the grand piano. She was wonderful. I glanced around the packed theater and knew I could never perform that way, no matter how simple the music was. I would die of stage fright before I ever played a single note. Surely that wasn't my calling, was it?

At last, Dwight L. Moody rose to stand behind the podium in the center of the stage. He was a sturdy-looking man with a wide forehead and an impressive beard. A deep stillness fell over the auditorium as he began to speak.

"We have for our subject today the Prodigal Son. Perhaps there is not any portion in Scripture as familiar as this fifteenth chapter of Luke. This young man was like thousands in our cities today who want to get away from home and do as they please. So the boy came to his father and said, 'Give me my portion and let me go.'

"He left home and went into that far country and got into all kinds of vice. He went to the theater every night and to the billiard hall and the drinking saloon. It does not take long for a young man to go to ruin when he gets in among thieves and harlots; that is about the quickest way down to hell."

Mr. Moody paused and stared out over the audience for a moment. I had heard the story of the Prodigal Son before in my church in Lockport, but this time it moved me deeply. I thought of how my Uncle Philip had left home to patronize saloons, and how my father had joined Mr. Moody's Yokefellows to search for him. I thought of my grandmother's long years of waiting for Philip to return, her heart breaking. My mother was a prodigal too, turning her back on her home and her family to pursue a stage career in Chicago. She must have broken my father's heart as he waited for her to return.

"At last the Prodigal's money was gone," Mr. Moody continued, "and he joined himself to a citizen of that country to feed swine. Now just for a moment think what that young man lost. He lost his home;

you may live in a gilded palace, but if God is not there, it is no home. He lost his food; he would have fed on the husks that the swine did eat. You can never get any food for the soul in the devil's country. Then he lost his testimony. No one believed him when he said he was a wealthy man's son.

"But there is one thing he did not lose. If there is a poor prodigal here tonight, there is one thing you have not lost. That young man never lost his father's love. When he came to himself and said, 'I will arise and go to my father,' that was the turning point in his life. If you are willing to admit your sin, and confess that you have wandered far from God, He is willing to receive you. I say to every sinner in Chicago, I do not care how vile you are in the sight of your fellow-men, the Lord Jesus loves you still."

When Mr. Moody paused again, I remembered what Grandmother had said about her husband—he had preached too much law and not enough love. Love was what my Uncle Philip had longed for, and what I longed for too. I had traveled to Chicago to search for my mother, desperate to know if she loved me. And I had wanted a beau who would offer me all of the love and romance I had craved when reading Ruth's novels. I wanted to find someone who loved me for myself, just the way I was, and God already loved me that way, right now.

"I can see the prodigal's father up there on the roof of his house," Mr. Moody continued, "watching for his boy. How his heart has ached for him! Then one day he sees that boy coming back. The father runs and leaps for joy. It is the only time God is seen running, just to meet a poor sinner. What joy there was in that home!

"No other subject in the Bible takes hold of me with as great force as the wandering sinner. The first thing I remember as a young boy was the sudden death of my father. The next thing was that my eldest brother left home and became a wanderer. How my mother mourned for her boy—waiting day by day and month by month for his return! Night after night she watched and wept and prayed. Our friends gave him up, but Mother had faith that she would see him again.

"Then one day in the middle of summer, a stranger approached the house. When my mother saw the great tears trickling down his cheeks, she cried, 'It's my boy, my dear, dear boy!'

"My brother stood in the doorway and said, 'Mother, I will never cross the threshold until you say you forgive me.' Do you think he had to stay there long? Oh, no! Her arms were soon around him, and she wept upon his shoulder, as did the father of the Prodigal Son.

"Oh, my friends, come home tonight. God's heart is aching for you. I do not care what your past life has been like—God is ready and willing to forgive you. There is no father in Chicago who has as much love in his heart as God has for you.

"You can leave the pigpens and the gutters of this world and come home to Him. Give every area of your life to Him, and He will show you how He wants you to live. Offer yourself to Him, and you can know His will. Rich people can serve Him, poor people, men and women, old and young alike. There is a place for you in the Father's house that only you can fill. And you begin to find it right here, when you give your life to Jesus."

I felt like cheering. Again, I recalled my grandmother's words: *"Violet, you be exactly who God created you to be, and don't let anyone tell you otherwise."*

"I'm going to ask you to come forward in a moment," Mr. Moody told us, "so you can come home to Jesus. And you'll never know if this may be your last chance to accept His invitation. I preached on the night of the Great Chicago Fire, but when I heard the alarm bells ringing, I dismissed the congregation without offering this invitation. That night some three hundred people lost their lives. Perhaps one of them had been about to surrender to Jesus—but I didn't offer him the chance.

"After the fire, I vowed never to preach another sermon without inviting people to come to Christ. This is your invitation. Come now.

The Father's arms are open wide, waiting for you to come home."

I longed to go forward. Mr. Moody's sermon was the most compelling one I'd ever heard. Louis and several of his friends moved into place in front of the stage and I knew that's what he'd meant when he'd said he would pray with people afterward. But I remained in my seat. I couldn't leave Aunt Birdie alone, and she would be too confused if I tugged her forward with me. Instead, I closed my eyes and prayed silently.

Okay, I'm yours. Whatever you want me to do, God, I'll do it. I know you have my best interests at heart, just like my father does when he tries to make plans for me. You know even better than he does what I should do with my life. I want to offer it to you now.

As people streamed forward, the choir sang the song about the shepherd searching for his lost lamb. My tears slowly fell. God loved me! It seemed so amazing. God felt as anxious and determined to find me as I had been to find poor, lost Aunt Birdie. He would search for me to bring me home to himself just as diligently as I was searching for my mother. He would search as hard as Grandmother had searched for her, as hard as Father had searched for his brother in all of Chicago's saloons. God loved me that much.

I remained in my seat as the service ended and the lights came on and people began to leave. And as strange and untrue as it might sound, I felt loved for the first time since my mother left me. I still didn't know what my future would be, yet I felt certain that if I came home to my Heavenly Father, then I could face anything in life.

I would put as much effort into learning about Him as I had into learning all of Madame Beauchamps' rules of etiquette. I would discover my "calling," as my grandmother referred to it. I would serve God the way He wanted me to.

Chapter

33

I was still sitting in my seat in the theater, still feeling God's love, when Louis came up the aisle to find me. I became aware of my surroundings again and saw the crowds filing slowly out of the auditorium and heard the rumble of excited voices.

"That was wonderful," I told him. "Thank you for inviting me."

"I'm so glad you came today, Violet. You have no idea how much it means to me—and to our future."

I remembered my rash promise to marry Louis Decker. Was that really God's will for me? I understood now why Louis didn't need love and romance; he had God's love. So why was he so eager to court me? He had never professed his love, yet he seemed to be in a big hurry to marry me, in spite of the fact that we hardly knew each other. Did he love me or didn't he?

"I'm working at another rally this weekend," Louis said. "We could go together and work side by side. You could play the piano and—"

"May I ask you a question?"

"Of course."

"You seem so busy with school and your volunteer work at the settlement house and with Mr. Moody's campaign. Why are you courting me right now? I would think that courtship would be the least of your concerns."

"Actually, it's very high on my list. There is a church here in Chicago where I would very much like to minister after I graduate, but the board is reluctant to hire a bachelor. They would prefer a pastor who is a settled family man with a wife, especially a wife who will be a partner with him in the ministry."

I stared at him in surprise. "So you won't be considered for the job unless you're married?"

"They'll give preference to a married applicant."

The news that Louis was using me to secure a job stunned me. But to be fair, hadn't I been using Louis too? I had asked him to take me to the Bohemian woman's tenement. And I had come to the rally today because Louis had promised to help me search for my mother.

"Which reminds me, Violet, what time is your father coming on Saturday? I would very much like to meet him and ask his permission to court you. Then I can tell the church board truthfully that I'm courting someone."

"Why me, Louis? Is the fact that I play the piano an asset?"

"Yes, a huge one. But it's not only that. You would be surprised how difficult it is to find a woman who is willing to marry a minister. When I learned that you came from a minister's family, I knew you would understand what's involved. I have the highest regard for your grandmother. She is such a wonderful woman."

I had to look away, alarmed by what Louis was saying. He hadn't mentioned any of my own qualities or why he had been drawn to me. The real me, Violet Rose Hayes, didn't seem to matter at all when he'd made his choice. And he still hadn't mentioned love.

My thoughts raced in every direction as I tried to digest Louis' words. Once again, I wasn't paying attention to Aunt Birdie. She turned to Louis and poked her finger in his chest.

"Why aren't you fighting in the war, young man?"

"I don't understand. Which war are you referring to?"

"The War Between the States, of course."

Aunt Birdie had her back to me, and I began waving my arms and shaking my head, signaling to Louis not to reply. He didn't get it.

"I think you're confused, Mrs. Casey. The war—" He stopped when I grabbed his arm.

"Louis, could I talk to you, please?"

"Just a minute, Violet." He held up his hand. "Mrs. Casey, that war is long over with."

"Louis, stop!" I shoved myself between them, but I was too late. Aunt Birdie had already heard him.

"It is? The war is finally over? Oh, that's wonderful! Did you hear what he said, Violet? The war is over!"

"Come on, Aunt Birdie. I think we should be going now." I took her arm and managed to drag her away from him, moving as quickly as I could make her go.

"Why didn't you tell me it was over, Violet? Matilda reads the newspaper every day and she never said a word about it either. And you would think that Gilbert would write immediately to tell me the good news."

"Maybe you'll get a letter today. Let's go home and see." I was trying to rush her out of the theater, but the crowd was still too thick. People stood talking in the aisles and in the lobby, and we could barely move.

I didn't realize that Louis had followed us until Aunt Birdie turned around and said, "Did we win the war, young man? Did we set the slaves free?"

"Yes, the North won and the slaves are free. But the War Between the States ended in 1865, Mrs. Casey, and this is—"

"Louis, no!" I was too late.

"—the year 1893. The war ended twenty-eight years ago."

"Oh, but that can't be true!" Aunt Birdie said. "If the war ended that long ago, then what has become of my husband?"

There was a terrible silence that no words could fill.

"Please, let's go home, Aunt Birdie," I begged.

"Maybe that soldier would know," she said, pointing.

"He isn't a soldier. He's a theater usher. We need to go home."

"Is your husband deceased?" Louis asked. I punched his arm. Again, I was too late.

"Deceased?" Aunt Birdie repeated. "Deceased? My Gilbert didn't come home . . . he went . . . he's in . . ."

The look of pain that suddenly filled her eyes broke my heart. I knew it was my fault for dragging her away from the refuge of her home, but I took it out on Louis.

"Couldn't you have just shut up?"

"I don't understand what's going on, Violet."

"That horrible undertaker came to my house!" Birdie cried. "He was dressed all in black . . . and he said . . . he said that Gilbert was *dead*!" I pulled Aunt Birdie into my arms and hugged her tightly as she finally grasped the truth. Her grief was heartrending.

"He's gone . . . he's gone! Oh, my Gilbert, my love—he's gone forever!"

"I'm sorry, Aunt Birdie. I'm so sorry." I wept along with her. Her beloved husband was dead, leaving a hole that nothing else had ever filled.

I remembered the day that I'd learned my mother was gone. I had wandered into her bedroom searching for her and found the bed neatly made. The room was still rich with the scent of roses, but her clothes and shoes were no longer in the wardrobe. Father sat down on the bed with me and told me Mother was sick—that she had gone away to get better. I remembered the aching emptiness I felt, the deep sorrow, the loss. He had lied to me, and I finally understood why.

"Why did you have to tell her the truth?" I asked Louis.

"Because it's wrong to lie. Satan is the father of lies."

"Well, sometimes it's better not to know. Sometimes it's better to say the kind and loving thing, instead of the brutal truth."

Louis seemed at a loss to know what to do. He tried to offer me his handkerchief, but I shook my head. I didn't dare release my arms from around Aunt Birdie, fearing that she would fall to pieces like a broken vase.

"Did her husband know Christ?" Louis asked. "Do you think he's in heaven?"

"Stop talking, Louis!" His insensitivity infuriated me. I knew that I could never marry Louis Decker. "Why did you have to tell her?"

"I'm sorry, Violet. I didn't know. . . . What can I do?"

"Go flag down a carriage so I can take her home."

"I can drive you—"

"No! I don't want you to. Just get us a cab. I'll meet you out front in a few minutes." He hurried away.

Aunt Birdie wept as if she never would stop. I rocked her in my arms, murmuring "Shh, shh . . ." I couldn't say *It'll be all right* because I knew that it never would be. We were the objects of many rude stares and odd looks, but I didn't care. Several choir members and people from Mr. Moody's team tried to approach us, obviously concerned, but I waved them away. It was my fault for dragging her with me on my useless quest. The best thing I could do for her was to take her home.

By the time we reached the door to the street, Louis had a hired cab waiting. Aunt Birdie and I climbed in. We wept all the way home.

The truth hurt. Love sometimes brought a great deal of pain with it. These were the hard lessons I had learned this summer. In the past I had often tried to escape the grown-up world of sorrow through my imagination, dreaming that a handsome young lieutenant would ride to my rescue, or that a great impresario would discover my musical talents and whisk me away. I had envisioned knights in shining armor and happily-ever-after scenes to escape from rules or boredom or pain, including a vision of my mother walking through our front door, whole and well again. But now I knew that a lifetime of escape led to a life like Aunt Birdie's.

My imagination was a gift, but I had to live in the real world. My eyes had been opened this summer to poverty and crime and abuse, and I needed to use my imagination—not to escape, but to help people like Irina and Katya; to make my own contribution, as the women in the Woman's Pavilion had done. I couldn't do it in the same way that Jane Addams and my grandmother and Aunt Matt were, but I would find my own way in my own time.

Aunt Birdie was still mourning when our carriage halted in front of our house. I saw someone sitting on our front steps and couldn't believe my eyes. It was Silas McClure. He leaped up and hurried over to the carriage to help Aunt Birdie climb down while I paid the driver.

"What are you doing here?" I asked. "We're not going to the fair until tomorrow night."

"I know. I came by to show you something."

"Well, this isn't a good time. Aunt Birdie has suffered a terrible shock."

"What happened?"

"My Gilbert is dead!" she moaned. She moved into Silas' open arms. He closed his eyes as he held her, rocking her gently in sympathy.

"I'm so sorry to hear that, Mrs. Casey. So sorry."

"Come into the house, Silas," I said after a moment. I couldn't have her weeping on the front steps for the entire world to see, and she was still clinging to Silas.

He led Aunt Birdie into the parlor and sat beside her on the sofa. She gazed around as if she had never seen this room before—then started crying all over again.

"Gilbert . . . Oh, my love, my Gilbert! What will I do without him? How can I go on?"

I had no idea how to console her. I could only cry along with her.

"The undertaker came and brought Gilbert home to me in a wooden box!"

Silas took her limp hands in his. "That wasn't him in the casket,

Mrs. Casey. Gilbert is alive and in heaven with the Lord, where he'll live forever. He's waiting there, waiting for the resurrection of the dead. Jesus rose from the dead on Easter—and that means all of His followers will live again one day. Gilbert is waiting for you."

His words astonished me. How could a thief like Silas suddenly start talking like a preacher? He must have astonished Aunt Birdie too, because she stopped crying and looked up at him in surprise.

"Yes . . ." she murmured. "That's what Gilbert promised me the day that he left. He promised that we would be together again—if not here on earth, then in paradise."

"Mrs. Casey, tell me again why Gilbert went away to war."

She drew a shuddering breath, as if for strength. "He wanted to end slavery. He worked so hard to abolish it—going to meetings, writing articles. For years and years. We both were involved. He saw me for the first time at a meeting of the Chicago Abolition Society . . . and he fell in love with me."

"He died a hero, you know. The slaves are all free. Millions of men, women, and children—and they'll never have to suffer as slaves again. Your husband did what he could to help make this country a better place."

"So their freedom was worth dying for?"

"Absolutely, Mrs. Casey. And he's still here with you, you know. We never lose our loved ones, because we always carry them in our heart. When we love someone as much as you loved him, we're changed. We become better people. That's how our loved ones always remain with us. We're different because of them."

"Have you lost a loved one too?" she asked.

"My mother—God rest her soul. But I remember all the things she taught me and the sacrifices she made to raise me—and I carry her here, in my heart."

"Gilbert used to help runaway slaves escape to Canada. He would risk going to prison himself just so they could be free. I used to be such a fearful person, but he taught me to be brave."

"And he would want you to be brave now, wouldn't he? As long as you remember his love, he will always be with you."

"But I can't hold him in my arms. I miss his arms . . ."

"I know, I know. That's why God gives us friends to hold." Silas drew Aunt Birdie into his arms and let her cry. I watched in amazement, aware that I never would have been able to console her the way he was doing.

"Did he send letters to you, Mrs. Casey?" he asked after a while. "I have letters from my mother, and sometimes when I read them, it helps me remember her voice and her smile."

"Yes." She pulled away to look up at Silas. "I have all of his letters. Every one he ever sent. He talked so much about the things he saw in Virginia and the horrible way that the slaves were treated. It made him want to fight all the harder for them."

"He sounds like an amazing man, Mrs. Casey."

By the time my grandmother came home, Aunt Birdie's tears had finally tapered off. But I knew Grandmother would see our red, swollen eyes and soggy handkerchiefs and know that something was wrong. I jumped up from the sofa and drew her aside.

"What happened, Violet? Is Birdie all right?"

"Louis Decker told her the truth about the war," I whispered.

"Louis did? But why?"

"He said that Satan is the father of lies." I was still furious with Louis and I wanted Grandmother to be too.

"Oh, dear. Come here, Birdie, dear." Silas helped Birdie to her feet, and Grandmother led her upstairs to her room. I drew a shaky breath and faced Silas. When I recalled everything he'd said to comfort Birdie, I could only stare at him, dumbfounded.

"I don't know what I would have done without your help. You knew exactly what to say. Thank you."

Where had all of his beautiful words about Jesus and heaven come from? Were they simply a memorized spiel, like his sales pitch for Dr. Dean's Blood Builder? I didn't think so—Silas had spoken as if he'd meant them. But then why did he consort with thieves? Why hadn't he revealed this side of himself before? Was he still being the professional con-artist—even now?

"Say, listen—I should go," he said, edging toward the door.

"Wait. Didn't you say you had something to show me? Was it about my mother?"

"It's nothing definite. It can wait until tomorrow night."

"You came all the way over here, Silas. You must have learned something definite." He rubbed his forehead as if it ached. He took a long time to reply.

"Your aunt kept saying that your mother loved the theater, and I began to wonder if maybe she was an actress or something. So I looked into it and found a showgirl who goes by the name of Angelina. No last name. I didn't speak with her, but I was able to take a photograph of her. I was going to show it to you and see if you recognized her, but . . . this isn't the time."

"I want to see it." He seemed very reluctant to hand it over. When I finally convinced him to show it to me, I immediately understood why. The woman wore a harem costume that looked like an illustration from the Arabian Nights. Her midriff was bare. She was very beautiful and had dark, curly hair like mine, but my heart rebelled at the idea that she was my mother.

"I didn't say anything to this woman about you," Silas continued, "because I didn't think it was a good idea to barge into her life until we're certain that it's her. If you want me to, I'll go back and talk to her."

"No, I don't want her to run away again. Please tell me where she is. Tomorrow might be my last chance to see her before my father comes to take me home."

"I don't think you should go there—"

"Why not? I've been to the tenements and the slums with my grandmother and to the Jolly Roger with you. . . . Can you go with me tomorrow?"

"Violet, it's not the neighborhood I'm worried about." Silas' smile was gone. He looked sorrowful. "I doubt that it's your mother."

"Why? What aren't you telling me?"

He hesitated a long time before saying, "This woman dances at a burlesque theater."

I should have been prepared for the truth after what the old Bohemian woman had told me about my gypsy ancestors, but I wasn't. I was sorry I had ever come to Chicago in the first place. I never would have tried to find my mother if I had known it would hurt this much. I was better off living with a lie, the way Aunt Birdie had.

"It can't be her!" I cried out. "It isn't my mother!"

I thought I had run out of tears, but I couldn't stop them from falling. I covered my face with my hands and wept. The next thing I knew, Silas had pulled me into his arms to console me the way he had consoled Aunt Birdie. He smelled like bay rum aftershave. I buried my face in his shoulder and sobbed.

I don't know how long we stayed that way before my good sense returned. My behavior was highly improper. I squirmed out of his arms and looked away, embarrassed. He handed me his handkerchief to dry my eyes.

"I'm sorry," I sniffed. "There has been entirely too much weeping here this afternoon. I'm sorry for subjecting you to it."

"No, I'm the one who's sorry, Violet. I never should have shown you the picture when you were already so upset. We don't even know if it is your mother. It might not be, you know."

"It isn't," I said, although I knew that it was.

"Anyway," he said with a sigh, "I should leave now and let you and your family recover. I guess I'll see you at the fair tomorrow night with your fiancé?"

"Nelson isn't my fiancé."

"I see." Silas was trying not to grin, but I could tell that the news delighted him. "Well, we can talk more tomorrow night."

"Thank you again for helping my aunt. I don't know how I will ever repay you."

"It isn't necessary."

He retrieved his hat, then turned to me, studying me for a long moment. I could only imagine how awful I looked with my bloodshot eyes and reddened nose. But his tender gaze told me he hadn't noticed.

"Good-bye, Violet."

"Good day, Silas."

When he was gone, I took the photograph over to the window and pulled back the lace curtains so I could see it in the light. Eleven years had passed since the last time I'd seen my mother, but she looked the same. I fought back my tears so they wouldn't blur my vision. If only Silas had told me where he had found her.

I decided to study the background for clues. That was when I spotted the familiar-looking steel girders and support trestles that held up Mr. Ferris' wheel. They were unmistakable. I also saw something that resembled a camel, half-hidden behind my mother's arm, and I remembered seeing the Bedouin Arab with his camel on the day I had visited the Midway with Silas. Herman Beckett had refused to tour the Midway because of the exotic dancers, improperly clothed. Misery Mary had called them hootchy-kootchy dancers.

This photograph of my mother had been taken on the Midway at the World's Columbian Exposition. I was certain of it. Tomorrow night, when Nelson took me to the fair, I would go over to the Midway and find her.

I hurried upstairs to splash water on my face and try to recover from all of the events of the day—and realized that I still had Silas' handkerchief in my hand. It was made from the finest quality linen, monogrammed in blue silk thread. But the letter wasn't an *S* for Silas or an *M* for McClure. It was monogrammed with the letter *A*. Silas had stolen it, no doubt.

He had so many wonderful qualities—why did he have to be a thief?

Chapter

34

Friday, July 14, 1893

On my last full day in Chicago I stayed home. It would be my last chance to make social calls with Aunt Agnes, but I'd seen all that phoniness for what it was. I received a note of apology from Louis Decker, asking if he still could meet my father on Saturday, but I was too disappointed with Louis to face him.

My grandmother left for the settlement house, promising to bring Katya home with her. Aunt Matt and I remained home to help console Aunt Birdie.

"How long will it take for her to forget again?" I asked Aunt Matt as I helped clean up the breakfast dishes.

"It varies each time. Maybe a week. We can hope and pray that it's sooner."

"I'm so sorry, Aunt Matt. I feel like it's all my fault."

"Sometimes the truth is very painful, Violet. I want you to remember that if you do find your mother someday. I would hate to see you get hurt."

I nodded and swallowed back my tears. I already knew that my mother was a dancer at a burlesque theater.

That afternoon, my grandmother brought Katya home with her. I was in the kitchen fixing a tea tray for Aunt Birdie and Aunt Matt, but I poured a cupful for Katya and myself.

"Let me take this tray upstairs to my aunts," I told her, "then we'll talk. Please go into the parlor and make yourself at home." She was still standing in the kitchen when I returned. I picked up our two teacups. "Let's go sit down," I repeated, gesturing to the parlor with a tilt of my head.

"Oh no. I could not do that."

"Why not?" I thought her hesitation came from mistrust, but her reason surprised me.

"It is not right for a person like me to sit in your parlor. I am only a servant."

"Katya, it's perfectly proper if I invite you."

She shook her head vigorously. "No, no, I could not."

"Okay, fine." I set our cups on the kitchen table and sank down in a chair, gesturing for her to sit. She hesitated, and as much as I disliked doing it, I knew I would have to command her as I would a servant. "Sit down and drink your tea, Katya. We're going to talk."

I offered her milk and sugar but she refused, obviously uncomfortable with being served by me. She seemed as fearful and skittish as a sparrow.

"Katya, please sit back and relax. I want to be your friend. I meant what I said the other day. I want to help you and Nelson."

"But why would you help me? You are going to marry him."

"No. I'm not going to marry Nelson. I want to help you because . . . because love is so precious and perhaps so fleeting that we need to hang on to it tightly when we do find it. My aunt Birdie taught me that lesson. Her husband died nearly thirty years ago and she's still mourning for him. So I made up my mind to help you and Nelson find a way to be together."

Tears filled her eyes. "But I am not a good wife for him—"

"Stop right there. You're wrong. The best wife for Nelson is the one who will bring him love and joy. You need to forget that you ever were a maid and start thinking of yourself as a woman—a very lovely woman. The only difference between you and me is where we were born, and birthplace has nothing to do with who we are on the inside. If I can learn all those fancy manners, so can you—if you want to, that is. Do you want to?"

"I will do anything for Nelson."

"Good. Then pick up your teacup and come into my parlor. We're going to sit down in there like two proper young ladies and drink it." I rose from my chair and led the way to the parlor, gesturing to Katya to sit on the sofa beside me. She did so, looking stiff and uncomfortable.

"Just watch me and do exactly as I do."

"I am always watching the fine ladies when I am serving the food."

"That's good. Pretend you're one of those fine ladies. It's all an act anyway."

"I do not know that word, 'act.'"

"It means make-believe, like a show in a theater. Everyone is pretending to be someone they aren't." I was confusing her. "Look, you had to learn the rules for being a good maid, didn't you? Being a lady is simply a matter of learning all new rules. Tell yourself that you are a lady, copy what the other ladies are doing—and pretty soon you'll begin to believe it." I lifted my teacup and sipped daintily. Katya did the same, but I saw the cup trembling in her hand.

"Tonight we'll be going to a private club at the fairgrounds. Nelson is coming for us, and—"

She gasped. "Does he know I am here?"

"Not yet. Look, this will be an experiment." Again, she seemed confused by the word. "What I mean is, tonight you and Nelson will have a chance to try being together in his world—the way you would try on a dress to see if it fits you. If you decide to get married, then you'll be going with him to fancy places all the time. Now finish your tea and we'll go up to my bedroom and try on some clothes."

"I cannot go up to your room! Maybe there is a room down here to dress? Where your servants stay?"

"Did you forget your first lesson already? You have to get rid of the idea that you're a servant. Someone told me yesterday that when we love somebody we are changed—we become better people. Let your love for Nelson change you, Katya. Tell yourself that you are the same kind of woman that I am. Now, come on."

I dragged her up the stairs and into my bedroom. We were nearly the same size, so it was easy to dress her in one of my gowns. She was so naturally elegant and graceful that she would never need to practice with a book on her head. I helped her arrange her fine, wheat-colored hair in an elegant, upswept style, then took her downstairs to look at herself in the hall mirror.

"See? You look beautiful, and as fine as any lady."

"But everyone will hear that my English is not so good."

"Stay beside me. I'll answer everyone's questions for you. Besides, for all they know, you could be an elegant European lady visiting Chicago to see the fair."

"I am scared. What will Nelson say when he sees me?"

"I don't know, but we'll soon find out. Listen, this night may not turn out the way we're hoping it will, but don't you want to know the truth? Don't you want to see if he loves you enough to try to make things work?"

As it turned out, Nelson was so stunned when he came to the door and saw Katya that he couldn't utter a single word. He didn't have to. The tender look in his eyes spoke for him. I saw the deep love he and Katya shared written on both of their faces, and I envied them. I'd had three marriage proposals, but not one of my suitors had ever looked at me that way.

"I think we should take your carriage to the fairgrounds," I told Nelson.

He nodded absently. He hadn't taken his eyes off Katya. I could have suggested that we walk to the fairgrounds in our undergarments and he would have nodded the same way. I explained my reasons, even if he didn't hear them.

"If we drive we can avoid running into the pea pods onboard the ship. They might ask too many questions. And if I know the pea pods, they'll be lining up to court Katya before the ship leaves the dock."

"What is that word—pea pod?" Katya asked.

"That's what I call Nelson's look-alike, act-alike, think-alike friends. They're like vegetables, like peas in a pod, all the same."

She nodded, but I could see that she still didn't understand. Playing fairy godmother in this Cinderella act might be more difficult for me than I had imagined. I thought of my mother, trying to adjust to life in Lockport. It must have seemed like another world to her.

We climbed into Nelson's carriage and started on our way. Nelson sat close to Katya, holding her hand all the way there. I sat opposite them, issuing instructions the way that my aunt Agnes had whenever she'd taken me places.

"I'll introduce Katya as a friend of mine. It's true enough, for now. But you'll have to escort me into the casino, Nelson, not her. Your friends will get suspicious if you arrive with another woman on your arm after courting me all of these weeks."

"I'm sorry," he told Katya. "I hate pretending."

"Your life is all about pretending!" I said. "It's knee-deep in phoniness! Remember how we talked about that? And how much we both hated it? You're not giving anything up, Nelson. You're gaining a real life. And true love."

Nelson grew increasingly nervous as we neared the fairgrounds. So did Katya. She had proper manners to worry about, but he had a pile of his father's money to win back.

"Are you sure this McClure fellow will show up?" he asked me.

"He said he would. I have no reason to doubt him."

"But will he have the money? I have to have the money, Violet."

"Listen, if he does give you a loan, I think you should use it to repay your father instead of gambling it all away again."

"That's impossible. I need to win enough to repay my father and have some left over so I can be my own man. Make my own rules."

"But you could also lose it all and end up in twice as much trouble as you're in now."

He shook his head. "I have to do it. For Katya's sake."

"If people respect you, Nelson, they'll respect your choice of a wife. The ones who don't accept Katya aren't worth having as friends. Let her be herself, not a copy of Haughty and Naughty. You fell in love with her, remember? Not them. You and I can both play the game and act phony, but we're much happier when we're ourselves."

That was what my grandmother had been trying to tell me. *"You be exactly who God created you to be, and don't let anyone tell you otherwise."* I still wasn't sure what I wanted to do with my life, but I was narrowing it down and eliminating several possibilities. I didn't want a life in Nelson's social circle, living with all of the suffocating rules and manners I'd learned at Madame Beauchamps' School for Young Ladies—no matter how wealthy my husband was. Money meant nothing if I'd never be allowed to be myself.

As for settling down in Lockport, I didn't think I was cut out for that life any more than my mother had been. And after what had happened with Aunt Birdie yesterday, I didn't want to be part of Louis' world either, always under scrutiny as a minister's wife, suffocating under a church board's expectations. Those rules and limitations were as foreign to me as mine were to Katya.

We got out of the carriage at the entrance gates. I glanced at Katya's face and saw her wonder and delight as she glimpsed the fair for the first time. Cinderella, arriving at the prince's ball, could not have been more awestruck. Nelson was watching her too, and I could hear the excitement in his voice as he described the pavilions as we strolled past them. I followed behind like a chaperone as we made our way to the casino, allowing the two of them to be alone for as long as possible.

I was as nervous as Nelson and Katya, but for a completely different reason. My mother was here at the fair. After eleven long years, I might find her tonight. But did I really want to? It would mean facing the truth about who she really was and why she had left me. I had seen firsthand how deeply the truth had hurt Aunt Birdie. Did I really want to uncover all of it? I had the next few hours to make up my mind.

Silas and his friend were waiting for us in front of the building. I didn't even recognize Silas at first. Dressed in an elegant tuxedo with a bow tie and white satin vest, he looked like a completely different man from the sleazy one I'd first encountered on the train. I decided Katya must have cinched my corset too tightly; I could scarcely breathe.

I was wearing the gown that Aunt Agnes' seamstress had made for me, and when Silas saw me, his smile faded to a look of awe. I saw love in his eyes. Love! He looked at me the same way Nelson had looked at Katya. But any future between us would be even more impossible than the future they faced. I remembered the monogrammed *A* on his linen handkerchief and wondered who he really was. For the first time, I felt relieved to be leaving Chicago tomorrow. I couldn't risk meeting up with Silas McClure ever again.

"This is the way we'll do things," Silas told Nelson. "I'll give you a small stake to get you started. You place the bets while my friend Jackson studies the dealers. If things are on the up-and-up, we'll talk about a loan."

I took Nelson's arm as we entered the private casino. Silas and his friend escorted Katya. I felt absurdly jealous.

Cigar smoke filled the opulent room, making it seem dingy. The atmosphere seemed darker and more oppressive than I'd remembered from last time. Perhaps it was because Nelson was so on edge. I felt sorry for him. He had more at stake than ever before—not only his father's money, but also his happiness with Katya. I followed him to the dice table and watched as he placed his first bet. He held out the dice to me.

"A kiss for luck, Violet."

I backed away, shaking my head. "Let Katya be your good luck charm."

I tugged on her arm. She had been holding on to Silas, but she let go as I nudged her forward. Silas' friend was watching the game, but Silas was studying the three of us.

I turned my attention to the game. Nelson's forehead shone with sweat, even though the room didn't feel at all warm to me. Katya looked as frightened as a doe in hunting season. Silas and his friend seemed very intent on the game, and I thought I saw them exchange knowing glances and sly hand signals from time to time.

I watched each roll of the dice until I could no longer stand the tension, then I turned away and watched all of the other well-dressed partygoers gambling away their money. A group of cigar-wielding men waved wads of it around like it was so much paper. I suddenly had a horrifying thought. What if Silas and his partner had used Nelson to get inside because they intended to rob everyone? What if they weren't watching for crooked dealers at all but for a chance to steal every last dollar in this place? Just because Silas had shown me a harmonica instead of a gun didn't mean he was unarmed tonight.

Why had I ever trusted him? I knew that his friends had committed robbery before—right here at the fair! I had to warn Nelson. I inched my way over to his side and bent to whisper in his ear.

"Nelson? May I have a word with you, please?"

"Not now." Sweat trickled down his brow.

"It's very important—"

"Shh!" He waved me away.

I'd had enough. My father was coming tomorrow, and I'd wasted six weeks on Nelson and his nonsense. It was his own stupid fault for being in this situation. Besides, he didn't have any money to steal. Who cared if Silas and his friend robbed everyone in this place? I didn't.

I slipped away from the gaming table and merged into the crowd. Everyone was occupied with money. No one cared where I went or what I did. My anger and disappointment made me courageous. My mother was at the fairgrounds, a short distance away. I needed to face the truth.

I left the smoke-filled casino and went to find my mother.

Chapter

35

~~~

I stopped outside the pavilion to get my bearings. I was alone, but I didn't feel at all afraid. The well-lit streets bustled with people, and colored searchlights crisscrossed the sky, lighting up the fair's golden domes and towers. The World's Columbian Exposition was beautiful, and I was seeing it for the last time. Tomorrow I would leave Chicago. In another three months all the grand pavilions would be torn down and the White City would disappear. Everything would change. That was the lesson I'd learned this summer: Life was all about change.

I scanned the horizon and saw the giant wheel, revolving slowly in the distance. I began walking in that direction, following the clues I'd found in Silas' photograph. I remembered that the entrance to the Midway was near the Woman's Pavilion, and I could see that graceful building across the lagoon.

Finding my mother's theater turned out to be easier than I'd expected. The turbaned Arab and his camel stood right in the middle of the Midway Plaisance, drumming up business for the Arabian Nights Show. The billboard outside the theater featured a woman in a harem outfit just like the one my mother wore in the photograph. According to the scheduled times, I had more than an hour to talk with her before the next show began.

I left the pathway and walked around to the back of the theater as if I knew exactly where I was going. It was what Louis had done when he'd led me backstage at the theater the other day. No one had stopped him then, and no one stopped me now. A sign above the backstage door read *Employees Only*. I tried the knob and found it locked. I drew a breath for courage and pounded on the door. It opened a crack, and a bearded man with oily hair peered out.

"What do you want?"

"I'm here to see Angeline ... um ... Angelina. She's expecting me."

He looked me over from head to toe like a greedy child eyeing an ice-cream cone. He didn't seem inclined to let me in.

"Angelina said she might have a job in the show for me," I added.

His lips curled into a smile. He opened the door very wide. "Second door on the right," he said, pointing.

My knees shook violently as I walked down the short corridor. I quickly knocked on my mother's door before I lost my nerve.

"Come in," someone called from inside. I turned the knob.

The scent of roses overwhelmed the tiny dressing room. I knew I had found my mother.

She sat before a mirror at a lopsided dressing table, brushing her dark, loose hair. I had loved to watch her do the very same thing in her bedroom in Lockport. She looked up at my reflection in the dingy mirror and knew in an instant who I was.

"Violet," she whispered. She stood and turned, and we rushed into each other's arms.

"Mama!" I wept. "Mama, I found you!"

Memories from childhood flooded back as I felt her familiar arms surrounding me and heard her murmuring in her native language. I don't know how long we remained that way. I only know that I had missed her embrace, her voice, her love, for eleven long years. I needed to make up for all that lost time.

"I've missed you so much, Mama!"

"And I have missed you, *ho-cheech-ka*," she cried. "You will never know how much!"

At last Mother released me. She held me at arm's length and gazed at me, her eyes brimming with love.

"Look at you," she murmured. "You are beautiful! And such a lady! A proper young lady, just as I hoped you would be."

I thought she would hug me again, but instead she turned away, tightening the belt on the ragged bathrobe she wore over her costume, drawing it closed. I saw shame in her eyes and in her manner as her gaze flitted around the shabby room, seeing it the way I would see it.

"I am sorry that you found me, Violet. Sorry that you see me this way."

"No, Mama, don't be sorry. I'm not—"

"Shh, shh . . . Listen, my darling. You must go back home. You must not let anyone see you here with me."

I shook my head, swallowing the lump of emotion in my throat. "But I want to talk to you. I want to know—"

"Shh . . . No, darling. No one must know that I am your mother. I do not want to tarnish you."

"You could never do that! I love you, Mama!" I moved toward her, longing to embrace her again, but she shook her head, holding up her hands to keep me away.

"You are very young, Violet. You do not understand how the world is."

"Then explain it to me." I sank onto her chair, wiping my tears as quickly as they fell. "I'm not leaving until you tell me everything I want to know. Why did you marry Father? Why did you have me?

And why . . . why did you abandon me?"

"Then will you go?"

"If you want me to." I couldn't understand how she could hold me in her arms and weep one moment and push me away the next. "I know that you and Father met on the night of the Great Fire. I know that he rescued you, but I don't know how."

She paced the cramped room for several moments as if gathering her thoughts, searching for a place to begin. I was struck by how lithe and graceful she was—and how beautiful. She looked very young to me, not yet forty, and I realized that she had been younger than I was now when she'd married Father. My hapless, straitlaced father must have been as attracted to the exciting young Angeline as stuffy Herman Beckett had been attracted to me in bloomers.

"Listen, I came to this country with my family when I was only a small girl," she began. "We were a family of gypsies—do you know what that means, what kind of life we led?"

"I-I think so." Thieves. Like Silas McClure.

"My father and older brothers started a theater here in Chicago. It was not a very nice place, and they made my sisters and me . . . We had to do whatever they said. I wanted to get away and have a better life, but they forced me to stay. My brothers locked me in my room every night with no shoes and no coat so I could not get away. I was their prisoner.

"That is where I was, locked inside, when the fire began. My brothers saw that the city was burning, so they left me there and went out to steal things from other people. I would have died that night if John hadn't saved me. He and his brother smashed down my door and helped me get out. Then John's brother ran back inside to save more people—but he never came out. The building fell into the street, and we had to run and run to get away.

"I hope you never have to live through a night like that one, *ho-cheech-ka*. It was worse than any nightmare I have ever dreamed of. The flames roared like a hundred trains, and buildings crashed to the ground. The sky was as light as daytime, the heat as warm as a summer day. We ran from the smoke and from the hot sparks that blew over us like snow. The cinders stung our skin, blown on the wind that howled in our ears. Some of the burning coals were as large as chestnuts.

"We ran as fast as we could, but the fire chased after us, a towering wave of flames that rolled toward us, trying to drown us. The streets were full of wagons and horses and screaming people trying to escape. They would leave things behind, dropping furniture and belongings to lighten their load until we had to climb over mountains of baggage just to get away. Behind us the flames leaped hundreds of feet in the air and swallowed buildings in one gulp. No one was fighting the fire. They could only watch helplessly as everything burned.

"John and I walked for miles and miles. My throat hurt from the smoke, and my feet ached because I had no shoes. John carried me on his back much of the way, like a child. We finally got to where all the streetcars had stopped. The men had driven them as far away as they could to get them out of the fire's path. They let us sit inside them to try to rest or maybe sleep.

"The city burned all night and all the next day. When the rain finally came and the fire stopped, my old life had all burned up. I could start all over again in a new place. John took me to his father's church in Lockport. I had never seen such a nice, quiet town.

"I fell in love with John, with his kindness and gentleness—and he loved me. But it was a terrible mistake to get married. I did not belong like all of the other people in that town. John's father disliked everything about me. The clothes I wore had too many colors. My hair should be put up, not hanging loose. I smiled too much; I was too foolish; I loved to dance. Everything was always wrong, and he said that I was turning you the wrong way too. He said I should not dance with you. And so I began to feel very sad. I stopped going out of our house. But I still had you and John. You brought me so much joy, Violet. I don't have enough words to tell you how much."

"Then why did you leave me?"

"After you were born, *ho-cheech-ka*, I had two more babies, but they died while they were still inside of me. Your grandfather said that God was punishing me for some sin in my life. I grew afraid that God would harm you or your father in order to punish me even more. I loved you both too much to let you suffer because of me."

"But that isn't true. God doesn't do things like that. And Father knows it isn't true. Why did you listen to Grandfather?"

"Do you remember the game we used to play together?"

"I don't remember very much . . ."

"I would ask something like: 'If you could choose, would you rather be a butterfly or a firefly?' And then you would have to choose."

I closed my eyes as tears flooded them.

"If you could choose, Violet, would you rather live on the moon or under the sea?"

"Mama, listen . . ."

"No, you need to listen to me, *ho-cheech-ka*. In the end, it was no longer a game for me. I had to make a choice and it was a terrible, terrible one—like choosing whether to be blind or to go deaf. Except that I had to choose between staying with the man I loved, the daughter I loved more than life itself, and ending up destroying them—or choosing to go away so they could live."

"I don't understand—"

"Have you ever been in love?"

I shook my head, trying not to think of the tender look I'd seen in Silas' eyes.

"Come back and talk to me when you do fall in love. Only then will you be able to understand."

"But I need to know now. I won't leave until you tell me everything."

I could see her frustration and her reluctance. But I had waited too long and searched too hard to leave my mother now.

"Very well," she said, exhaling. "Do you remember how I used to tell you tales about a princess who battled evil sorcerers and monstrous dragons and finally married a handsome prince? That was my life, Violet. My brothers were evil men, monsters who held me captive until a handsome prince came and rescued me. I did some very bad things before I met John Hayes. My father, my brothers—they were not good people, and they made me do bad things. John knew the truth about my past. When I told him, he said that Jesus forgave a woman in the Bible for the sinful life she lived, and He would forgive me too. But we never told John's father the truth.

"Then one terrible day my two older brothers found me. They came to our little town and told John's father. My brothers demanded a lot of money from him to keep quiet about all the things I had done. Your grandfather hated me even more for bringing this shame upon his family. Everyone in his church and in the nice little town would hear the truth unless he paid the money. I knew that my brothers would never be satisfied if we paid one time. They would always come back for more and more and more. So I chose to leave and go with them instead."

"Father told me you left because you didn't want to feel tied down anymore."

"That's what I told him. I wanted to make him angry with me so he would not follow me and beg me to come home. I left so that you and John could have the best possible life, not stained by my past. And look at you! You are beautiful. You look like a princess in your magnificent gown. You must have many rich young princes who want to marry you. And that is what I wanted most of all for you. A life of love and happiness—not a life like mine. The only way I could give that to you was to leave. I did it for you and for John. And now you must go and marry well, live well. You must forget all about me."

"But I can't forget you, Mama. I love you! I don't care about your family. I want to stay with you."

"No. That's not possible. Don't you see what I am?"

"Please, Mama. I could—"

"I don't want you here!" she said harshly. "You need to leave! It's time for the next show!" She opened the door and pointed to the hallway. Exotic music had begun playing in the background, and I heard drums pounding in the distance. "If you love me, then live the rest of your life without me, Violet. . . . Go!"

I didn't move.

She untied her ragged bathrobe and let it drop to the floor, revealing her flimsy costume. Then she turned her back on me and hurried away in the direction of the drums. The scent of roses trailed behind her. I ran outside, blinded by tears.

And I ran straight into Silas McClure.

Chapter

36

"H ey, hey—whoa!" Silas said as he caught me by the arm.

"Let me go!" I wanted to run and run and never stop, but he didn't ease his grip.

"There's no place to go, Violet. Just take a minute, okay? Take a deep breath." I did what he said. I had no choice. He wouldn't let go of me. I could hear the music from my mother's theater drifting faintly through the walls along with the relentless drumbeat.

"W-what are you doing here?" I asked when I could speak.

"I saw you leave the casino all alone, and I followed you. I was afraid you'd do something crazy like come over here. I figured I'd better come after you."

"I found her," I said, my voice shaking. "I found my mother. The woman in your picture—"

"I figured as much. There's a very strong resemblance."

"But she sent me away!" My tears started falling again.

Silas relaxed his grip on my arm and reached for my hand. "Come on. This is a lousy place to talk."

He led me around the building to the Midway's main street. The noise and bright lights and activity made my head swim. I was afraid that Silas was going to take me back to the smoke-filled casino, and I didn't want to go there. But he led me in the opposite direction and stopped at the base of the giant wheel. He bought two tickets. A few minutes later we were slowly rising above the bustle and confusion. Silas was a strong, silent presence at my side, saying nothing as we ascended. Lights twinkled below us and in the starry sky above us, and I felt my sorrow slowly ease. By the time we stopped at the very top, my tears were under control.

"Do you want to tell me what your mother said, Violet? I'm sure there was a very good reason why she sent you away."

The glorious wheel had worked its magic, and I was able to see past my bruised feelings and recall her words. "She left home because she loved me. She wanted a better life for me than the one she'd had. She thought I would be better off without her."

"And is that why she sent you away now?"

I nodded, remembering her shame as she'd pulled her robe closed over her costume.

"Violet, I'm so sorry," he murmured.

"My mother loves me. I finally understand that. She loves me so much she gave up her happiness for mine."

By the time we reached the bottom again I was calm. "Thank you for finding her for me."

"You did as much of the work as I did."

I felt drained as I stood in the bustling Midway, hearing the excitement and laughter all around me. "I guess we can go back to the casino now," I said with a sigh.

"No, Violet. I'm taking you home."

I wondered if he and his friend had already robbed the casino and he was using me to make his getaway again.

"What about Nelson and the others?"

"I'm sorry to say that your friend is a fool. That casino is as crooked as a witch's nose. If he borrows money to gamble in that place, he'll lose it all. He might as well toss his money into Lake Michigan."

"But what else can he do? He has to pay his father back."

"Well, my advice to him was to tell his father the truth and suffer the consequences. From what I hear, his father will never miss a few hundred bucks. I'm not sure your friend was listening, though."

We walked to the entrance gate, and Silas flagged down a cab. He helped me climb inside and sat opposite me. I couldn't stop thinking about love on the long ride home, and what a truly powerful force it was. It made people take enormous risks and make huge sacrifices. There was so much more to it than what I'd learned from reading Ruth's romance novels. Aunt Birdie had been the wisest of all the Howell sisters. I needed to make certain I married for love. And none of the three men who had proposed to me had loved me—the real me.

Now my time was up. Father was coming tomorrow. I would have to join Aunt Matt's suffragettes and remain a spinster because I didn't want to marry Herman Beckett or Nelson Kent or Louis Decker. I had thrown away my chances with any of Aunt Agnes' other suitors, even if I had wanted to live that phony life.

My parents had truly loved each other, but like Romeo and Juliet, interference from their families had doomed them. Katya and Nelson would likely face similar opposition from their families. Even so, I would be rooting for them to overcome all of their obstacles. I remembered the kiss they had shared and sighed.

What would it feel like to be kissed that way? Too bad none of my suitors had ventured to steal a kiss from me. At least I would have something to remember in my old age. I wondered if Aunt Matt's beau had kissed her before she'd learned the truth about him. Did she have the memory of that one kiss to see her through the lonely nights? If only there was a way I could experience a kiss—just once—before I gave up men forever.

Silas didn't say a word on the journey home. I noticed that he was no longer smiling. He paid for the carriage and let it drive away, then walked with me to the front steps.

"Are you still planning on leaving tomorrow?" he asked, pausing outside our front door.

"Yes. My father is coming to take me home to Lockport."

"Listen, before you go, I need to tell you the truth about myself."

"I already know the truth, Silas."

"You do? How did—?"

"I found out about the robbery on the day we went to the fair because my aunt works in the Woman's Pavilion. She told me the guards caught one of the thieves but that the other one got away. It wasn't hard to figure out."

"That was a real mess. I'm sorry—"

"Josephine and Robert were in disguise, weren't they?"

"Violet, I'm so sorry about all of that. I didn't know where else to get a chaperone, and I wanted to take you to the fair so badly."

"I understand."

"Just so you know, they were working the fair that day, but I wasn't."

"But you were working on the train the day we met, weren't you?" If I had learned anything at all this summer about being a detective, it was to plunge right in and pretend I knew the truth, then wait and see what people told me. "That's why you were in disguise on the train. I know all about that too, Silas. And that you aren't a salesman."

"Guilty as charged," he said, holding up his hands in surrender. "Listen, I'm sorry that I didn't tell you the truth about myself sooner, but I was afraid you would tell me to get lost—and I wouldn't blame you. I know I'm unworthy of you. I was going to tell you the truth last night when I brought you the photograph, but then your aunt was so upset and—"

"You really helped her, Silas. I want to thank you again for being so good with her."

"I don't suppose you'd be willing to reconsider—?"

"It's not a good idea. Besides, I'm leaving Chicago, probably for good. But thanks for helping me find my mother."

"If there's anything else I can ever do for you, just ask, okay?"

I had nothing to lose. I didn't want to die an old maid who had never been kissed. It was just an experiment, I told myself. Silas was a confessed thief, but in his fine tuxedo and white bow tie, he was a very respectable-looking one. If he could pretend to be a gentleman for an evening, then I could pretend that he was one.

"Now that you mention it, I would like to ask one more favor of you, Mr. McClure, but I hope you won't get the wrong idea about me. I would like . . ." All of my courage fled. I couldn't go through with it. I turned away. "Never mind."

"No, wait." He caught my arm. "I'll do whatever I can, Violet. And I could never think ill of you. Please tell me."

I made the mistake of looking into his eyes. The tenderness and love that I saw in them began to hypnotize me. I couldn't seem to look away.

"You're right about Nelson being a fool. My other suitors turned out to be disappointing too. And so it is starting to appear that I will never marry."

"Never marry? A girl as smart and as pretty as you? I don't believe it."

"It's too complicated to explain. But the truth is . . . you see . . . I mean, the favor I would like to ask . . . if you wouldn't mind . . ."

"Just ask me, Violet."

"I have never been kissed, Mr. McClure. And I would like to be—kissed, that is. Just once. So I could see what it's like."

"And you want me to be the one?" he asked breathlessly.

"I-if you wouldn't mind."

"Whoa," he said, exhaling. "I never saw that coming! But I would be honored." He looked into my eyes for a very long time as if trying to steady himself. "Are you ready?" he finally asked.

"Yes," I whispered.

Silas leaned toward me. I closed my eyes. His lips touched mine, as softly as a butterfly landing, and rested there for a moment. Then he moved closer and his mouth seemed to melt into mine as he kissed me. It was the most wonderful sensation I had ever felt. It started where his warm, tender lips joined mine and traveled slowly through me like a wave of warm water.

Much too soon, the kiss ended. Silas moved away.

"How was that?" he murmured. In the moonlit darkness, his eyes looked as though they were made of navy blue velvet.

"Oh my . . ." I breathed. "I had no idea that a kiss traveled all the way to your toes."

"Yeah. I felt it too."

"Why are we whispering?" I asked.

"I don't know."

He moved toward me again and this time he took my face in his hands. He was going to kiss me again. And I wanted him to.

The second kiss was much firmer and lasted much longer. I felt the stubble of his chin as his face brushed against mine. This time the sensation that washed over me was like falling into a raging river and being swept downstream. The power of it came not only from the touch of his lips against mine but from the warmth of his hands on my face and in my hair. My knees turned so weak I thought I might fall over. He finally pulled away once again, but I didn't want him to.

"That . . . that was even more wonderful," I whispered.

"Yeah . . ." We both sounded like we had just swum across a river and collapsed on shore. "Violet? May I . . . ?"

"Yes, please . . . one more . . ." I closed my eyes. This time his arms encircled me, and he pulled me close. I clung tightly to him, no longer simply being kissed, but kissing him in return. It was every bit as passionate as the kiss Nelson and Katya had shared—but I wasn't observing this time. I was drowning in it.

The sensation was the most amazing, terrifying, wonderful,

frightening one I had ever felt. All of it—the feel of his strong arms around me, his sturdy body close to mine, the way he breathed, the way his skin caressed my skin, his scent. As his warm lips melted into mine, I decided that a kiss was the most wonderful thing in the world. And now that I had experienced one, I didn't want to spend the rest of my life without another. No wonder Aunt Birdie hugged every man she met.

When our lips finally parted, Silas crushed me against his chest for a moment. I was glad that he did. I felt so weak and breathless and dizzy that I could barely stand.

At last my strength returned and I pulled away.

"Thank you." I still was able only to whisper, for some reason. "Now I know what it feels like and—"

"I love you, Violet."

I couldn't speak. Tears filled my eyes.

"It's the truth. I love you. I've never been in love before, but I've fallen in love with you. I don't suppose I could get you to change your mind? About never getting married? Because I don't think I can live without you."

I longed to ask if he loved me enough to change; enough to give up stealing and find a legitimate occupation. But I remembered Nelson Kent's indecision when I'd asked if he would surrender all of his wealth for Katya, and I was afraid to ask. If Silas hesitated, if he was unable to decide—or if he lied to me—it would break my heart. He would have to choose to change on his own.

"No, I won't change my mind. Good-bye, Silas."

"Violet, wait—"

"I'll remember that kiss for the rest of my life, but now I have to go." I was going to burst into tears, and I didn't know why. I fled into the house and up the stairs to my room.

As soon as I closed my bedroom door, I took off my dress and unlaced my corset. To my despair, all of the symptoms of love that every romance novel had ever described were still there. My heart raced wildly. I was breathless, weak, dizzy. His last kiss had left me so dizzy, in fact, that I had leaned against him to keep from falling over. And the symptoms were still there, even after I'd torn off my corset and tossed it onto the floor. I was in love with Silas McClure. I had fallen in love with a thief.

True love was much more devastating than in a romance novel. More devastating than the Great Chicago Fire. The flames of love were all-consuming, and there was nothing you could do to stop them or hold them back. You either saved yourself or ended up destroyed.

I cried inconsolably.

After a while, I heard my bedroom door creak open. Aunt Birdie floated into the room in her nightgown and gazed down at me, her head tilted to one side in sympathy.

"You must be in love," she said. I could only nod. "Make certain you marry for love, dear."

"I know, Aunt Birdie, I know!" I sobbed as her arms surrounded me. "I want to marry for love, but he is completely unsuitable. He's a thief. He even confessed that he was one tonight. My father would never approve of him, even if I got up the nerve to ask him."

"Your father, of all people, would understand."

"What do you mean?"

"Well, he defied his father, you know. Angeline was totally unsuitable too. But he married her for love."

The mention of my mother brought another flood of tears. "I found her, Aunt Birdie. I found my mother tonight."

"Oh, how nice."

"And she didn't abandon me after all. My mother left me because she loved me."

"Well, then," she said as she hugged me tightly. "That says it all, doesn't it."

Chapter

37

Saturday, July 15, 1893

I was packing the last of my things on Saturday morning when I remembered the journal I'd stuffed beneath the mattress. I took a moment to leaf through the record of my time in Chicago and paused when I found my entry from June twentieth.

I had written *Mysteries to Solve* on the top of the page. I had arrived in town with two of them and had added several more. Now that I was going home, it surprised me to see how many of them I could cross off.

1. Why did Mother leave us? Where is she?
2. Did Maude O'Neill murder her first husband? How can I stop the wedding?
3. Why did Father change from being one of Mr. Moody's Yoke-fellows to being indifferent about religion?
4. Why are Grandmother and Father estranged? What were the "sorrows" she mentioned in her life with my grandfather? Why won't Father let her talk about my mother?

5. Was Aunt Matt's fiancé, Robert Tucker, really a thief, or was Aunt Birdie simply rambling? Did Mr. Tucker get caught? Is he in prison?

6. Does Nelson Kent really love Katya, or is he using her? Is he using me?

7. And speaking of being used—is Silas McClure using me, or does he truly have feelings for me?

The last question brought tears to my eyes. Silas was the only man I'd met this summer who had truly loved me. And I loved him. I dried my eyes with his handkerchief, which still bore his faint scent. I finished packing my trunk, then went downstairs to wait for my father. I had just reached the foyer when Aunt Agnes burst through our front door without even knocking.

"Violet! Oh, you poor dear," she said breathlessly. "You had better sit down. I'm afraid you're in for a terrible, terrible shock."

"What's wrong?"

"I have scandalous news. Outrageous news! Nelson Kent eloped with his grandmother's serving girl last night!"

"Good for him." I couldn't help smiling.

Aunt Agnes gripped my shoulders. "But, my dear, aren't you positively heartbroken? He proposed marriage to you!"

"And I turned him down. He's in love with that serving girl, Aunt Agnes, and I'm thrilled for both of them. I hope they figure out a way to make it work."

"Oh, my dear," she moaned as she pulled me into her arms. "You must be in shock. I'm sure the truth hasn't sunk in yet. I feel so bad for dragging you into this mess."

"You don't have to feel bad at all." A giggle escaped from my lips, and Agnes pulled away to stare at me.

"I knew you'd be upset," she said. "You're hysterical!"

"I'm not. Please believe me, Aunt Agnes. I know all about Nelson and Katya. I loaned her the gown she eloped in."

Agnes pulled a collapsible fan from her handbag and flicked it open. She fanned herself vigorously, causing the papers on the hall table to flutter in the breeze.

"Oh, Violet, I'm so sorry."

"Listen, I had a good time with you and your friends. I learned a lot. You helped me decide some things in my life."

"I'm acquainted with plenty of other young men from good families. I could make introductions for you."

I smiled, wondering what she would think of the nickname I'd given them: pea pods. "I have to go home today, Aunt Agnes. But who knows? Maybe I'll visit Chicago again someday."

"What's all the fuss?" Aunt Matt asked as she marched out from the kitchen. "What's going on?"

"I've come with dreadful news," Agnes said. "Violet's beau eloped with another woman!"

"He wasn't my beau—"

"Oh, is that all?" Matt asked. "Will you be staying for lunch, Agnes?"

"Not today. I must go and comfort my dear, dear friend, Sadie Kent. She is simply devastated that her Nelson would do such a thing and run off that way. The family is worried sick about a breach of promise suit, so I offered to come over and talk with you, Violet." She sniffled as Aunt Matt stomped back to the kitchen, shaking her head.

"I'm not going to sue anyone, Aunt Agnes. I never accepted Nelson's proposal."

"Oh, thank goodness. The Kents will be so relieved. Disappointed, mind you, but relieved to know they won't face a lawsuit. I'd better go and tell them right away. *Au revoir*, my dear. And give my apologies to your father. I'm afraid I've failed him miserably."

I watched Aunt Agnes hurry away to comfort Mrs. Kent and realized that while many things in her life were superficial, the friendships she shared with the other women were not. There was a solidarity in their lives that I had experienced only at school with

Ruth Schultz. I no longer wanted a life like Aunt Agnes', but I admired her a great deal. She had taken her sorrows and tragedies and allowed good to come from them, just as Grandmother had advised me to do.

I went into the parlor and found Aunt Birdie seated on the sofa, reading a letter from Gilbert. I could tell by the faded ink and tissue-thin paper that it was many, many years old. I still hoped she would forget that Gilbert was dead, but for now she had found comfort in his letters. She looked up when she saw me and smiled through her tears.

"Your young man was right, Violet. I hear Gilbert speaking to me."

I couldn't reply around the lump in my throat. She had referred to Silas as "my young man." I wondered how long it would take for me to forget him. Did people ever find true love more than once in a lifetime? Birdie and Aunt Matt never had. I hoped I would.

I heard my grandmother puttering around in the kitchen with Aunt Matt, fixing lunch, and I wandered out to talk with her. She stood at the kitchen stove, stirring a pot, and I slipped into place beside her.

"I hope you aren't too disappointed that things didn't work out for Louis Decker and me."

She circled her arm around my waist and laid her head against my shoulder. "Not at all, my dear. You would make a dreadful minister's wife. You're much too high-spirited and unconventional. There are people in the church, I'm sorry to say, who would try to put you into a mold and squeeze your wonderful imagination right out of you. God has a purpose for your life. You would be wrong to marry Louis for my sake."

"And there is much more to life than getting married," Aunt Matt added. "But if you do get married, Violet, make sure you and your husband want the same things in life."

"I know. I want to do something useful with my life, the way both of you do. I'm just not sure what that will be. I'll never forget all those wonderful displays you showed me at the Woman's Pavilion, Aunt Matt. You really inspired me. You both did."

Father arrived in time for lunch. I listened as he chatted with Grandmother at the dining room table, and it seemed to me that they had reconciled a bit. He kissed her cheek when it was time to go.

"Good-bye, Mother," he said. "I trust I'll see you in Lockport for the wedding?"

"Of course, dear. And don't be a stranger, John. Bring Violet back to see us once in a while. We love her dearly, you know."

We all wept as I said good-bye. Even Aunt Matt brushed a tear from her eye. Father finally pried me out of Aunt Birdie's arms and towed me out to the waiting carriage, grumbling about missing our train. We chugged away from Union Station an hour later, but my tears didn't stop falling until we reached the outskirts of the city.

We would be back in Lockport in another hour, so I drew a deep breath to gain control of my emotions. I still had a few things that I needed to discuss with my father. He was engrossed in the newspaper he had purchased from one of the street urchins at the train station, but I cleared my throat, signaling for his attention.

"I know why Grandmother came to Chicago after her husband died," I began. "And I know why she didn't come to live with us." He folded his newspaper and laid it aside, frowning.

"It was because your Aunt Bertha—"

"No. She came here to search for Mother."

His frown deepened. "Did she tell you that?"

"Yes. She started working in all of those poor areas so she could look for Mother and convince her to come home to us."

"She promised me that she wouldn't talk to you about your mother."

"And she didn't break that promise. I learned everything on my own. I came to Chicago to find Mother too."

"You what?"

"That was the real reason I asked to visit the city—not to see the fair. I needed to know why she left me."

"Violet, I already told you—"

"I found her. And now I know exactly why she left. I know the truth about her past—that her family were gypsies and that she worked in a burlesque theater."

He closed his eyes. When he finally opened them again, he gazed out of the window not at me. "How is she?" he asked quietly.

"Still beautiful."

He nodded silently.

"Mother told me the whole story, her side of it. She didn't go away because she was discontented with you. She left because she loved you. Your father told her that the reason her babies died was because God was punishing her. She didn't want anything bad to happen to us because of her. Then her brothers found her and threatened to expose her past to all of Lockport if Grandfather didn't pay them money. She was afraid the scandal would ruin you and me. So she left."

Father's lips drew into a tight, angry line. "So it wasn't just Philip who my father destroyed."

"I know how strict your father was and how he made your brother run away. But I would like to hear your side of the story. All of it. Starting with the night of the fire when you and Mother met."

He was silent for so long that I began to believe he wouldn't speak. But at last he started talking, hesitantly at first. His voice was very soft.

"I was in Chicago that night with Philip. I found him in the saloon that he and Lloyd O'Neill ran together. Philip wanted to become an actor, and he enjoyed the theater and all of those other vices that our father railed against. I made a deal with Philip to come to Dwight Moody's church with me—just once—so he could see how the Gospel was supposed to be preached. I kept telling him that Mr.

Moody's portrait of Christ was much different than our father's. I convinced him to come, promising that I would never ask another thing of him if he did. And Moody's sermon didn't disappoint me. I remember they sang a song that night called 'Today the Savior Calls.'"

My father began to sing softly, surprising me with his beautiful tenor voice:

"Today the Savior calls
For refuge fly
The storm of justice falls
And death is nigh."

"We had no idea how true those words would be," he continued. "Mr. Moody was still preaching his sermon when fire engines started thundering past and the bell in the old courthouse began to toll nearby. Everyone grew restless, and there was so much noise and confusion in the street outside that Mr. Moody decided to close the meeting. He didn't invite the congregation to come to Jesus—so I never knew if Philip . . ."

I took my father's hand in mine, waiting until he could continue. He had suffered more losses in his life than I had ever realized.

"Philip was worried about the saloon, worried that his friend O'Neill would be too drunk to get himself out of there with his bad leg. O'Neill had saved Phil's life during the war, so I went along with him. The fire was spreading very close to the saloon, and we found it empty except for looters who were stealing as much liquor as they could carry. I told Philip it was time for both of us to get to safety, but he wanted to go to the theater first and make sure his friends had all escaped.

"On the way we passed a building that had just caught fire. Your mother was leaning from a third-story window, screaming for help. Her father had locked her inside. Philip and I broke the door down and I carried her out. But then he went back inside to make sure no one else was trapped."

Father paused. I saw him struggling to compose himself.

"Philip never made it out. I watched the place collapse on top of him."

"He sounds like a great man," I murmured. Father nodded wordlessly, then cleared his throat.

"Our church in Lockport was taking in refugees, so I brought Angeline home. I was grieving for Philip, and she helped me through it. She always said that I saved her, but she saved me too, Violet. I fell in love with her.

"Looking back," he said, after clearing his throat again, "I can see how hard it was for her to adjust to Lockport. She didn't fit in. Her family were gypsies—thieves and rogues—and she didn't know what a real family was supposed to be like. She loved you though. You and I were her life, especially after she stopped trying to find acceptance in town. I never knew that my father was the one who drove her away . . . just like he drove Philip away. She never told me what he'd said about our children dying. I wish she had. And I never knew that her brothers had found her. . . ."

He turned to gaze out of the window at the flat prairie land we were passing. I could see his reflection in the window. There were tears in his eyes.

"If I could offer you any advice, Violet, it would be to marry someone who comes from the same background as you do and has the same values. That's why I want to encourage you to consider Herman Beckett. He's a nice young man. Bright, capable . . . I offered him a job with me if he does marry you."

"You—*what*? When did you tell him that? Was it before the Fourth of July?"

"Well, yes it was, in fact. He came to see me the day after he took you to the fair. He told me that the outing had gone very well and that he had grown fond of you."

"Don't you see? That's the only reason he proposed to me. He wants a job with you!"

"Well, why not? I don't have a son to inherit my business."

"Take away the job offer and see if he still wants me. Go ahead, I dare you."

He stared at me in surprise, then murmured, "You're so much like your mother."

"And that's another reason why I can't marry Herman Beckett. I want more than a life in Lockport. Maybe it's my gypsy blood, I don't know, but Herman and I have nothing at all in common. Besides, I don't love him. Please don't make me marry a man I don't love."

I was still holding my father's hand, and he squeezed mine gently. "I know what it's like to have a father who tries to control your life," he said. "It's just that I'm concerned about your future—but perhaps my father felt the same way."

We traveled in silence for several minutes. "You need to finish your story," I finally said. "Tell me about Maude and Lloyd O'Neill."

Father exhaled. Again, he took a long time to reply.

"O'Neill lost his leg during the war while saving Philip's life. That's why I wanted to help him, even though he was a drunk. He would dry up for a little while and get a respectable job, but he always returned to the city to start drinking again. Whenever he got drunk he would go after Maude and start beating her. She would send the children down into the cellar because he had a wooden leg and couldn't manage the steps very well. That's what happened the day he died. He was drunk, and he came after her and the children. She fled into the basement with them, and when he tried to follow, he fell and cracked his skull. Maude and her children have been through so much, Violet, and seen so much. I would like to provide them with a peaceful home."

"Do you love her?"

"I married for love the first time. Now I simply want companionship."

"Well, I want to marry for love. I want to fall madly, passionately in love with someone, and I want him to love me the same way in return, and—"

I had to stop or I was going to cry. We were nearing Lemont, where Silas McClure had boarded the train and I'd seen him for the first time. Father wrapped his arm around my shoulder and pulled me close.

"I won't make you marry Herman Beckett—or any other man— unless you want to. But please think about what I said. Two people need more in common for a good marriage than passion."

"I know. I've learned a lot in these past few weeks. I'm not the timid, fragile girl I used to be. When I first arrived in Chicago and no one was there to meet me at the train station, I had no idea what to do. Madame Beauchamps' School for Young Ladies never prepared me for real life. I was scared and foolish and much too sheltered." I recalled how I nearly had gone off alone with Silas that day and shuddered. "But I've grown up since then. I don't need to be protected and sheltered from bad news anymore. And I don't want to hide away in Lockport living a safe, comfortable life. I want to live. I want to discover new things about myself and see new places."

"I wish you would take time to get to know Maude since she's going to be your stepmother."

"All right, I will." I finally accepted it. "But then I want to go back to Chicago and find my place in life. I don't want to look for a husband right now. I won't be twenty-one for nine more months. Just give me some time to figure out what I'm supposed to do with my life, okay? That's what we're put on earth for, isn't it? I need to serve God in my own way, just like you and Uncle Philip had to find your own way."

"Are you going to see your mother again?"

"I want to see her, if she'll let me. Someone needs to tell her that all those things Grandfather said were wrong. I think she should know the truth—even if she never does come home to us. Maybe she and I can learn together."

"You're so much like her," he said again. "So lively and dramatic. That's why I worry so much about you."

"I don't want to be an actress," I said, smiling. "And I'm not going to marry one of Grandmother's religious zealots or be brainwashed by Aunt Matt. I want to be my own person. I know that worries you, but remember how your father tried to put you into a box that didn't fit? Remember what it did to Philip? And to Mother? Let me find my own box. I'll be okay—I promise."

He tightened his grip on my shoulder.

"I'll stay home with you for a few months," I told him. "I'll be nice to Maude and her children. I'll stay until after the wedding. But please let me go back to Chicago in the fall. I have so much more to learn."

"All right, Violet," he said with a sigh. "You can go back."

Chapter

38

On the second Saturday in September I stood in the train station in Lockport, saying good-bye to my father once again. He was allowing me to return to Chicago with his blessing, as he'd promised. Maude and her imps were at the station too. Her wedding to my father had been simple and brief, and she had moved into our house on the same day. I no longer resented her for coming between my father and me now that I had my own life to look forward to.

I settled comfortably in the seat as the train began to move, excited to be on my way back to the city. I would have two more months to revisit the World's Fair before it closed, to see all of the sights I had missed. I was especially eager to attend the festivities on Chicago Day, October 9—the anniversary of the Great Fire. It still amazed me to realize how quickly the city had risen from the ashes after that tragedy twenty-two years ago. It was a good lesson for my own life. Tragedies can mean a new beginning as well as an ending.

Within minutes the train was moving fast, chugging past the

boring Illinois terrain. Some of the leaves had begun to change colors, but not enough of them to make the view a scenic one. I had a book to read in my satchel, but my thoughts were racing much too quickly to be able to concentrate as I anticipated all of the new discoveries that lay ahead for me. I would visit my mother again—of that much I was certain. And I would try to discover what God wanted me to do with my life.

Some time later, I felt the locomotive slowing down as it prepared to stop at the station in Lemont. Silas had boarded the train here the last time I had traveled to Chicago, wearing his garish plaid suit and hauling his satchel full of elixir. I closed my eyes to erase that image of him, preferring to remember Silas the way I last had seen him, wearing a tuxedo and bow tie and white satin vest.

"Is this seat taken, Miss Hayes?"

I opened my eyes, and there he was! Silas McClure! I blinked, wondering if I was dreaming.

His grin was as brilliant as the electric lights at the White City. My heart began thumping. I stared up at Silas in surprise, then quickly looked away, remembering the kisses we had shared. He was a rogue, stalking me, hoping to seduce me into kissing him again. I never would have asked him to kiss me in the first place if I had known we would meet this way. I had been certain that our paths would never cross again.

He stood beside my seat, waiting for me to answer his question. But first I had one of my own.

"What are you doing here?"

"I'm going to accompany you to Chicago."

"I'm sorry, Mr. McClure, but my father would never allow you to do that."

His brow furrowed in confusion. "Violet, your father is the one who hired me."

"Hired you. . . ?"

"Yes, just like he hired me the first time. Well, not me specifically—either time—but since I ended up with the assignment last June, I was able to arrange things so I could accompany you again."

"What are you talking about?" The train lurched as it pulled out of the station. Silas gripped the back of the seat to keep from losing his balance.

"May I sit down?" he asked again, gesturing to the seat beside mine. I nodded. My heart raced much faster than the train. "Violet, you said you knew the truth about me."

"Yes, that you're a thief."

"A what?"

"You know . . . the robbery at the fair, your trial at the courthouse, all your underworld connections to find my mother—I know that you're a thief."

"Violet, I work for Pinkerton's."

His words seemed to hang suspended in the air between us. I couldn't comprehend them.

"The . . . the detective agency?"

"Yeah. You said that you knew."

"You mean . . . you don't commit crimes? You . . . you solve them?"

"Well, we do a lot more than solve crimes. And some of our work is pretty routine. A law firm might hire us to conduct an investigation or serve a subpoena. And I've also been hired to guard payrolls or to travel by train undercover to watch for thieves. That's what my salesman garb was for. It was pure chance that I got picked to accompany you that first day. . . . And I have to say that I never expected you to be so beautiful. I figured I'd be accompanying an ugly old spinster— not you. That's why I couldn't stop staring at you that day. And why I was horrified to be seen wearing that corny getup and—"

"Wait a minute. Back up. . . . My father hired you to spy on me?"

"Well, I wouldn't want to call it that. Our company has done security work for your father in the past and—"

"That's outrageous!"

"Hey, don't get mad at me," he said after I punched his arm. "He cares about you. He wanted to make certain you arrived safely. He was afraid you'd meet up with someone unsavory or unscrupulous."

"Like a sleazy elixir salesman?"

"Exactly."

"And now my father hired you to keep track of me again?"

"If not me, then it would have been someone else," Silas said with a shrug.

"Were you being paid to follow me all around Chicago too? Is that why I kept running into you and—?"

"Hey, no! Not at all! Just to the train station. After that, it was my own idea to keep track of you."

"Then the robbery at the fair ... Your two friends must have been the *guards*, not the thieves!"

"Right. Joe decided to pose as a woman to try to catch the thieves who were snatching purses at the Woman's Pavilion. Robert caught one of them and had to testify in court the day I met you downtown."

"So that's how you were able to find my mother. You're a detective!"

"A pretty good one, eh?" He couldn't help grinning.

"What about the night at the casino, with Nelson? Were you working then?"

"The fair administrators knew about the gambling and suspected a scam, but the room was rented privately. Admission was by invitation only, so they couldn't gather any proof. Thanks to your friend, we were able to get inside and check it out for them."

"I understand the dealers were all arrested. I read about it in the paper." When I saw his look of surprise, I added, "I read the newspaper every day now. My aunt Matt is right. You can learn a lot about the world that way."

"Well, thanks to you and your gambling friend, I got a nice bonus from the fair's administrators for my night's work."

"Does that mean you won't have to sell Dr. Dean's Blood Builder anymore?"

"That's right—and it's a shame too, because our specially patented formula is made from the highest quality beef extract, fortified with iron and celery root. If you're suffering from extreme exhaustion, brain fatigue, debility of any kind, blood disorders, or anemia, our blood builder will enrich your blood and help your body throw off accumulated humors of all kinds. You should try it, Miss Hayes. It's guaranteed to stimulate digestion and improve your blood flow or we'll give you your money back."

I laughed and laughed—so hard that I could no longer sit up straight. Silas laughed with me. It was a wonderful sound.

"May I ask you a question?" I said when we finally paused for breath. "When you comforted my Aunt Birdie and you talked about heaven and Jesus . . . do you . . . are you. . . ?"

"I'm a believer, Violet. My saintly mother made sure of that."

"I see." I couldn't stop smiling. "Me too. And one more question? What does the *A* on your monogrammed handkerchief stand for?"

"It's an *A* for agent. It's so we can recognize each other when we're working undercover. It's less obvious than *P* for Pinkerton's."

"But suppose there's an innocent bystander whose name just happens to begin with an *A* and he—?"

"You've asked enough questions," he said, putting his fingers over my lips. "Now it's my turn. Tell me, if you loved someone, and you had never fallen in love before, and you couldn't stop thinking about her day and night, would you let her walk out of your life or would you follow her to the ends of the earth and fight to win her hand?"

I didn't think my heart could pound any harder or faster but it did. "I-I'd fight to win her hand."

"I was hoping you would say that." He grinned and took my hand in his, twining our fingers together. "Okay, now it's your turn to ask me one. I love your questions, you know."

I was so rattled I couldn't think. I asked the first one that came to mind. "If you could choose, would you rather be a butterfly or a firefly?"

"I'd rather be a moth."

"Ugh!" I shuddered. "I hate moths."

He leaned his head back and smiled. "Now that's a mystery I'll never understand. A moth is just a butterfly without the fancy clothes, isn't it? But if a moth flutters around your head, you women scream and shoo it away like it was some kind of monster. If a butterfly does the same thing, you're entranced. You say, 'Oh, how lovely!' and you stick out your finger and try to get it to land there. It's the same insect, isn't it? Except for the color?"

"Yes, I suppose it is," I said with a smile. "So why would you choose to be a moth?"

"Because I'd like to make my way in life without all the fancy colors and be judged by who I am, not by what I look like from the outside."

"You're right," I said, grinning as broadly as he did. "One should never judge someone by outward appearances. I'll remember that the next time an elixir salesman in a baggy plaid suit boards my train."

And that, dear reader, was how I solved my first *True Crime* and found *True Romance* in . . .

❧ The End ❧